COLORIMETRIC
METHODS OF ANALYSIS

Including Some Turbidimetric and
Nephelometric Methods

By

FOSTER DEE SNELL, Ph.D

and

CORNELIA T. SNELL, Ph.D.

THIRD EDITION

VOLUME III

ORGANIC—I

1953

D. VAN NOSTRAND COMPANY, Inc.

TORONTO NEW YORK LONDON

NEW YORK

D. Van Nostrand Company, Inc., 250 Fourth Avenue, New York 3

TORONTO

D. Van Nostrand Company (Canada), Ltd., 25 Hollinger Rd., Toronto

LONDON

Macmillan & Company, Ltd., St. Martin's Street, London, W.C. 2

Press of
GEORGE S. FERGUSON CO.
Philadelphia, Pa.

PREFACE TO THE THIRD EDITION

As in the second edition the aim of this edition has been completeness but so many new methods appear in this field that much condensation is necessary. We have attempted to include, or to refer to, the methods that have been published since the second edition, up to the time of publication. This has meant deleting many of the older references. Alternative methods for a particular substance are still given, because a method suitable for one purpose may not be suitable for another. For example, some methods are for determination of 0.0001 mg. or less, others for the order of 0.1 mg. of active ingredient. Some methods are very precise, others much less so.

Substances that interfere with a determination are usually mentioned in the introductory paragraph. Available methods for removal of these are described under "sample." The preparation of samples is given in great detail because much of the applicability of a method depends on proper treatment of the sample to remove substances which would interfere with the color development, and on preparation of a solution with a suitable concentration of active ingredient.

Because so much detail must be given, explanatory matter is condensed as much as possible. It is expected that the reader will be able to decide from the introductory paragraph, which explains the principle and limitations of each method, which one to choose among alternative methods.

The authors had hopefully expected to put all organic and biological material in this third volume, but the amount precluded incorporation in a single book. Therefore, as of the end of 1953, chapters written to follow in Volume IV, not necessarily in that order, are the following: Sterols; Hormones; Amino acids; Proteins; Nitrites, nitrates, and nitro compounds; Aliphatic amines and amides; Aromatic primary, secondary, and tertiary amines; Azo compounds, and nitrogen-containing cycles; Urea and related compounds; Compounds with inorganic radicals; Alkaloids; Enzymes; Antibiotics; Hemoglobin and related compounds; Pigments; and Color of liquids.

Acknowledgement is made of editorial assistance by Sally Cohen and Elsie Testa, and of secretarial help by Dorothy Bevilacque Kruk and others. Acknowledgement to all who have assisted would be impossible.

FOSTER DEE SNELL

CORNELIA T. SNELL

New York, N. Y.
August, 1953

CONTENTS

TABLES

ILLUSTRATIONS

CHAPTER 1

INTRODUCTORY

IT IS the intent of the authors to assemble in this chapter a host of miscellaneous comments in regard to organization of the book and instructions for its use.

The volume of literature and the number of individual substances to be covered are so great that every possible method of condensation has been applied. Thus a characteristic ending of a procedure will be: "Read at 560 mμ against a reagent blank." It is not felt that one need add thereafter: "Compare with a calibration curve prepared under the same conditions." Similarly, unless there is something unique about the preparation of a blank, it is not described. Ordinarily the color developed is suitable for colorimetric estimation. This fact will not be mentioned unless there is some reason to do so: for example, when the color that appears first cannot be read, but changes to one that can. Similarly, if Beer's law holds, this will not be mentioned unless there is some reason for it, as when the law holds over a limited concentration range only. It is our belief, or at least hope, that this will not reduce the usefulness of the book, although it will reduce an otherwise necessarily large bulk.

It has not seemed worth while to specify the use of a "250-ml. beaker" or a "250-ml. Erlenmeyer flask" for carrying out a reaction. Often some other container may be more available and will be used. Thus, if a 10-gram sample is digested with 150 ml. of water at 70°, it is assumed (1) that it will be put in a container and (2) that the container will be put in a water bath or an oven. Of course, if special conditions to protect from oxidation are necessary, they are included.

Few volumetric flasks are mentioned. If a 100-mg. sample is dissolved in acetone and diluted to 10 ml., the operator will naturally dilute with an accuracy comparable to that desired. For control work of a "go-no-go" type, dilution may be in a graduated cylinder. Usually dilution will be in a volumetric flask. By this form of expression the typographers have missed many hundreds of mentions of such flasks, and many thousands of words as a result.

As an example the phrase "Transfer to a 100-ml. volumetric flask

1

and dilute to volume with distilled water" is replaced by "Dilute to 100 ml. with water."

Methods of specification of solutions vary widely. For example, when a N solution of sodium hydroxide is mentioned there is usually no criticality as to whether it be 0.9 or 1.1 N; often it is added to obtain a rough end point. Hence, usually such solutions have been given in per cent, a 4 per cent solution rather than a N solution. The same applies to acids often prepared by dilution, 1:35 sulfuric acid rather than normal. If no concentration is mentioned, the common commercial concentration is meant; for example, ethanol means 95 per cent ethanol, and concentrated sulfuric acid means that of density 1.86.

No calibration curves are reproduced because they must be prepared with the reagents being used. Aside from the space they occupy, if present there is a temptation to assume that maybe they will be accurate enough. Standard solutions for calibration are rarely shown, it being left to the worker's option to select such concentrations as will be applicable to his specific problem.

Much of the same basic principle applies to weights cited. A reference may call for 1, 1.0, or 1.00 mg. The accuracy of taking the sample depends on the purpose of the analysis rather than on an arbitrary indication of accuracy possibly desirable. Hence, with rare exceptions, volumes or weights cited do not go beyond the last numeral or the decimal point, whichever is the smaller. The worker can readily select the accuracy needed for his purpose. Whether it is attainable is another subject.

Problems of classification are complex. Thus there is a chapter on sterols. If classified entirely by structure, the majority of hormones would appear there. Yet the hormones are so closely integrated as a unit that to break them up would be unwise. Should vitamins appear together? There is no direct relationship between thiamine and ascorbic acid. Should thiamine appear with aliphatic amines and ascorbic acid with substituted aliphatic monobasic acids? Should acetoacetic acid appear as a substituted monobasic acid or as a ketone? The net conclusion is to classify primarily by chemical structure when there is not a good reason to do otherwise as in the case of the hormones. But there are so many exceptions that the simplest way to find a compound is through the index rather than thumbing through the chapter where it might be.

Details of infrared and ultraviolet determinations are rarely given, an exception being vitamin A where the spectrophotometric method has become USP. The reason is that a line has to be drawn somewhere to encompass the material in a single volume. That was selected as the fringe with references often given to such methods.

With the heterogeneity of expression of weights in grams, milligrams, micrograms, etc., an effort has been made to translate all to grams and milligrams, even though fractional in terms of the latter. For good reasons there are a few exceptions, usually because the amounts are fractions of even gamma.

CHAPTER 2

HYDROCARBONS *

HYDROCARBONS, even though unsaturated, rarely have determinable chemical properties. An exception is acetylene which forms red copper acetylide. Generally, the aliphatic hydrocarbons are not determinable colorimetrically. Aromatic hydrocarbons nitrate readily which gives a method of introducing chemical properties and therefore colorimetric reactions.

There is no appreciable absorption at longer wave lengths than 200 mμ by paraffins, naphthenes, monoolefins, and unconjugated diolefines.[1] Absorption for conjugated diolefines begins at about 230 mμ. The region 250-280 mμ is characteristic of 6 carbon cycles regardless of side chains or heterocycles attached. Unsaturated side chains may introduce additional bands around 290 mμ if the benzene ring and the olefin are conjugated. The naphthalene bands are characteristically 300-330 mμ with the lower bands substantially fading out by that time. Acenaphthene, fluorene, and some other polycyclics have absorption in that region, but are separable by their boiling points.

Hence benzene, toluene, xylenes, and possibly other hydrocarbons are readable in the ultraviolet [2] when dissolved in ethanol [3,4] or isooctane.[5] The absorption coefficients in ethanol are particularly different at 247.5, 257.5, and 265 mμ. Similarly naphthenic type hydrocarbons are read directly in kerosene at 310-330 mμ.[6] This is applied to 1-methylnaphthalene, 2-methylnaphthalene, and naphthalene at 300-330 mμ,[7] prefer-

---

* See Chapter 1 for details of organization, condensation, etc.

[1] Gilbert N. Lewis and Melvin Calvin, *Chem. Rev.* **25**, 273-328 (1939).

[2] P. A. Cole and D. W. J. Armstrong, *J. Optical Soc. Am.* **31**, 740-2 (1940).

[3] Daniel Florentin, Marguerite Heros, and René Heros, *Bull. soc. chim. France* **1947**, 92-5.

[4] A. Luszczak, *Abh. Gesamtgebiete Hyg.* **1935**, No. 17, 1-18; cf. *Gas- u. Wasser fach* **79**, 733.

[5] D. D. Tunnicliff, R. Robert Brattain, and L. R. Zumwalt, *Anal. Chem.* **21**, 890-4 (1949).

[6] Alden P. Cleaves and Mildred S. Carver, *Natl. Advisory Comm. Aeronautics*, Tech. Note. No. 1243, 13 pp. (1947).

[7] Alden P. Cleaves, Mildred S. Carver, and Robert R. Hibbard, *Ibid.* No. 1608, 22 pp. (1948).

ably at 318 mμ,[8] with correction for the vehicle. Minor amounts of impurities in toluene are read directly in the infrared.[9]

Biphenyl is read at 251 [10] or 247 [11] mμ in cyclohexane. When orange oil is present, it is read at 375 mμ and the correction applied to the reading at the shorter wave length. A spectrophotometer [12] is designed for continuous ultraviolet estimation of diolefines.

ACETYLENE

Acetylene added to an ammoniacal solution of cuprous chloride produces a colloidal solution of copper acetylide having an intense red color.[13] This is sometimes designated as the *Ilosvay reagent*. Additional ammonia alters the color toward orange. The colored product is stable for only a few moments but is made more permanent by the addition of gelatin, starch, gum ghatti, or other colloids. Hydrogen sulfide and large amounts of oxygen or carbon dioxide interfere, the interference being increased by greater alkalinity of the solution. These are removed by passing the gas to be examined through a hot alkaline solution of pyrogallol. A brown scum often appears on the surface of the solution in the absorber but, unless excessive, does not interfere. It is believed due to small amounts of carbon dioxide which in the solution act as an electrolyte to tend to coagulate the colloid.

The method will detect about 0.15 ml. of gaseous acetylene. The accuracy depends largely on the source and handling of the sample.

Samples—*Air*. Prepare 10 per cent pyrogallol in 10 per cent sodium hydroxide solution. Heat this to boiling and pass a measured volume of 0.5 to 2.0 liters of air through it prior to passing through the absorber. During this operation keep the wash bottle containing pyrogallol solution in a water bath nearly at boiling temperature. For very low concentrations of acetylene in air, such as 0.005 ml. per cubic meter, sorb the acetylene on activated carbon, cooled by liquid air, and later recover by desorbing in nitrogen at 100°.[14] Another technic is to absorb in ace-

---

[8] Norman D. Coggeshall and Alvin S. Glessner, Jr., *Anal. Chem.* **21**, 550-3 (1949).
[9] R. C. Gore and J. B. Patberg, *Ind. Eng. Chem., Anal Ed.* **13**, 768-71 (1941).
[10] H. E. Cox, *Analyst* **70**, 373 (1945).
[11] A. P. Steyn and F. Rosselet, *Ibid.* **74**, 89-95 (1949).
[12] Eugene J. Rosenbaum, U. S. Patent 2,468,638 (1949).
[13] E. R. Weaver, *J. Am. Chem. Soc.* **38**, 352-61 (1916).
[14] E. A. Finkelshteïn, *Zavodskaya Lab.* **9**, 52-4 (1940).

tone cooled with solid carbon dioxide, the method being adaptable to use of a portable apparatus.[15]

Illuminating gas. Pass a measured volume of 0.5 to 2.0 liters through the absorber, without preliminary purification.

Liquid oxygen.[16] Set up the special apparatus shown in Figure 1. Flask A is 250-ml. for more than 0.7 ppm. of acetylene, larger for lower contents. Place it in a 1-liter beaker packed with rock wool. Cool the condensers with liquid air.

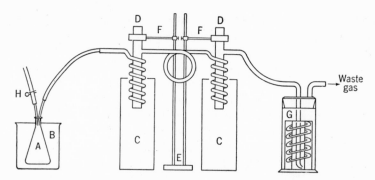

FIG. 1. Apparatus for acetylene test

A. Erlenmeyer flask
B. Pyrex beaker
C. Pyrex thermos bottles
D. Oks condensers

G. Milligan absorption bulb
H. Pinchclamp
F. Buret clamps
E. Double ring stand

Place the sample in the flask and allow it to evaporate with clamp H closed. Completion of evaporation will be evidenced by disappearance of frost from the rubber tubing leading from A to D. Lift the condensers and examine for liquid oxygen by observation. Its presence indicates that the condenser was too deep in the coolant. If any is present, hold the condenser just above the coolant until the oxygen has evaporated.

Then remove the coolant and blow the acetylene through the absorbing solution with nitrogen. Some acetylene is lost in boiling off the liquid oxygen, but by rigid standardization of conditions, duplicable comparative results are obtained. In the solid form recovered, the vapor pressure

---

[15] B. J. Purser, *Analyst*, **74**, 237-9 (1949).

[16] I. I. Strizhevskii, *Bull. Acad. Sci.* U.S.S.R. Ser. technol. **1939**, No. 3, 51-62; H. P. McKoon and Henry D. Eddy, *Ind. Eng. Chem., Anal. Ed.* **18**, 133-6 (1946); T. A. Geissman, Samuel Kaufman, and David Y. Dollman, *Ind. Eng. Chem., Anal. Ed.* **19**, 919-21 (1947).

of acetylene is 89-105° K.[17] This corresponds to a maximum loss of 0.037 ppm. of acetylene. Sweeping out the acetylene with ammonia gas has also been recommended.[18]

Procedure—As reagent prepare freshly each day a mixture of 10 ml. of 20 per cent aqueous copper sulfate pentahydrate, 60 ml. of 30 per cent hydroxylamine hydrochloride, 30 ml. of 1:1 ammonium hydroxide, and 100 ml. of 0.5 per cent gelatin solution. Mix 10 ml. of reagent with 10 ml. of ethanol and pass the acetylene sample through this, or transfer the gas to a closed container in which it can be shaken with the sample. Unless excessive amounts of oxygen are present, the initial blue will be reduced by the hydroxylamine hydrochloride. Dilute the pink to red solution to a suitable volume with water and read at 515 mμ.

HYDROCARBONS

Hydrocarbon oils, extracted into carbon tetrachloride, are read in the infrared at 3.4 microns.[19]

CYCLOPENTADIENE AND DICYCLOPENTADIENE

While cyclopentadiene is colorless, it condenses with aldehydes and ketones to give highly colored fulvenes.[20] The most satisfactory selection for the purpose is benzaldehyde, giving a yellow to orange color.[21] Dicyclopentadiene does not so react, but is readily depolymerized to the monomer under controlled conditions. Inhibitor must be absent. Acetone gives an unstable colored derivative. The ultraviolet absorption spectrum is suitable for reading only if interfering conjugated diolefines and aromatics are absent.[22] The average error is 0.03 mg. and no interfering substances are likely to be present. Thus ethyl mercaptan, thiophene, methyl sulfide, isoprene, and piperylene are without effect. Cyclopentadiene also gives a reddish-violet color with chloroform and acetic acid.[23] The only known interference is acetylene.

[17] P. Z. Burbo, *J. Tech. Phys.* (*USSR*) **13**, 116-22 (1943).

[18] I. I. Strizhevskii, *Avtogennoe Delo* **10**, No. 9, 30-1 (1939).

[19] R. G. Simard, Ichiro Hasegawa, William Bandaruk, and C. E. Headington, *Anal. Chem.* **23**, 1384-7 (1951).

[20] J. Thiele, *Ber.* **33**, 666 (1900).

[21] Karl Uhrig, Eleanor Lynch, and Harry C. Becker, *Ind. Eng. Chem., Anal Ed.* **18**, 550-3 (1946).

[22] L. W. Pickett, E. Poddock, and E. Sackter, *J. Am. Chem. Soc.* **63**, 1073-7 (1941).

[23] B. N. Afanas'ev, *Zavodskaya Lab.* **14**, 1492 (1948).

Procedure—*With benzaldehyde. Cyclopentadiene.* Dilute the sample with pentane so that under 1 mg. of cyclopentadiene per ml. is present. Mix 1 volume each of diluted sample, 3 per cent potassium hydroxide solution in ethanol, and 20 per cent solution of benzaldehyde in ethanol. Let stand for 3 minutes and read around 425 mμ. Subtract the reading of a blank in which the 20 per cent alcoholic benzaldehyde has been replaced by absolute ethanol.

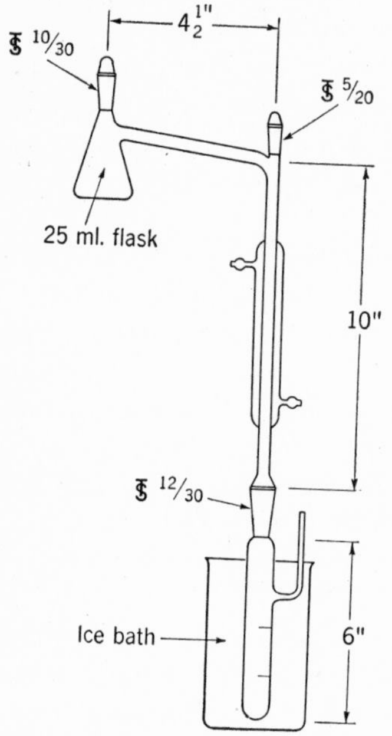

Dicyclopentadiene. Mix 5 ml. of sample or a sample diluted to 5 ml. with pentane, 5 ml. of decahydronaphthalene to serve as carrier, and 5 ml. of mineral oil of 100 viscosity at 100° to serve as residue in the distillation. Insert in the depolymerization apparatus shown in Figure 2, adding a boiling stone. Place the flask directly on the heating coil of a 550-watt electric heater with a rheostat. Distil approximately 5 ml. over 20 minutes. Then heat to distil another 6 ml. in not less than 40 minutes. Then raise the heat for 1 minute and discontinue. Do not take to dryness as explosive peroxides may be present. Rinse the condenser with ethanol, dilute to 100 ml. with that solvent, and use an aliquot for estimation as cyclopentadiene. Subtract the content of cyclopentadiene found by direct determination, the difference being dicyclopentadiene.

Fig. 2. Apparatus for quantitative depolymerization of dicyclopentadiene

BENZENE

When benzene is nitrated under optimum conditions it gives about 95 per cent of *meta*-dinitrobenzene [24] and the balance *ortho* and *para* isomers. For color development, the aci-nitro form of the *meta* isomer condenses with the enol form of a ketone in the presence of alkali with elimination of a molecule of water.[25] Aldehydes also react in some cases.

[24] Ladislaus von Szécsényi-Nagy, *Biochem. Z.* **281**, 178-80 (1935).
[25] H. D. Baernstein, *Ind. Eng. Chem., Anal. Ed.* **15**, 251-3 (1943).

Some methods provide for reading of toluene and xylene if present. As benzene would usually be most toxic, that is of major importance.

Butanone, methyl ethyl ketone, is suitable for development of color as a micro [26] or macro estimation. The presence of toluene or xylene introduces complications which necessitate varied forms of color development. Sodium hydroxide is the most satisfactory alkali for neutralization of the mixture after nitration. Ammonia causes fading after a few hours. Potassium hydroxide gives a deeper color, but precipitation of salts during extraction interferes. Increased concentration of alkali gives increased intensity of color, but the use of a sodium hydroxide solution stronger than 40 per cent causes turbidity and precipitation of salts during extraction.

Acetone gives a suitable color development but cannot be satisfactorily separated from the neutralized mixture. Pentanone gives a satisfactory color but results are erratic. Neither hexanone nor methylisobutyl ketone gives a satisfactory color.

As applied to gas the results are accurate within 5 per cent and applicable to below 25 ppm. With extreme care, accuracy to 2 per cent is obtainable. With blood and urine 0.001 mg. can be detected and 90 per cent can be recovered in the range of 0.01-0.9 mg. per 10 ml. Accuracy with tissue approaches this. The errors where results are low are largely in the isolation of benzene from the sample.

Toluene gives a similar color, but 15 parts are required to equal 1 part of benzene. About 2-3 parts of ethylbenzene equal 1 part of benzene. Chlorobenzene gives a color of similar intensity but changing from red to orange. Naphthalene gives an orange and aniline a pink color. If the color is developed by butanone and the solution then acidified,[27] interference by toluene and xylene is prevented. Where in alkaline solution, benzene gives a red to violet color, toluene gives a blue which quickly turns to violet, and xylene a blue. They may be read separately at suitable wave lengths. For determination only of benzene, acidify the solution with glacial acetic acid which destroys the other colors and read that due to benzene. There is then no interference by other aromatic hydrocarbons, methanol, ethanol, ethyl acetate, isopropanol, butanol, butyl acetate, acetone, and other commercial paint and lacquer thinners and solvents. Accuracy to ±0.9 per cent is obtained. An alternative is

---

[26] H. H. Schrenk, S. J. Pearce, and W. P. Yant, *U. S. Bur. Mines Investigation* **3287**, 11 pp. (1935); *Ibid.* **3293**, 2 pp. (1935).

[27] B. H. Dolin, *Ind. Eng. Chem., Anal. Ed.* **15**, 242-7 (1943); Reginald Milton, *Brit. J. Ind. Med.* **2**, 36-8 (1945).

to develop as the sodium and potassium salts and solve simultaneous equations for both benzene and toluene.[28]

For development of the color with acetone, it is necessary to separate the *m*-dinitrobenzene prior to color development. The method permits estimation of 0.025 mg. of dinitrobenzene in 10 ml. of final solution.[29] When toluene has been nitrated to trinitrotoluene it does not

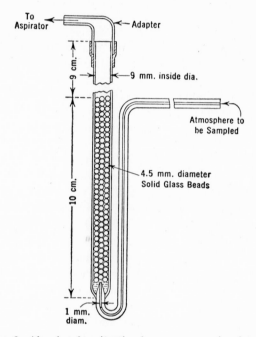

To Aspirator

Adapter

9 cm.

9 mm. inside dia.

Atmosphere to be Sampled

4.5 mm. diameter Solid Glass Beads

10 cm.

1 mm. diam.

FIG. 3. Absorber for nitrating benzene vapor-air mixture

interfere because in alkaline solution it hydrolyzes to a phenolate which is insoluble in the ether used for extraction.[30] Dimethylether may replace the acetone.[31]

Another technic is by conversion of benzene to nitrobenzene and subsequent reduction to aniline. The latter is determined [32] to 3 per cent

[28] René Fabre, René Truhaut, and Marcel Péron, *Ann. pharm. franç.* **8**, 613-26 (1950).

[29] S. I. Sinyakova, *J. Appl. Chem.* (USSR) **9**, 2109-14 (1936).

[30] M. S. Bykhovskaya, *Zavodskaya Lab.* **11**, 537-41 (1945).

[31] M. V. Alekseeva, *Okhrana Truda* **1939**, No. 8, 38.

[32] A. A. Gavrilov, *J. Chem. Ind.* (Moscow) **8**, 23-4, 26-9 (1931).

accuracy with calcium hypochlorite. Reading in the ultraviolet at 254.7
mμ, corrected for toluene, gives quantitative data.[33]

Samples—For general use, prepare a nitrating mixture of equal
parts of concentrated sulfuric acid and fuming nitric acid of d. 1.50.
This will convert benzene to the m-dinitro compound in the cold within
30 minutes, provided the volume of acid is at least 10 times the volume
of benzene.

Gases. Place 2 ml. of the nitrating acid in a suitable absorber, such
as that shown in Figure 3. Use of rubber for conduction of the gas is
not permissible. Bubble the gas through it at 20-30 ml. per minute. For
25 ppm. of benzene a 500-ml. sample is adequate. After 30 minutes,
transfer the acid and beads to a 100-ml. flask. Rinse the absorber with
five 1-ml. portions of distilled water and add this to the sample solution
in the flask. Cool the sample solution to 20° and slowly neutralize to
litmus by addition of 40 per cent sodium hydroxide solution. Add 1 to
2 drops in excess, as a yellow color will develop with the reagent if even
a slight acidity is present. Dilute to volume and develop the color with
butanone in an aliquot.

Alternatively, wash the gas sample by bubbling through petroleum
naphtha and then nitrate all or an aliquot as described for solvents
(page 13).

If the benzene is to be nitrated only to mononitrobenzene for reduction to aniline, use less drastic conditions. Prepare a mixture of 4 parts
of concentrated sulfuric acid and 1 part of fuming nitric acid of d. 1.50.
Charge two efficient gas absorption bottles and pass a suitable sample of
air according to the benzene content.

Rinse the contents from the gas absorption bottles and dilute to about
100 ml. with distilled water. Add 1:1 ammonium hydroxide until alkaline
to litmus. Cool the solution and extract with 3 successive 10-ml. portions
of ether. Add 1 ml. of concentrated sulfuric acid to the ether extract
and follow with 1 gram of zinc dust in several portions, agitating during
the addition. Evaporate the ether and take up the residue with about
50 ml. of water. Add saturated sodium carbonate solution until alkaline
to litmus, and filter to remove any solid impurities. Dilute to 100 ml.
and use an aliquot for development as aniline.

As another technic,[34] shake 1 liter of gas with 10 ml. of the nitrating
mixture for making the dinitro compound, for 30 minutes. Add 4 ml.

---

[33] Per Lundgren and Olle Wallén, *Svensk Farm. Tid.* **54**, 273-8 (1950).
[34] B. S. Boĭkina, *Zavodskaya Lab.* **16**, 1400-1 (1950).

of the mixture to water, make just alkaline with 30 per cent sodium hydroxide solution, and develop with acetone.

Gasoline. Agitate a 1-ml. sample with a mixture of 4 ml. of concentrated sulfuric acid and 1 ml. of fuming nitric acid of d. 1.50 for 1 hour. Dilute to 100 ml. and continue as for the second technic for benzene in gases starting at "Add 1:1 ammonium hydroxide until alkaline to litmus."

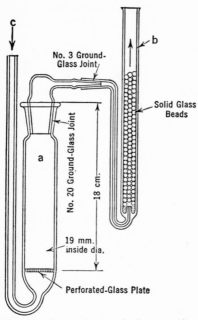

FIG. 4. Apparatus used for aeration and nitration of benzene from blood or urine

Blood.[35] Place 5-10 ml. of sample in *a* of the apparatus shown in Figure 4. Add 0.5 ml. of 1.3 grams of calcium stearate triturated with 20 ml. of white mineral oil of medicinal grade, to prevent foaming. Place 2 ml. of the mixed nitration acids in the bubbler, *b*. Connect *a* and *b*, wetting the ground-glass joint with water as a lubricant. Connect a calibrated aspirator bottle to *c* with rubber tubing carrying a screw clamp, being sure that there is a positive pressure in the bottle. Open the clamp carefully so as to deliver benzene-free air at 3-6 liters per hour. For 0.01-0.03 mg. of benzene per 10 ml. of blood, aerate with 6-10 liters of air. For higher benzene concentrations an even greater volume of air will be required. Formation of small bubbles and good agitation are important.

About 80 per cent of the benzene is removed in the first half of the aeration. For maximum accuracy check the efficiency of the aeration by replacing the tube *b* with a duplicate and continue aeration for 1 hour. Treat the contents of this tube separately to determine whether benzene is present. After 30 minutes, transfer to a 100-ml. flask and complete as described in the first method for gas samples starting with "Rinse the absorber . . ."

Urine. Follow the method of treatment of the sample described for

---

[35] S. J. Pearce, H. H. Schrenk, and W. P. Yant, *U. S. Bur. Mines Investigation* **3302**, 8 pp. (1936); L. Truffert, *Ann. fals et frandes* **45**, 181-5 (1952).

blood with these exceptions. Add a few crystals of citric acid instead of the calcium stearate to prevent foaming. Aspirate with only about 6 liters of benzene-free air for recovery of 2.5 mg. of benzene in 10 ml. of urine.

Tissue.[36] Benzene is aerated slowly from fatty materials. Therefore the aeration is accompanied by heating. Set up a flask in a water bath with an inlet tube for aeration and a water-cooled vertical reflux condenser as exit. Connect the top of the condenser to an absorber similar in type to that used with blood and urine.

Specimens of 5 grams or less of tissue having a high fat content will usually be sufficient. Freeze tissue specimens in liquid air as soon as collected. Grind quickly in a meat grinder while frozen and transfer at once to the apparatus. Alternatively cut the weighed specimen of tissue into small cubes, place in glass tubes or bottles, and fill with medicinal mineral oil. There should be 25-50 per cent excess volume to allow for this. Store the entire specimen in a refrigerator until ready to use and transfer the entire contents including the covering oil to the distillation flask.

Add 2 parts of 1:200 sulfuric acid for every part of tissue. Connect the apparatus and heat the flask at a rate which will slowly eject the air through the absorber. After refluxing has become definitely stabilized this will nearly or entirely cease. Start the bubbling of nitrogen through the boiling contents of the flask and continue for 1-2 hours. Nitrogen avoids possible oxidation of benzene to phenols in the presence of the biological material.

When the gas has been stopped for 30 minutes, transfer the contents of the absorber to a 100-ml. flask and complete as in the first method for gas samples starting at "Rinse the absorber . . ."

Solvents. Chill a 50-ml. flask containing a 0.5-ml. sample with a 0.25-75 per cent benzene content in ice and salt. Add the nitrating mixture at 2 drops per second with rotation of the flask until 10 ml. have been so added. Remove from the cooling bath, add 35 ml. of water, and cool to room temperature. Extract with 25 ml. of ether, followed by three 10-ml. portions. Extract the combined ether extracts with 10 ml. of 10 per cent sodium hydroxide solution, then with two 10-ml. portions of water. Dilute the washed ether extract to 100 ml. with 95 per cent ethanol. Similarly dilute a 10-ml. aliquot of this to 50 ml. Develop with butanone and acid.

---

[36] W. P. Yant, H. H. Schrenk, and P. H. Mautz, *U. S. Bur. Mines Investigation* **3282,** 7 pp. (1935).

If both toluene and benzene are to be read, chill 5 ml. of 1:1 sulfuric acid and fuming nitric acid to zero and add 0.5 ml. of the solvent. After 1 hour at zero, dilute with 50 ml. of water and neutralize with 30 per cent sodium hydroxide, usually requiring about 15 ml. Extract with 50 ml. of ether in 3 portions. Evaporate the ether extract and take up in 50 ml. of butanone as sample. Dilute 1 ml. with butanone to 50 ml.

Procedure—*With butanone*. Warm the slightly alkaline sample solution containing *m*-dinitrobenzene to 25-30°, add 10 ml. of methylethyl ketone, and shake occasionally for 10 minutes. The higher temperature prevents crystallization of salts. Transfer to a separatory funnel and remove the methylethyl ketone layer. Add 1.5 ml. of 40 per cent sodium hydroxide solution to the solvent solution. Shake vigorously for several minutes and occasionally for 1 hour to develop the color. During this period of color development protect from exposure to light. Read at 570 mμ against a reagent blank.

If the color extracted is too intense for reading, separate the methylethyl ketone layer and measure the volume accurately. Dilute an aliquot with methylethyl ketone to the same volume previously present. If the aliquot is 1 ml. or less add 0.7 ml. of an aqueous solution containing 1.7 per cent of sodium nitrate and 0.86 per cent of anhydrous sodium sulfate. As the volume of the aliquot is increased, reduce the amount of nitrate-sulfate solution added. Then treat the diluted aliquot with 1.5 ml. of 40 per cent sodium hydroxide solution as before. This technic maintains the amount of water and salts present in the methylethyl ketone layer the same as that in the solutions used in preparation of the standard curves.

With butanone and acid. To 10 ml. of sample solution in ether-ethanol add 1 ml. of butanone and 0.5 ml. of 4 per cent alcoholic sodium hydroxide solution. Agitate and let stand for 5 minutes. Add 0.5 ml. of a 1:9 dilution of glacial acetic acid with 95 per cent ethanol. Agitate, let stand for 10 minutes, and read at 25° and 570 mμ.

Benzene and toluene with butanone. The nitrated sample is in butanone. Mix 10 ml. with 2 ml. of a solution containing 16 per cent of sodium hydroxide and 12 per cent of sodium chloride. This gives 25 times as much color with benzene as with toluene and is the Na test. Mix another 10-ml. portion with 2 ml. of 50 per cent potassium hydroxide solution. This gives only 1.5 times as much color with toluene as with benzene. This is the *K* test. After shaking each frequently for an hour, read at 570 mμ against a butanone blank. The readings are linear up to 0.1 mg.

Calculate from the equations

$$K_1 = rb + r't$$
$$K_2 = pb + p't$$
$$\text{Benzene} = (K - r't)/r$$
$$K_2 = (p/r)(K_1 - r't) + p't$$
$$\text{Toluene} = (K_2 - (p/r)K_1)/[p' - (pr')/r]$$

where

$r = $ extinction coefficient in Na test for 1 unit of benzene
$r' = $ extinction coefficient in Na test for 1 unit of toluene
$p = $ extinction coefficient in K test for 1 unit of benzene
$p' = $ extinction coefficient in K test for 1 unit of toluene

With acetone. Extract the *m*-dinitrobenzene from the alkaline solution of the nitration mixture with 10 ml. of ether. Separate the ether and repeat 3 times more. Combine the extracts and evaporate the ether. Take up the dried residue in acetone and dilute to 10 ml. According to concentration take an aliquot of this, such as 1-5 ml. and dilute to 10 ml. with acetone. To this add 2 ml. of 33 per cent sodium hydroxide solution and let stand for 30 minutes. Read the violet color against a reagent blank.

As aniline. Follow the method for aniline by treatment with hypochlorite (Vol. IV).

TOLUENE

The necessity of estimation of toluene vapors has led to development of a method [37] similar in many respects to that for benzene as *m*-dinitrobenzene. Toluene is changed to unidentified nitrotoluenes which give a reddish-blue color with methylethyl ketone, butanone. There are some important differences from the benzene method. Fuming nitric acid replaces a mixture of nitric and sulfuric acid because the latter diminishes the color developed, and if heated no color is given. The use of fuming nitric acid greatly reduces interference by benzene. Many alcohols and esters develop yellow colors, but only benzene, chlorobenzene, xylene, and thiophene give colors similar to that developed with toluene. Results are accurate to 10 per cent for 0.05-0.25 mg. of toluene. Both benzene and toluene are determined by simultaneous equations by a technic described under benzene.

[37] W. P. Yant, S. J. Pearce, and H. H. Schrenk, *U. S. Bur. Mines Investigation* 3323, 12 pp. (1936).

The violet color of trinitrotoluene in alkaline ethanol solution is also suitable for its estimation.[30] Toluene is read in the ultraviolet at 268.7 mµ, corrected for benzene.[38]

Sample—*Air*. For development with butanone, draw an air sample of suitable volume through 2 ml. of fuming nitric acid of d. 1.50, in the

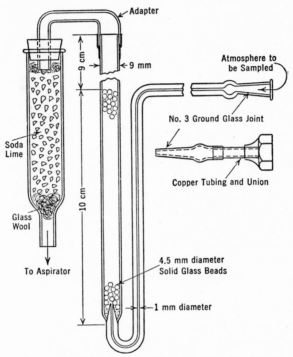

FIG. 5. Bubbler for nitrating toluene vapor-air mixture

bubbler shown in Figure 5. The soda-lime tube protects the aspirating device. If necessary to draw the sample through fine-bore copper tubing from an inaccessible point, the combined glass joint and copper union illustrated is convenient. Rubber absorbs toluene and cannot be used for sampling. When nitration is complete transfer the acid and beads to a small flask or bottle with a glass stopper. Rinse the bubbler with six 1-ml. portions of water and add to the acid. The sample may be stored at this stage for 2 weeks.

[38] Per Lundgren and Olle Wallén, *Svensk Farm. Tid.* **54**, 273-8 (1950).

Alternatively, nitrate to trinitrotoluene. As nitrating mixture dissolve 10 grams of ammonium nitrate, dried at not over 80°, in 10 ml. of concentrated sulfuric acid. Pass the sample through two successive 2-ml. portions of this reagent in efficient gas absorption units. When absorption is finished, complete the nitration by heating the absorbers for 30 minutes in a boiling water bath. Cool the absorbers and transfer their contents to a flask containing 12 ml. of water. Rinse the absorbers with two 2-ml. portions of water. Divide the combined solution and washings into two parts and use one portion, after neutralizing, for estimation of any benzene with butanone (page 14). Use the other portion for toluene.

Procedure—*With butanone*. Neutralize the acid solution of sample at 25-30° by slow titration with 50 per cent potassium hydroxide solution, using litmus paper as indicator. Add 2-3 drops of alkali solution in excess to avoid later development of an interfering yellow color.

If an amber color is present, extract the neutralized solution with 10 ml. of ether, let the ether evaporate spontaneously, and dissolve the residue in 9 ml. of butanone. This avoids interfering colors. Otherwise add 10 ml. of methylethyl ketone to the neutralized solutions and shake occasionally for 10 minutes. Keep at 25-30° to prevent crystallization of salts. Separate the methylethyl ketone, add 1.5 ml. of 50 per cent potassium hydroxide solution, and shake vigorously for several minutes. Let stand for 60 to 90 minutes for complete development of color. The color is stable for at least a month if protected from light. Read against a reagent blank.

If the color being developed appears to be too deep within the first 10 minutes separate the methylethyl ketone layer and dilute a suitable aliquot with fresh solvent. If 1 ml. or less is used add 0.45 ml. of 3.5 per cent potassium nitrate solution; if more, use a proportionately lesser amount of the potassium nitrate solution. This addition is necessary when so diluting to avoid unduly high results. The acid solution can also be aliquoted and then diluted to 2 ml. with a mixture of equal volumes of concentrated nitric acid and water. Similarly the neutralized solution can be diluted and an aliquot taken.

As trinitrotoluene. Neutralize the nitration mixture by dropwise addition of 1:3 ammonium hydroxide with cooling. Extract with two 10-ml. portions of ether. Evaporate the combined extracts and take up the residue in 10 ml. of ethanol. Take half for development of color and add 1 drop of 3 per cent potassium hydroxide. Read against a reagent blank.

Styrene

Styrene absorbs in the ultraviolet at 251 mμ, 282 mμ, and 219 mμ, whereas polystyrene does not. This is the basis of methods of determination of monomer.[39] The relative absorption at the three wave lengths is 15:25:1. Therefore readings in the vicinity of 250 mμ are most accurate. The equivalent reaction is used to read styrene in ethyl benzene.[40] Toluene or benzene within reasonable concentrations in the ethylbenzene does not affect the results. Photometric results are more accurate than titration below 1 per cent.

A method for terminal olefinic bonds has been worked out for undecylenic acid (page 309). Preliminary results indicate that it is applicable to styrene in the absence of other compounds having terminal olefinic groups. Styrene is also determined by nitration in toluene, the technic being described in full under polystyrene [41] (page 19).

Sample—Air.[42] Pass a known volume of air through a suitable cold absorbent in a bead-packed absorber.

Procedure—*In chloroform.* Dissolve 0.1 gram of polymer in chloroform and dilute to 250 ml. Read at 250 mμ, 255 mμ, and 260 mμ. Then calculate styrene monomer by the formulas

$$\% \text{ styrene} = 0.743 \ (E_{250} - 1.34)$$
$$\% \text{ styrene} = 0.876 \ (E_{255} - 1.80)$$
$$\% \text{ styrene} = 1.178 \ (E_{260} - 2.12)$$

Average the three results provided they are in agreement to a degree acceptable for the purpose of the analysis.

In ethyl benzene. Read directly at 290-310 mμ.

Polystyrene

Polystyrene is determined by alteration to the monomer, nitration, and reading in the ultraviolet.[43] The calibration curves for derivatives such as *p*-chlorostyrene and 3,5-dimethylstyrene are different.

[39] J. S. Owens, *Ind. Eng. Chem., Anal. Ed.* **11**, 643-6 (1939); J. J. McGovern, J. M. Grim, and W. C. Teach, *Anal. Chem.* **20**, 312-14 (1948); J. E. Newell, *Anal. Chem.* **23**, 445-7 (1951).

[40] Nina Hadden and John A. Perry, *Anal. Chem.* **23**, 1337 (1951).

[41] Cf. M. I. Poletaev, *Gigieni i. Sanit.* **1952**, No. 3, 46-7.

[42] V. K. Rowe, G. J. Atchison, E. N. Luce, and E. M. Adams, *J. Ind. Hyg. Toxicol.* **25**, 348-53 (1943).

[43] Raymond C. Crippen and Charles F. Bonilla, *Anal. Chem.* **21**, 927-30 (1949).

Sample—The apparatus for the determination is shown in Figure 6. Add a sample of about 3 grams to the depolymerization flask. Add 100 ml. of carbon tetrachloride to the recovery flask and close the system. Cool the recovery flask and the traps ahead of the vacuum pump with dry ice and acetone. Evacuate to the vapor pressure of the cold carbon tetrachloride in the recovery flask. Turn on the steam generator and the superheater and heat the depolymerization flask to 300-400° at

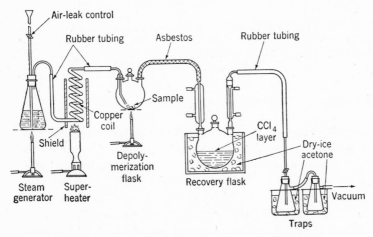

FIG. 6. Apparatus for depolymerization of polystyrene

5-10 mm. of mercury. Control the rate of steam generation to a slow stream of air bubbles in the steam generator by a capillary tube, hose and pinch clamp. After the flow of steam starts, apply a flame directly to the sample flask. Turn on water in the condensers and melt and evaporate the sample slowly. When all of the sample is distilled, distil splashes on the walls with a flame applied to the surface of the flask. By this time water condensation should be about 100 ml. Shut off the flames and dismantle. Rinse the condenser tubes and flasks with the carbon tetrachloride in the recovery flask. Dilute the carbon tetrachloride to a known volume and use an aliquot.

Procedure—Dilute an aliquot of 2-8 mg. of styrene monomer in carbon tetrachloride to about 15 ml. with carbon tetrachloride. Add 2 ml. of a mixture of equal parts of freshly boiled and cooled concentrated nitric acid and concentrated sulfuric acid. Shake for 10 seconds every 2 minutes for 10 minutes. Add 15 ml. of water, shake, and remove the water layer. Wash the carbon tetrachloride with 15 and 15 ml. of water. Dilute the combined aqueous layers to 50 ml., filter or let stand until clear, and read at 365 mμ. Multiply by 2 as an empirical factor to give styrene in the polymer.

POLYMERIZED HYDROCARBONS TURBIDIMETRICALLY

The method has been worked out for determining polystyrene in styrene.[44]

Procedure—Dilute one volume of sample with two volumes of absolute methanol. No cloud indicates less than 0.0005 per cent of polymer present. Otherwise compare with known standards or read in an electric turbidimeter and compare with a calibration curve for that instrument.

o-XYLENE

The method for estimation of benzene as m-dinitrobenzene [45] is applicable to a specific aromatic cut, that is o-xylene in styrene monomer. Interfering unsaturated hydrocarbons are reacted with mercuric acetate to permit separation of the o-xylene by steam distillation, sometimes with ethyl benzene.[46] Then it is dinitrated and color developed with acetone.

For samples containing less than 0.2 per cent of o-xylene and not over 5 per cent of alkyl benzenes the accuracy may be ±5 per cent. Less than 0.01 per cent of o-xylene is detectable. Fractionation will usually prepare a sample within the optimum limits.

Sample—The preparation of a sample containing over 99 per cent of styrene and less than 0.5 per cent of o-xylene is typical. To 60 ml. of propylene glycol in a glass-stoppered flask add 5 ml. of sample. If less than 60 ml. of mercuric acetate reagent is to be used later, reduce the glycol to the same volume.

Add 0.2 ml. of ethyl benzene and 75 ml. of a solution containing 320 grams of anhydrous mercuric acetate per liter. This 15:1 ratio gives 1.5 moles of mercuric acetate per mole of sample. If 1,4-vinyl-cyclohexane is present which has two olefinic linkages, increase accordingly. With small amounts of olefines the reagent may be reduced. Shake

---

[44] Bassett Ferguson, Jr., and Mark D. Snyder, *Ind. Eng. Chem., Anal Ed.* **14**, 135 (1942).

[45] R. W. Bost and F. Nicholson, *Ind. Eng. Chem., Anal. Ed.* **7**, 190-1 (1935).

[46] Roland P. Marquardt and E. N. Luce, *Ind. Eng. Chem., Anal. Ed.* **16**, 751-3 (1944).

mechanically for 2 hours. If polymer-free the solution is clear and water-white.

Steam-distil from the flask, with a minimum amount of reflux, using a Babcock bottle with a graduated neck as receiver. Before the flask containing the sample is heated, have steam passing, to minimize the time for distillation of alkyl benzenes. Unless this is done a secondary reaction may precipitate mercuric acetate, an oily liquid distil, and accuracy be lessened. Some acetic acid which distils does not interfere. Collect 35-40 ml. of distillate. Dilute so that the distillate can be read in the calibrated neck after centrifuging. Polymer present is permissible, provided the liquid can be pipeted. Remove the sample and reserve for nitration. Some loss has occurred, as by solubility, and must be corrected by a predetermined value which for the usual Babcock bottle is 0.05 ml.

Procedure—Prepare a 1:1 nitration mixture of sulfuric and nitric acids. Add 0.05 ml. of sample with a pipet graduated to 0.01 ml. to a 200-ml. volumetric flask. Wash down at once with 10 ml. of nitrating mixture and shake for a few seconds. After occasional shaking for an hour cool in an ice bath and gradually add 25-30 ml. of water with shaking. Add 10 ml. of concentrated nitric acid to help dissolve the nitro compounds. Dilute to volume and transfer a 5-ml. aliquot to 10 ml. of water. Make just alkaline by dropwise addition of 1 ml. of 50 per cent potassium hydroxide solution. Extract with 10 ml. of ether, then with 5 ml. Evaporate the ether from the combined extracts but leave the water which was dissolved. Complete evaporation will reduce the intensity of the colors.

Add 20 ml. of acetone, 1 ml. of monoethanolamine, and 2 ml. of 50 per cent potassium hydroxide solution in that order. Close with a cap lined with silver foil and shake mechanically for 15 minutes. After waiting 2 minutes for the caustic to separate from the solution in the dark, read the transmittance at 660 mμ. Accept the first reading as the color fades slowly.

The per cent by weight of *o*-xylene in the original sample is $A(B + C)DE$/sample weight, in which

A = Volume per cent of *o*-xylene in the alkyl benzenes as derived from the ethyl benzene added.
B = Volume read of alkylbenzenes.
C = Correction discussed at the end of sample preparation.
D = Correction for impurity in the standard if necessary.
E = 0.87, specific gravity of *o*-xylene.

DIPHENYL, BIPHENYL

In hexane solution, biphenyl is read in the ultraviolet at 251 mμ.[47] Similarly a carbon tetrachloride solution is read in the infrared at 14.34 μ.[48]

AROMATIC HYDROCARBONS

Aromatic hydrocarbons extracted from aqueous solution react with sulfuric acid containing formaldehyde to give a brown coloration [49] which is suitable for colorimetric estimation.[50] The method has a sensitivity of ±1 ppm. for samples of 1-10 ppm. For samples up to 500 ppm. it is necessary to dilute the sample and multiply the answer by a dilution factor. Thus the accuracy remains at about ±10 per cent.

When applied to benzene, toluene, ethylbenzene, and styrene, and probably to related hydrocarbons, alone or in combination, the different hydrocarbons give different degrees of discoloration with the reagent. For very accurate work it is necessary first to identify the hydrocarbon present. for work of lesser accuracy it is not. Thiophene and unsaturated hydrocarbons interfere.

Procedure—Prepare a formaldehyde-sulfuric acid reagent by mixing 1 ml. of 37 per cent USP formaldehyde with 100 ml. of concentrated sulfuric acid. The carbon tetrachloride must be CP or purified by washing with sulfuric acid until it remains colorless in contact with the reagent.

Shake 100 ml. of the aqueous sample with 25 ml. of carbon tetrachloride. Allow the layers to separate and carefully draw off the carbon tetrachloride layer. Only a single extraction is necessary. Add it to 5 ml. of the formaldehyde-sulfuric acid reagent. Shake vigorously for 1 minute and allow to stand for 5 minutes. Since the intensity of the brown discoloration changes on standing, it is important that it be

---

[47] H. E. Cox, *Analyst* **70**, 373 (1945).

[48] L. Robert Knodel and Evert J. Elvin, *Anal. Chem.* **24**, 1824-6 (1952).

[49] Dept. Sci. Ind. Research, ''Methods for Detection of Toxic Gases in Industry,'' Benzene Vapour, Leaflet **4**, p. 43, London, H. M. Stationery Office (1938).

[50] J. B. Ficklen, ''Manual of Industrial Health Hazards,'' p. 43, Lancaster, Pa., Science Press Printing Co., (1940); Morris B. Jacobs, ''Analytical Chemistry of Industrial Poisons, Hazards, and Solvents,'' pp. 399-415, New York, Interscience Publishers (1941); H. E. Morris, R. B. Stiles, and W. H. Lane, *Ind. Eng. Chem. ,Anal Ed.* **18**, 294-5 (1946).

observed at a standard time interval after shaking. Compare with a standard prepared under exactly similar conditions.

TURPENTINE

Turpentine in alcohol gives an initial pink color with vanillin in concentrated hydrochloric acid which quickly changes with evolution of heat to a green-blue color and intensifies for about 30 minutes.[51] The reagent turns brown in 2-3 hours, but the fully developed color does not change for several hours. The sensitivity can be increased by warming to detect 0.02 mg. of turpentine; without warming, not less than 0.15 mg. can be detected. Benzene, naphtha, acrolein, etc., do not affect the color. The reaction is common to compounds with mobile double bonds. Aromatics with double bonds not sufficiently mobile do not give the reaction. Acetone and methylethyl ketone give the initial pink color but not the green-blue, unless the solution is heated. Phenol interferes.

Also, in the absence of substances such as highly unsaturated petroleum hydrocarbons giving color under similar conditions, turpentine vapors are absorbed in concentrated sulfuric acid and estimated colorimetrically.[52] Fairly large amounts of naphtha and benzene do not affect the color produced.

Sample—Place 50 ml. of ethanol in a gas wash bottle. Pass 30 liters of air to absorb the turpentine vapor. Dilute this solution to an approximately known concentration but containing less than 1 mg. of turpentine per ml. for development with vanillin.

Alternatively, place 50 ml. of concentrated sulfuric acid in each of two 125-ml. fritted glass bubblers in succession. Draw the air through these at 1 liter per minute for 10 minutes for direct reading.

Procedure—*With vanillin.* Mix 5 ml. of the alcoholic solution of turpentine with 5 ml. of a fresh 1 per cent solution of vanillin in concentrated hydrochloric acid. Read after 30 minutes against a reagent blank. If the color of the sample and standards varies in quality it is

[51] Rosentaler, *Z. anal. Chem.* **44**, 292-301 (1905); V. D. Bogatskii and V. A. Biber, *J. Chem. Ind.* (Moscow) **5**, 645-7 (1928); *Z. anal. Chem.* **76**, 103 (1929); A. S. Zhitkova, S. I. Kaplun, and Joseph B. Ficklen, "Estimation of Poisonous Gases and Vapors in the Air," p. 177, *Service to Industry,* West Hartford, Conn. (1936).

[52] P. N. Andrev and A. A. Gavrilov, *J. Chem. Ind.* (Moscow) **5**, 1282-7 (1928); *Chem.-Ztg.* **53**, 870-1, 889-91 (1929); Marion T. Yates and Seymour Levinson, *U. S. Naval Med. Bull.* **41**, 1138-42 (1943).

usually due to variation in the terpene hydrocarbons present in the sample and standard. Use distillation fractions such as that below 155°, 155-160°, 160-165°, 165-170°, and above 170° to attempt to match the color. Precautions to use the turpentine which is the source of con tamination will usually be sufficient.

Direct reading. Read the color at once as it increases with time.

TERPINOL

When terpinol, a mixture of terpene hydrocarbons with oxygenated derivatives, in drug mixtures is dehydrated with sulfuric acid, it is estimated by the blue to blue-green color with phosphomolybdic acid.[53] The determination is accurate to 3-4 per cent in the presence of codeine, potassium guaicol sulfonate, sugar, soda, and licorice.

Sample—*Tablets.* These normally contain only starch and terpinol hydrate. Treat 0.25 gram of tablets with ethanol on a water bath. Filter, cool, and dilute to 100 ml. with ethanol. Dilute 1 ml. of the solution to 10 ml. with ethanol. Use 5 ml. of this dilution as sample.

Powders. These normally contain 5 per cent as much codeine as terpinol hydrate. The codeine reacts the same as the terpinol hydrate and a correction must be applied. Sugar is usually present. Treat a suitable amount of powder with a mixture of 93 parts by volume of chloroform and 7 parts by volume of ethanol. Extract several times and filter. Wash the filter with the solvent and remove the solvent by blowing with clean air. Dissolve the residue in ethanol and dilute to a suitable volume. Use 5 ml. as sample.

Procedure—Mix the sample with 5 ml. of 5 per cent aqueous phosphomolybdic acid solution. Add 5 ml. of concentrated sulfuric acid in 1-ml. portions and mix after each addition. Let stand for 30 minutes to cool and dilute with ethanol to 25 ml. Read against a reagent blank.

CEDRENE

Cedrene, a sesquiterpene hydrocarbon, and cedrol, a tertiary alcohol, constitute major ingredients in oil of cedar. Since cedrene in ethanol reacts like other terpenes with vanillin, it follows that, in the absence of terpenes, this reaction is applicable to estimation of cedrene.[54] Unlike

---

[53] J. Perelmann, *Pharm. Z.* **77**, 1204-6 (1932).
[54] F. W. Hayward and R. B. Seymour, *Anal. Chem.* **20**, 572-4 (1948).

turpentine, the initial red-violet is relied on for the determination. Cedrol does not so react but is easily dehydrated by phosphoric acid to cedrene. Hence by using two aliquots of the sample, total cedrene and cedrol are determined, as well as cedrene alone, cedrol being found by difference.

As little as 0.01 mg. of cedrene or cedrol is detectable by this method. Air from cedar chests contains 0.05-0.6 mg. of cedrene or cedrol per liter of air. It is probable that minor unsaturated constituents such as cedrenene or cedrenol will react with the reagent and be calculated as cedrene or cedrol. The color does not fade for 16 hours.

Sample—*Atmosphere of a cedar chest.* Replace the lock of the chest being tested with a rubber stopper containing a glass tube. Have a rubber tube located inside so that the air sample comes from the middle of the chest. Close the tube and let the chest stand until equilibrium is reached. Withdraw 1 liter of air slowly through 10 ml. of ethanol in a gas wash-bottle, using a calibrated siphon bottle as a measure of the sample taken. Dilute the ethanol to 10 ml. for taking samples.

Procedure—Dilute an aliquot of sample containing 0.3-2 mg. of cedrene to 5 ml. with ethanol. As reagent add 5 ml. of a 0.1 per cent solution of vanillin in concentrated hydrochloric acid. Mix by five inversions and allow to stand for 30 minutes. Read the color at 525 mμ against a tube of ethanol and subtract a reagent blank.

INDENE

The reaction to produce fulvenes described for cyclopentadiene is also applicable to indene.[55] Benzaldehyde is the preferred reagent, giving an intense yellow color of 1-(a-hydroxylbenzyl)-3-benzalindene. The maximum absorption is in the ultraviolet, but that in the visible spectrum is suitable for reading. Color develops slowly but is accelerated by heating. No change in color occurs within 72 hours. Only cyclopentadiene and methyl indenes interfere. The latter are determinable by the same method. As with various other hydrocarbons, absorption by other aromatic compounds interferes with determination by direct ultraviolet reading.

Procedure—Dilute the sample with benzene or petroleum ether to

---

[55] D. A. Skoog and H. D. DuBois, *Anal. Chem.* **21**, 1528-9 (1949).

0.2-2 mg. per ml. To a 5-ml. aliquot add 20 ml. of a 2 per cent solution of benzaldehyde in ethanol and 5 ml. of a 3 per cent solution of potassium hydroxide in methanol. Heat just to boiling for 10 minutes and cool, or let stand for 8-24 hours. Add 1-2 ml. of glacial acetic acid and dilute to 50 ml. with ethanol. Read around 420 mμ against the reagent blank.

BENZOPYRENE

Benzopyrene is a carcenogenic hydrocarbon present in tars. It is read fluorescently.[56]

Procedure—Dissolve the sample in light paraffin oil and read the fluorescence. The method will detect 0.005 per cent.

AZULENE

Azulene, $C_{15}H_{18}$, is a hydrocarbon which in solution in petroleum solvent has a blue color.[57] It is an ingredient of the oil in yarrow and various other drugs. The color can be matched with ammoniacal copper sulfate as an artificial standard.[58]

Procedure—Steam-distil a suitable portion of sample according to the azulene content. Extract the steam distillate with petroleum ether, dilute to a known volume, and read at 580 mμ.

ACENAPHTHYLENE

Since the contaminants are largely colorless, acenaphthylene is read in toluene.[59]

Sample—Prepare a solution in toluene of appropriate concentration, not over 0.15 per cent.

Procedure—Read with a mercury light and Ilford filter 601.

---

[56] A. A. Il'ina, *Zhur. Anal. Khim.* **5**, 90-3 (1950).

[57] H. Kaiser and H. Frey, *Dent. Apoth.-Ztg.*, **54**, 882-5 (1939); *Ibid.* **57**, 155-6, 163-4 (1942).

[58] K. Koch, *Ibid.* **55**, 758-9 (1940).

[59] M. Kaufman and A. Fowler Williams, *Analyst* **76**, 109-12 (1951).

Anthracene

Anthracene is read in the ultraviolet at 376 mμ with suitable correction for impurities.[60] The solvent is chloroform. Carbazole and phenanthrene do not interfere. Accuracy to ± 1 per cent is obtainable.

Carotenoids

Carotene is a highly unsaturated hydrocarbon, $C_{40}H_{56}$, closely related to vitamin A, the alcohol $C_{20}H_{29}OH$. Carotenoids in general are hydrocarbons of such molecular size as to be colored in the visible spectrum while the smaller molecule of vitamin A absorbs in the ultraviolet. Various carotenoids are included in this topic. The carotenoids are read by their natural color. At least α-, β-, and γ-carotene, cryptoxanthin, aphanin, and myxoxanthin are precursors of vitamin A. Thus in animal feedstuffs the precursors are usually present, changed by the animals to the vitamin and then stored in the liver.[61]

Carotenoids present in natural material are usually in combined form, as esters or protein complexes. They are segregated by saponification with alcoholic potassium hydroxide solution and extraction with organic solvents. The solvent affects stability. Thus blood carotene is more stable when extracted into petroleum ether than in chloroform.[62]

Often the carotenoids are separated and determined as a group. Interfering pigments such as xanthophylls must be removed to read the carotene.[63] By older technics the carotenoids in petroleum ether are shaken with 90 per cent methanol and the xanthophylls enter the alcohol phase while the provitamins remain behind. More specific chromatographic methods of separation are available. Xanthophylls are often eliminated chromotographically when the other carotenoids are not separated.

Properly prepared dicalcium phosphate,[64] calcium hydroxide,[65] alum-

---

[60] Frank P. Hazlett, Roy B. Hannan, Jr., and Joseph H. Well, *Anal. Chem.* 22, 1132-6 (1950).

[61] G. S. Fraps, *Ind. Eng. Chem., Anal. Ed.* 10, 525-7 (1938).

[62] Wilhelm Halden and Günther K. Unger, *Mikrochemie, Festschr. von Hans Molisch* 1936, 194-200.

[63] D. M. Hegsted, J. W. Porter, and W. H. Peterson, *Ind. Eng. Chem., Anal. Ed.* 11, 256-8 (1939).

[64] L. A. Moore, *Ind. Eng. Chem., Anal. Ed.* 12, 726-9 (1940); L. A. Moore and Ray Ely, *Ind. Eng. Chem., Anal. Ed.* 13, 600-1, (1941); L. A. Moore, *Ind. Eng. Chem., Anal. Ed.* 14, 707-8 (1943).

[65] Akizi Huzita, Tunesaturo Narita, and Masanobu Azisaka, *Biochem. Z.* 308, 420-9 (1941).

inum hydroxide, magnesium carbonate,[66] magnesium hydroxide,[67] or magnesium oxide[68] will selectively sorb xanthophyll without affecting carotenes.

The absorption curves for β-carotene and neo-β-carotene differ and may introduce discrepancies unless read with a sharp band at 436 mμ.[69] For further subdividing, by elution from calcium hydroxide petroleum ether gives neo-β-carotene B, then with 5 per cent of acetone present, all-*trans*-β-carotene, followed by neo-β-carotene U.[70]

The maximum absorptions in carbon bisulfide are α-carotene 511, 478, 446 mμ, β-carotene 520, 485, 451 mμ, γ-carotene 533, 496, and 463 mμ.[71] The maximum absorption band of all types of carotenoid pigments can be calculated by formulas not reproduced here.[72] Reading of β-carotene in petroleum ether at 470 mμ is proposed as a standard Swiss method.[73] Other carotenoids or fat-soluble dyes must be separated chromatographically.

Carotenes are subject to oxidation and isomerization unless suitable protective measures are taken which may either increase or decrease color intensity.[74] Oxidation of carotene in oil by air causes a temporary increase in absorption at 337.5 mμ.[75] Carotene in oil can be separated nonquantitatively as salts with strong acids sorbed on diatomaceous earth.[76]

Comparison can be with artificial standards such as azobenzene[77] or potassium dichromate. A 0.025 per cent aqueous dichromate solution in distilled water is equivalent to 0.158 mg. of β-carotene per 100 ml. in petroleum ether.[78] Many others have been used. If potassium dichromate is used as an artificial standard, it is desirable that the pH be kept

[66] A. R. Kemmerer, *J. Assoc. Official Agr. Chem.* **24**, 859-65 (1941).

[67] G. S. Fraps and A. R. Kemmerer, *J. Assoc. Official Agr. Chem.* **22**, 190-4 (1939).

[68] G. Rozenberg, *Bull. biol. med. exptl.* (URSS) **5**, 363-4 (1938).

[69] F. P. Zscheile and B. W. Beadle, *Ind. Eng. Chem., Anal. Ed.* **14**, 633-4 (1942).

[70] E. M. Bickoff, M. E. Atkins, G. F. Bailey, and Fred Stitt, *J. Assoc. Official Agr. Chemists* **32**, 766-75 (1949).

[71] R. A. Morton, *The Application of Absorption Spectra to the Study of Vitamins, Hormones, and Coenzymes,* Adam Hilger, London (1942).

[72] Louis F. Fieser, *J. Org. Chem.* **15**, 930-43 (1950).

[73] P. B. Muller and H. Moor, *Mitt. Lebensm. Hyg.* **40**, 358-415 (1949).

[74] Gábor Vastagh, *Magyar Gyógyszerésztud. Társaság Értesitojh.* **20**, 203-21 (1944).

[75] Ralph T. Holman, *Arch. Biochem.* **21**, 51-7 (1949).

[76] Willy Lange and Robert G. Folzenlogen, U. S. 2,484,040 (1949).

[77] D. I. Sapozhikov, *Doklady akad. Nauk.* (USSR) **60**, 1013-14 (1948).

[78] R. O. Davies et al, *Rept. Grass Driers' Assoc.* 1941, 20 pp.

constant, as by use of a phosphate buffer.[79] Such methods are suitable only as first approximations,[80] considering that pure crystalline carotene is available.

While photoelectric readings are most accurate,[81] nearly as good results are obtainable by filter photometry.[82] Dihydrocarotene in liver oils of fresh-water fish introduces complications.[83] The carotene of dried grass is almost entirely β-carotene. Carotene is added as a concentrate to milk to improve the color.[84]

Check results on carotenoids are obtainable by the antimony trichloride reaction, which they give in the same way as vitamin A. The maximum color is reached in 5-10 seconds and then fades rapidly. That from 0.1 mg. of carotene is equal to that from 0.0056 mg. of vitamin A.[85] Partially oxidized carotene develops color for as long as 15 minutes, hence the necessity of purifying by chromatography. Carotene also gives a color with 1,3-dichloro-2-propanol.

The complex pigment mixture in flour includes alpha and beta carotenes, free and esterified xanthophyll, and flavone pigments such as tricin and others unidentified.[86] The spectral distribution suggests that the pigments of high-grade flour are mainly of a carotenoid type. Flavone pigments are associated with the bran and appear to increase in the low-grade flours.[87] Since a variable mixture is being measured, results can only be relative between samples in terms of an absolute standard such as β-carotene. The efficiency of various solvents in extraction of wheat and flour pigments is in decreasing order; tertiary alcohols, secondary alcohols, primary alcohols, hydrocarbons, ethers, esters, halogen derivatives, ketones and aldehydes. Butanol is preferable to hydrocarbons or hydrocarbon-ethanol mixtures.[88]

---

[79] A. Krogis, *Biochem. Z.* **287**, 226-34 (1934).

[80] S. M. Bolotnikov, *Farmatsuja* **8**, No. 3, 25-30 (1945).

[81] V. E. Munsey, *J. Assoc. Official Agr. Chem.* **21**, 626-31 (1938), *Ibid.* **22**, 664-73 (1939); Alfredo Castro Alarco, *Rev. facultad farm. y Bioquim., Univ. nacl. major San Marcos* **7**, 53-66 (1946).

[82] R. J. Taylor, *Analyst* **71**, 566-73 (1946).

[83] E. A. Lederer and V. A. Rozanova, *Biokhimiya* **2**, 293-303 (1937).

[84] Edwin B. Williams, L. H. Burgwald, and R. G. Washburn, *J. Dairy Sci.* **25**, 1003-14 (1942).

[85] R. M. Johnson and C. A. Baumann, *J. Biol. Chem.* **169**, 83-90 (1947).

[86] M. C. Markley and C. H. Bailey, *Cereal Chem.* **12**, 33-48 (1935).

[87] D. S. Binnington, W. S. Hutchinson, and Charles G. Ferrari, *Cereal Chem.* **18**, 10-19 (1941).

[88] D. S. Binnington, L. D. Sibbitt, .and W. F. Geddes, *Cereal Chem.* **15**, 119-32 (1938).

Samples—*General.* See chlorophylls (Vol. IV) for separation of carotenes from xanthophylls and chlorophylls for reading.

Milk. The preparation of the sample is fully described under determination of vitamin A (page 82), carotenoids being read before development of the vitamin A color reaction.

Butter. Follow the technic described for vitamin A determination (page 84).

Dried whole eggs.[89] Technics are described under vitamin A (page 86) for separate successive elution of β-carotene, cryptoxanthol, the vitamin A, luteol, and zeaxanthol containing isomerized material.

Carotenoids in dried eggs are alternatively measured by a formula in which the absorption at two wave lengths is applied to an extract without saponification.

Egg yolk. Follow the preparation of separate flour pigments (page 36) but use a 2-gram sample. The methanol separation of xanthophyll may require as much as 10 extractions.

Carotene dissolved in vegetable oils.[90] As a sorption column pack an 11-mm. inside diameter Tswett tube with 12 grams of 80-mesh aluminum oxide. Adjust the column to a height of 10 cm. by applying gentle suction and tamping lightly with a footed glass rod.

Dilute 1 gram of carotene-vegetable oil to 100 ml. with petroleum ether. Run a 10-ml. aliquot of the solution on the column. Develop the column and elute the carotene with petroleum ether containing 2 per cent of acetone. The volume of eluant needed varies from lot to lot of aluminum oxide. Dilute the eluate to 100 ml. with the solvent and read as under procedure. This measures α-, β-, and neo-β-carotene. The β-carotene is eluted off last.

Dried hay, grasses, and materials other than yellow corn, sweet potatoes, and carrots.[91] Reflux a 5-gram sample with 100 ml. of 12 per cent

---

[89] Cf. S. M. Hauge, F. P. Zschiele, C. W. Carrick, and B. B. Bohren, *Ind. Eng. Chem.* 36, 1065-8 (1944); W. G. Schrenk, Douglas S. Chapin, and Ralph M. Conrad, *Ind. Eng. Chem., Anal. Ed.* 16, 632-4 (1944); Gaston Dalby, *Cereal Chem.* 25, 413-17 (1948).

[90] Emanuel Bickoff and Kenneth T. Williams, *Ind. Eng. Chem., Anal. Ed.* 15, 266-8 (1943).

[91] Walter J. Peterson, J. S. Hughes, and H. F. Freeman, *Ind. Eng. Chem. Anal. Ed.* 9, 71-2 (1937); F. Genin, *Lait* 18, 1049-52 (1938); Donald W. Bolin and Assad M. Khalapur, *Ind. Eng. Chem., Anal. Ed.* 10, 417-18 (1938); Loran O. Buxton and Bernard A. Dombrow, *Ibid.* 10, 262-3 (1940); E. J. Lease and J. H. Mitchell, *Ibid.* 12, 337-8 (1940); R. A. Morton, *Analyst* 65, 266-81 (1940); L. A. Moore and Ray Ely, *Ind. Eng. Chem., Anal. Ed.* 13, 600-1 (1941); G. Mackinney, G. Aronoff

alcoholic potassium hydroxide solution for 30 minutes. Rinse down the sides of the flask with ethanol if necessary. The hot alkali saponifies the fats and chlorophylls and disintegrates the cells. Cool, add 50 ml. of petroleum ether, shake for 1 minute, and allow the sediment to settle. Decant into a 500-ml. separatory funnel, separate the extract, and repeat the extraction twice with 25-ml. portions of petroleum ether. Break up the residue by shaking with 15 ml. of ethanol. Make additional extractions with 25-ml. portions of petroleum ether until the final extract is colorless.

Gently pour 100 ml. of water through the alkaline alcohol-petroleum ether solution in the separatory funnel. The resulting alcohol-water solution contains most of the alkali, chlorophyllins, and flavones. Withdraw this solution and extract it by shaking with 30 ml. of petroleum ether. If there is any emulsion, clear by adding 1 ml. of ethanol. Combine the petroleum ether extracts and wash 5 times with 50-ml. portions of distilled water until free of chlorophyllins and alkali. The final washings should not be alkaline. Filter over anhydrous sodium sulfate and dilute to 100 ml. for aliquoting.

Prepare a sorption column about 10 mm. wide and 15 cm. tall, constricted at one end and plugged with cotton. As the sorbent, use 2 grams of either magnesium carbonate or dicalcium phosphate. Apply suction and pack the sorbent firmly, but not tightly. Concentrate *in vacuo* a 50-ml. aliquot of the carotene solution to about 10 ml. Place a few ml. of petroleum ether on the column and apply suction. Before the petroleum ether is drawn through, place the concentrated aliquot in the tube. When the extract is nearly drawn into the column, add petroleum ether. Keep the surface of the column covered with petroleum ether at all times. Wash the column with petroleum ether several times to wash through all the carotene. Dilute the eluate to 50 ml. for reading according to the procedure.

Dehydrated carrots and sweet potatoes. Add 8 ml. of water to 2 grams of finely ground sample and allow to stand for 30 minutes. If the sample

and B. T. Bornstein, *Ibid.* **14**, 391-5 (1942); A. J. Haagen-Smit, C. E. P. Jeffreys, and J. G. Kirchner, *Ibid.* **15**, 179-80 (1943); Monroe E. Wall and Edward G. Kelley, *Ibid.* **15**, 18-20 (1943); Cf. C. R. Austin and J. Shipton, *J. Council Sci. Ind. Research* **17**, 115-26 (1944); A. R. Kemmerer, *J. Assoc. Official Agr. Chemists* **29**, 18-24 (1946); R. T. O'Connor, D. C. Heinzelman, and M. E. Jefferson, *Ind. Eng. Chem., Anal. Ed.* **18**, 557-62 (1946); F. P. Zscheile and J. W. Porter, *Anal. Chem.* **19**, 47-53 (1947); F. P. Zscheile and R. A. Whitmore, *Ibid.* **19**, 170-2 (1947) James V. Derby, Jr., and James B. DeWitt, *J. Assoc. Off. Agr. Chem.* **31**, 701-8 (1948); Cf. Victor L. Guzman, *Inform. mem. soc. ing. Peru* **51**, 71-6 (1950).

cannot be ground in a mill, soak 5 grams of unground material in 20 ml. of water for 2 hours and grind with a mortar and pestle. Add 50 ml. of ethanol and reflux for 15 minutes. Filter through fritted glass and wash the residue with small portions of ethanol. Add 25 ml. of ethanol to the residue and reflux for 15 minutes. Filter and wash again as above. If the residue is more than slightly yellowish, reflux a third time. Add 50 ml. of petroleum ether to the combined alcoholic solution and shake. Add 50 ml. of water, and allow the layers to separate. Draw off the aqueous-alcoholic layer and extract with 25 ml. of petroleum ether. Repeat the extraction until the last petroleum ether extract is colorless. Wash the combined petroleum ether extracts 5 times with 50-ml. portions of distilled water. Concentrate the petroleum ether extracts if necessary, filter over anhydrous sodium sulfate, and dilute to 100 ml.

Continue as for dried hay, etc., starting at "Prepare a sorption column . . ."

Green plant tissue.[92] Cut the sample fine. Grind with sand in a mortar and proceed as for dried hay or dry, grind, and extract.[93] Green grass may be partially dehydrated by immersion in saturated salt solution.[94]

Mixed carotenes in plant tissue. A sample was extracted into 85 per cent acetone for estimation of total chlorophylls (Vol. IV). Add 50 ml. to about 1 gram of finely divided anhydrous barium hydroxide free from carbonate. Mix well, rinse down with 85 per cent acetone, and reflux for 30 minutes, shaking occasionally. Detach, cool, and filter the yellow solution through sintered glass or paper which will retain the barium hydroxide-chlorophyll precipitate. Wash with 85 per cent acetone until the washings are colorless. Transfer the washings to a 500-ml. separatory funnel with 50 ml. of petroleum ether. Rinse traces from the prior flask with three 10-ml. portions of 85 per cent acetone. Swirl gently to collect as much carotene as possible in the petroleum ether layer. Draw off the acetone layer and extract thrice with 10-ml. portions of petroleum ether. Discard the acetone and wash the combined petroleum ether layers twice with 20-ml. portions of water. Discard these washings. Extract the petroleum ether solution with 30-ml. portions of 90 per cent methanol saturated with petroleum ether until the extract is colorless. Extract the methanol extracts with 10 ml. of petroleum ether.

[92] Walter J. Peterson, *Ind. Eng. Chem., Anal. Ed.* 13, 212-15 (1941); Cf. J. W. Thomas, C. G. Melin, and L. A. Moore, *Anal. Chem.* 21, 1363-5 (1949).

[93] Bhupal Chandra Rai Sircar, *J. Indian Chem. Soc.* 17, 412-15 (1940).

[94] A. M. Mikmin and A. A. Tupikova, *Biokhimiya* 6, 373-8 (1941).

Add this extract to the petroleum ether layer containing the carotene. Wash twice with a few ml. of water to remove methanol. Filter the petroleum ether solution through anhydrous sodium sulfate. Wash the paper with petroleum ether until colorless and dilute the petroleum ether extract to 100 ml. Mix and read.

Alternatively,[95] grind a 1-gram fresh sample, not rehydrated, with 1 gram of quartz powder. Then grind with 1:1 light petroleum ether-acetone containing 0.01 per cent of quinol. Decant without filtering and repeat 6-7 times to remove all pigment. Wash out the acetone by an automatic extractor in which water is dropped through the petroleum ether layer and overflows automatically. Pigments remain in the petroleum ether. Sorb the pigments by passing through a column of alumina-sodium sulfate predried for 12 hours at 150°. Elute the carotene with 2 per cent of acetone in petroleum ether for reading.

Yellow corn.[96] Grind dried mature corn in a hammer mill. Soak a 20-gram sample in a Soxhlet extractor with about 6 ml. of water for 5 minutes, then extract with acetone so long as color is being removed. For immature corn this extraction is abbreviated by treatment of a sample corresponding to 20-grams, dry weight, in a Waring Blendor with 200 ml. of acetone for 5 minutes and filtering.

In either case, add an equal volume of ether to the acetone extract and cautiously dilute with three volumes of water. The carotenoids are in the ether extract. Wash the separated ether layer with five successive 25-ml. portions of water. Add 10 ml. of 12 per cent solution of potassium hydroxide in ethanol and reflux the ether for a half hour. Wash the ether with 100 ml. of water, then with 25-ml. portions until the washings are not alkaline. Evaporate the ether to just short of dryness.

Prepare aqueous diacetone alcohol by mixing 100 ml. with 28 ml. of water. Mix this as solvent 1:1 with hexane and take up the residue in the phases. Add each solvent until about 25 ml. of each phase is present. Shake vigorously and separate the diacetone alcohol phase. Extract the hexane layer with two additional portions of aqueous-diacetone alcohol. Extract the combined diacetone-alcohol extracts with 15 ml. of hexane

[95] V. H. Booth, *Anal. Chem.* **21,** 957-60 (1949); A. L. Bacharach, et al., *Analyst* **75,** 568-73 (1950); W. B. Deys and H. J. Immink, *Landbourok. Tijdschr.* **63,** 125-30 (1951).

[96] Jonathan W. White, Jr., Arthur Brunson, and F. P. Zscheile, *Ind. Eng. Chem., Anal. Ed.* **14,** 798-801 (1942); Cf. George L. Clark and John L. Gring, *Ind. Eng. Chem., Anal. Ed.* **9,** 271-4 (1937); Loran O. Buxton, *Ibid.* **11,** 128-9 (1939); G. S. Fraps and A. R. Kemmerer, *Ibid.* **13,** 806-9 (1941).

and wash that extract with 15 ml. of aqueous diacetone alcohol. Reserve all the hexane extracts. Mix the combined diacetone alcohol solutions with an equal volume of ether and cautiously add 3 volumes of water to transfer the carotenoids to the ether phase. Wash the ether extract with five 25-ml. portions of water. Evaporate just to dryness, take up in ethanol, and read as carotenoids except cryptoxanthol.

Extract the reserved solution of the carotenoids in hexane three times with 25-ml. portions of a mixture of 100 parts of 2-methyl-2,8-pentanediol and 9 parts of water. Add 15 ml. of hexane and cautiously add 300 ml. of water to transfer the cryptoxanthol to the hexane. Wash the aqueous layer with 10 ml. of hexane. Combine these hexane extracts, wash with five 5-ml. portions of water, and dilute to a known volume for reading of cryptoxanthin.[97]

Alfalfa.[98] Freeze the samples with dry ice and so maintain until subsampled and enzymes are destroyed. Add 5 grams to 25 ml. of 10 per cent potassium hydroxide in 80 per cent ethanol. Mix and simmer under a reflux for 10 minutes. Cool, fill the flask with low-boiling petroleum ether, close with a rubber stopper, and store at $-1°$ until ready to proceed. Transfer to a Waring Blendor and agitate for 2 minutes. Filter through cloth and wash the residue with petroleum ether.

Shake with 25 ml. of 10 per cent potassium hydroxide in 80 per cent ethanol to remove chlorophyll. Discard the lower layer and repeat. Shake with 100 ml. of 1:25 sulfuric acid and discard the washings. Wash gently with 200 ml. of water, discard the washings, and repeat this operation. Carotene remains in the petroleum ether.

To chromatograph pass through a layer of sodium sulfate over a sorption tube containing a 5-cm. layer of 1 part of magnesia to 8 parts of soda ash, with a 50-ml. graduated cylinder as receiver. Wet the column with petroleum ether before adding the water-free sample. As soon as the sample solution is all added, rinse in with 25 ml. of petroleum ether and wash with another 25 ml.

Elute with petroleum ether containing 1 per cent of ethanol until the upper pigment bands begin to move down. There is then no carotene in the column. Dilute the percolate to a known volume and read.

Alternatively,[99] extract a 1-2 gram sample in the dark with 3 parts

[97] For more details, see page 91.

[98] L. W. Charkey and H. S. Wilgus, Jr., *Ind. Eng. Chem., Anal. Ed.* **16**, 184-7 (1944); Cf. A. R. Kemmerer, *J. Assoc. Official Agr. Chem.* **25**, 886-91 (1942).

[99] E. M. Bickoff and C. R. Thompson, *J. Assoc. Official Agr. Chem.* **32**, 775-80 (1949); C. R. Thompson and E. M. Bickoff, *Ibid.* **34**, 219-24 (1951).

of acetone and 7 parts of low-boiling petroleum ether. Dilute to 100 ml. with the petroleum ether. Chromatograph a 5-ml. aliquot on a 12 × 40 mm. column of 50 per cent magnesium oxide 2642 and 50 per cent diatomaceous earth. Elute with 1 part of acetone and 9 parts of the petroleum ether until 25 ml. is collected and read. Neo-β-carotene U is more strongly sorbed and comes off last and most difficultly.

Silage.[100] Mix and grind a representative sample of fresh silage. Reflux 25 grams with 200 ml. of ethanol for 40 minutes and decant the extract. Repeat the extraction of the residue and decant. Combine the alcoholic extracts and add 40 ml. of a 20 per cent alcoholic potassium hydroxide solution. Shake and allow to stand overnight.

To recover any carotene not extracted by the ethanol, add 80 ml. of low-boiling petroleum ether to the residue, heat to boiling, and allow the flask to cool.

Take aliquots from the combined alkaline ethanol extract and the petroleum ether supernatant layer which represent equivalent amounts of silage. This will usually be based on 5 ml. of the petroleum ether extract and 25 ml. of the ethanol extract. Add 2 ml. of 20 per cent alcoholic potassium hydroxide solution to the petroleum ether extract and shake in a separatory funnel. Then add the aliquot of the alcoholic extract, 15 ml. of petroleum ether, and 8 ml. of water. Shake well and allow the layers to separate. Draw off the alcoholic solution and re-extract with two 15-ml. portions of petroleum ether.

Combine the petroleum ether extracts and wash free of alkali with four 15-ml. portions of water. Remove noncarotene pigments by extracting the petroleum ether solution with four 10-ml. portions of diacetone solution made up of 100 parts diacetone and 6 parts of water. Shake vigorously after each addition of diacetone solution and allow to stand until complete separation of the phase occurs. Discard the extracts.

Wash the carotene solution twice with water to remove the diacetone, dilute to 50 ml., and read according to the procedure.

Pigments in flour.[101] Shake 10 grams of flour for 1 minute with 50 ml. of water-saturated *n*-butanol. After 15 minutes protected from daylight,

---

[100] D. M. Hegsted, J. W. Porter, and W. H. Peterson, *Ind. Eng. Chem., Anal. Ed.* 11, 256-8 (1939); Cf. L. A. Moore, *Ibid.* 12, 726-9 (1940).

[101] D. S. Binnington and W. F. Geddes, *Cereal Chem.* 16, 252-62 (1939). Official and Tentative Methods of the Association of Official Agricultural Chemists, 7th edition, p. 206, Association of Official Agricultural Chemists, Washington, D. C. (1950).

reshake, and filter through a folded filter paper. Read according to a technic given under procedure.

Separate flour pigments.[102] Reflux 20 grams of flour with 50 ml. of 10 per cent alcoholic potassium hydroxide solution for a half hour, rotating the flask at intervals. Cool and filter through a fritted-glass Buchner-type filter. Transfer the last residues with ether. Repeat this refluxing with ethanolic potassium hydroxide twice more.

Add 175 ml. of cold tap water to the combined filtrates and rotate several times. When the ether layer has separated, draw off the lower aqueous alcohol layer. Extract this with 25 ml. of ether. Discard the lower layer and combine the ether layers. Wash the combined ether layers by pouring 50 ml. of water through it and discard the aqueous washings. Add 50 ml. of petroleum ether to the ether layer and wash gently 5 times with 50-ml. portions of water.

Concentrate the ether-petroleum ether extract at 45-50° *in vacuo* to about 5 ml. Filter through anhydrous sodium sulfate on paper, wash the filter with petroleum ether, and dilute to 100 ml.

Read an aliquot of this solution at 440 mμ according to the procedure and return quantitatively to the solution. Add 15 ml. of 92 per cent methanol and shake mechanically for 10 minutes. Separate the lower methanol layer containing xanthophyll and extract until colorless. This is usually 6 times for flour.

Wash the xanthophyll-free extract thrice with 25-ml. portions of water. Concentrate the washed petroleum ether-extract *in vacuo* at 45-50° to about 15 ml. Filter through paper containing sodium sulfate and wash the paper with petroleum ether. Dilute to 25 ml. or 50 ml. and read at 440 mμ according to the procedure.

The first reading represents carotenoids plus xanthophylls, the last only carotenoids. Therefore, xanthophylls are obtained by difference.

Macaroni and noodles. Grind in a coffee mill to as near the fineness of flour as possible. Follow the preparation of separate flour pigments, using as sample 20 grams of seminola, or macaroni, or 10 grams of egg noodles.

Paprika. Treat as for dried plant tissue.

Serum. Use the sample as prepared for estimation of vitamin A (page 88).[103]

---

[102] Official and Tentative Methods of the Association of Official Agricultural Chemists, 7th edition, pp. 217-19, Associated Official Agricultural Chemists. Washington, D. C. (1950).

[103] Cf. G. Baldassi, *Atti. soc. lombardo sci. med. biol.* **1**, 285-8 (1946).

Blood of dairy cattle. Follow the technic given under vitamin A (page 87).[104]

Procedure—*Carotenes by direct reading.* Read in hexane or light petroleum ether at 440 mμ, or multiply L_{440} by 0.028 to give mg. of carotene per 10 ml. of solvent. A convenient artificial standard for rechecking the instrument from time to time is 0.02 per cent potassium dichromate solution. If its reading changes, the instrument requires recalibration against carotene. A reading at 320 and 380 mμ is due to phytofluene. In some technics carotenes and other carotenoid pigments are separately eluted for determination.

For total pigments in butanol extracts such as from flour, read at 435.8 mμ against the solvent. Report by the formula: carotene in ppm. = (50 × density)/(cell thickness × 1.6632). The value 1.6632 is the specific transmissive index for carotene at the specified wave length and solvent.

For carotenoids in ether extracts of dried eggs (page 86) read the solution in ether at 380 mμ and 445 mμ against a solvent blank. Calculate as micrograms per gram by the formula 110 (D_{445} − 0.395 D_{380}).[105]

Carotenes with antimony trichloride. Follow the technic for vitamin A (page 89) but with a calibration curve prepared with carotene.

Carotenes with activated 1,3-glycerol dichlorohydrin. The technic for reading of vitamin A is applicable to carotene at 800 mμ [106] as described under vitamin A.

Reading of xanthophylls. Read after separation from chlorophylls and carotenoids. See Vol. IV for the determination on green leaves.

LYCOPENE

Lycopene is the typical red pigment of tomatoes, closely related to the carotenes and having the formula $C_{40}H_{56}$.[107] The pigment is extractable with acetone, benzene,[108] or gasoline [109] for reading.

104 Cf. L. A. Moore, *J. Dairy Sci.* **22**, 501-11 (1939).

105 J. A. Pearce and M. W. Thistle, *Can. J. Res.* **20D**, 276-82 (1942).

106 Albert E. Sobel and Abraham A. Rosenberg, *Anal. Chem.* **21**, 1540-3 (1949).

107 W. B. Davis, *Anal. Chem.* **21**, 1226-8, 1500-3 (1949); Cf. F. P. Zscheile and J. W. Porter, *Ibid.* **19**, 47-51 (1947).

108 Amihud Kramer, R. B. Guyer, and H. R. Smith, *Proc. Am. Soc. Hort. Sci.* **51**, 381-9 (1949).

109 O. B. Darbishire, *Analyst* **73**, 457-8 (1948).

Standard—Mix a 6- or 8-ounce can of bright red tomato paste thoroughly with 250 ml. of 30 per cent potassium hydroxide in methanol.[110] Store overnight at 5°. Disperse the paste with water and filter aid and apply to a suction funnel precoated with filter aid. Wash the cake with water until alkali-free, keeping the cake covered with liquid at all times.

Add 75-ml. portions of acetone at 35° until the lycopene is extracted from the filter cake. The suction reduces this to about 20°. About 300 ml. per ounce of paste is required. The first fractions contain little lycopene and are best discarded. Let the filtrate stand at 0° for the red crystals to settle. Deterioration is slow at this temperature. Decant most of the solution containing other carotenes.

Filter the crystals on hard filter paper. Wash with a little cold acetone, and dissolve in freshly distilled chloroform.[111] Filter and recrystallize by addition of methanol.[112] Vacuum-dry at 1-3 mm. over calcium chloride which should require only about an hour. Work rapidly and avoid strong light. As a stock solution dissolve 20 mg. of the crystals in 3 ml. of chloroform and dilute to 200 ml. with hexane. For use dilute a portion of this to 1 mg. per liter.

Procedure—Mix a 1-gram sample of tomato paste with sufficient 1 per cent metaphosphoric acid to cover the blades of a Waring Blendor. Add 2 teaspoonfuls of filter aid and filter with suction on a 2.5-cm. circle. Wash the filter cake thoroughly to remove all yellow carotenes and metaphosphoric acid.

Extract the filter cake with acetone at 25-30°, added in small portions under suction, and dilute the resulting lycopene solution to 50 ml. with acetone. Dilute a 5-ml. aliquot to 25 ml. with acetone and read at 440 mμ as the color index of the tomato paste. This is not strictly a determination of lycopene but correlates with analysis for lycopene and carotenoids.

---

[110] A. J. Haagen-Smit, E. P. Jeffreys, and J. G. Kirchner, *Ind. Eng. Chem., Anal. Ed.* **15**, 179-80 (1943).

[111] Byron C. Brunstetter and H. G. Wiseman, *Plant Physiol.* **22**, 421-37 (1947).

[112] G. S. Fraps and A. R. Kemmerer, *Chem. Eng. News* **19**, 846-7 (1941).

CHAPTER 3

ALCOHOLS AND THEIR ESTERS [1]

ALCOHOLS, per se, have insufficient chemical properties for making good colorimetric derivatives. By oxidation to aldehydes they are more readily determined, but unfortunately with a question as to the completeness of conversion. Because of its greater stability, ethanol is not readily converted to an aldehyde. Therefore, the main method is one of oxidizing with dichromate and estimation of the change of color. Methods for other alcohols are largely but not entirely modifications of these two basic types of determination.

ALCOHOLS IN GENERAL

The alcoholic hydroxyl group can be determined by the red coordination complex produced upon addition of ammonium hexanitratocerate (IV) solution.[2] Primary and secondary alcohols reduce the cerium to the trivalent state with the result that the color slowly disappears. In order to increase color stability, the cerate solution should be prepared without acidification, although sensitivity of the method will be impaired. The rate of decay is eliminated by extrapolation back to zero time.

Phenols, enols, and aromatic amines produce interfering colors. Tetravalent cerium is reduced by 1,2-oxygen-containing compounds and they therefore should be absent. Ethylene glycol is the only member of this series which yields a color stable enough for determination. Formaldehyde interferes by reduction of cerium, acetaldehyde and propionic aldehyde by producing color. Inorganic reducing agents and alkalis must be absent.

Procedure—As ammonium hexanitratocerate (IV) reagent, dissolve 667 grams of the commercial product, $(NH_4)_2Ce(NO_3)_6$ in a minimum

---

[1]See Chapter 1 for details of organization, condensation, etc.

[2] Frederick R. Duke and G. Frederick Smith, *Ind. Eng. Chem.*, *Anal Ed.* **12**, 201-3 (1940); Frederick R. Duke, *Ibid.* **17**, 572-3 (1945); V. W. Reid and R. K. Truelove, *Analyst* **77**, 325-8 (1952).

amount of water and dilute to 1 liter. Filter through sintered glass if the solution is cloudy.

Mix a sample of the alcohol solution containing 0.05-0.5 mg. of an alcohol with 2.5 ml. of stock cerate solution and dilute to 25 ml. Read at 475 mμ against a reagent blank. Note the time of mixing and the time of reading and make one or two additional readings at 2- and 3-minute intervals.

Correct the extinction to zero time from the formula.

$$E_x = \frac{100\, E_m}{100\, A_t}$$

where

E_x = extinction at zero time
E_m = measured extinction
A = percentage decay per minute
t = time in minutes

Apply this to a curve for the specific alcohol present.

MONOHYDRIC ALCOHOLS

A general reaction for water-soluble monohydric alcohols is to convert to the nitrite by treatment with nitrous acid. After extraction this is used to form the diazo compound of sulfanilic acid from which an equivalent amount of dyestuff of high tinctorial power is formed.[3] Thus the reaction is suitable for estimation of methanol in the absence of ethanol, and vice versa. It is also given by acetic acid, but not quantitatively. Since reaction or separation may be incomplete at several stages, it follows that conditions must be rigidly standardized.

The procedure [4] will determine 0.005-0.025 per cent of ethanol within ±3 per cent in 20 minutes.

Procedure—The apparatus required is a 200-ml. glass cylinder with a funnel and stopcock at the upper end and a stopcock at the lower end. Connect the lower end to a source of suction and reduce the pressure in this reaction tube to about 500 mm. Introduce through the funnel, 1 ml. of 50 per cent sodium nitrite solution, 20 ml. of sample, and 1 ml. of 1:1 hydrochloric acid. Shake the reaction tube for about 30 seconds.

---

[3] Z. T. Tikhonova, *Lesophim. Prom.* **1939**, No. 2, 24-8; *Khim. Referat. Zhur.* **1939**, No. 8, 59-60.

[4] W. M. Fisher and Arvid Schmidt, *Ber.* **59B**, 679-82 (1926); N. V. Chalov and L. P. Volskaya, *Zavodskaya Lab.* **12**, 286-91 (1946).

Alkyl nitrite will form and fill the space above the liquid. To remove nitrogen oxides which form simultaneously, add 2 ml. of 25 per cent sodium hydroxide solution, and shake vigorously. Connect the reaction vessel to a suction flask and draw off the reaction mixture, leaving a 3-ml. layer of the liquid in the tube above the stopcock to prevent loss of alkyl nitrite. Add 0.5 ml. of 25 per cent sodium hydroxide solution and 10 ml. of 2 per cent potassium permanganate solution simultaneously. Shake for 30 seconds to oxidize the remaining nitrogen oxides and traces of sodium nitrite to nitric acid. Remove the alkaline potassium permanganate solution. Wash the walls of the vessel twice with 10-ml. portions of water. Add to the reaction tube containing the purified alkyl nitrite a 0.6 per cent solution of sulfanilic acid in 1:120 hydrochloric acid. Shake for 30 seconds to convert the alkyl nitrite to nitrous acid and in turn to form the colorless diazo sulfanilic acid. Add 10 ml. of a 0.32 per cent solution of α-naphthylamine containing 0.6 ml. of 1:1 hydrochloric acid per 100 ml.

After 2 minutes to form the azo dye, add water to give a final volume of 250 ml., and read the color. Since recovery is not complete, the calibration curve must be based on carrying through the entire technic with the same alcohol.

METHANOL AND METHOXYL GROUPS

The major method of conversion of methanol to a colorimetrically determinable derivative is by oxidation to formaldehyde. Then varied methods are applicable[5] for its estimation. While various oxidizing agents have been applied with greater or lesser degree of success, the determination has pretty much settled down to oxidation with potassium permanganate. The reaction to form formaldehyde is incomplete and affected by time, acidity, amount of permanganate, temperature, and the reducing agent used to remove excess permanganate.[6] Therefore stand-

---

[5] G. Deniges, *Compt. rend.* **150**, 832-4 (1910); C. Simmonds, *Analyst* **37**, 16-8 (1912); Leslie D. Wright, *Ind. Eng. Chem.* **19**, 750-2 (1927); G. F. Beyer, *J. Assoc. Official Agr. Chem.* **22**, 151-6 (1939); Elmars Bremanis, *Z. Lebensm. Untersuch. u.-Forsch.* **93**, 1-7 (1951).

[6] Th. von Fellenberg, *Congn. intern. tech. chim. ind. agr., Compt. rend. Ve Congr.* **1**, 184-96 (1937); Olli Aut-Wuorinen and Eeva Kotonen, *Z. Untersuch. Lebensm.* **74**, 273-81 (1937); S. S. L. Ginzburg, *Org. Chem. Ind. (USSR)* **6**, 177-9 (1939); Gabriel Bertrand and Lazare Silberstein, *Compt. rend.* **226**, 365-7 (1948); *Ibid.* **227**, 245-8 (1948); *Ann. inst. Pasteur* **74**, 233-41 (1948); James F. Guymon, *J. Assoc. Official Agr. Chemists* **34**, 310-28 (1951).

ardization of conditions of preparation of sample and standards is essential, and it is inadvisable to apply photometric methods using a prepared curve unless checked by a standard run at the same time.

Chromic acid is objectionable as the oxidizing agent only because of the green color of the residual chromic compound. Glycerol gives about 10 per cent as much color as methanol after oxidation. Dimethyl ether is equivalent to 93 per cent of methanol by weight.[7] Normal amounts of aldehydes, isobutyl, amyl, and propyl alcohols, acetic and tartaric acids present as impurities in beverages do not interfere.[8] Estimation of methanol in essential oils or their solutions by controlled oxidation is unsatisfactory because a large number of constituents of essential oils give formaldehyde on oxidation.[9]

Alkaline hydrolysis of methoxyl compounds permits their estimation by the same method. Varied methods of estimation of the formaldehyde with correspondingly varied kinds of interference are applicable. For glucosides acid hydrolysis followed by this method is entirely suitable as an alternative to the Zeisel method.[10] With methanolated cellulose the Zeisel method is grossly inaccurate. Some ether-linked methoxyl also reacts by hydrolysis and correction must be applied. The method is inapplicable with a compound which will distil with the methanol.

The steps for estimation of methanol are preliminary preparation of the sample, oxidation and destruction of excess oxidizing agent, and development of color by one of the methods available. Practically the oxidation step often has to be adjusted to the conditions of the color development.

Using Schiff's reagent, accuracy is about ±5 per cent in 1 per cent solution and ±1 per cent at around 0.05 per cent. By micro manipulation it will detect 0.005 mg. of methanol.

Chromotropic acid, 1,8-dihydroxynaphthalene-3,6-disulfonic acid, in the presence of sulfuric acid, gives an intense violet-red color with formaldehyde.[11] The method is rapid, accurate, and specific for quantitative

---

[7] Barnett F. Dodge, *Ind. Eng. Chem., Anal. Ed.* **4**, 23-4 (1932).

[8] Norberto S. Espinosa, *Anales assoc. quim. Argentina* **18**, 57-73 (1930).

[9] Y. R. Naves, *Parfumes de France* **13**, 60-73, 91-104 (1935).

[10] Carroll L. Hoffpauir and Richard E. Reeves, *Anal. Chem.* **21**, 815-17 (1949).

[11] E. Eegriwe, *Z. anal. Chem.* **110**, 22-5 (1937); Walter C. Gakenheimer and Walter H. Hartung, *J. Am. Pharm. Assn.* **30**, 49-50 (1951); M. John Boyd and Milan A. Logan, *J. Biol. Chem.* **146**, 279-87 (1942); Clarke E. Bricker and Hilding R. Johnson, *Ind. Eng. Chem., Anal. Ed.* **17**, 400-2 (1945); George F. Beyer, *J. Assoc. Official Agr. Chem.* **34**, 745-8 (1951); K. Agner and K. E. Belfrage, *Acta Physiol. Scand.* **13**, 87-95 (1947).

estimation.[12] Acetaldehyde, propionaldehyde, butyraldehyde, isobutyraldehyde, isovaleraldehyde, crotonaldehyde, chloral hydrate, glyoxal, benzaldehyde, and phthalylaldehyde give no color. Glyceraldehyde gives a yellow color.

Formaldehyde reacts with phenylhydrazine hydrochloride in the presence of potassium ferricyanide to give the violet compound [13] suitable for estimating much smaller amounts than the color developed with Schiff's reagent.[14]

Sample.—*Air*.[15] Prepare a series of 3 gas absorbers which may be stock bottles fitted with inlet and outlet tubes. Place 150 ml. of 0.5 per cent phosphoric acid solution containing 1 per cent of barium chloride in the first bottle. This removes formic-, acetic-, and sulfurous-acid vapors. Place 200 ml. of 5 per cent alkaline potassium permanganate in the second bottle. This removes methanol. In the third absorber, 225 ml. of Schiff's reagent removes formaldehyde. For the procedure adjust the contents of the second bottle to 35° and make just neutral with 1:1 sulfuric acid. Follow the procedure but omit addition of more potassium permanganate. Reserve the bottle in which the formaldehyde was absorbed for that determination (page 257).

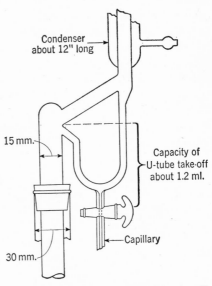

Fig. 7. Upper part of still and take-off for isolation of ethanol

Solutions containing ethanol.[16] Use a still with a column about 500 mm. long packed with small single-turn glass helices in a 30-mm. glass tube with a take-off shown in Figure 7. If more than 0.5 per

[12] R. N. Boos, *Anal. Chem.* **20**, 964-5 (1948).

[13] S. B. Schryver and C. C. Wood, *Analyst* **45**, 164-70 (1920).

[14] H. Lapp and H. Reimers, *Z. anal. Chem.* **128**, 290-8 (1948).

[15] C. F. Ackerbauer and R. J. Lebowich, *J. Lab. Clin. Med.* **28**, 372-7 (1942).

[16] F. R. Georgia and Rita Morales, *Ind. Eng. Chem.* **18**, 304-6 (1926); Official and Tentative Methods of the Association of Official Agricultural Chemists, 7th Ed., p. 131-2, Association of Official Agricultural Chemists, Washington, D. C. (1950).

cent of methanol is present, dilute to below that concentration with 50 per cent ethanol. Distil a 25-ml. sample keeping the column under total reflux for about 30 minutes and then collecting at about 20 drops a minute until about 8.5 ml. is collected. Keep the U-tube filled and the ratio of reflux to take-off at least 5:1. Distillate should be about 94 per cent alcohols. Dilute the distillate about 4 times with water and then to 50 ml. with 23 per cent ethanol. Develop with Schiff's reagent or chromotropic acid. Distillation is probably only about 95 per cent efficient so that standards must be similarly treated.[17]

Distilled liquors.[18] Transfer a sample according to proof containing 25 ml. of absolute ethanol and dilute to 100 ml. with water. Distil collecting 50 ml. of distillate. Add 20 grams of sodium chloride and shake at intervals over several hours to saturate. Transfer to a separatory funnel and wash in with about 10 ml. of saturated sodium chloride solution. Extract successively with three 25-ml. portions of petroleum ether, washing each extract successively with the same 25 ml. of saturated salt solution. Discard the petroleum ether extracts and add the washings to the extracted solution. Distil about 48 ml. and dilute to 50 ml. Develop an aliquot with Schiff's reagent or chromotropic acid.

Lemon, orange, and lime extracts and flavors.[19] Dilute a 50-ml. sample to nearly 200 ml. and let the oil separate on top. Dilute to 200 ml. exclusive of the oil. Mix with 5 grams of light magnesium carbonate, shake well, and filter. Add 50 ml. of water to 100 ml. of filtrate and distil for methanol collecting 100 ml.

Methoxyl groups in plant products. Extract 1 to 2 grams of finely powdered sample on a folded filter paper with several portions of boiling ethanol to remove essential oil. Keep the funnel covered. When the washings amount to 40 ml., pour several portions of ether, totaling about 40 ml., over the residue. Dry on a water bath and transfer the dry material to a flask. If the original sample contains no essential oil, this extraction may be omitted.

Add 40 ml. of water to the dried sample and evaporate to 20 ml. to drive off the last trace of essential oil. With products rich in

---

[17] James F. Guymon, *J. Assoc. Off. Agr. Chem.* **34,** 310-27 (1951).

[18] Peter Valaer, *Ibid.* **31,** 178-84 (1948).

[19] *Official and Tentative Methods of the Association of Official Agricultural Chemists,* 7th Ed. p. 308, Association of Official Agricultural Chemists, Washington, D. C. (1950).

starch omit this evaporation and add only 20 ml. of water. Treat the hot mixture with 5 ml. of 10 per cent sodium hydroxide solution, stopper, shake, and let stand for 5 minutes for hydrolysis to take place. Add 2.5 ml. of 1:4 sulfuric acid and distil off 60 per cent of the volume. The distillate will contain all the methoxyl groups as methanol. Distillation separates from pectin and glycerol which interfere in the color determination. Concentrate the methanol by redistillations, if necessary, each time collecting 60 per cent of the volume of solution used.

Glucocidic methoxyls. Ether-linked methoxyl absent. Dissolve a sample containing 0.3-2 mg. of methoxyl in 5 ml. of 3:2 sulfuric acid by occasional swirling with 3 glass beads. After standing overnight at approximately 27°, add 55 ml. of water. Distil to collect at least 36 ml. of distillate. Dilute to 50 ml. and develop aliquots by Schiff's reagent.

Ether-linked methoxyl present. Dissolve 8 or more samples as before to "... with 3 glass beads." Store at 27° and at 24-hour intervals dilute a sample with 55 ml. of water and "Distil to collect...". Complete and plot the results. Extrapolate the straight line reached after 48 hours to zero time. The point of intersection measures the glycosidic methoxyl.

Procedure—*With Schiff's reagent.* As the reagent dissolve 1 gram of pure crystalline fuchsin in 1 liter of water and add 7-8 grams of sodium bisulfite dissolved in 25-30 ml. of water. Store in the dark for several days. Remove excess sulfur dioxide by vacuum. If necessary decolorize with activated carbon. Store 2 days more before using. The solution must be colorless.

Heat 0.25 ml. of sample at 35° for 5-10 minutes. Add 2 ml. of 3 per cent potassium permanganate solution in 1:5 syrupy phosphoric acid prewarmed to the same temperature. Shake occasionally for 10 minutes and add 2 ml. of 5 per cent oxalic acid solution in 1:1 sulfuric acid. Exactly 2 minutes after the oxalic acid has been added, add a 5-ml. portion of reagent. Stir, keep at 35° for 1 hour, and read at 560, 580, or 600 mμ against 23 per cent ethanol developed as a reagent blank.

With chromotropic acid. Oxidize 0.25 ml. of the test solution containing 0.02-0.1 mg. of methanol by adding 2 ml. of 3 per cent potassium permanganate solution in 15 per cent phosphoric acid. Keep at room temperature for about 4 minutes with occasional swirling. Reduce excess permanganate by adding solid sodium bisulfite.

Add 0.6 ml. of 10 per cent aqueous chromotropic acid solution. Slowly add 10 ml. of concentrated sulfuric acid with agitation. Swirl, chill, and dilute to 50 ml. Read at 570 mμ and subtract a reagent blank.

With phenylhydrazine and ferricyanide. Proceed as for development by Schiff's reagent through ". . . add 2 ml. of 5 per cent oxalic acid solution in 1:1 sulfuric acid." After 2 minutes add 2 ml. of a 1 per cent solution of phenylhydrazine hydrochloride, 2 ml. of a 2.5 per cent solution of potassium ferricyanide, and 3 ml. of concentrated hydrochloric acid. Read against a reagent blank.

ETHANOL

Potassium bichromate in acid solution oxidizes ethanol completely to acetic acid. In the absence of other reducing agents this is used as a means of estimation, with the amounts of bichromate and acid accurately standardized. Since the final color is a composite of chromic and bichromate ions, either a method using a series of standards or photometric examination at 600 mμ is necessary.[20] The color does not follow Beer's law because of the shift in the point of maximum absorption between blue-green and green-yellow but will determine 1-10 mg. per liter in blood with accuracy to ±5 per cent, and in beer within 1.4 per cent.[21]

The method is subdivided into those which distil and condense the sample, and those which absorb the vapors directly in acid or in acid dichromate solution.[22] Some variations providing for bichromate in nitric acid [23] are less accurate.

By oxidation of ethanol with bichromate, on dilution to under 1 mg. of chromium per liter, the green and yellow do not interfere with determination of the excess bichromate by the violet color with s-diphenyl-carbazide.[24] Results [25] are very close to or on the theoretical curve.

[20] R. Fonteyne and P. de Smet, *Mikrochemie* **13**, 289-304 (1933); Lloyd M. Shupe and Kurt M. Dubowski, *Am. J. Clin. Path.* **22**, 901-10 (1952).

[21] Gh. Ghimicescu, *Mikrochemie*, **22**, 326-8 (1937).

[22] Richmond K. Anderson, *Am. J. Clin. Path.*, Tech. Sect. **6**, 85-9 (1942); Henry W. Newman and Mason Abramson, *J. Pharmacol.* **74**, 369-71 (1942); Lennart Smith, *Svensk. Kem. Tid.* **56**, 153-6 (1944); Walter W. Jetter, *Am. J. Clin. Path* **20**, 473-5 (1950); George R. Kingsley and Hazel Current, *J. Lab. Clin. Med.* **35**, 294-6 (1950).

[23] H. Agulhon, *Bull. soc. chim.* **9**, 881-5 (1911); W. R. Fearon and D. M. Mitchell, *Analyst* **57**, 372-4 (1932); E. C. Craven, *J. Soc. Chem. Ind.* **52**, 239-42T (1933); D. A. Webb, *Sci. Proc. Roy. Dublin Soc.* **21**, 281-4 (1936).

[24] Max B. Williams and H. Darwin Reese, *Anal. Chem.* **22**, 1556-61 (1950).

[25] For more details of this system see Vol. II, pp. 274-5.

Other oxidizable substances, tetravalent molybdenum, mercury, ferric iron, and pentavalent vanadium may interfere. The reaction is read best in about 1:180 sulfuric acid solution. The color fades slowly at lower concentrations, more rapidly at higher concentrations. A large excess of the reagent to develop the color is always present.

After ethanol is oxidized to acetic acid, this gives a color reaction with p-hydroxybiphenyl.[26] The results are accurate within 6 per cent and there is no interference from methanol and acetone.

Ethanol of the order of 0.5-1 per cent in ether is important in some uses, such as extraction of propellant mixtures. The color with ceric ion is suitable [27] for its estimation. Rapid fading of the color requires comparison within a few minutes. The reaction is given by all the lower alcohols. Aldehydes and amines interfere.[28] An error of 3 per cent occurs with 0.1-0.2 per cent ethanol. If necessary a sample may be cut back to that range with known ethanol-free ether. The method is applicable down to 0.01 per cent ethanol.

Sample—*Blood.*[29] Add 2 ml. of oxalated blood to 20 ml. of saturated picric acid solution. Distil [30] 9-10 ml. and dilute to 10 ml. Mix well and pipet off a 5-ml. aliquot for oxidation by dichromate.

Alternatively,[31] take 2 ml. of oxalated blood with 14 ml. of water and add 2 ml. of 10 per cent sodium tungstate solution. Shake and add 2 ml. of 1:1 sulfuric acid to precipitate serum protein and hemoglobin. Filter or centrifuge. Distil 10 ml. of clear solution collecting 5-6 ml. and dilute to 10 ml. for oxidation by dichromate.

Urine. Treat by the alternative method for blood, using from 1 to 10 ml. diluted to 10 ml., according to the amount of ethanol expected. Results will include other reducing substances such as acetone.

Blood or urine. Complexities arising from other volatile substances in either blood or urine are avoided by use of a purifying train.[32] In

---

[26] Richard J. Henry, Carol F. Kirkwood, Sam Berkman, Riley D. Housewright, Jane Henry, and Renate Hirsch, *J. Lab. Clin. Med.* **33**, 241-5 (1948).

[27] J. Lamond, *Analyst* **74**, 560-1 (1949).

[28] Frederick R. Duke, *Ind. Eng. Chem., Anal. Ed.* **17**, 572-3 (1945).

[29] R. Gingras and R. Gaudry, *Laval Med.* **9**, 661-5 (1944); Cf. Milton Lessa Bastos, *Engenharia e quim.* (Rio de Janeiro) **4**, No. 2, 10-15 (1952).

[30] A recommended apparatus is shown by Maurice Nicloux, *Bull. soc. chim. biol.* **13**, 857-918 (1931).

[31] R. Fleming and E. Stotz, *Arch. Neurol. and Psychiat.* **33**, 492 (1935); John G. Gibson, 2nd, and Harry Blotner, *J. Biol. Chem.* **126**, 551-9 (1938).

[32] Teresa Meneses Ruiz, *Farmacia y quim.* (Lima, Peru) **2**, 3-13 (1945).

the first of four test tubes place 4 ml. of blood or urine and 4 ml. of saturated picric acid solution. The second tube contains 5 ml. of 10 per cent sodium carbonate solution, the third 5 ml. of 10 per cent tartaric acid, the fourth 5 ml. of 0.33 per cent potassium chromate in 1:1 sulfuric acid. Heat the train in boiling water and bubble air through until the color no longer changes in the fourth tube. Read as preoxidized by dichromate. A simpler but less specific technic [33] reports all volatile reducing substances in blood or urine as ethanol and is applicable to 0.05-0.5 ml. of blood.

Macro. Cut two segments from a piece of hardened filter paper so that the remaining portion corresponds to half of the paper with a projecting strip from the center as a tab. Roll up the paper and stitch with thread. The rolled paper has a projecting flap with which to handle it.

Place 1 ml. of 0.4262 per cent solution of potassium dichromate in 1:1 sulfuric acid in the bottom of a 50-ml. Erlenmeyer flask. Pipet 0.5 ml. of blood onto the filter paper roll. Use the projecting tab to suspend the roll carrying the sample in the flask by inserting the tab between the stopper and neck of the flask. The closure must be reasonably but not absolutely tight. Heat the flask in boiling water or a 100° oven for 15-30 minutes. The alcohol and water of the sample are volatilized and absorbed by the reagent. Cool to condense the vapors and remove the paper roll which carried the sample. Use water to transfer the reduced reagent, dilute to 10 ml. with water, and read as preoxidized by dichromate.

Micro. Sterilize the skin with 1 per cent picric acid solution. Puncture and remove 0.05 ml. of blood. Transfer to a roll of hardened filter paper similar to that described for the macro method but smaller. Transfer 0.2 ml. of the reagent to 5-ml. flask. Suspend the sample as for the macro method and heat for 20 minutes in a 100° oven. Cool and remove the stopper and paper. Rinse out with water, dilute to 1 ml., and read as preoxidized by dichromate.

Separation as acetic acid. To distil the ethanol from any acetic acid present, neutralize a suitable volume of sample with 10 per cent sodium hydroxide solution and add 0.1 ml. in excess. Distil 5 ml. or more. Transfer the distillate to a flask containing 2.5 ml. of saturated aqueous potassium dichromate solution and 0.5 ml. of concentrated sulfuric acid. Distil the acetic acid which forms and dilute to a known volume.

---

[33] Julius C. Abels, *Proc. Soc. Exptl. Biol. Med.* **34,** 346-51 (1936) ; A. G. Sheftel, *J. Lab. Clin. Med.* **23,** 534-6 (1938) ; Jess Shapiro, *Am. J. Clin. Path., Tech. Sect.* **12,** 66-9 (1942).

Procedure—*Oxidation of distillates by dichromate.* To 5 ml. of sample solution containing 0.1-10 mg. of alcohol, in a glass-stoppered container add 10 ml. of 0.5 per cent potassium dichromate solution and 5 ml. of 1:1 sulfuric acid. Mix and heat for 1 hour at 80-85°. Allow to cool and read the green color of chromic sulfate at 600 mμ [34] or with an orange filter with maximum transmittance at 600-610 mμ.[35]

Preoxidized by dichromate. When the sample is absorbed in the reagent, read photometrically at 600 mμ.

Dichromate oxidation with development with s-diphenylcarbazide. Dilute a sample containing up to 0.1-50 mg. of ethanol to 10 ml. and add exactly 5 ml. of dichromate reagent in concentrated sulfuric acid called for in Table 1, slowly from a microburet with shaking. Cooling is not

TABLE 1. ETHANOL BY *s*-DIPHENYLCARBAZIDE

Dichromate Reagent (mg. per ml.)	Ethanol (mg. per 10 ml.)	First Dilution of Reaction Mixture with Water	Final Volume to Develop Color from 10 ml.	1:5 Sulfuric Acid Added to Final Solution	Saturated s-Diphenyl-carbazide in 95 per cent Ethanol to Develop Color
50	10-50	2 liters	500 ml.	16.7	5
10	2.5-10	2 liters	100 ml.	3.3	1
1	0.5-1	500 ml.	100 ml.	3.3	1
0.2	0.01-0.1	none	500 ml.	1.7	5

necessary. Stopper with a capillary provided to release the pressure and heat in boiling water for 2 minutes. Cool in water and dilute with water to the volume indicated in Table 1. If called for there, take an aliquot, add the specified volumes of 1:5 sulfuric acid and s-diphenyl-carbazide reagent. Dilute to 100 ml. with water and read at 540 mμ within 10 minutes against a reagent blank.

As acetic acid. To 1 ml. of the distillate containing the ethanol as acetic acid add 1 drop of 5 per cent copper sulfate solution. Next add 6 ml. of concentrated sulfuric acid with shaking in an ice bath. Add 0.1 ml. of 1.5 per cent solution of *p*-hydroxybiphenyl in a 0.5 per cent sodium hydroxide solution. Heat the tube at 30° for 30 minutes, then in boiling water for 90 seconds. Let cool to room temperature and read the deep-violet color at 560 mμ. Correct for a reagent blank.

---

[34] R. Gingras and R. Gaudry, *Laval Med.* **9**, 661-5 (1944).
[35] Roger Gaudry, *Rev. can. biol* **3**, 328-32 (1944).

Ethanol in ether by ceric nitrate. As reagent dissolve 667 grams of ammonium hexanitratocerate (IV), $(NH_4)_2Ce(NO_3)_6$, in a minimum quantity of water and dilute to 1 liter. Filter, if the solution is cloudy. This reagent keeps for an indefinite period.

For the determination, extract 50 ml. of ether with three 15-ml. portions of water. Combine the extracts in a tube. In another tube, take 40 ml. of distilled water and 5 ml. of reagent. Add 5 ml. of reagent to the cylinder containing the aqueous extract. Rapidly titrate the blank with 3 per cent ethanol in water. When the color of the blank almost matches that of the sample, adjust the volumes in the two tubes so that they are equal and complete the colorimetric titration.

β-NAPHTHOXYETHANOL

β-Naphthoxyethanol is a local anesthetic which when extracted into chloroform is read in the ultraviolet at 272 mμ or 325 mμ.

ISOPROPANOL, ISOPROPYL ALCOHOL

Isopropanol is determined as acetone after oxidation.[36] Results obtained by 7 collaborators averaged 95 per cent recovery.[37]

Procedure—Add 10 ml. of distillate sample, such as is described under ethanol (page 47), containing isopropanol to 50 ml. of 9 per cent potassium dichromate and add 100 ml. of 1:3 sulfuric acid. Stopper the flask, swirl, and let stand for 30 minutes. Add 100 ml. of 30 per cent ferrous sulfate solution and connect the flask to a vertical condenser through a foam trap. Distil slowly about 100 ml. into a flask in ice, containing 100 ml. of cold water. Dilute to 250 ml.

Dilute an aliquot containing 0.1-0.3 gram of acetone to 100 ml. Read against a water blank at 265 mμ.

If acetone is present in the original sample, determine the amount and deduct this from that obtained from oxidation of isopropanol. Multiply by 1.0347 to give the amount of isopropanol.

AMYL ALCOHOL, AMYL ACETATE AND FUSEL OIL

When amyl alcohol in ethanol is treated with furfural and sulfuric

---

[36] Anon. *J. Assoc. Offic. Agr. Chemists* **35**, 77-8 (1952).
[37] Robert D. Stanley, *Ibid.* **35**, 272-7 (1952).

acid, the rose-red color produced is used for colorimetric estimation.[38] The reaction is general for aldehydes with higher alcohols which probably partially dehydrate to C_nH_{2n} hydrocarbons, all of which, except ethylene, so react.[39] Exceptions are polyalcohols, o- or p-substituted phenols, alcoholic and phenolic acids, and aromatic derivatives having an ethylene group and carboxyl group on the side chain.

The color becomes more intense on heating, and the ester then gives a color equivalent to the same molar concentration of the alcohol, probably from saponification of the ester on heating. The method therefore gives the combined value for the two when both the alcohol and its ester are present, and neither can be estimated individually. The method will estimate 0.001 per cent of amyl alcohol in ethanol. Interference of acetaldehyde is prevented by 50 per cent dilution with water. Methanol and acetone give the color in 0.1 per cent solution. To a lesser extent toluene and xylene give the color. Normally these do not interfere. Oil of turpentine gives an intense reaction. Other terpenes, such as lemon or orange oils, pinene, limonene, terpineol, menthol, citral, and citronella also give the color. Unsaturated hydrocarbons from petroleum give the color. No reaction is given by menthone, camphor, and fenchon. Not only the concentration of test substance but also of the reagents affect the color, indicating incomplete reaction.

Of the higher alcohols, the ratio of intensities with furfural is isobutyl alcohol:isoamyl alcohol:n-propyl alcohol $= 1:3:9$. Since the principal ingredient of fusel oil is isoamyl alcohol, the method is used for its estimation. The error by this method varies from 3 to 11 per cent.

As in the case of furfural, amyl alcohol reacts with salicylic aldehyde and sulfuric acid to give a color [40] which varies from yellow in transmitted light and reddish in reflected light to garnet red in transmitted light at 0.01 per cent.[41]

The same reaction has been applied with benzaldehyde and derivatives. Isoamyl alcohol gives a raspberry color with p-hydroxybenzaldehyde, which changes to violet on long standing. The reagent is a 2 per

[38] Ladislaus V. Udránszky, *Z. Physiol. Chem.* **13**, 248-63 (1889) ; A. Komarowsky, *Chem.-Ztg.* **27**, 807-8 (1903).

[39] I. M. Korenman, *J. Applied Chem.* (U.S.S.R.) **4**, 940-9 (1931) ; *Arch. Hyg. Bakt.* **109**, 108-23 (1932) ; G. Guerin, *J. pharm. chim.* (6) **21**, 14-7 (1905) ; L. Ekkert, *Pharm. Zentralhalle* **69**, 289-96 (1928).

[40] T. von Fellenberg, *Chem.-Ztg.* **34**, 791-2 (1910) ; Hans Kreis, *Chem.-Ztg.* **31**, 999-1000 (1907).

[41] A. Komarowsky, *Chem.-Ztg.* **27**, 807-8 (1903).

cent solution in 50 per cent alcohol. Under similar conditions benz-aldehyde gives a brick-red color. o-Hydroxybenzaldehyde [42] is also suit-able for application in this reaction.

Higher alcohols [43] of the paraffin series,[44] esters of these alcohols, hydroaromatic alcohols, and phenols are dehydrated by concentrated sulfuric acid. Ethylene compounds when present as a straight chain possess the same structure. Aromatic aldehydes such as p-dimethyl-aminobenzaldehyde then combine to give the color. The reaction is not given by polyalcohols, ortho- and para-substituted phenols, alcoholic and phenolic acids, and aromatic derivatives having an ethylene group and carboxyl group on the side chain.

A threshold concentration of sulfuric acid must be reached before the color appears. Phosphoric acid acts similarly but produces a less intense color. Factors increasing color intensity in addition to the amount of higher alcohol are: Increase in aldehyde, increase in sulfuric acid, heating, and time. The colored complex is not extractable with butanol but can be sorbed on fuller's earth and eluted after washing. Applied to ethanol it will show 10 grams of contaminant per 100 liters and by applying the reagent in the sulfuric acid this can be increased to 1 gram per 100 liters.

Sample—*Air.* Collect the air to be examined in a flask of known size. Add 20 ml. of 50 per cent ethanol. Close and shake for 2-3 hours. This dissolves the amyl alcohol and amyl acetate vapors. Develop with furfural or salicylic aldehyde.

Distilled liquor. To 25 ml. of distilled liquor add 5 ml. of 4 per cent sodium hydroxide solution. Digest for 1 hour with refluxing to saponify the esters present. Distil 25 ml. Add 5 ml. of water and distil 5 ml. more. Add 0.2 gram of m-phenylenediamine hydrochloride and reflux for 1 hour to destroy aldehydes. Distil 25 ml., add 5 ml. of water, and distil 5 ml. more. Develop with furfural or salicylic aldehyde. An alternative for destruction of aldehydes is to reflux with aniline and sulfuric acid.[45]

[42] I. M. Korenman, *J. Applied Chem.* (U.S.S.R.) **4**, 940-9 (1931); *Arch. Hyg. Bakt.* **109**, 108-23 (1932).

[43] A. Komarowsky, *Chem.-Ztg.* **27**, 807-8, 1086-7 (1903).

[44] G. Guerin, *J. pharm. chim.* **21**, 14-19 (1905); L. Ekkert, *Pharm. Zentralhalle* **69**, 289-96 (1928).

[45] Ramon Bonaterra, *Anales direc. gen. ofic. quím. nacl.* (Buenos Aires) **2**, 90-1 (1949).

Mashes.[46] To a 75-ml. sample of filtered mash add 0.5 gram of silver sulfate and 1 ml. of 1:1 sulfuric acid. Dilute to 110 ml. and reflux for 15 minutes. This removes aldehydes. Add 5 ml. of 50 per cent sodium hydroxide solution with a few pieces of granulated zinc to avoid bumping and reflux for 30 minutes.

Distil this saponified sample, collecting 75 ml. of distillate, and use a 2-ml. aliquot as sample for development with *p*-dimethylamino-benzaldehyde.

Procedure—*With furfural.* To 1 ml. of the sample solution add 0.1 ml. of a 1 per cent solution of furfural. Carefully pour 1.5 ml. of concentrated sulfuric acid down the side of the test tube. Mix with cooling under the tap. Similarly treat standard amyl alcohol solutions. Heat the sample and standards together in boiling water for 3 minutes. Cool and compare at once.

With salicylic aldehyde. To 1 ml. of sample solution add 3 drops of a 1 per cent solution of salicylic aldehyde in ethanol. Similarly treat standards. Carefully pour 2 ml. of concentrated sulfuric acid down the side of each tube of sample and standards. Shake all samples and standards simultaneously and compare when cool.

With p-dimethylaminobenzaldehyde. To the sample in a tube chilled in ice and water add 20 ml. of chilled concentrated sulfuric acid. Add 2 ml. of a 1 per cent solution of *p*-dimethylaminobenzaldehyde dissolved in ethanol. Mix well and place the tube in boiling water for exactly 20 minutes. After this, immerse the tubes in ice water. Remove from the ice water and allow to come to 25°. Read at 395, 465, or 535 mμ against a reagent blank.

CINEOLE, EUCALYPTOL

Cineole gives colors with aldehydes. Reaction with *p*-dimethylamino-benzaldehyde in 75 per cent sulfuric acid gives a red color which can be read with an accuracy of ±0.5 per cent.[47] Thymol hinders color development so that 10 minutes then replaces the usual 6-minute period. There is no interference by menthol, benzyl alcohol, or camphor. Related terpenes give color at other wave lengths.

---

[46] W. B. D. Penniman, D. C. Smith, and E. I. Lavshe, *Ind. Eng. Chem., Anal. Ed.* **9**, 91-5 (1937); Harold W. Coles and William E. Tournay, *Ibid.* **14**, 20-2 (1942); *Ibid.* **19**, 936-7 (1947).

[47] Eric W. Martin and Joseph W. E. Harrisson, *J. Am. Pharm. Assoc.* **39**, 677-9 (1950).

Procedure—The sample should be available in anhydrous methanol at 0.05-0.25 mg. of cineole per ml. As reagent add 64 ml. of concentrated sulfuric acid to 40 ml. of water with cooling. Then dissolve 0.5 gram of p-dimethylaminobenzaldehyde per 100 ml.

Dilute a 2-ml. sample to 25 ml. with the reagent. Mix and read at 555 mμ against a reagent blank six minutes after adding the reagent.

CEDROL

Cedrol is determined by difference after dehydration to cedrene (page 24).

Procedure—Mix an aliquot containing 0.3-2 mg. of cedrene and cedrol with 1 ml. of syrupy phosphoric acid. Shake and allow to stand for 30 minutes. Dilute to 5 ml. with ethanol and continue as for cedrene from "As reagent add 5 ml. . . ." Subtract a separate determination of cedrene to get the corrected value for cedrol.

POLYVINYL ALCOHOL

The orange-red color of iodine with polyvinyl alcohol varies with grades of the alcohol so that standard and sample should be of the same relative degree of polymerization.[48] The color is also affected by temperature. Reading a natural standard at the same time is preferable to use of a calibration curve.

Sample—*Sera and body fluids.* To a sample containing approximately 5-10 mg. add double the volume of 22.2 per cent sodium sulfate solution to throw down the protein precipitate. After decanting, drain well. Disperse the precipitate in 5 ml. of 10 per cent trichloroacetic acid solution and 5 ml. of water, and centrifuge again.

Procedure—Decant the clear extract and add a drop of 1.25 per cent iodine in aqueous potassium iodide. Read at 490 mμ against a reagent blank.

OCTADECANOIC ALCOHOLS

The reading of this in the infrared is given under octadecanoic acid (page 310).

---

[48] H. Leverne Williams, *Can. J. Med. Tech.* **7**, 127-30 (1945).

β-Pyridylcarbinol, 3-Pyridinementhol

Opening up of the pyridine ring with cyanogen bromide followed by conjugation with an aromatic amine to form a polymethine dye is applicable to β-pyridylcarbinol.[49,50] With *p*-aminoacetophenone as the amine the original yellow color turns to purple on standing. Colorless fresh reagents are essential. Results are reproducible to ±2 per cent. No interference occurs with phenol, *o*-cresol, *p*-hydroxybenzoic acid esters, chlorobutanol, or benzyl alcohol.

Sample—*Tablets*. Dissolve an amount of crushed tablets approximately equivalent to 40 mg. of β-pyridylcarbinol in 50 ml. of 0.4 per cent sodium hydroxide solution. Dilute to 1 liter with water, filter, discarding the first 100 ml., and use an aliquot.

Ampoules. Dilute a portion of solution containing about 40 mg. of β-pyridylcarbinol to a liter, after adding 50 ml. of 0.4 per cent sodium hydroxide solution.

Procedure—Dilute a 2-ml. aliquot of the sample with 11.5 ml. of water and 0.5 ml. of 5 per cent *p*-aminoacetophenone in ethanol. Add 1 ml. of 4 per cent aqueous cyanogen bromide and mix. Immerse in an 80° bath for 2 minutes, then in ice water for 2 minutes. Add 10 ml. of 1:60 hydrochloric acid and dilute to 25 ml. Read the color at 560 mμ against a blank exactly 20 minutes after immersion in the 80° bath. Use a sample blank from which cyanogen bromide has been omitted rather than the more conventional reagent blank with the sample omitted.

Ethylene Glycol

Oxidation of ethylene glycol with periodic acid converts it to formaldehyde.[51] The same reaction is given whenever two hydroxyl groups or an amine and a hydroxyl are on adjacent carbon atoms. It follows that the reaction gives aldehydes with propylene glycol, glycerol, etc.

Procedure—Mix 5 ml. of 4 per cent solution of the sample and 2.5 ml. of 6.6 per cent sodium iodate solution. Cool to 0° after 20

---

[49] Ernest G. Wollish, G. P. Kuhnis, and R. T. Price, *Anal. Chem.* **21**, 1412-15 (1949).

[50] For more detail of the Koenig reaction involved here see Vol. IV.

[51] P. Desnuelle and M. Naudet, *Bull. soc. chim.* **12**, 871-4 (1945); *Industries corps gras* **1**, 113-14 (1945).

minutes and add 0.5 ml. of saturated aqueous potassium nitrate to precipitate periodate. After 10 minutes use an aliquot of the supernatant layer, suitably diluted, for estimation of formaldehyde by phenylhydrazine and ferricyanide (page 258). Compare with a curve developed from ethylene glycol.

Propylene Glycol

1,2-Propylene glycol is converted to acetaldehyde by oxidation with periodic acid.[52] The acetaldehyde is then determined as iodoform, or by piperazine hydrate and sodium nitroprusside. This gives the same reaction as diethylene glycol and triethylene glycol, with 1-naphthol in sulfuric acid. It is shown for the latter but is applicable to propylene glycol in the absence of interference. It is also determinable by reduction of bichromate in much the same way as glycerol (page 64).

Procedure—*As acetaldehyde.* Dilute a sample containing 2-4 grams of 1,2-propylene glycol to 250 ml. with water. Distil a 5-ml. aliquot diluted to 50 ml. with water after adding 0.5 gram of periodic acid. The rate of 3-5 ml. per minute should continue until only about 1 ml. of solution remains in the flask. Have the condenser dip below the surface of the liquid in the receiver in an ice bath. Dilute to 50 ml. at room temperature and analyze for acetaldehyde as iodoform (page 263).

2,3-Butylene Glycol

By oxidation of 2,3-butylene glycol with bromine, diacetyl is formed which is appropriate for colorimetric estimation.[53] The color developed with dinitrobenzoic acid is applicable to estimation of butylene glycol in the absence of diacetyl, creatinine, and acetoin.

Procedure—Mix 10 ml. of sample solution containing 0.3-1.5 mg. of 2,3-butylene glycol with 0.5 ml. of 1:8 sulfuric acid and add 3 ml. of fresh 0.32 per cent bromine solution. Dilute to 20 ml. and seal. Heat at 80° for 20 minutes in the dark and cool similarly protected. Reduce the excess bromine and steam-distil the diacetyl which has been formed. Determine it by one of the methods for that compound (page 300).

---

[52] P. Desnuelle and M. Naudet, *Bull. soc. chim.* **12**, 871-4 (1945); *Industries corps gras* **1**, 113-14 (1945); Stephen Dal Nogare, T. O. Norris, and John Mitchell, Jr., *Anal. Chem.* **23**, 1473-8 (1951).

[53] Michael Hooreman, *Compt. rend.* **225**, 208-9 (1947).

Dipentaerythritol

The band at 1115 cm.$^{-1}$ is suitable for estimation of dipentaerythritol acetate.[54] Therefore, pentaerythritol is acetylated to determine the contamination with dipentaerythritol. For reading to 10 per cent the content of dipentaerythritol should be 10-70 per cent. Any higher polymer of pentaerythritol is read at the same time.

Sample—Reflux the sample with 5 parts by weight of acetic anhydride and 1.5 parts of anhydrous sodium acetate. After 6 hours dilute cautiously with 10 parts of water to destroy excess anhydride. Cool and extract with carbon tetrachloride. Filter and dilute the extract to a known volume.

Procedure—Read in the infrared at optical density 0.2-0.5 in the 1115 cm.$^{-1}$ band. Calculate x, dipentaerythritol, as follows.

$$d = \frac{a \times \dfrac{x}{100} \times 1.99}{v} \times l \times 41 + \frac{a\left(1 - \dfrac{x}{100}\right) \times 2.24}{v} \times l \times 6$$

$$x = \frac{1.47 \times d \times v}{a \times l} - 19.7$$

where a = weight of sample, grams
       v = final volume of solution in carbon tetrachloride, ml.
       l = length of cell, mm.
       d = optical density of solution at 1115 cm.$^{-1}$
    1.99 = ratio of molecular weights of dipentaerythritol hexaacetate
           (506) and dipentaerythritol (254)
    2.24 = ratio of molecular weights of pentaerythritol tetraacetate
           (304) and pentaerythritol (136)

Diethylene Glycol

This gives the same reaction as propylene glycol and triethylene glycol, with 1-naphthol in sulfuric acid. It is shown for the latter (page 59), but is applicable to diethylene glycol in the absence of interference.

Triethylene Glycol

Triethylene glycol, propylene glycol, and diethylene glycol in sulfuric acid all react with 1-naphthol. The method presented is for the most

---

[54] Joseph H. Jaffe and Shraga Pinchas, *Anal. Chem.* **23**, 1164-5 (1951).

important of the series for air disinfection, triethylene glycol.[55] It depends on reading the intensity of yellow color resulting from heating with the reagents. When collecting samples from the air by absorption in sulfuric acid, increasing moisture results in decreasing color. The humidity must therefore be taken into consideration. This means, in practical terms, that a psychrometric determination must be made with each sample. This dependence on the humidity of the air introduces no drawback to the method because relative humidity of the air is of primary importance in any program of glycol aerial disinfectant.

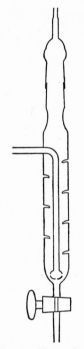

FIG. 8. Absorption tube for triethylene glycol

Normal air may contain interfering contaminants. Large amounts of tobacco smoke give a red-orange color. Dust or traces of rubber or soap in the ignition tubes impart a deep red color to the samples. Copper and iron cause a green color. The method is accurate to ±5 per cent. Results conform to Beer's law over the range of 0.0005-0.00035 mg. in a 30-liter sample.

The green color of chromic ion resulting from reduction of bichromate is also a sensitive method for estimation of glycols.[56] It requires large samples, 300 liters for triethylene glycol and 50 liters for propylene-glycol determination. The intensity of the color can be judged visually to 0.1 mg. or photometrically to 0.05 mg.

Since the oxidation reaction is not specific, care should be taken to exclude other reducing substances. Air samples containing no glycol will produce a blank value, depending upon the amount of dust, sulfur dioxide, and other substances present in the air. These blanks are of the order of 0.0006 mg. of glycol per liter in the air of occupied rooms and about 0.0003 mg. per liter of glycol for outside air. In the case of propylene glycol the blank is insignificant, but in the case of triethylene glycol, the amount is more serious.

Sample—*Air.* The technic as developed provides for sampling by drawing air at 15 liters per minute for 2 minutes through an absorber shown in Figure 8. For use, dispense 10-ml. portions of concentrated sulfuric acid into 25 × 200 mm., borosilicate glass ignition tubes, by

[55] Saul Kaye and Anna C. Adams, *Anal. Chem.* **22**, 661-3 (1950).

[56] H. Wise, T. T. Luck, and H. M. Stral, *J. Biol. Chem.* **150**, 61-7 (1943).

means of an acid buret. Cover the tubes and place them in a rack. For every sample determination, pour the contents of the ignition tube into the absorption tube and clamp the tube below to receive the liquid after the air has been drawn through. After the sample is absorbed, 9.8 of the 10 ml. will drain through the apparatus in 15 seconds. Use for development with 1-naphthol and sulfuric acid.

For development by oxidation, absorb in water. The original work on this method used two Folin aeration tubes. With that form, place each in a test tube with the 2-holed bulb close to the bottom and held in place by a rubber stopper. Add about 12 ml. of water, connect to a pump, and pass air at 20-30 liters per minute. Disconnect the aeration tubes and wash down into the test tubes with 2 ml. of water, collecting the washings in the respective absorption tubes. Add enough water to each tube to bring the level to 15 ml. and mix. Develop with bichromate and sulfuric acid.

Procedure—*With 1-naphthol in sulfuric acid.* Place the 25×200 mm. tubes containing a series of samples in boiling water for 30 minutes, remove, and place in water at 30°. Prepare the fresh reagent by dissolving 0.1 gram of 1-naphthol in 21 ml. of concentrated sulfuric acid. Add 1 ml. of the reagent to each tube when cooled to 30°. Shake and allow to stand for an additional 15 minutes for full color development. Read at 410 mμ against a reagent blank. Then results are translatable, subject to being checked on any specific instrument by the formula in which D is optical density and RH is relative humidity.

$$\text{Micrograms of triethylene glycol per liter} = \frac{1780 \, D}{145 - RH}$$

With bichromate. Dissolve 2 grams of potassium bichromate in 20 ml. of water and dilute to 1 liter with concentrated sulfuric acid. Store the solution in a glass-stoppered bottle in the dark. Transfer aliquots of sample solutions to contain not more than 2.4 mg. of glycol to tubes. Place the tubes in cold water and slowly add 10 ml. of the reagent to each sample. Mix each solution thoroughly and heat in boiling water for 15 minutes. Cool to room temperature by immersing in cold water. Read at 610 mμ or compare visually with standards.

3-(o-Toloxy)-1,2-propanediol, Myanesin

The strongly alkaline myanesin is extracted with chloroform and color developed in either of two ways.[57] In the first, myanesin is coupled with diazotized 2,4-dinitroaniline in 85 per cent phosphoric acid and the red color measured at 520 mμ. This technic is applicable to plasma and urine.

In the second method, the glycerine side chain is oxidized with periodic acid to formaldehyde [58] and the liberated formaldehyde determined by the chromotropic acid method at 570 mμ.[59] The method is suited to plasma but not urine because of interfering substances.

Procedure—*With diazotized 2,4-dinitroaniline.* As reagent dissolve 1 gram of 2,4-dinitroaniline in 5 ml. of concentrated sulfuric acid by warming gently on a steam bath and cool in an ice-salt bath. Dissolve 0.5 gram of sodium nitrite in 5 ml. of concentrated sulfuric acid which has been cooled to 0° and mix the two solutions. Keep at 0° and stir mechanically for 1 hour, meanwhile adding 20 ml. of 85 per cent phosphoric acid dropwise. To decompose excess nitrite, add 670 mg. of urea, dilute the mixture to 100 ml. with 85 per cent phosphoric acid, and refrigerate. Dilute 8 ml. of this stock solution to 100 ml. for use. It is stable for 2 months under refrigeration.

Add 0.5 ml. of plasma or urine to 9 ml. of chloroform and 5 ml. of 8 per cent sodium hydroxide solution. Shake mechanically for 10 minutes and centrifuge. Remove the gel and aqueous phase with a capillary tube. Shake a 7-ml. aliquot of chloroform extract with 7 ml. of 85 per cent phosphoric acid mechanically for 10 minutes and centrifuge. Remove the upper layer and to 6 ml. of the remaining phosphoric acid layer add 0.5 ml. of reagent. Read at 520 mμ against 85 per cent phosphoric acid within 24 hours.

By chromotropic acid. As chromotropic acid reagent, dissolve 1 gram of 1,8-dihydroxynaphthalene-2,6-disulfonic acid in 20 ml. of water. Before using dilute 1 part of this with 9 parts of 1:2 sulfuric acid. Shake vigorously 1 ml. of urine or plasma and 0.1 ml. of 4 per cent sodium hydroxide solution for 3 minutes with 25 ml. of chloroform. Remove the upper layer. Evaporate 20 ml. of the lower layer *in vacuo*. To the residue add 0.4 ml. of 2.5 per cent sodium bicarbonate solution and 0.4 ml. of 0.25 per cent potassium periodate solution. Allow to stand for 1 hour, then add 0.1 ml. of 1:1.5 hydrochloric acid and 0.2 ml. of 0.65 per cent sodium

[57] Elwood Titus, Stanley Ulick, and Arthur P. Richardson, *J. Pharmacol. Exptl. Therap.* 93, 129-34 (1948).

[58] Richard E. Reeves, *J. Am. Chem. Soc.* 63, 1476-7 (1941).

[59] Douglas A. MacFadyen, *J. Biol. Chem.* 158, 107-33 (1945).

arsenite solution. Allow to stand for 20 minutes to insure complete fading of the iodine color. Add 4 ml. of chromotropic acid reagent and immerse in a boiling water bath for one hour. Cool to room temperature and read at 570 mμ against a reagent blank.

POLYETHYLENE GLYCOLS

The familiar molybdenum blue reaction (Vol. II, page 660), has been adapted to polyethylene glycols, whether solid or liquid, and more particularly to biological samples.[60] The method is useful for determining 0.05-1 mg. of polyglycol at as low as 0.01 mg. per ml. There is no interference by 50 mg. of glycine, tyrosine, methionine, cystine, cysteine, choline, creatinine, uric acid, allantoin, phenol, catechol, or hydroquinone. Phosphomolybdic acid reacts with all the polyglycols from molecular weight 200 up, including Carbowax 6000.

Sample—*Blood.* Prepare deproteinizing reagents [61] consisting of 5 per cent zinc sulfate heptahydrate and about 5 per cent barium hydroxide octahydrate. The concentrations of the solutions are not as important as the fact that the amounts used must neutralize. To check this, dilute 10 ml. of the zinc sulfate solution, using phenolphthalein as indicator with 100 ml. of water. Run in the alkali dropwise with stirring until phenolphthalein turns pink and the color persists for 1 minute. Do not let the alkali run in rapidly, as this gives false end points. On the basis of the titration, dilute the more concentrated solution so that they are volumetrically equal.

Take a sample of blood in a measured amount of water and add 2 volumes of the barium hydroxide solution for one volume of blood. Mix well. Follow this with 2 volumes of the zinc sulfate solution. Shake vigorously and filter. Exact precipitation is manifested by the absence of foaming on shaking and ease of filtration. Add dropwise 1 per cent barium chloride solution to the filtrate to precipitate excess sulfate, if present, and digest until this can be removed by filtration.

Procedure—To 10 ml. of the plasma filtrate add the following successively, mixing after each addition: 1 ml. of 1:4 hydrochloric acid, 1 ml. of 10 per cent barium chloride solution, and 1 ml. of 10 per cent phosphomolybdic acid. Let stand for 1 hour. A flocculent, greenish precipitate

---

[60] C. Boyd Shaffer and Frances C. Chitchfield, *Anal. Chem.* **19**, 32-4 (1947).

[61] M. Somogyi, *J. Biol. Chem.* **160**, 69-73 (1945).

results from reaction of phosphomolybdic acid with polyglycol present. Centrifuge for 10 minutes and withdraw the supernatant liquid without disturbing the precipitate. Wash the inside walls with 3 ml. of 1:100 hydrochloric acid. Break up the precipitate with a glass rod, then wash down the rod and the walls with 7 ml. of water. Centrifuge and repeat this washing procedure. Transfer the precipitate, using as little water as possible. Add 3 ml. of concentrated sulfuric acid and digest with 1 ml. of concentrated nitric and 1 ml. of 70 per cent perchloric acid. Cool the residue, add about 20 ml. of water, and neutralize with 40 per cent sodium hydroxide to a phenolphthalein end point. Add 1 or 2 drops of 1:9 sulfuric acid so that the mixture is slightly acidic. Dilute to 100 ml.

As reducing reagent, mix 60 ml. of 1:20 sulfuric acid with 3 ml. of freshly distilled phenylhydrazine. Shake well to dissolve the precipitate, dilute to 100 ml., and store in a brown bottle under refrigeration when not in use.

Mix a 10-ml. aliquot of prepared sample and 5 ml. of the phenylhydrazine reagent in the colorimetric tube. Close with a rubber stopper pierced by a fine capillary and place in water at $81° \pm 2°$ for exactly 15 minutes. Let cool to room temperature and read against a reagent blank at 490 mμ.

Glycerol

The quantitative oxidation of glycerol with potassium bichromate and sulfuric acid is well known. The reaction has been applied to colorimetric estimation of glycerol, with the amounts of sulfuric acid and potassium bichromate accurately standardized.[62] Since the point of maximum absorption shifts with glycerol concentration only the method by series of standards is applicable. The estimation is accurate to better than 10 per cent. Studies [63] of the spectrophotometric characteristics offer promise for reading the excess bichromate at 350 mμ without interference by chromic ion. Thus by quantitative addition of the chromate reagent at a controlled acidity, an indirect method is feasible.

Glycerol is determined by oxidation to dihydroxyacetone with bromine. This product is changed to the anhydrous derivative, methylglyoxal. The latter develops a bluish-green color with codeine in sulfuric

---

[62] R. Fonteyne and P. de Smet, *Mikrochemie* 13, 289-304 (1933).

[63] D. T. Englis and Louis A. Wollerman, *Anal. Chem.* 24, 1983-5 (1952).

acid at 100°.[64] Provided that excess is present, the amount of bromine-water does not affect the end result,[65] and it does not matter how fast the excess is expelled. The blue color that develops increases up to 25 minutes after the addition of codeine and 20 minutes after the addition of sulfuric acid. Oxidation may also be by heating to 180-200° with vanadium pentoxide.[66]

Glycerol is determined in biological samples by its red color with catechol in sulfuric acid solution.[67] Carbohydrate material and organic acids are removed from samples by copper-lime precipitation, lipides by ether extraction. Carboxyl carbonyl groups such as in succinic, fumaric, and butyric acids are unreactive. The method is accurate to ±1 per cent. Oxidation with periodic acid gives equal moles of formic acid and formaldehyde.[68] The method of oxidation is described under ethylene glycol (page 55) which interferes. Propylene glycol gives acetaldehyde and formaldehyde.

Sample—Soap.[69] Add 100 ml. of water to a 10-gram sample and dissolve by boiling. Add powdered lead subacetate until precipitation of soap and salt is completed. Usually about 5 grams will be required. Boil to coagulate the precipitated soap and clear the solution. Decant and wash the precipitate with 10 ml. of hot water. Add 1:1 sulfuric acid dropwise until excess lead is completely precipitated, and filter. Dilute to a known volume for the development of aliquots by oxidation with potassium bichromate.

Wine. Decolorize red wine with activated carbon. To 1 ml. of decolorized wine add 1 ml. of 2.5 per cent sodium hydroxide solution, 2 grams of talc, and 10 ml. of ethanol. Shake, filter, and heat 6 ml. of filtrate in boiling water for 1 hour without evaporating to dryness. Add 1.5 ml. of 1:9 sulfuric acid and 2 ml. of saturated bromine-water. Dilute to 10 ml., heat for 20 minutes in boiling water, then boil until all the bromine has been driven off. Cool and dilute to 20 ml. for development of the methyl glyoxal present.

---

[64] Georges Deniges, *Bull. soc. chim.* **5,** 421-5 (1907) ; *Bull. soc. pharm. Bord.* **49,** 161-7 (1911) ; C. de Coquet, *Ibid.* **66,** 69-78, 235-50 (1928).

[65] Hogai Ka, *Rept. Inst. Sci. Research Manchoukuo* **4,** 141-61 (1940) ; *Bull Agr. Chem. Soc. Japan* **18,** 22-3 (1941).

[66] Emon. Pozzi-Escot, *Bull. assoc. chim.* **55,** 353-4 (1938).

[67] Stewart C. Harvey and Velma Higby, *Arch. Biochem.* **30,** 14-24 (1951).

[68] P. Desnuelle and M. Naudet, *Bull. soc. chim.* **12,** 871-4 (1945) ; *Industries corps gras* **1,** 113-14 (1945).

[69] K. E. Johnson and H. W. Ladyn, *Oil and Soap* **21,** 141-3 (1944).

General. Remove all other reducing substances, such as by the method of defecating soap solutions with lead subacetate. Dilute to a glycerol concentration of 1-10 mg. per ml. for development of a suitable aliquot by oxidation with potassium bichromate.

For development as methylglyoxal,[70] treat 50 ml. of a solution containing not more than 1 gram of glycerol with 50 ml. of saturated bromine-water. Remove excess bromine by heating on a steam bath for 20 minutes and then boiling for 5 minutes. Allow to cool and then dilute to 1 liter. Use a suitable aliquot for development.

Biological material, tissue, etc. Homogenize a suspension of material and acidify with 0.1 ml. of concentrated sulfuric acid for each 3 ml. of sample. Extract 5 times with equal volumes of ether or continuously in an extractor to remove lipids. To 1.8 ml. of extracted aqueous dispersion add 0.2 ml. of 20 per cent copper sulfate pentahydrate solution. After 5 minutes add 0.28 gram of calcium hydroxide, with mixing, and let stand for at least 30 minutes. Centrifuge and withdraw the supernatant liquid. Wash the residue 3 times by shaking with 2-ml. portions of 90 per cent acetone-free ethanol for 10 minutes at 75°. Centrifuge and add the washings to the supernatant liquid. Evaporate to 1-1.5 ml. Dilute to a volume containing 0.04-0.2 mg. of glycerol per ml. Develop with catechol.

Procedure—*Oxidation with bichromate.* Measure 10 ml. of clarified sample into a tube. Into similar tubes measure a standard glycerol solution at 1-mg. intervals covering the range in which the sample is expected to fall. Dilute each to 10 ml. To the sample and each standard add 5 ml. of a 7.5 per cent aqueous solution of potassium bichromate and 30 ml. of 1:1 sulfuric acid. Mix well and heat the sample and standards in boiling water for 15 minutes. Cool and dilute each to 50 ml. Compare without dilution or balancing. If many series are to be run with very low glycerol concentrations, a higher degree of accuracy of reading is obtained by reducing the concentration of potassium bichromate reagent or by using a smaller volume of reagent. Standards may be preserved for reuse if protected from evaporation.

As Glyoxal. Mix a 4-ml. aliquot of prepared sample with 1 ml. of a 5 per cent solution of codeine in ethanol. Dilute to 5 ml. with water. Add 2 ml. of concentrated sulfuric acid and cool rapidly in running water. Heat for 2 minutes in boiling water, cool to room temperature,

---

[70] V. Helweg Mikkelsen, *Analyst* **73**, 447-9 (1948).

and dilute to 25 ml. with concentrated sulfuric acid. Allow to stand for 30 minutes and read the blue color against a reagent blank at 600 mμ.

With catechol. To 1 ml. of sample in a tube immersed in an ice bath, add 1 ml. of freshly prepared 10 per cent catechol solution and 4 ml. of 3:1 sulfuric acid, and stir. Treat a control standard similarly at the same time. No color should appear if the solutions are kept cool. Transfer to a bath at 140-5° and leave for 10 minutes for development of color. Immerse again in a crushed-ice bath and read against a reagent blank at 510 mμ.

HEXITOLS

The class of compounds called hexitols or their simple derivatives includes sorbitol, sorbitan, and sorbide as well as mannitol and isomannide. The determination is done by the color with alkaline picrate.[71]

Procedure—*Plasma.* Add 4 ml. of plasma dropwise to 12 ml. of saturated picric acid solution and heat in boiling water for 12-15 seconds. Filter and make 10 ml. of cooled filtrate alkaline with 0.5 ml. of 10 per cent sodium hydroxide solution. Read at 520 mμ after 20 minutes.

Alternatively, add 4 ml. of 17 per cent ferric sulfate to a mixture of 4 ml. of plasma and 32 ml. of water. Add 6 grams of precipitated barium carbonate, stopper, and shake till all carbon dioxide has been given off. Centrifuge and filter through washed cotton or paper. Add 9 drops of saturated sodium sulfate solution and allow to stand for 15 minutes. Centrifuge to remove the barium sulfate and refilter the liquid. To 10 ml. of filtrate add 5 ml. of a solution of 5 parts of saturated picric acid solution and 1 part of 10 per cent sodium hydroxide solution. Read at 520 mμ after 10 minutes.

Urine. Add 3 ml. of sample to 9 ml. of saturated picric acid solution. Next add 0.6 ml. of 10 per cent sodium hydroxide solution and read at 520 mμ after 10-20 minutes. This may also be developed by 1:9 dilution and addition of the picric acid-sodium hydroxide reagent.

MANNITOL

Mannitol is oxidized by periodic acid to two moles of formaldehyde and four moles of formic acid. After removal of excess periodic acid with stannous chloride, the formaldehyde determined by reaction with

---

[71] Alexander Steiner, Frank Urban, and Edward S. West, *J. Biol. Chem.* **98**, 289-93 (1932); H. Popper, E. Mandel, and N. Mayer; *Biochem. Z.* **291**, 354 (1937); Willie W. Smith, Norma Finkelstein, and Homer W. Smith, *J. Biol. Chem.*, **135**, 231-50 (1940).

chromotropic acid is a measure of the mannitol.[72] The same reaction applies to sorbitol. Accuracy to ±2 per cent is usual.

Compounds that produce formaldehyde are fructose, α-glycerophosphate, ethylene and propylene glycol, and most compounds which contain either a –CHOH–CH$_2$OH or a –CO–CH$_2$OH grouping. Substances with a –CHOH–CHOH– or a –CO–CHOH– or a –CO–CO– group are oxidized but do not yield formaldehyde. They will interfere, however, if present in such concentrations that they decrease periodic-acid content and cause reduction of formaldehyde by excess stannous chloride. In biological samples, glucose is the chief source of interference. The oxidation of mannitol takes about 3-5 minutes. Oxidation should not be prolonged beyond 10 minutes or there will be higher yields of formaldehyde from glucose.

Samples—*Blood.* Prepare as described for polyethylene glycols (page 61).

Urine. Dilute with water so that 2 ml. contains 0.007-0.04 mg. of mannitol.

Procedure—As color-development reagent, dissolve 0.15 gram of chromotropic acid, 1,8-dihydroxynaphthalene-3,6-disulfonic acid in 20 ml. of 1:3 sulfuric acid, and dilute to 200 ml. with concentrated sulfuric acid. Add the first 25 ml. of concentrated acid slowly with cooling in a water bath. Store in the dark at refrigeration temperatures. As periodic acid reagent, use 0.18 per cent in 1:140 sulfuric acid. The reducing agent is 3 per cent stannous chloride dihydrate in 1:40 hydrochloric acid. Immediately before use dilute so that 10 ml. titrate 10.2 ml. of the periodic acid reagent.

Pipet out 2 ml. of sample containing 0.007-0.04 mg. of mannitol. Add 0.5 ml. of the potassium periodate reagent and mix immediately. After 8 minutes at room temperature, add 0.5 ml. of the stannous chloride reagent. Mix well and place the tube in cold water. Add 5 ml. of the chromotropic acid reagent and mix. Immerse in a boiling water bath for 30 minutes, remove, and cool. Add 10 ml. of 10:7 sulfuric acid and mix thoroughly. Read the sample and a reagent blank against distilled water

---

[72] D. A. MacFadyn, *J. Biol. Chem.* **158**, 107-33 (1945); A. C. Corcoran and Irvine H. Page, *J. Biol. Chem.* **170**, 165-71 (1947); Clark D. West and Sam Rappaport, *Proc. Soc. Exptl. Biol. Med.* **70**, 141-2 (1949); Nicole Argant, *Bull. soc. chim. biol.* **31**, 485-91 (1949).

at 570 mμ. The color does not change if the tubes stand several hours before reading.

Apply a correction for the slight oxidation of glucose which occurs under these conditions by developing a series of mannitol standards containing known amounts of glucose. The density per mg. of glucose can be expected to be around 17 per cent of that of mannitol. Thus the calculation will be

$$D_o - D_B - (K_G \times \text{mg. glucose in sample})/K_m = \text{mg. of mannitol}$$
in the sample

with D_o = observed density, D_B = density of blank, K_G = density per mg. of glucose, and K_m = density per mg. of mannitol.

SORBITOL

The same oxidation by periodic acid applied to mannitol is applicable to sorbitol with development of the resulting formaldehyde with chromotropic acid. Apply the method for mannitol (page 65), substituting the word ''sorbitol'' for ''mannitol.''

INOSITOL

Inositol is a vitamin for yeast and mice. Only the *meso* variety is active for both, esters only for mice. It is developed turbidimetrically in an appropriate medium by yeast growth.[73]

Sample—*Natural products.* Reflux a sample expected to contain about 0.02 mg. of inositol in 1:1 hydrochloric acid solution for 6 hours. After hydrolysis, concentrate under reduced pressure to dryness, take up in water, neutralize with 10 per cent sodium hydroxide solution, and filter. Adjust the volume to 10 ml.

Medium—As a medium, heat vitamin-free casein in an autoclave at 15 pounds pressure for 16 hours with 1:5 sulfuric acid. Remove the acid with barium hydroxide, filter, and adjust the filtrate from the barium sulfate to pH 6 with 1 per cent sodium hydroxide solution. Mix an aliquot of the hydrolysate equivalent to 2.5 grams of casein with 100 grams of glucose, 8.3 grams of ammonium nitrate, 4.2 grams of monobasic potassium phosphate, 2.1 grams of magnesium sulfate heptahydrate,

---

[73] D. W. Woolley, *J. Biol. Chem.* **140**, 453-9 (1941).

0.7 gram of calcium chloride hexahydrate, and approximately 300 ml. of water. Heat in an autoclave for 15 minutes at 15 pounds pressure. Remove the precipitate which forms. Prepare rice-bran extract by dissolving in water and dialyzing against running water for 48 hours. Add to the filtrate 10 grams of this extract (vitab), 0.5 mg. of thiamine, 0.5 mg. of riboflavin, 0.5 mg. of vitamin B_6, 1 mg. of nicotinic acid, 2.5 mg. of choline chloride, 1 mg. of pimelic acid, 5 mg. of asparagine, 0.05 mg. of biotin, 0.5 mg. of sodium pentothenate, 2.5 mg. of uracil, and 2.5 mg. of adenine. Add a concentrate of bios II [74] equivalent to 10 grams of malt sprouts. Adjust the volume to 500 ml. and preserve the solution with toluene.

Procedure—To 5-ml. portions of basal medium, add aliquots of the prepared samples to cover the range of 0.001-0.0001 mg. of inositol per ml. in the final solution. Prepare also a series to contain 0.001 to 0.010 mg. of inositol per ml. Dilute each flask to 11 ml. with water. Place the flasks in an autoclave at 15 pounds pressure for 15 minutes. Inoculate with *Saccharomyces cereviseae* and place in a water bath at 30° for 16 hours. Examine the contents of each flask for turbidity in a photoelectric colorimeter.

Prepare a standard curve relating colorimeter turbidity to micrograms of inositol. From the curve determine quantities of inositol in the various dilutions of the unknown. An average of these values give the inositol content of the sample.

POLYOXYETHYLENE STEARATE

Polyoxyethylene stearate is estimated by its effect on the potato starch amylose-iodine complex.[75] With polyoxyethylene approximating 40 moles of ethylene oxide, the method estimates to 0.05 per cent with reproducibility to 0.01 per cent. Hydrolytic products of the ester do not interfere.

Procedure—As buffer for pH 5 neutralize 800 ml. of 1:700 acetic acid to pH 5 with 4 per cent sodium hydroxide solution and dilute to 1 liter. As reagent suspend 0.4 gram of dry starch in 500 ml. of the buffer for pH 5. Heat to boiling, hold for 5 minutes, and cool. Filter through asbestos and dilute to 1 liter.

---

[74] G. H. W. Lucas, *J. Phys. Chem.* **28**, 1180-200 (1924).

[75] Robert V. MacAllister and Raymond J. Lisk, *Anal. Chem.* **23**, 609-10 (1951).

Mix 15 ml. of filtered sample solution containing not over 5 mg. of polyoxyethylene stearate per ml. with 5 ml. of the starch solution. Add 2 ml. of 0.05 per cent iodine solution in 0.1 per cent potassium iodide solution. After 1 minute read at 590 mμ against a reagent blank. A new calibration curve is needed for each batch of starch.

BENZYL ALCOHOL

Benzyl alcohol is polymerized in aqueous solution with sulfuric acid which is heated and is read turbidimetrically.[76] The variables aside from concentration of benzyl alcohol are (1) amount of sulfuric acid present, (2) manner of addition of the acid, (3) period of standing after mixing, (4) period and temperature of heating, and (5) period of standing after heating. There is interference only by substances darkened by heating with sulfuric acid and by dioxane and ethyl acetate because they dissolve the colloid. In the range of maximum sensitivity, the method is accurate to ±3 per cent.

Procedure—To 5 ml. of aqueous benzyl alcohol containing 0.05-0.25 mg. per ml. add 5 ml. of concentrated sulfuric acid and stir. Heat in boiling water for 10 minutes and chill in cold water for 5 minutes. Read at 410 mμ against distilled water.

MENTHOL

Menthol, a white crystalline alcohol, is separated from interfering substances in biological samples by micro aeration. The red color developed with dimethylaminobenzaldehyde can then be used for estimation by comparison with a suitable buffered phenol red solution.[77]

Sample—*Tissue.* Mix 1 gram of pulped tissue with 1 ml. of water and add ethanol to a total volume of 6 ml. Mix to deproteinize. Filter and take 3 ml. of filtrate for further treatment.

Set up a micro distillation apparatus. Add the 3 ml. of sample solution and 5 grams of anhydrous sodium sulfate to the apparatus. Warm the distillation tube to 70° and cool the condenser to −10°. Slowly draw air, washed with concentrated sulfuric acid, through the apparatus. After about 15 minutes add 1 ml. of ethanol and continue to draw air

---

[76] Max Kaufman, *Anal. Chem.* **24**, 683-5 (1952).

[77] Hajime Masamune, *J. Biochem. (Japan)* **18**, 277-83 (1933).

through the apparatus for another 15 minutes. Measure the volume of distillate for aliquoting.

Blood. Mix 1 ml. of blood and 1 ml. of water. Dilute to 8 ml. with alcohol and mix to deproteinize. Filter and use 4 ml. of filtrate for micro distillation.

Procedure—As reagent mix 1.6 volumes of concentrated sulfuric acid and 1 volume of water. Cool and dissolve 0.5 gram of dimethyl-aminobenzaldehyde in 100 ml. of the mixture.

Mix 1 ml. of sample solution with 5 ml. of reagent. Close the tube with a cork stopper carrying a fine capillary and heat for 2 minutes in boiling water. Cool under running water and compare with a standard.

As a convenient artificial standard, dissolve 0.1 gram of phenol red in water with the addition of 5.7 ml. of 0.05 N sodium hydroxide solution. Dilute to 100 ml. Add 0.3 ml. of this solution to 10 ml. of a boric acid-chloride buffer for pH 8.0 (Vol. I, p. 175). Add 10 ml. of water and mix. In a colorimeter at 8.2 mm. this is equal to the color of 0.1 mg. of menthol at 10 mm.

VITAMIN A

One of the most complex vitamins is the polythene alcohol vitamin $A(C_{20}H_{29}OH)$. The majority of methods for its estimation are based more on the unsaturation than the single slightly reactive group. The subject is complicated by isomers and by precursors, such as carotene, $C_{40}H_{56}$, converted in the body to a biologically active form.

In the absence of interference, preformed vitamin A is read in the ultraviolet at approximately 325 mμ with corrections, or color is developed with antimony trichloride or glycerol dichlorohydrin. Usually isolation of the unsaponifiable portion of the sample is necessary to avoid interferences. The necessity of control of size of samples is illustrated by the variation from 1 unit per gram in milk through roughly 2000 units per gram in cod-liver oil to upward of 3 million units per gram in rich concentrates. The vegetable provitamin, carotene, is included in the hydrocarbon chapter (pages 27 to 37). Kitol from whale-liver oil is a provitamin of animal origin, with a maximum absorption at 293 mμ.[78]

Observation [79] that the maximum absorption by vitamin A occurs

---

[78] Henri Chatain and Marcel Debodard, *Compt. rend.* **233**, 105-7 (1951).

[79] K. Takahashi, Z. Nakamiya, K. Kawakani, and T. Kitosato, *Sci. Papers Inst. Phys. Chem. Research* (Tokyo) **3**, 81-148 (1925); R. A. Morton and Ian M. Heilbron, *Biochem. J.* **22**, 988-96 (1928); J. C. Drummond and R. A. Morton, *Biochem. J.* **23**, 785-802 (1929).

around 325 mμ led to approval of the direct spectrophotometric method in 1934 [80] by the International Committee. Knowledge of the source, treatment, and conditions of storage is important.[81]

In diffuse daylight in chloroform, ethanol, or petroleum ether, deterioration is demonstrable in 2-5 hours, but none in 48 hours in the dark.[82] The successive use of methanol, ethanol, propanol, and butanol gives successively lower absorbency, as does also increase in temperature.[83] Other substances give absorption at the same wave length. Various approaches have been made for correcting this. One is to destroy vitamin A by ultraviolet irradiation,[84] reread, and so correct. This depends on the assumptions that (1) the end product from vitamin A has no appreciable absorption at 328 mμ, (2) other substances absorbing at 328 mμ are unaffected, and (3) destruction of vitamin A is complete.[85] In at least some cases technics meet these requirements. Vitamin A is very stable in hot alcoholic potassium hydroxide solution [86] in an atmosphere of nitrogen.[87] Diethyl ether is largely used as extractant [88] although some higher boiling solvents are superior. Larger amounts of soap than 5 per cent interfere markedly with the extraction from 50 per cent ethanol with petroleum ether.[89] A single extraction recovers 95 per cent of the vitamin A, three extractions only 97 per cent. Where loss of 1-4 per cent of the vitamin A occurs during saponification and

[80] R. M. Hume and H. Chick, *Med. Research Council, Special Rept.*, Ser. 202, IV (1935).

[81] J. B. Wilkie, *J. Assoc. Official Agr. Chem.* **20**, 208-12 (1937); *Ind. Eng. Chem., Anal. Ed.* **13**, 209-11 (1941).

[82] L. Fuchs and E. Soos, *Vitamine u. Hormone* **4**, 155-61 (1943).

[83] H. W. Rawlings and G. H. Wait, *Oil and Soap*, **23**, 83-7 (1946).

[84] Beaumont Demarest, *Z. Vitaminforsch.* **9**, 20-1 (1939).

[85] P. R. Peacock, *Lancet* **11**, 328-30 (1926); Robert W. Little, *Ind. Eng. Chem., Anal Ed.* **16**, 288-93 (1944); Cf. N. K. De, *Indian J. Med. Research* **24**, 737-49 (1937); A. C. Dornbush, W. H. Peterson, and F. R. Olson, *J. Am. Med. Assoc.* **114**, 1748-51 (1940).

[86] William J. Dann, *Biochem. J.* **26**, 666-78 (1932); G. H. Benham, *Can. J. Research* **22B**, No. 2, 21-31 (1944); J. I. M. Jones, *Analyst* **68**, 8-13 (1943); Bernard L. Oser, Daniel Melnick, and M. Pader, *Ind. Eng. Chem., Anal. Ed.* **15**, 717-24 (1943); E. M. Hume and H. Chick, *Medical Research Council Special Rept.*, Series 202 (1942).

[87] Norris Dean Embree, *Ind. Eng. Chem., Anal. Ed.* **13**, 144-5 (1941); Ernest L. Smith and Violet Hazley, *Biochem. J.* **24**, 1942-51 (1930).

[88] S. Yudkin, *Biochem. J.* **35**, 551-6 (1941).

[89] Willis D. Gallup and J. A. Hoefer, *Ind. Eng. Chem., Anal. Ed.* **18**, 288-90 (1946).

extraction [90] with some oils but not with others, it is attributed to manipulation. Conventional saponification to give potassium soaps results in some solubility of vitamin A in the micelles.   Precipitation of barium soaps avoids this, giving slightly better recovery.[91]

Qualitative chromatography with calcium carbonate [92] has been made quantitative as a means of separation of some materials absorbing at the wave length for vitamin A.   It is desirable to chromatograph not more than 3000 USP units as a sample. By reading the unsaponifiables in benzene, removal of the vitamin A in a column of Floridin, and reading again as a correction, good values were obtained with margarine.[93] Chromatographic separation of low concentrations of vitamin A on aluminum oxide and of higher concentrations on tricalcium phosphate is also practical.[94] It is sorbed from petroleum ether and eluted with 2 per cent of ethyl ether in petroleum ether.

Carotenes in butterfat prevent direct spectrophotometric reading with the desired degree of accuracy,[95] but corrections have been applied to both butterfat [96] and margarine.[97] Good correlation with biological methods is obtained.[98] Application to extracts of dried eggs was unsatisfactory.[99]

Partially oxidized carotene introduces an error which must be compensated.[100] Factors affecting the correction to be applied are the solvent employed and whether the vitamin is free or esterified. Some fish oils

---

[90] M. E. Chilcote, N. B. Guerrant, and H. A. Ellenberger, *Anal. Chem.* 21, 1180-88 (1949).

[91] Dirk Verhagen and Robert W. Parent, *Anal. Chem.* 21, 1584-5 (1949).

[92] Albert E. Gillam and Ian M. Heilbron, *Biochem. J.* 29, 834-6 (1935).

[93] Jorge Arvapera, Fred H. Mattson, John W. Mehl, and Harry J. Duel, Jr., *Science* 104, 602-4 (1946).

[94] W. Hjarde, *Acta Chem. Scand.* 4, 628-40 (1950).

[95] F. P. Zscheile, R. L. Henry, J. W. White, Jr., H. A. Nash, C. L. Shrewsbury, and S. M. Hauge, *Ind. Eng. Chem., Anal. Ed.* 16, 190-3 (1944).

[96] J. R. Edisbury, *Analyst* 65, 484-93 (1940); R. H. Neal, C. H. Haurand, and F. H. Luckmann, *Ind. Eng. Chem., Anal Ed.* 13, 150-4 (1941).

[97] R. H. Neal and F. H. Luckmann, *Ind. Eng. Chem., Anal. Ed.* 16, 358-62 (1944).

[98] Hans W. Vahlteich and R. H. Neal, *Food Industries* 16, 90 (1944).

[99] S. M. Hauge, F. P. Zscheile, C. W. Carrick, and B. B. Bohren, *Ind. Eng. Chem.* 36, 1065-8 (1944); Charles A. Denton, C. A. Cabell, Harry Bastron, and Russell Davis, *J. Nutrition* 28, 421-6 (1944); C. R. Thompson, M. A. Ewan, S. M. Hauge, B. B. Bohren, and F. W. Quackenbush, *Ind. Eng. Chem., Anal Ed.* 18, 113-15 (1946); Cf. C. J. Koehn and W. C. Sherman, *J. Biol. Chem.* 132, 527-38 (1940); W. G. Schrenk, Douglas S. Chapin, and Ralph M. Conrad, *Ind. Eng. Chem., Anal. Ed.* 16, 632-4 (1944).

[100] W. A. McGillivray, *Anal. Chem.* 22, 494 (1950).

contain as much as 5 per cent of their vitamin A as the alcohol.[101] High values for the alcohol but not for the ester have been reported [102] with isopropanol as solvent. Although a correction for interfering factors has been derived,[103] it is not indiscriminately applicable. Fish-liver oils cause distortion of the curve and vertical displacement by nonvitamin A materials. A simplified form [104] is by the nomogram shown as Figure 9.

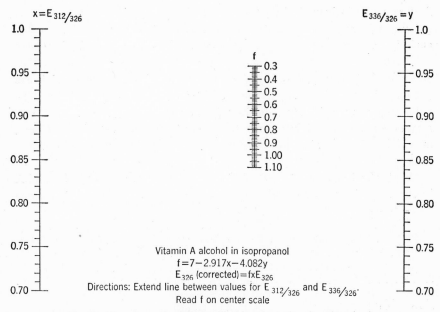

FIG. 9. Nomogram for Morton-Stubbs correction for vitamin A

Crystalline vitamin A acetate is the most satisfactory standard,[105] being stable in isopropanol for at least 24 hours. The absorption curve of 2-phenylazo-p-cresol between 290 mμ and 370 mμ is practically identi-

[101] H. M. Kasher and J. G. Baxter, *Ind. Eng. Chem., Anal Ed.* **17**, 499-503 (1945).

[102] Kenneth Morgareidge, *Ibid.* **14**, 700-2 (1942).

[103] R. A. Morton and A. L. Stubbs, *Analyst* **71**, 348-56 (1946); *Biochem. J.* **41**, 525-9 (1947); *Ibid.* **42**, 195-203 (1948); Aurelio Mariani, *Ann. chim. applicata* **39**, 227-33 (1949); Aurelio Mariani and Aldo Gaudiano, *Rend. ist. super. sanitá* (*Rome*) **13**, 632-58 (1950).

[104] Bernard L. Oser, *Anal Chem.* **21**, 529 (1949).

[105] M. E. Chilcote, N. B. Guerrant, and H. A. Ellenberger, *Anal. Chem.* **21**, 960-3, 1180-8 (1949); N. B. Guerrant, M. E. Chilcote, H. A. Ellenberger, and R. A. Dutcher, *Ibid.* **20**, 465-9 (1948).

cal with that of vitamin A.[106] Results by different operators or on duplicate samples are reproducible within 1 per cent.[107]

Much work has been done to establish the conversion factor.[108] Samples oxidize on exposure and are reported to give either increase [109] or decrease [110] in potency.

Determination of deterioration of the carrier oil by measuring $E^{1\%}_{1\ cm.}$ 300/328 by setting a limit of 0.72 for this ratio [111] is not satisfactory for fish-liver oils.[112] The method is not applicable to vitamin A potency of animal feeds because, other than in yellow corn, it is due entirely to carotene;[113] corn contains the related cryptoxanthin (page 91). Absorption at 325 mμ may be corrected for carotene as read at 450 mμ.[114] For both vitamin A and carotene in butter, where both are present, the vitamin A is extracted with ether and read at 324 mμ. The value tends to be high due to contamination with carotenoids. Azo dyes may be extracted and interfere. Carotenoids are often read at 437 mμ, at which point the absorptions of β-carotene and neo-β-carotene are the same.

With the issuance of USP XIV [115] the direct reading of vitamin A in the ultraviolet around 310-334 mμ became an official method, became

---

[106] Henry P. Kreider, *Ind. Eng. Chem.*, *Anal. Ed.* 17, 694-5 (1945).

[107] F. P. Zscheile and R. L. Henry, *Ind. Eng. Chem.*, *Anal. Ed.* 16, 436-8 (1944).

[108] E. M. Hume, *Nature* 139, 467-8 (1937); *Ibid.* 143, 22-3 (1939); *Ibid.* 151, 535-6 (1943); *Expt. Sta. Record* 91, 249 (1944); C. L. Barthe, F. F. Berg, E. B. Carter, D. M. Copley, R. J. Fosbinder, T. Lewis, and F. O. Taylor, *J. Am. Pharm. Assoc.* 28, 661-72 (1939); N. H. Coy, H. L. Sassaman, and Archie Black, *Ind. Eng. Chem.*, *Anal Ed.* 13, 94-6 (1941); F. P. Zscheile and R. L. Henry, *Ind. Eng. Chem.*, *Anal. Ed.* 14, 422-5 (1942); Norris D. Embree and Edgar M. Shantz, *J. Biol. Chem.* 132, 619-26 (1940); W. S. Metcalf, *Nature* 155, 575-6 (1945); Paul B. Müller and Marc Reinert, *Nature* 157, 876 (1946); A. Lee Caldwell, *Proc. Am. Drug Manufrs. Assoc.* 1948, 170-7.

[109] F. P. Zscheile and R. L. Henry, *Ind. Eng. Chem.*, *Anal. Ed.* 16, 436-8 (1944).

[110] N. H. Coy, H. L. Sassaman, and Archie Black, *Ibid.* 13, 74-6 (1941); *Ibid.* 15, 441-3 (1943); Ronald L. McFarlan, Philip K. Bates, and Edward C. Merrill, *Ibid.* 12, 645-7 (1940).

[111] Bernard L. Oser, Daniel Melnick, Morton Pader, Roslyn Roth, and Mona Oser, *Ind. Eng. Chem.*, *Anal. Ed.* 17, 559-62 (1945).

[112] George R. Halpern, *Ibid.* 18, 621-5 (1946).

[113] G. S. Fraps, *Ibid.* 10, 525-7 (1938).

[114] A. K. R. McDowell, *J. Dairy Research* 16, 348-55 (1949).

[115] Norris Dean Embree, *J. Am. Oil Chemists' Soc.* 27, 235-6 (1950); *The Pharmacopoeia of the United States of America*, Fourteenth Revision, Mack Printing Co., Easton, Pa., pp. 784-5 (1950).

official in Canada in 1951,[116] and is proposed for similar official status
in Switzerland by reading at 328 mμ.[117] Tocopherol interferes.[118] Forti-
fication of margarine with vitamin A is read with a high degree of
accuracy at 328 mμ against the unfortified margarine oil.[119] The lecithin
of the margarine must be in the blank.

Deterioration of vitamin A is minimized by avoiding at all times
undue exposure to oxidizing agents and bright light. Reagents free
from peroxides and non-actinic glassware [120] are therefore indicated. A
quartz spectrophotometer is required. Varied special designs have been
developed [121] and results with standard instruments correlated.[122]

A solution of anhydrous antimony trichloride [123] in chloroform gives
an immediate intense blue with vitamin A in the same solvent. The color
fades rapidly and therefore is read seconds after development. Efforts
to stabilize the color with acids, dehydrating agents, and phenols so that
it need not be read between 5 and 30 seconds have been unsuccessful.[124]
Natural inhibitors prevent reading vitamin A by the antimony trichloride method directly on natural oils, the colors being too low. Saponification removes the inhibitors. By application to the unsaponifiables,
color present in the original sample is largely eliminated. Members of
the carotenoid family give a color also, but not necessarily identical with
that from vitamin A and carotene. The intensity is much lower,[125] that

[116] A. J. Campbell, *Can. Pharm. J.* **84**, 342-7 (1951).

[117] Paul B. Müller and H. Moor, *Mitt. Lebensm. Hyg.* **40**, 358-415 (1949).

[118] Serek H. Fox and Alexander Mueller, *J. Am. Pharm. Assoc.* **39**, 621-3 (1950).

[119] Frederick H. Luckmann, Chester M. Gooding, and Daniel Melnick, *J. Am. Oil Chem. Soc.* **29**, 174-7 (1952).

[120] Norris Dean Embree, *Ind. Eng. Chem., Anal Ed.* **13**, 144-5 (1941); Cf. G. H. Benham, *Can. J. Research* **22B**, No. 2, 21-31 (1944); F. P. Zscheile, R. L. Henry, J. W. White, H. A. Nash, C. L. Shrewsbury, and S. M. Hauge, *Ind. Eng. Chem., Anal Ed.* **16**, 190-3 (1944).

[121] Ronald L. McFarlan, J. Wallace Reddie, and Edward C. Merrill, *Ind. Eng. Chem., Anal. Ed.* **9**, 324-6 (1937); Beaumont Demarest, *Ibid.* **13**, 374-6 (1941); U. S. Patent 2,265,357; Allen E. Parker and Bernard L. Oser, *Ind. Eng. Chem., Anal. Ed.* **13**, 260-2 (1941).

[122] D. T. Ewing, J. M. Vandenbelt, A. D. Emmett, and O. D. Bird, *Ind. Eng. Chem., Anal. Ed.* **12**, 639-44 (1940).

[123] Francis H. Carr and E. A. Price, *Biochem. J.* **20**, 497-501 (1926); F. Wokes and S. G. Willimot, *Analyst* **52**, 515-24 (1927).

[124] R. B. French, *Ind. Eng. Chem., Anal Ed.* **12**, 351-2 (1940).

[125] Richard Kuhn and Hans Brockmann, *Z. physiol. Chem.* **206**, 41-64 (1931); Cf. A. A. Klose, G. I. Jones, and H. L. Fevold, *Ind. Eng. Chem.* **35**, 1203-5 (1943).

of β-carotene being of the order of one-twentieth that of vitamin A [126] and reached more slowly. No carotenoid gives one-tenth of the color intensity at 620 mμ that vitamin A does.[127] Vitamin A$_2$, the less common form occurring in fresh fish, gives the reaction but with a maximum at 693 mμ [128] instead of 620 mμ. Interference by water is eliminated by adding a drop of acetic anhydride before the antimony trichloride.[129] The relative proportions of vitamin A$_1$ and A$_2$ are determinable by two-component analysis.[130] The Carr-Price value in arachis oil and olive oil is confusing and limits the use of the method to oils with over 3000 International Units per gram.[131]

As applied to fish-liver oils and concentrates the spectrophotometric and antimony-chloride methods are about equally accurate.[132] Cod-liver oil may contain inhibitors for the reaction.[133] Vitamins D and K diminish the intensity of blue developed. Kitol gives a stable but weak color; its diacetate, an intense violet which alters toward the red. The reaction product of the diacetate therefore interferes with reading of vitamin A. By reduction of the concentration of the antimony trichloride to 6 per cent instead of 20 per cent or 25 per cent, the time for reaching the maximum color is lengthened with the general form of the curve unchanged.[134]

Addition of pyrocatechol and heating at 60° for 2 minutes modifies the color toward a purple.[135] A 5 per cent solution of polyphenols such as guaicol in chloroform gives a somewhat more permanent blue to vio-

---

[126] Bernard L. Oser, Daniel Melnick, and Morton Pader, *Ind. Eng. Chem., Anal. Ed.* **15**, 724-9 (1943).

[127] M. J. Caldwell and J. S. Hughes, *J. Biol. Chem.* **166**, 565-72 (1946).

[128] Edgar M. Shantz, *Science* **108**, 417-19 (1948).

[129] Paul D. Boyer, Robert Spitzer, Curtis Jensen, and Paul H. Phillips, *Ind. Eng. Chem., Anal. Ed.* **16**, 101-2 (1944).

[130] E. Lederer and F. H. Rathmann, *Compt. rend.* **206**, 781-3 (1938).

[131] N. K. Iyengar and H. K. Biswas, *Indian J. Med. Research* **37**, 311-18 (1949).

[132] Arthur D. Holmes, Frances Tripp, and G. Howard Satterfield, *Ind. Eng. Chem., Anal. Ed.* **9**, 456-7 (1937); W. D. McFarlane and A. J. Sutherland, *Can. J. Research* **16B**, 421-31 (1938); A. Black, R. D. Greene, H. L. Sassaman, and C. Sabo, *J. Am. Pharm. Assoc.* **27**, 199-205 (1938).

[133] A. Emmerie, *Rev. trav. chim.* **57**, 776-80 (1938).

[134] James A. Brown, *J. Am. Pharm. Assoc.* **39**, 699 (1950).

[135] Jenö Rosenthal and János Erdélyi, *Biochem. Z.* **267**, 119-23 (1933); Jenö Rosenthal and Margit Weltner, *Magyar Orvosi Arch.* **36**, 93 (1935); Jenö Rosenthal and Catherine Szilard, *Biochem. J.* **29**, 1039-42 (1935).

lèt-red color.[136] In another modification, saturated sulfur oxychloride solution is used.[137] Antimony trichloride is also replaceable by trichloroacetic acid to give a similar color development.[138]

Simultaneous development and reading of sample and standard is one way of avoiding error due to fading.[139] The rate of fading is partially a function of the light intensity used in the colorimeter [140] and is greatly reduced by working at a light intensity of the order of 10 per cent of the usual. Necessarily calibration curves are prepared with the same photometer.[141] Interfering greenish color can be screened out by a low red glass for visual observation.[142]

The color conforms to Beer's law [143] on whole shark-liver oil below 50 per cent extinction, and to much higher levels on the unsaponifiable fraction. Theoretical yields are obtained from cold-saponified milk.[144] A special colorimeter has been designed for margarine [145] and the Spekker instrument modified for use in this test.[146]

In examination of unfortified oils, margarine, capsules of high-potency vitamin-A ester concentrate, pharmaceuticals, and fortified foods, the correlation of the antimony-chloride method with bio-assay is much better than that of direct spectrophotometric reading, with use of an internal standard.[147]

Saponification and chromatography will eliminate extraneous mate-

---

[136] Jenö Rosenthal and János Erdélyi, *Magyar Orvosi Arch.* **35**, 232-7 (1934); *Biochem. Z.* **271**, 414-9 (1934); Jenö Rosenthal, *Klin. Wochschr.* **14**, 307 (1935); A. Przezdziecka, *Biol. Lekarska* 1935, No. 6; Jenö Rosenthal and János Erdélyi, *Biochem. J.* **29**, 2112-13 (1935).

[137] Jenö Rosenthal and Margit Weltner, *Biochem. J.* **29**, 1036-8 (1935).

[138] G. Nogràdy, *Magyar Orvosi Arch.* **45**, 135-46 (1944).

[139] Walter Koch and Deborah Kaplan, *J. Biol. Chem.* **173**, 363-9 (1948).

[140] M. J. Caldwell and D. B. Parrish, *J. Biol. Chem.* **158**, 181-6 (1945).

[141] M. J. Caldwell, D. B. Parrish, and W. G. Schrenk, *Trans. Kansas Acad. Sci.* **49**, 197-204 (1946).

[142] K. A. Williams, *Analyst* **70**, 21-2 (1945).

[143] Olav Notevarp and Harold W. Weedon, *Biochem. J.* **30**, 1705-18 (1936); W. J. Dann and K. A. Evelyn, *Biochem. J.* **32**, 1008-17 (1938); R. B. French, *Ind. Eng. Chem., Anal. Ed.* **12**, 351-2 (1940).

[144] Melvin Hochberg, *J. Dairy Sci.* **31**, 315-21 (1948).

[145] J. T. Bowen, N. T. Gridgeman, and G. F. Longmann, *Analyst* **71**, 20-9 (1946).

[146] R. F. Innes and H. F. Birch, *Analyst* **70**, 304-5 (1945); Cf. V. L. Solyanikova and G. V. Troitskii, *Biokhimiya* **2**, 850-8 (1937); L. Westenberg, *Verslag. Landb. Onderzoek* No. 45, E, 587-90 (1939).

[147] E. E. Rice, E. Primm, and A. I. Coombes, *J. Assoc. Offic. Agr. Chemists* **31**, 621-33 (1948); Cf. J. B. Wilkie, *J. Assoc. Offic. Agr. Chemists* **32**, 455-9 (1949).

rial from fish oils [148] or margarine [149] without serious loss of vitamin A and with good agreement with the biological method. Arratto and azo dyes permissible in butter do not interfere with the antimony-trichloride reaction.[150] By extraction with methylene chloride, the sample solution can be used directly as compatible with the antimony chloride reagent.[151] For indirect estimation the vitamin A and carotenes are estimated with antimony trichloride and the value for carotenoids obtained separately is subtracted. Interfering materials offer problems and separation of the test substance is out of the question. The conventional calibration curve is replaced by additions of standards to portions of the test solution. The method requires only the assumption that positive or negative catalysis of the color reaction has the same effect on added standard as on test substance already present. Prior to the availability of crystalline vitamin A, a standard containing 0.020 gram of β-carotene per 100 ml. of chloroform was used for calibration.[152]

A practical grade of activated glycerol dichlorohydrin or 1,3-dichloro-2-propanol gives a violet color with vitamin A.[153] This reaction due to an impurity in the reagent can be duplicated by activating pure material by distillation with antimony trichloride.[154] The color conforms to Beer's law over a considerable range and is stable for 2-10 minutes after addition of the reagent. There are practical conveniences over the antimony trichloride reaction and the reagent is not adversely affected by atmospheric humidity. The maximum color intensity is only about one-fourth that developed by the antimony trichloride reagent.

The reagent contains a trace to 0.67 per cent of antimony trichloride, but such addition without distillation does not activate the reagent. Activation also occurs by treatment with concentrated hydrochloric acid, acetyl chloride, phosphorous pentachloride, anhydrous aluminum chloride, benzoyl chloride, concentrated sulfuric acid, or chlorosulfonic acid,

---

[148] M. E. Chilcote, N. B. Guerrant, and H. A. Ellenberger, *Anal. Chem.* **21**, 1180-8 (1949).

[149] Mario Lodi, *Intern. Z. Vitaminforsch.* **21**, 17-26 (1949).

[150] F. P. Zscheile, H. A. Nash, R. L. Green, and L. F. Green, *Ind. Eng. Chem., Anal. Ed.* **16**, 83-5 (1944).

[151] Paul C. Tompkins and Rene A. Bolomey, *Ibid.* **15**, 437-9 (1943).

[152] Gábor Vastagh, *Ber. ungar. pharm. Ges.* **17**, 23-39 (1941).

[153] Louis Feinstein, *J. Biol. Chem.* **159**, 569-70 (1945); Albert E. Sobel and Harold Werbin, *Ibid.* **159**, 681-91 (1945); Chikataro Kawasaki and Senji Suenaga, *J. Pharm. Soc. Japan* **69**, 460-3 (1949).

[154] Albert E. Sobel and Harold Werbin, *Ind. Eng. Chem., Anal. Ed.* **18**, 570-3 (1946); *Anal. Chem.* **19**, 107-12 (1947).

but the color with vitamin A is not as stable as when the reagent is distilled with antimony trichloride.[155]   Glycerol 2,3-dichlorohydrin and glycerol 1,3-dibromohydrin can also be activated.   Pyridine, aniline, n-butylamine, and epichlorohydrin inhibit the color reaction with this reagent.   A lesser inhibitory effect is given by potassium hydroxide, ethanol, water, and dioxane.

Blood plasma or milk should be saponified when this reagent is to be used.[156] Saponified milk requires several extractions. Saponification of serum is not required [157] To correct for carotene, subtract a correction from a chart. To do so, the carotene content is read at 800 mμ (page 91), and the corresponding correction at 550 mμ is applied. Kitol, while giving absorption at 325 mμ, gives no color with glycerol dichlorohydrin, thus furnishing a method of estimation of kitol by difference.[158] The reaction of the mixture of 2 ml. of glyceroldichlorohydrin, 50 mg. of antimony trichloride, and 0.1 ml. of concentrated hydrochloric acid with 1 ml. of liver oil in chloroform is more sensitive and also not disturbed by kitol.[159]

Purity of Reagents and Precautions—The use of reagents of a high degree of purity is even more necessary than usual in dealing with vitamin A because of its ready oxidizability.   Therefore methods of preparation are grouped here with other necessary general precautions.

Peroxide-free ether. Shake 20 volumes with 1 volume of a solution of 5 per cent ferrous sulfate and 2.5 per cent potassium hydroxide until the washed ether gives no color with a dilute solution of ferrous sulfate and potassium thiocyanate. Wash the ether with water and dry over anhydrous sodium sulfate. Store in the dark until used. Unless ether is peroxide-free, destruction of vitamin A may exceed 30 per cent. Other solvents are superior to ether for the purpose but have too high boiling points.

Aldehyde-free ethanol. Add silver nitrate to 95 per cent ethanol and make alkaline with potassium hydroxide to remove aldehydes. Filter, reflux with m-phenylenediamine hydrochloride, and distil. Store in the

[155] R. S. Allen and Sidney W. Fox, *Anal. Chem.* **22**, 1291-5 (1950).

[156] R. S. Allen, G. H. Wise, and N. L. Jacobsen, *J. Dairy Sci.* **32**, 688-94 (1949); Albert E. Sobel and Abraham A. Rosenberg, *Anal. Chem.* **21**, 1540-3 (1949).

[157] Albert E. Sobel and Selig D. Snow, *J. Biol. Chem.* **171**, 617-32 (1947); Monroe E. Wall and Edward G. Kelley, *Anal. Chem.* **20**, 757-9 (1948).

[158] Olaf R. Braekkan, *Anal. Chem.* **21**, 1530-1 (1949).

[159] Akiji Fujita and Maasataro Aoyama, *Inst. Kitsato-vitamins* (Japan) **4**, 127-8 (1951).

dark in full bottles and test with Schiff's reagent before use. Aldehydes in ethanol form yellow resins soluble in chloroform and ether which give a blue color with antimony trichloride reagent. This can cause 10-50 per cent error.

Chloroform. This must be anhydrous. Dry over anhydrous sodium sulfate and redistil. Store over sodium sulfate. Should those precautions prove inadequate, wash with seven equal portions of distilled water. Then shake the chloroform with an excess of phosphorous pentoxide and run rapidly through filter paper. Fractionate the chloroform and discard the first cloudy portions and the last 10 per cent.

Petroleum ether. Some petroleum ether contains material which will carry through to give a green color with antimony trichloride. To purify, percolate through silica gel, stir with two successive portions of concentrated sulfuric acid, wash with alkali, stir with alkaline potassium permanganate, distil, and dry over anhydrous sodium sulfate.

Cyclohexane. To remove benzene, if present, agitate with fuming sulfuric acid, separate, neutralize, and redistil.

Antimony trichloride. Where necessary, purify this reagent by crystallization from absolute ethanol. Some minor amounts of ethanol present in the reagent do not alter the result.[160]

All-glass apparatus. This is essential for most methods. For example, petroleum ether extracts material from rubber stoppers which gives a blue-green with the antimony trichloride reagent.

Non-actinic glass. Destruction by exposure to bright light can exceed 50 per cent. Use of non-actinic glass is one method of avoiding this; working away from sources of bright light is another.

Samples *—Fats or oils of relatively low potency.*[161] Transfer not more than 1 gram of sample containing not less than 400 USP units to a flask. Add 3 ml. of 50 per cent potassium hydroxide solution and 30 ml. of ethanol. Reflux in an all-glass apparatus for 30 minutes. Cool and add 30 ml. of water. Extract with 4 successive 30-ml. portions of ether. Wash the combined extracts gently with 50 ml. of water. Repeat the washing with successive portions of water until they show no color with phenolphthalein. Evaporate the washed ether extract to about 50 ml., mix with 5-10 grams of anhydrous sodium sulfate, and let settle. Decant into a 100-ml. volumetric flask, wash the sodium sulfate with ether, and dilute

---

[160] Mario Lodi, *Vitamine u. Hormone* **4**, 401-16 (1943).

[161] *The Pharmacopoeia of the United States of America,* Fourteenth Revision, Mack Publishing Co., Easton, Pa., pp. 784-5 (1950).

the extract and washings to volume with the same solvent. Confirm that vitamin A has been removed from the sodium sulfate by testing with antimony trichloride reagent. The solution so obtained is suitable for direct reading in the ultraviolet, except that whale-liver oils have an interfering ultraviolet absorption, principally from kitol. The glycerol-dichlorohydrin method is then satisfactory.

For development with activated glycerol dichlorohydrin, take up a 0.03-0.2 gram sample of whale oil, or the unsaponifiable fraction from such an oil, in chloroform and dilute to 25 ml. Vitamin D does not interfere when the ratio of A to D is 5:3, but does at 1:2.5.[162]

Capsules. Weigh not less than 5 capsules accurately. Open without loss of the capsule material and collect the contents. Wash the emptied capsules with small amounts of ether, collecting the washings with the oil. Dry the capsules and weigh, thus getting the weight of oil by difference. Evaporate the ether from the oil and proceed as for samples of fats or oils by direct reading.

Tablets. Crush and extract with ether. Evaporate the ether and proceed as for samples of fats or oils by direct reading.

Fish-liver oils.[163] Weigh 0.1-0.25 gram of oil, depending on the potency, into a 25 x 150-mm. low-actinic tube fitted to an air condenser with a standard-taper joint. Add 0.6 ml. of 50 per cent potassium hydroxide solution and 6 ml. of ethanol. Reflux until the oil has completely reacted, but not less than 15 minutes. Evaporate the ethanol *in vacuo* with nitrogen and at once add 20 ml. of 1.5 per cent barium chloride solution saturated with chloroform. When cool add 20 ml. of chloroform. Shake thoroughly and centrifuge until the solvent layer is clear. The barium soaps deposit at the interface.

For use of the antimony chloride reagent dry part of the chloroform layer with anhydrous sodium sulfate and use directly.

For correction of the ultraviolet reading, fill a 10-ml. amber or red volumetric flask with the chloroform layer. Add 0.3 ml. of isopropanol and evaporate to dryness in the flask. For this heat at 60-65° at an angle under a stream of nitrogen and apply vacuum cautiously at first. As soon as the flask is dry—do not overheat—fill almost to the mark with isopropanol. Mix well, let cool, and make up to volume. Centrifuge or filter through sintered glass under a slight pressure of nitrogen if not clear after 1-2 minutes. Subtract the reading for this from that obtained with the sample.

---

[162] Louis Feinstein, *J. Biol. Chem.* **159**, 569-70 (1945).
[163] Cf. John Lie, *Tids. Kjemi, Bergvesen Met.* **5**, 18-20 (1945).

Whale-liver oil.[164] Saponify a 5-gram sample in 40 ml. of ethanol and 5 ml. of 60 per cent potassium hydroxide solution for 25 minutes in the presence of 50 mg. of quinol as antioxidant. Dilute with water and ethanol to 40 per cent ethanol and 2.5-4 per cent soap. Extract with 100, 50, 50, and 50 ml. of 1:1 ethyl ether—40-60° petroleum ether. Wash the extracts with four 50-ml. portions of 40 per cent aqueous potassium hydroxide. Filter and evaporate to 5-10 ml. Remove the remaining ether with a stream of nitrogen. Add 2-3 ml. of ethanol and evaporate the solvent. Cool and weigh. Dissolve the unsaponifiable matter in petroleum ether and dilute to 50 ml. Chromatograph on a 6.5 x 470 mm. column of 100-200 mesh activated alumina. Elute the vitamin A with ether and read in the ultraviolet.

Liver.[165] Mix 1 gram of well-homogenized liver and 5 ml. of 5 per cent aldehyde-free alcoholic potassium hydroxide in a 50-ml. heavy-walled centrifuge tube with a constricted neck. Distribution of vitamin A in different parts of the liver varies considerably. Digest at 75° in a water bath until disintegration is complete. Cool, dilute to the original volume with ethanol, and add an equal volume of water. If large amounts of vitamin A are present, take an aliquot and dilute to 10 ml. with 50 per cent ethanol.

Add exactly 10 ml. of petroleum ether, shake vigorously for 2-3 minutes, and let separate. An aliquot of that solution is suitable for use in the antimony trichloride procedure.

Milk.[166] Mix 20 ml. of fresh whole milk and 30 ml. of 20 per cent potassium hydroxide in 90 per cent ethanol in a separatory funnel. Let stand for 3 hours, disregarding the formation of a yellow coloration. Extract with 25 ml. of ether, retaining any small emulsified layer in the funnel when withdrawing the lower layer into a second funnel. Extract this with 20 ml. of ether and discard the aqueous layer. Wash the contents of the first funnel with 75 ml. of water by a single inversion. Withdraw the wash water to the second funnel and wash that ether layer by vigorous shaking. Discard the washings.

Add 10 ml. of 10 per cent ethanol containing 1 ml. of concentrated hydrochloric acid per liter to the first funnel and shake. Transfer this washing to the second funnel, shake, and discard. Add 3 ml. of petroleum

164 N. T. Gridgeman, G. P. Gibson, and J. P. Savage, *Analyst* **73**, 662-5 (1948).

165 Willis D. Gallup and J. A. Hoefer, *Ind. Eng. Chem., Anal Ed.* **18**, 288-90 (1946).

166 Paul D. Boyer, Robert Spitzer, Curtis Jensen, and Paul H. Phillips, *Ind. Eng. Chem., Anal. Ed.* **16**, 101-2 (1944).

ether to each funnel to reduce the water content. Wash the first funnel with two 10-ml. portions of the acid-ethanol solution, extracting each in the second funnel before discarding. Combine the ether extracts and after 15-20 minutes carefully remove all separated water. Evaporate the ether cautiously *in vacuo* at 30-40°, finishing off at 60-70° with shaking. Take up the cooled residue in exactly 5 ml. of ether. Shake with 5 ml. of saturated sodium-chloride solution, add exactly 10 ml. of petroleum ether, and shake again. Let the clear layer separate and before proceeding further read at 440 mμ for total carotenoids (page 37). Then take a 10-ml. aliquot for analysis by the antimony trichloride technic.

Alternatively,[167] take a 100-ml. sample of milk in a separatory funnel. Add successively with shaking after each addition: 15 ml. of concentrated ammonium hydroxide, 100 ml. of ethanol, 75 ml. of ether, and 25 ml. of petroleum ether boiling at 60-70°. After 20 minutes withdraw the lower layer and extract it with 25 ml. of ether and 10 ml. of petroleum ether. Combine the extracts and separate the suspended matter which settles out.

Prepare a vacuum-distillation unit with a small separatory funnel in the stopper of the flask. Evaporate the solvents *in vacuo* at not over 70°. Add 10 ml. of ethanol through the separatory funnel before releasing the vacuum. Transfer with 35 ml. of ethanol to a reflux and add 2.5 grams of potassium hydroxide. Reflux in a nitrogen atmosphere for 20 minutes, add 100 ml. of water, and cool to 4°. Extract successively with 75, 25, and 25 ml. of ether.

Wash the combined extracts gently with two 100-ml. portions of water, then vigorously with two 50-ml. portions. Chill the washed ether in solid carbon dioxide to freeze out the water. Filter through cotton and wash the filter with precooled ether. Distil the ether *in vacuo* at not over 70°. Add 5 ml. of methanol before releasing the vacuum. Transfer to a 10-ml. centrifuge tube and dilute to volume with methanol. Centrifuge to clarify and use aliquots of the upper layer for direct reading of carotene (page 37) and for vitamin A by reading spectrophotometrically in the ultraviolet.

Micromethod. Mix 1 ml. of 5.6 per cent potassium hydroxide in 90 per cent ethanol with 1 ml. of milk in an 18 x 100-mm. test tube. Heat at 60° for 35 minutes, then cool. Add 2 ml. of petroleum ether boiling at 30-60° and shake mechanically for 10 minutes. A rubber stopper pre-extracted with pretroleum ether is suitable. Centrifuge and transfer

---

[167] F. R. Olson, D. M. Hegsted, and W. H. Peterson, *J. Dairy Sci.* 22, 63-6 (1939).

the extract to another tube. Carry out two 5-minute extractions with 1-ml. portions of petroleum ether.

Evaporate the combined extracts at 40-50° with a stream of nitrogen. Take up the residue in 1 ml. of chloroform as sample for development with activated glycerol 1:3-dichlorohydrin. In that case read carotene at 800 mμ after development.

Butter.[168] Saponify a 10-gram sample of filtered butterfat or solid butter with 5 ml. of saturated aqueous potassium hydroxide and 20 ml. of aldehyde-free methanol in an all-glass apparatus. Boiling for 10 minutes is usual. Add 40 ml. of water and cool. Transfer to a separatory funnel with 50 ml. more of water and extract with 100 ml. of ether. Further extract with three 50-ml. portions of ether. Wash the combined extracts with water until free of alkali, usually 4-6 times. Evaporate to about 80 ml. Dry the ether solution over anhydrous sodium sulfate and transfer. Wash the sodium sulfate 3 times with 10-ml. portions of ether and add the washings to the main solution. Evaporate the ether *in vacuo.* Do not heat after the ether has been removed. Add about 15 ml. of ether before releasing the vacuum. Cool the flask and dilute to 50 ml.

For vitamin A read directly in the ultraviolet on this solution. Alternatively transfer to chloroform by the technic under procedure and determine by the antimony trichloride reagent.

For carotene, extract a 25-ml. aliquot, with three 10-ml. portions of 94 per cent diacetone alcohol to remove noncarotene pigments. Wash with 10 ml. of water, dilute to 50 ml. with low-boiling petroleum ether, and read at 440 mμ (page 37).

Margarine. Saponify 20 grams of the fat obtained by filtering through paper at 60°, with 30 ml. of 20 per cent alcoholic potassium hydroxide. Usually refluxing for 15 minutes will suffice. Add 3 volumes of water and cool with ice. Extract successively with 200, 150, 100, 50, 50, and 50 ml. of cold ether. Wash the combined extracts with water until alkali-free, merely pouring the water through the ether on the first two washes. Filter and concentrate to 25-50 ml. on a steam bath. Complete the evaporation under carbon dioxide to prevent oxidation. Cool and take up the residue in cyclohexane or methylcyclohexane. Dilute to 50 ml. and store at 4-10° until examined spectrophotometrically. As a correction, irradiate one por-

---

[168] F. P. Zscheile, H. A. Nash, R. L. Green, and L. F. Green, *Ind. Eng. Chem., Anal. Ed.* **16**, 83-5 (1944); Soll Berl and W. H. Peterson, *J. Nutrition* **26**, 527-38 (1943); Cf. Willis D. Gallup and A. H. Kuhlman, *Oil and Soap* **18**, 71-3 (1941).

tion under a Cooper-Hewitt Uviarc in a quartz flask which has been allowed to heat up for at least 10 minutes. Have the bulb of the flask about 10 cm. from the lamp with an aluminum reflector about 7.5 cm. beyond the flask. About 2.5 hours are required for destruction of all vitamin A to a negative antimony chloride test. Subtract this correction from the value for the sample.

The vitamin A is also separated from a benzene solution of unsaponifiables by chromatographing on aluminum oxide, and cutting out the appropriate section for extraction with benzene and petroleum ether.[169]

Uncolored margarine.[170] The unfortified margarine oil must also be available. Dilute the fortified and unfortified oils to the same concentration in cyclohexane. Set the spectrophotometer at 100 per cent transmission with the unfortified oil in hexane as a blank. Read directly at 328 mμ.

Baked goods.[171] Extract with ether a sample of suitable size to give about 10 grams of fatty extract, and evaporate the solvent without oxidation. Use by the technic described for butter by adding the alkali and methanol directly to the residue.

Feedstuffs.[172] As a chromatograph tube seal a 23 × 200 mm. tube to a 4 × 80 mm. one. Attach to a receiver connected in turn with a vacuum pump. Place glass wool in the bottom of the tube and pack to a depth of 100 mm. with 1:1 Hyflo Super Cel and magnesia. Tamp well in several well-mixed portions with vacuum on. Add 1 cm. of anhydrous sodium sulfate to the top of the column.

Reflux a 10-gram sample with 100 ml. of 60-71° petroleum ether for 15 minutes. Let cool and settle without evaporation and apply 50 ml. of the clear upper layer to the column. Draw the liquid through with suction and discard. Add about 35 ml. of 10 per cent acetone in the petroleum ether so that the first portion of the carotene band goes through the column. Only a trace of carotene need pass to insure all the vitamin A being eluted. Stop the suction and dilute

[169] W. Heimann, *Z. Untersuch. Lebensm.* **85**, 502-7 (1943); Cf. Maxwell L. Cooley, James B. Christiansen, and Carl H. Schroeder, *Ind. Eng. Chem., Anal. Ed.* **17**, 689-92 (1945).

[170] Frederick H. Luckmann, Daniel Melnick, and Hans W. Vahlteich, *J. Am. Oil Chemists' Society* **29**, 121-6 (1952).

[171] A. Anderson and E. Nightingale, *J. Soc. Chem. Ind.* **48**, 139-140T (1929).

[172] William Brew and Mary Beth Scott, *Ind. Eng. Chem., Anal. Ed.* **18**, 46-8 (1946); Maxwell L. Cooley, James B. Christiansen; and Ray C. Koehn, *Anal. Chem.* **21**, 593-5 (1949).

the eluate to 50 ml. Evaporate 25 ml. *in vacuo* at a mild heat. Transfer by solution in ether and evaporate the ether. Take up the residue in chloroform for development with antimony trichloride.

Cocoa and chocolate.[173] Reflux a 5-gram sample with 30 ml. of ether in an all-glass apparatus. Let cool, add filter aid, filter, and wash with 10 ml. of ether. Return the sample to the flask and extract by again refluxing with another 30 ml. of ether. Combine the extracts and washings, and evaporate the ether. Add 15 ml. of 3 per cent alcoholic potassium hydroxide and reflux for 20 minutes. Cool, add 15 ml. of water, and transfer to a separatory funnel with 20 ml. of wash water. Extract successively with 50, 40, and 40 ml. of ether. Wash the combined ether extracts until the washings are neutral to phenolphthalein.

Filter and evaporate nearly to dryness. Complete on a boiling water-bath with vacuum. Cool *in vacuo* to prevent oxidation. Take up the residue in exactly 20 ml. of chloroform and use an aliquot for development with antimony trichloride.

Dried whole eggs.[174] Combine a 5-gram sample with 20 ml. of absolute methanol and 5 ml. of saturated aqueous potassium hydroxide. Stir until the particles remain suspended and heat on a water bath until the particles are disintegrated, not less than 10 minutes. Cool the hydrolyzate and transfer to a separatory funnel. Extract successively with 35 ml. and four 25-ml. portions of ether. Wash the combined ether extract with five 25-ml. portions of water, then dry it with 20 grams of anhydrous sodium sulfate for 1 hour. Evaporate the extract to about 15 ml. at 50° under slightly reduced pressure. Dilute to 25 ml. with petroleum ether.

Prepare a chromatograph column 20 × 135 mm. of 3 parts of calcium hydroxide and 2 parts of Hyflo Supercel, which has been kept dry by storage over sulfuric acid. Pass 10 ml. of the solution through this, then develop the chromatogram with a 60:40 mixture of benzene and petroleum ether. Such a column will handle 50-80 units of vitamin A and 0.15-0.2 mg. of carotinoids. About 500 ml. of total solution will result. Elute the two lowest bands of β-carotene and cryptoxanthin separately. Then collect vitamin A until xanthophyll begins to give a yellow color to the eluate. This band should

[173] E. G. Raynes and B. G. McLellan, *Analyst* **68**, 109-11 (1943).

[174] C. R. Thompson, M. A. Ewan, S. M. Hauge, B. B. Bohren, and F. W. Quackenbush, *Ind. Eng. Chem., Anal. Ed.* **18**, 113-15 (1946); Cf. W. G. Schrenk, Douglas S. Chapin, and Ralph M. Conrad, *Ind. Eng. Chem., Anal. Ed.* **16**, 632-4 (1944).

be sharp as it nears the bottom of the column, since it follows the vitamin A closely. These bands, except for vitamin A, are confirmed by their absorption curves.[175] The xanthophyll and zeaxanthin fractions can be separately eluted if readings are desired. Usually they are not, because they are not known to be precursors of vitamin A. That of zeaxanthin which is above that for xanthophyll contains large amounts of isomerized material.

Evaporate the solvent from the β-carotene and cryptoxanthin fractions, take them up in 10 ml. each of petroleum ether, and read at 440 mμ (page 37). These fractions contain some vitamin A. Then combine with the vitamin-A fraction and evaporate to about 15 ml. at 50°. Dilute to 25 ml. with chloroform, a superior solvent. Use an aliquot for development of color with antimony trichloride.

The error due to color developed from β-carotene and cryptoxanthin is minor as they develop 7 per cent and 11 per cent respectively of the color of vitamin A with the reagent.

Blood of dairy cattle.[176] Centrifuge venous blood as soon as possible after clot formation. Store the serum in the dark at 4° and analyze as soon as feasible, usually within 24 hours. Most of the vitamin A in the serum is present as the alcohol, the ester rarely exceeding 30 per cent. Mix 10 ml. of serum in a glass-stoppered centrifuge tube with 10 ml. of aldehyde-free ethanol and 20 ml. of ether.[177] Shake for two minutes and centrifuge. Transfer the clear layer to a flask and re-extract with two 10-ml. portions of ether. Evaporate the ether from the combined extracts and add 10 ml. of 10 per cent potassium hydroxide in 30 per cent ethanol. Reflux for 20 minutes, cool and transfer to a separatory funnel, rinsing with 10 ml. of ethanol and 15-20 ml. of water. Shake for 1 minute with 40 ml. of ether. Transfer the lower layer to another separatory funnel containing 30 ml. of ether and shake. Discard the aqueous layer. Wash the first ether layer gently with 80 ml. of water and transfer the washings to the second funnel where it is similarly used. Discard the washings. Wash the ether extracts successively with 40 ml., then 25 ml. of 1:99 hydrochloric acid.

[175] F. P. Zscheile, J. W. White, B. W. Beadle, and J. R. Roach, *Plant Physiol.* **17**, 331-46 (1942).

[176] D. B. Parrish, G. H. Wise, and J. S. Hughes, *Anal. Chem.* **20**, 230-3 (1948); P. D. Boyer, P. H. Phillips, and J. K. Smith, *J. Biol. Chem.* **152**, 445-52 (1944).

[177] G. H. Wise, F. W. Atkeson, M. J. Caldwell, D. B. Parrish, and J. S. Hughes, *J. Dairy Sci.* **30**, 279-91 (1947).

Combine the ether extracts and add 10 ml. of petroleum ether [178] to reduce the water content. Wash with 25 ml. of water. After 15 minutes discard this wash water. Evaporate the solvent in glass under low vacuum at 60°. Add a few ml. of petroleum ether as the vacuum is released. Cool and dilute to 10 ml. Of this solution use 9 ml. for estimation of vitamin A and 1 ml. for carotenoids (page 37).

Human blood serum.[179] Heat 10 ml. of serum with 1 ml. of 60 per cent potassium hydroxide solution in boiling water for one-half hour. Cool and add 5 ml. of ethanol. Extract the mixture with 50- and 25-ml. portions of ether. Wash the combined ether extracts twice with 10 ml. of water, then with 20 ml. of 3 per cent potassium-hydroxide solution and twice with 50 ml. of water. Dry the ether extract over anhydrous sodium sulfate, and evaporate in an atmosphere of carbon dioxide. Dissolve the residue in light petroleum ether and concentrate to 0.2 ml. Read carotene directly [180] (page 37), and then use for development of color with the antimony trichloride reagent. The same technic is applicable to 0.5-1.0 ml for microestimation.[181]

Urine.[182] Mix a 50-ml. sample with 3 ml. of 60 per cent aqueous potassium hydroxide and heat for 30 minutes in a boiling water-bath. Cool, add 25 ml. of ethanol, and extract with two successive 50-ml. portions of ether. Combine the ether extracts and proceed as for serum starting at ''Wash the combined ether extracts . . .''

Separation by chromatography.[183] Saponify the sample with sodium ethylate in absolute ethanol and extract any unsaponifiable material with petroleum ether containing a trace of tocopherol as antioxidant. Sorb the vitamin A by passage through a column of clean iron filings somewhat coarser than 300 mesh. Wash the column with petroleum ether and dry in the absence of air by passage of illuminating gas. Recover the vitamin A by solution in 60 per cent ethanol.

[178] L. R. Hines and H. A. Mattill, *J. Biol. Chem.* **149**, 549-54 (1943).

[179] M. van Eekelen and A. Emmerie, *Acta Brevia Neerland. Physiol., Pharmacol., Microbiol.* **4**, 171-2 (1935); Cf. Margaret Kaser and Jakob Torsten Lindquist, *Acta Med. Scand., Suppl.* **97**, 314 pp. (1939); A. Stekol, *J. Lab. Clin. Med.* **28**, 904-9 (1943).

[180] Y. Raoul and M. M. Janot, *Bull. soc. chim. biol.* **23**, 78-89 (1941).

[181] Harm Veldman, *Nederland. Tijdschr. Geneeskunde* **85**, 3837-44 (1941); *Acta Brevia Neerland. Physiol., Pharmacol., Microbiol.* **11**, 178-80 (1941).

[182] Johan Hedberg and Tosten Lindquist, *Acta Med. Scand., Suppl.* **90**, 231-47 (1938).

[183] Marcel Servigne, M. Pinta, and P. Guerin de Montgaruil, *Bull. soc. chim. biol.* **30**, 454-64 (1948).

Procedure—*Direct Reading*. Evaporate a 25-ml. aliquot of the sample solution to about 5 ml. Complete the evaporation without heat *in vacuo*. Alternatively, use a stream of inert gas. Take up the residue in isopropanol and dilute to a volume having 8-15 USP units per ml. Determine the absorbency at 325, 310, and 334 mμ. Calculate as below:

where A = absorbency

L = length of cell in cm.

C = sample in grams, capsules, or tablets per liter of solution read

$$A \text{ (corrected)} = 7A_{325} - 2.625\ A_{310} - 4.375\ A_{334}$$

$$\frac{A \text{ (corrected)}}{L \times C} \times 5700 \times \frac{1}{0.3} = \text{USP units per sample unit}$$

With antimony trichloride. Chloroform solutions. Set the photometer at 100 with 1 ml. of chloroform and 9 ml. of a 25 per cent solution of anhydrous antimony trichloride in chloroform. Add 1 ml. of a chloroform solution of sample containing 5-15 USP units of vitamin A to a dry cell. Add 9 ml. of reagent from a quick delivery pipet, such as that shown in Figure 10,[184] swirl and read within 4 seconds at 620 mμ. If the developed solution shows turbidity, repeat, adding a drop of acetic anhydride to the 1 ml. of sample solution and mixing before adding the reagent. Apply a correction for any color in the sample solution at 620 mμ by reading 1 ml. with 9 ml. of chloroform. To correct for turbidity, read at 720 mμ where the colored product

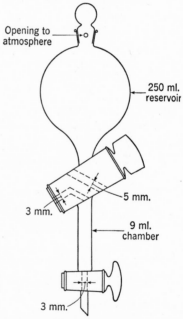

FIG. 10. Nine-ml. automatic pipet for delivery of antimony trichloride reagent

[184] Bernard L. Oser, Daniel Melnick, and Morton Pader, *Ind. Eng. Chem., Anal. Ed.* **15**, 724-9 (1943); Lyle A. Swain, *Ibid.* **16**, 241 (1943); Cf. D. B. Parrish and M. J. Caldwell, *J. Lab. Clin. Med.* **29**, 992-3 (1944).

does not react. To correct for carotene, read after 2 hours. The blue due to carotene remains; that due to vitamin A has faded completely.

Solutions in other solvents. Transfer an aliquot containing 5-15 USP units of vitamin A to the colorimeter tube. Evaporate to dryness *in vacuo* at 45°. The presence of a glass bead is helpful and a stream of nitrogen may be used to avoid oxidation. Take up the residue in 1 ml. of chloroform and proceed as for chloroform solutions starting at "Add 9 ml. of reagent . . . ."

Use of internal standard. After development as for a comparison curve, transfer 1 ml. of sample in chloroform to a dry tube. Add 0.1 ml. of a solution containing 100 USP units of vitamin A in chloroform. Develop as for chloroform solutions, starting at "Add 9 ml. of reagent . . . ."

Then calculate from the photometric densities as follows:

$$\frac{\text{Sample} - \text{Blank}}{1.01 \ (\text{Sample} + \text{standard}) - \text{Sample}} \times 10 \times \text{dilution factor} = \text{USP units per gram of sample}$$

As a more detailed procedure add to one aliquot of sample an appropriate amount of vitamin A to add 10 units per ml. to the final solution, to another add none. Evaporate both to dryness *in vacuo* and take up in chloroform to contain about 15 units per ml. in the sample and 25 units in the standard. Read the sample at 620 mμ as A within 10 seconds after development of a 1-ml. portion with 10 ml. of reagent. Irradiate at 30°, 30 cm. from opposite 150-watt reflector flood lamps. Read after 5 minutes as B, irradiate, and read after 10 minutes as C. Read the developed standard as D. Read 1 ml. of sample with 10 ml. of chloroform at 440 mμ against chloroform as a blank to correct for carotenoids. Then vitamin A per gram is $[10 \ (A - 2B + C - 0.067 E) \ \text{ml.}]/[D - A]$ (sample in grams).

Development with activated glycerol chlorohydrin. As reagent, add 25 grams of antimony trichloride in 100 ml. of chloroform to 1 liter of glycerol dichlorohydrin. Distil *in vacuo* at 30-40 mm. of mercury. Discard the chloroform fraction which comes over first and collect the 86-92° fraction.[185] The reagent is colorless and gives L (35-mμ band) $\frac{1\%}{1\text{cm.}}$ at 550 mμ of 1150-1250 with vitamin A. It is stable for at least 2 months and when stored in the dark in Pyrex-brand glass lost only 5 per cent of its activity in 14 months.

Add 1 ml. of prepared sample in chloroform to 4 ml. of the acti-

[185] Commercially available from Shohan Laboratories, Newark 5, N. J.

vated reagent, stopper, and place in a water bath at 25°. Read at 555 mμ after 2 minutes and compare with a calibration curve prepared under the same conditions. Read the carotene at 800 mμ 4 minutes after adding the reagent and apply a correction for it. Apply a blank obtained with 1 ml. of chloroform and 4 ml. of reagent. If necessary for instrumental reasons the amount of reagent may be increased to 5 ml.

Cryptoxanthin

Cryptoxanthin, $C_{40}H_{55}OH$, is closely related to the hydrocarbon carotenoids and is a precursor of vitamin A. It is read directly like the carotenoids.

Sample—*Yellow corn.* See details of isolation under carotenoids (page 33).

Green plant material.[186] Rub a weighed sample to a sludge with sand. Dilute with methanol and pass through an inorganic filter. Wash the residue with methanol and then with petroleum ether until the washings are colorless. Shake the extracts with one-tenth volume of water. This separates the methanol and petroleum ether layers. Separate the methanol layer and extract with petroleum ether. Evaporate the combined petroleum ether extracts to 20-30 ml. and mix with an equal volume of 5 per cent ethanolic potassium hydroxide. After 20 hours at room temperature, add 1.5 volumes of water. Shake, separate, and extract the aqueous soap solution with several successive small volumes of petroleum ether. Evaporate the combined petroleum ether extracts to a small volume and extract with an equal volume of 90 per cent methanol. Discard the extracts and wash the petroleum ether phase with several successive portions of water. Evaporate the petroleum ether phase to 1 ml. and pass through a column of aluminum oxide. Develop the chromatogram with 1:1 benzene-petroleum ether. Remove the orange-yellow zone about 1 cm. below the top of the column and elute with petroleum ether. Read as for carotene. (Page 37.)

Tocopherols, Vitamin E

There are at least four forms of tocopherols, designated as α-, β-,γ-, δ-forms, usually not differentiated. α-Tocopherol is (2,5,7,8-tetramethyl-2)-4,8,12-trimethyltridecyl-6-chromanol. The term vitamin E is applied

---

[186] Masanobu Azisaka, *J. Biochem.* (Japan) **35**, 119-32 (1942).

to α-tocopherol and its esters. It is synthesized from trimethylquinone and phytyl bromide. The ultraviolet absorption at 298 mμ can be used to read the synthetic product or the total of the four natural tocopherols.[187] The methods of colorimetric estimation are based on oxidation-reduction reactions. After reduction of a known amount of ferric ion, ferrous ion can be measured [188] by the red color formed with 2,2-bipyridine. While very sensitive, the method requires that all other materials which affect the color such as vitamin A, carotenoids, chlorophyll, fats, etc. be substantially absent. Under suitable conditions 0.01-0.4 mg. is an appropriate sample, but 0.01 mg. of carotene interferes. Pure cholesterol does not interfere but some sterols do.[189]

The rate and amount of color developed with different tocopherols vary with the solvent. The reagent in ethanol gives similar rates of color development with α, β and γ tocopherols, considering the differences in molecular weight while that in acetic acid does not. Even then the δ compound develops at a different rate and gives more final color unless the time of reading is carefully selected. Probably the first three oxidize to the quinone in 2 minutes, but the δ compound probably goes beyond that stage. Exposure to light must be avoided throughout and the photometer used should be one with a low light intensity. Accuracy to ± 2 per cent is readily obtainable with concentrates. Unsaponifiables associated with the glycerides of sesame oil and soya bean oil inhibit the color development quite materially so that a correction must be introduced. Some mineral oils also inhibit color development. The amount of ferrous ion formed by reduction can also be read as the blue with ferricyanide at 720 mμ[190] or as the red with 2,2'-bipyridine.[191]

[187] R. A. Dunford, *Can. Chem. Process Inds.* **35**, 47-9, 57 (1951).

[188] A. Emmerie and Chr. Engel, *Nature* **142**, 873 (1938); *Rec. trav. chim.* **57**, 1351-5 (1938); *Ibid.* **58**, 283-9, 895-902 (1939); *Z. Vitaminforsch.* **13**, 259-66 (1943); H. W. Rawlings, *Oil and Soap* **21**, 257-8 (1941); Henry B. Devlin and H. A. Mattill, *J. Biol. Chem.* **146**, 123-30 (1942); Leonard R. Hines and H. A. Mattill, *Ibid.* **149**, 549-54 (1943); H. Kaunitz and J. J. Beaver, *Ibid.* **156**, 653-71 (1944); Mary Louise Quaife and Philip L. Harris, *Ibid.* **156**, 499-505 (1944); Mary Louise Quaife and Raymond Biehler, *Ibid.* **159**, 663-5 (1945); Monroe E. Wall and Edward G. Kelley, *Ind. Eng. Chem., Anal. Ed.* **18**, 198-201 (1946); Max H. Stern and James G. Baxter, *Anal. Chem.* **19**, 902-5 (1947); J. G. Baxter, R. W. Lehman, E. L. Hove, Mary Louise Quaife, Leonard Weisler, and M. H. Stern, *Biol. Symposia*, **12**, 484 (1947); G. Funes and M. Massei, *Farm. sci. e. tec. (Pavia)* **5**, 417-24 (1950); Cf. S. A. Kibardin, *Fiziol. Zhur, SSSR* **35**, 472-5 (1949).

[189] A. Emmerie, *Rev. trav. chim.* **65**, 489-92 (1946).

[190] K. Ramachandran and Y. V. S. Rau, *Current Sci.* **12**, 147-8 (1943)

[191] Claude Domart, *Ann. pharm. franc.* **10**, 199-204 (1952).

Tocopherols in absolute ethanol are oxidized by nitric acid successively to yellow, orange-red, and bright red.[192] The quinones formed may react further in the process. The reaction is quite specific and is sensitive to 0.05 per cent. Susceptibility of the tocopherols to oxidation leads to the necessity for manipulation in an air-free atmosphere with air-free reagents. Alternative solvents are isobutanol, benzene, toluene, and xylene.[193] Pyrocatechol interferes but can be sorbed with aluminum hydroxide. The color can be extracted into ether from ammoniacal solution.[194]

A variation of this is to dilute the oil with acetic acid-chloroform and oxidize and read immediately in the cuvet.[195]

Much the same method of reduction with hydrogen in the presence of Raney nickel, and subsequent treatment with 2,6-dichloroindophenol, which is applied to vitamin K (page 166) is applicable to tocopherols.[196] Correction for the slowly reducing action of tocopherolquinones is necessary in determining vitamin K. Methods avoiding such complexity of apparatus are available for tocopherols.

The γ- and δ-tocopherols can be estimated from the difference in intensity when coupled with diazotized o-dianisidine in solutions made alkaline with sodium carbonate. Then α-tocopherol which has no unsubstituted position is determined by difference.[197] By this method β-tocopherol is included with α-tocopherol. This is a modification developed from the use of diazotized p-nitroaniline [198] and has the advantage of 10-day stability of the reagent at room temperature.[199] The γ form in sodium carbonate has maxima at 398 and 515 mμ; in potassium hydroxide at 395 and 510 mμ. Corresponding maxima for the δ form are at 395 and 510 mμ; and at 385 and 490 mμ. The upper values are preferable

---

[192] M. Furter and R. E. Mayer, *Helv. Chim. Acta.* **22**, 240-50 (1939); D. S. Binnington and John S. Andrews, *Cereal Chem.* **18**, 678-85 (1941); G. Secchi, *Ren. inst. super.* sanita **5**, 926-31 (1942); W. Hurka, *Mikrochaine ver. Mikrochim. Acta* **32**, 210-23 (1944); Bela Bencze, *Kem Lapja* **5**, 87-9 (1944); J. R. Chipault, W. O. Lundberg, and G. O. Burr, *Arch. Biochem.* **8**, 321-35 (1945).

[193] Gilberto Guineraes Villela, *Rev. brasil. biol.* (Rio de Janeiro) **1**, 285-91 (1941).

[194] Claudio Antoniani, L. Frederico, and M. Uniseroli, *Chimica e Industria* (Milan) **30**, 72 (1948).

[195] G. S. Fisher, *Ind. Eng. Chem., Anal. Ed.* **17**, 224-7 (1945).

[196] John V. Scudi and Rudolf P. Buhs, *J. Biol. Chem.* **146**, 1-6 (1942).

[197] Leonard Weisler, Charles D. Robeson, and James G. Baxter, *Anal. Chem.* **19**, 906-9 (1947).

[198] M. L. Quaife, *J. Am. Chem. Soc.* **66**, 308-9 (1944).

[199] N. B. Talbot et al, *J. Biol Chem.* **134**, 319-30 (1940).

for use, since the base color from oil samples interferes less and 520 mμ is more convenient to use. Errors vary from 1 to 13 per cent.

There is interference by phenols including gossypol, by 25 per cent of fatty acids, carotenoids and other pigments having intrinsic color, and a substance in wheat-germ oil, but all of these after coupling show different colors. At least 10 per cent of reactive tocopherols should be present in sodium carbonate solution. With potassium hydroxide in absolute ethanol as low as 0.1 per cent can be developed. Molecularly distilled samples do not contain these interferences and are of sufficient concentration. Samples saponified under nitrogen and hydrogenated (page 166) are suitable. Separation of α- and part of the γ-tocopherols by sorption on 70:30 zinc carbonate-Celite mixtures is satisfactory.

Alternatively the nitroso derivatives are formed from β-, γ-, and δ-tocopherols and either separated by elution or determined as a group.[200]

Samples—*Dried leaf meal.* Extract 25 grams of 30-40 mesh material in a Soxhlet with petroleum ether boiling at 60-70° for 5-8 hours and dilute the extract to such a volume that 25 ml. contains 0.3-1 mg. of tocopherols.

Prepare a sorbant by mixing 3 parts by weight of Hyflo Supercel [201] and 1 part of activated magnesium oxide No. 2641.[202] Put a plug of cotton in the bottom of a 40 × 20 cm. tube and connect through a receiver to suction. Fill the tube two-thirds to three-quarters of the height under vacuum and press down well with a rod and cork. Wash with 50 ml. of the petroleum ether and discard the washings.

Pass a 25-ml. aliquot of the sample solution through the column, which will remove all of the pigments and vitamin A. After sorption, elute the column with about 80 ml. of 1:19 acetone-low-boiling petroleum ether and then with 20 ml. of 1:9 acetone-petroleum ether. Xanthophyll and chlorophyll are retained, but carotene elutes with the tocopherol. Evaporate the eluate to 25 ml. in a water bath at 40-50° under vacuum and nitrogen. Add 2 ml. of 17:3 sulfuric acid and shake mechanically for 3 minutes. The decomposed carotene colors the solution blue. If necessary add 2 ml. more of acid for the purpose. Rinse into a separatory funnel with petroleum ether boiling at 60-70°, shake, and withdraw the acid layer to waste. Wash the petroleum ether solution with aqueous 5 per cent sodium sulfate solution, then with 1 per cent potassium

---

[200] Mary Louise Quaife, *J. Biol. Chem.* **175**, 605-17 (1948).

[201] Johns Manville Co., New York, N. Y.

[202] Westvaco Chlorine Products Co., Newark, California.

hydroxide solution. Wash with more 5 per cent sodium sulfate solution until the aqueous washings are almost neutral and the extract is colorless to pale yellow. Without drying dilute to 100 ml. with petroleum ether.

Evaporate a 25-ml. aliquot almost to dryness on a warm water bath under vacuum and nitrogen. Dissolve the residue in redistilled absolute ethanol for development of an aliquot by ferric ion and 2,2′-bipyridine.

For development of the sample by nitric-acid oxidation to the quinone, prepare as above for the ferric choride–2,2′-bipyridine method up to "... and the extract is colorless to pale yellow." Dry with sodium sulfate and evaporate almost to dryness for use of all or an aliquot in the procedure.

Fresh vegetable matter. Disintegrate a 25-gram sample in a Waring Blendor with 150 ml. of ethanol and 75 ml. of petroleum ether boiling at 60-70°. After 10 minutes add more ethanol if the mixture does not foam. Filter under suction through an inorganic filter and wash alternately with ethanol and low-boiling petroleum ether until the washings are colorless. Add 100 ml. of 5 per cent sodium sulfate solution and separate the aqueous layer. Extract that layer with three 30-ml. portions of the petroleum ether and discard the aqueous layer. Wash the combined petroleum ether fractions with 50 ml. of water and dry with anhydrous sodium sulfate. Evaporate the solvent under vacuum and nitrogen to about 25 ml. and complete as under dried leaf meal starting at "Prepare a sorbant . . ."

Molecularly distilled products. Dissolve in redistilled absolute ethanol, dilute to 0.05-0.15 mg. of tocopherols per ml., and develop with ferric chloride and 2,2′-bipyridine.

Crude soybean oil. Degum by stirring at 40° with 2 per cent by weight of water. Let stand overnight and filter the oil through anhydrous sodium sulfate to dry it. Dissolve 0.1 gram of oil in 10 ml. of petroleum ether boiling at 60-70° and add 2 ml. of 17:3 sulfuric acid. Shake, centrifuge, and wash the petroleum ether layer with 1 per cent potassium hydroxide solution. Evaporate a 3-ml. aliquot in nitrogen, take up in 1 ml. of petroleum ether boiling at 60-70°, and develop with ferric chloride and 2,2′-bipyridine.

Saponifiable oils.[203] Reflux a 5-gram sample under nitrogen for 10 minutes with 10 ml. of 11.2 per cent potassium hydroxide in methanol.

[203] A. Emmerie and Chr. Engel, **59**, 246-8 (1940); Cf. T. Tošić and T. Moore, *Biochem. J.* **39**, 498-507 (1945).

Cool and add 15 ml. of methanol and 40 ml. of water. Extract with 50-ml. portions of peroxide-free ether. Wash the combined ether extracts successively with 50 ml. of water, 50 ml. of 1 per cent potassium hydroxide solution, and two 50-ml. portions of water. Dry over calcium chloride and evaporate to dryness *in vacuo* protected by carbon dioxide. Take up in redistilled absolute ethanol for development with ferric chloride and 2,2'-bipyridine.

Butter.[204] Saponify a sample as described for saponifiable oils until the extracts have been dried ". . . over calcium chloride. . . ." Dilute to

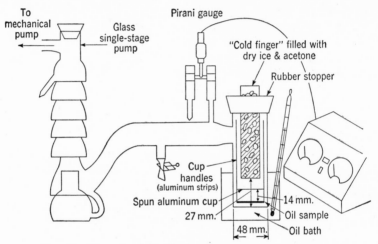

FIG. 11. Diagram of distillation apparatus for tocopherols

a known volume and use a one-fifth aliquot as described for serum (page 98) starting at "Filter the dried solution in a nitrogen atmosphere. . . ."

Food.[205] Wash, blot dry, and remove inedible portions. Cut the food into 1- or 2-inch cubes and freeze at −22°. Dry in a vacuum of 1-2 mm. of mercury to constant weight. Grind to pass 20-mesh.

Extract tocopherols and lipides for 2 hours from a 10-gram sample with 50 ml. of hot absolute ethanol. The extraction thimble should be suspended in the vapor as in a rubber extractor. Avoid exposure to direct light from this point on. After extraction is complete add 10 ml. of ethanol, 60 ml. of water, and a pinch of anhydrous sodium sulfate.

---

[204] A. Emmerie, *Rec. trav. chim.* **60**, 104 (1941).

[205] Mary Louise Quaife and Philip L. Harris, *Anal. Chem.* **18**, 707-8 (1946); *Ibid.* **20**, 1221-4 (1948).

Cool to room temperature and add 25 ml. of redistilled petroleum ether boiling at 60-70°. Shake mechanically for 10 minutes and allow the layers to separate.

To separate tocopherols from most of the triglycerides, chlorophyll, and carotenoids, run a laboratory molecular distillation. Pipet an aliquot of the petroleum ether layer containing 1 gram of fat or less into an aluminum cup designed to fit the still. Evaporate under a stream of nitrogen and weigh the amount of fat extracted. Transfer the cup to the apparatus shown in Figure 11. Reduce the pressure to 0.001 mm.

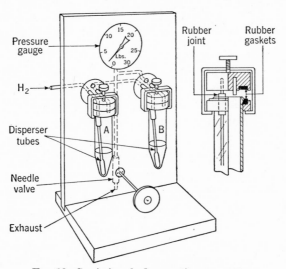

FIG. 12. Semimicro hydrogenation apparatus

Then cool the condenser by inserting an aluminum cylinder containing dry ice and acetone. Fill the space between that and the glass with acetone. Adjust the surface of the oil in the bath level with the bottom of the condenser. Heat the bath at 215-220° for 30 minutes, then when distillation is complete remove the bath and metal cooling element and let the still cool to room temperature. Remove the acetone from the condenser and fill it with water at 70°. Break the vacuum and rotate the removed condenser in 25 ml. of absolute ethanol. If the vitamin does not remain on the condenser take up in chloroform and evaporate the chloroform under nitrogen in the presence of ethanol for transfer.

Just prior to determination transfer 10 ml. of the ethanol solution to the tube B of the hydrogenation apparatus [206] shown in Figure 12.

[206] Mary Louise Quaife and Raymond Biehler, *J. Biol. Chem.* **159**, 663-5 (1945).

At room temperature add the Raney nickel catalyst and turn on 15 pounds of hydrogen, first saturated with ethanol by passing through tube A. With the needle valve adjust to give a flow of gas which will agitate the catalyst without the solution contacting the rubber. After one minute turn off the hydrogen and use the hydrogenated sample at once for development with ferric chloride and 2,2'-bipyridine.

Vegetable oil.[207] Dissolve 1-2 grams in low-boiling petroleum ether. Add 10-20 ml. of 85 per cent sulfuric acid, mix well, and centrifuge. Wash with 20 ml. of 1 per cent potassium hydroxide solution and centrifuge again. This removes pigments, peroxides, and tocoquinones. Evaporate an aliquot of the solvent layer in the cuvet in an inert atmosphere and develop with nitric acid.

For dilute oils, saponify in the presence of pyrogallol to protect against oxidation.[208] Extract with ether, dry the ether, dilute to a known volume, and proceed as for solutions in petroleum ether.

Serum.[209] Use amber glassware throughout and otherwise protect from light by working in subdued light. Deproteinize a 10-ml. sample by thorough shaking with 5 ml. of 1.1 per cent potassium hydroxide solution, 15 ml. of 37 per cent formaldehyde solution neutralized to phenolphthalein, and 15 ml. of ethanol. Without filtration, extract with 50 ml. of ether and separate the extract. Add 10 ml. of ethanol to the aqueous layer and extract with two 50-ml. portions of ether. Wash the combined ether extracts containing vitamins A and E and carotenoids with 25 ml. of 2 per cent potassium hydroxide solution. To remove phosphatides shake the ether layer with two 15 ml. portions of 1 per cent cadmium sulfate in 1:100 sulfuric acid. Turbidity may persist but disappears on shaking the ether layer with three 25-ml. portions of 0.5 per cent sodium sulfate solution. Dry the ether for 1 hour over anhydrous sodium sulfate. Filter the dried solution in a nitrogen atmosphere through an anhydrous sodium sulfate layer into a filter flask. Evaporate the ether by immersing in water at not over 55°.

Before dryness is reached, add 10 ml. of redistilled benzene which has been kept over sodium wire. Evaporate the benzene. Repeat until the residue forms a clear solution with 5 ml. of benzene, usually 4-5 times. Pass the clear yellow solution, under nitrogen, through a nitrogen-filled column of 30-60 mesh Floridin which has been activated at 480°.

207 W. E. Parker and W. D. McFarlane, *Can. J. Research* **18B**, 405-9 (1940).

208 T. Moore and J. Tošić, *Biochem. J.* **37**, No. 4, XIV (1942).

209 A. Emmerie, *Rec. trav. chim.* **61**, 305-8 (1942); Gerda Gernsheim Mayer and Harry Sobotka, *J. Biol. Chem.* **143**, 695-9 (1942).

The column is 12 mm. in diameter and 30 cm. in height, and removes vitamin A and carotenoids. Wash the column with about 25 ml. of dry benzene and evaporate the colorless filtrate to dryness under nitrogen. To insure dryness of the sample, add another 10 ml. of benzene, and evaporate to dryness. Take up the residue in redistilled anhydrous ethanol for development with ferric chloride and 2,2′-bipyridine. The standard should be of the same isomer as present in the sample, often dl-a-tocopherol.

Tissue. Mince 10 grams and homogenize [210] with 40-50 ml. of ethanol. Filter through an extraction thimble and place the thimble in a Soxhlet extractor with the filtrate and washings as solvent, adding more ethanol as necessary. Extract for 18 hours.

Remove the condenser and add to the flask 10 ml. of 2 per cent potassium hydroxide in ethanol containing 0.5 per cent of p-acetylaminophenol. The latter serves as antioxidant. Concentrate to about 50 ml. by heating for 30 minutes to saponify. Cool, add an equal volume of water, and saturate with sodium sulfate. Extract the unsaponifiable matter with 25 ml. of hexane by 10-minute shaking. Remove the solvent layer and dry it with anhydrous sodium sulfate.

Evaporate an aliquot of the hexane solution containing not over 1 mg. of tocopherols to dryness *in vacuo* and dissolve in 2 ml. of benzene. Sorb this on a 4-5 cm. column of Floridin pretreated with stannous chloride, washing the column with benzene to give a total of 10 ml. This removes carotenoids and vitamin A. Evaporate an aliquot containing 0.02-0.12 mg. of tocopherols to dryness *in vacuo* and take up in 8 ml. of absolute ethanol. Develop with ferric chloride and 2,2′-bipyridine.

Tocopherol acetates. Add 20 ml. of isopropanol to a sample containing about 0.2 gram of tocopherol acetate. Reflux, add 0.5 gram of potassium hydroxide, and reflux for 30 minutes. Add 2 ml. of concentrated hydrochloric acid dropwise and transfer to a separatory funnel with warm water. Cool and extract succesively with 50, 25, 25, and 25 ml. of ether. Wash the combined extracts with four 50-ml. portions of water and dry with anhydrous sodium sulfate. Evaporate in a stream of carbon dioxide and take up the extract in isopropanol. Dilute to a known volume for development of aliquots with ferric chloride and 2,2′-bipyridine. The tocopherol multiplied by 1.098 gives the content of acetate.

---

[210] R. W. Swick and C. A. Baumann, *Anal. Chem.* **24**, 758-60 (1952); Cf. Mary Louise Quaife and Mei Yu Dju, *J. Biol. Chem.* **180**, 263-72 (1949); P. Karrer, W. Jaerger and H. Keller, *Helv. Chim. Acta* **23**, 464-5 (1940).

Procedure—*With ferric chloride and 2,2'-bipyridine.* As reagents, prepare 0.1 per cent ferric chloride hexahydrate and 0.25 per cent 2,2'-bipyridine in absolute ethanol redistilled from alkaline permanganate. In black bottles these keep for 2 weeks. Redistill hexane after shaking with concentrated sulfuric acid and washing with dilute alkali.

As sample, use in a black bottle a 1-ml. aliquot in ethanol containing 0.05-0.15 mg. or, if glycerides are present, dissolved in hexane. Add in sequence 1 ml. of bipyridine reagent, 1 ml. of ferric chloride reagent, and 22 ml. of redistilled ethanol. Timing from that point, swirl to mix and read after exactly 2.5 minutes at 520 mμ against a reagent blank. The calibration curve is preferably prepared with equal parts of α and γ tocopherols. If constant ratios of the tocopherols are present a 10-minute reaction time can be used with suitable corrections. If the sample contains a glyceride oil, the same amount of the same kind should be present in standards used for calibration.

INDIVIDUAL TOCOPHEROLS

With diazotized o-dianisidine. Reagent. To prepare the reagent, boil 100 grams of technical *o*-dianisidine with 140 ml. of water and 6 ml. of concentrated hydrochloric acid until dissolved. Add 0.5 gram of stannous chloride and continue to boil for 5 minutes. Remove the remaining color with 2 grams of activated carbon by boiling for 5 minutes, and filter through Celite. Add 50 ml. of concentrated hydrochloric acid to the hot filtrate to precipitate the dihydrochloride. Cool in an ice bath and filter by suction. Wash three times with absolute ethanol, once with ether, and dry at 40° for an hour.

Dissolve 0.5 gram of the colorless reagent in 60 ml. of water and add 6 ml. of concentrated hydrochloric acid. Mix with 12 ml. of 5 per cent sodium nitrite solution, and after 5 minutes with 12 ml. of 5 per cent aqueous urea solution. Store in a dark bottle for 24 hours before use.

γ- and δ-Tocopherols. Coupling in sodium carbonate solution. Dilute a sample containing 0.05-0.1 mg. of γ- and δ-tocopherols to 3 ml. with absolute ethanol and add 7.5 ml. of 2 per cent sodium carbonate solution. Next add 1 ml. of the diazotized reagent and shake. After 5 minutes add 0.5 gram of sodium sulfate and 12 ml. of low-boiling petroleum ether. Shake vigorously three times, letting the phases separate between shakings. A precipitate at the interface occurs in both sample and blank. Discard the lower brown layer and dry the solvent layer with anhydrous sodium sulfate. Read at 520 mμ against a reagent blank.

Coupling in potassium hydroxide solution. Dilute a sample containing 0.05-0.2 mg. of γ- and δ-tocopherols to 4 ml. with absolute ethanol. Add 2 ml. of 2 per cent sodium hydroxide in absolute ethanol and mix, then add 0.3 ml. of diazotized reagent. Shake and let stand for 2 minutes. Add 8 ml. of water, 12 ml. of petroleum ether, and 0.5 gram of anhydrous sodium sulfate. Complete as in sodium carbonate solution starting at "Shake vigorously three times. . . ."

The results follow from the following derived equations in which $E^{1\%}{}_{1cm.}$ may replace L values.

$$\% \; \delta = 0.702 \; L^s{}_{C_s} - 0.597 \; L^s{}_{H_s}$$
$$\% \; \gamma = 0.948 \; L_H - 0.461 \; L_C$$

in which values marked C are developed in sodium carbonate solution and those marked H in potassium hydroxide solution.

a-Tocopherol. Subtract the values for γ- and δ-tocopherols from the total obtained by the preceding method of development with ferric chloride.

As nitroso compounds. Mix 5 ml. of a solution of oil sample in absolute ethanol containing 0.25-1 mg. of tocopherols other than a, with 0.2 ml. of glacial acetic acid. Add 3 ml. of 2 per cent sodium nitrite solution and mix. Swirl vigorously for 5 seconds, let stand for 60 seconds and add 2 ml. of 20 per cent potassium hydroxide solution, 10 ml. of water, a pinch of anhydrous sodium sulfate, and 12 ml. of low-boiling petroleum ether. Stopper, shake for 30 seconds, and let separate.

Total non-a-tocopherols. Read the upper layer at 400 mμ or 410 mμ against a reagent blank. Calculate the tocopherols other than a and get that by difference from results with 2,2'-bipyridine.

Separation of β-, γ-, and δ-tocopherols. Shake the solvent layer and an equal volume of distilled water containing a pinch of anhydrous sodium sulfate to wash out a trace of ethanol. Separate the solvent layer and adjust to a known volume to take an aliquot.

Prepare a packed 15×1.3 cm. column of 7:3 precipitated zinc carbonate and Celite 501. Pass 10 ml. of nitrosotocopherol solution in petroleum ether through the column previously washed with petroleum ether under suction. Do not let air intervene. Wash in the last traces with several successive fractional-ml. portions of petroleum ether and rinse the walls with 5 ml. of the solvent. Again without letting the column go dry, elute the lowest ring of nitroso-γ-tocopherol through with benzene, then the nitroso-β-tocopherol into another receiver. Elute the δ-tocopherol with 1:1 ether-ethanol. Evaporate each eluate to dryness under nitrogen and take up in 10 ml. of petroleum ether for reading at 400 mμ.

γ-Tocopherol in vegetable oils by nitric acid. Dilute a weighed sample not exceeding 1.5 grams, free from interfering pigments, in the cuvet with 3:2 acetic acid-chloroform to exactly 9.6 ml. Use to set the instrument at 420 mμ, remove the sample, and read. Repeat at 490 mμ. Mix with 0.4 ml. of concentrated nitric acid, free from oxides of nitrogen, and read after 30 seconds at 490 mμ. Read at 420 mμ.

For calculation C_a and C_γ are the concentrations of α- and γ-tocopherol in appropriate units, $L = 2 - \log$ galvanometer reading at the specified wave length, K is a specific value for known standards.

$$C_\gamma = (K_a{}^{490} L^{420} - K_a{}^{420})/(K_a{}^{490} K_\gamma{}^{420} - K_\gamma{}^{490} K_a{}^{420})$$

DORMISON, 3-METHYLPENTYNE-3-OL, METHYL PARAFYNOL

Dormison is determined by formation of an insoluble silver derivative, elimination of excess silver, followed by liberation and determination of the silver in the complex.[211] Two moles of silver react with each acetylenic group in the compound. Recovery of the drug added to physiological specimens varied. With urine, it was about 100 per cent, with blood 73 per cent, with most tissues 90-108 per cent, but with liver only 70 per cent.

Sample—*Urine.* Collect in the presence of 2 ml. of concentrated nitric acid and filter. Adjust the pH of a 75-ml. aliquot in a glass-stoppered centrifuge bottle to pH 8 with concentrated ammonium hydroxide. Add 75 ml. of ether, seal the stopper, and shake mechanically for 15 minutes. Transfer to a separtory funnel. Transfer the aqueous layer and any emulsion back to the centrifuge bottle. Transfer the ether layer to a second glass-stoppered centrifuge bottle.

Repeat the extraction of the urine and emulsion layer with an additional 75 ml. of ether, but keep the emulsion separate. Centrifuge the emulsion. Collect all the ether extracts in the second centrifuge bottle.

As the silver reagent add 15 ml. of 24 per cent sodium hydroxide solution to 125 ml. of 1.72 per cent silver nitrate solution. Then add concentrated ammonium hydroxide until the preciptate is dissolved, then 10 ml. excess, and dilute to 250 ml.

Add 4 ml. of the silver reagent to the combined ether extracts. Stopper and shake mechanically for 30 minutes. If a large amount of

---

[211] Preston L. Perlman and Carol Johnson, *J. Am. Pharm. Assoc.* **41**, 13-16 (1952).

precipitate is formed, add more alkaline silver reagent. Centrifuge, pour off the ether layer, and remove the last of the ether by blowing a stream of air over the surface of the aqueous phase. The silver complex floats on the surface of the aqueous layer. Suspend the complex in 15 ml. of water and again centrifuge. Filter the supernatant layer, retaining as much complex as possible in the bottle. Resuspend and centrifuge the contents of the bottle twice more with water. Transfer any precipitate on the filter paper back to the bottle with a small amount of water.

Add 2 ml. of concentrated nitric acid to the silver complex, immerse the bottle in a steam bath for 1 hour to decompose the complex, and filter, rinsing with water. Adjust the pH to 7 with concentrated ammonium hydroxide and dilute to 250 ml.

Blood. Transfer 5-10 ml. of blood to an oxalated centrifuge tube. After oxalated, transfer the blood to a separatory funnel, rinse three times with 10 ml. of water and add to the funnel. If necessary, add ammonium hydroxide to give a pH of 8. Extract three times with 50-ml. portions of ether. Collect the ether extracts in a 200-ml. glass-stoppered centrifuge bottle. Extract with ether as for urine, starting "Add 75 ml. of ether, seal. . . ."

Tissue. Place tissue samples on crushed ice. Weigh and mince with four volumes of ice-cold 0.08 per cent sodium fluoride and homogenize. Transfer the homogenate to a pointed centrifuge tube, rinsing with cold 0.08 per cent sodium fluoride solution. Mix the contents and centrifuge. Transfer the supernatant layer to a separatory funnel and wash the residue twice more with 10-ml. portions of the sodium fluoride solution, adding the supernatant layers to the separatory funnel. Adjust the pH to 8 with concentrated ammonium hydroxide and extract three times with 50-ml. portions of ether. Collect the ether extract in a glass-stoppered centrifuge bottle. Proceed as for urine, starting with "Add 75 ml. of ether, seal. . . ."

Procedure—Dilute a 1-4 ml. aliquot containing up to 0.8 mg. of silver to 5 ml. Add 1 ml. of gelatin-ammonium acetate solution prepared by filtering a 1 per cent gelatin solution and stirring 25 grams of ammonium acetate with 100 ml. of filtrate until dissolved. Add 2 ml. of diluted rhodanine dye solution to each tube. Prepare this by saturating acetone with *p*-dimethylaminobenzalrhodanine and filtering. Dilute the saturated solution 1:5 with acetone.

Mix the contents of the tubes and read at 550 mμ within 5 minutes.

CHAPTER 4

PHENOLS [1]

However simple and specific one might hope to keep a subject, that of phenols becomes complicated. The term in general means that an aromatic hydroxyl group is present. That simplicity is destroyed by the term being also used for the simplest member of the series, C_6H_5OH, which could also be designated monohydroxybenzene. Necessarily confusion arises in methods where phenol as determined may be true phenol, phenol plus cresol, or all phenolic bodies if many are present. Further complications arise from the phenolic group being inherently acid in reaction so that cresylic acids are phenols. Some phenol carboxylic acids appear here as phenols rather than as substituted aliphatic acids.

General methods of determination are by reduction of some complex molybdenum compound—for more than one is applicable—to molybdenum blue and by coupling with a diazo compound. There are a great many other applicable methods, the color with ferric salts, the combination with 2,6-dibromoindophenol, oxidation to indophenol, etc.

PHENOL

A general reaction of phenols is that with a mixture of phosphotungstic and phosphomolybdic acids known as the Folin phenol reagent.[2] When this labile complex acid is reduced by phenols, molybdenum blue is obtained. Thus it is a reagent for phenol only when other phenols are absent. Typically it is reduced by m-cresol, p-cresol, p-chloro-m-cresol and p-chlorophenol in alkaline solution.[3] It is reduced by hydroquinone without being made alkaline.

Many other reducing agents produce the same result; among the few exceptions are nitrous acid and aldehydes. Among the interfering substances are hydrogen sulfide, ammonium sulfide, sulfurous acid, hydrogen iodide, hydrogen peroxide, stannous and ferrous ions, unsat-

---

[1] See Chapter 1 for details of organization, condensation, etc.
[2] Otto Folin and W. Denis, *J. Biol. Chem.* 22, 305-8 (1915).
[3] N. Ray and U. P. Basu, *Indian J. Med. Res.* 32, 57-60 (1944).

urated aliphatic compounds, glucose, aromatic amines, urea, uric acid, and hemoglobin.[4] These must be removed before development of the color. Many substances closely related to phenol, such as naphthols, cresols, thymol, and others, produce a similar color and according to the usual procedures are reported in terms of a chemically equivalent amount of phenol. The tendency is for phenol values by this method to be high because of the presence of interfering substances.

Uric acid gives a color about one-third as intense as that produced by an equal weight of phenol. Uric acid can be determined in one sample with the uric acid reagent, in another, uric acid and phenol with the phenol reagent, and the true phenol content obtained by difference.[5] Removal of uric acid from the protein-free filtrate with silver lactate renders this involved procedure unnecessary.[6] A study of monohydric phenols indicates that the color is proportional to the molecular concentration of the various phenols. Deproteinizing with sodium tungstate is common for phenol determination, yet the precipitate may sorb up to 25 per cent of the phenols.[7]

When sensitivity is desirably less, the production of molybdenum blue by reaction of phenol with phosphomolybdic acid in alkaline solution is used.[8] Generally the cresylic types are more sensitive than the phenolic type, with compounds of mixed function, such as salicylic acid, insensitive. Up to 0.6 per cent the solution conforms to Beer's law. The color increases linearly with time after 4 minutes. The nature of the color is independent of the phenol. A single determination seldom deviates by ±3 per cent.

The reaction of phenols with diazotized amines gives orange to red azo dyes. One of rather general use is that with p-nitroaniline.[9] Interference of polyphenols is removed by ammoniacal hydrogen peroxide after which the excess peroxide is destroyed by manganese dioxide.[10]

---

[4] E. Scheiner, *Biochem. Z.* **205**, 245-55 (1929); Hidekatsu Fujiwara and Eisei Kataoka, *Z. physiol. Chem.* **216**, 133-7 (1933).

[5] Stanley R. Benedict and R. C. Theis, *J. Biol. Chem.* **36**, 95-103 (1918).

[6] Yutaka Asada, *Tohoku J. Exptl. Med.* **15**, 363-8 (1930); Carleton Henningson, *Ind. Eng. Chem.* **15**, 406-7 (1923).

[7] E. G. Schmidt, *J. Biol. Chem.* **150**, 69-73 (1943).

[8] V. M. Platkovskaya and S. G. Vatkina, *J. Applied Chem.* (USSR) **10**, 202-7 (1937); Robert E. Snyder and Ralph O. Clark, *Anal. Chem.* **22**, 1428-31 (1950).

[9] J. Moir, *J. South African Chem. Inst.* **5**, 8-9 (1922); R. C. Theis and Stanley R. Benedict, *J. Biol. Chem.* **61**, 67-71 (1924); A. D. Marenzi, *Anales farm. bioquím.* (Buenos Aires) **10**, 82-7 (1939); R. H. De Meio, *Science* **108**, 391-3 (1948).

[10] I. I. Ioffe and E. V. Sokolova, *J. Applied Chem.* (USSR) **18**, 273-7 (1945).

Another coupling agent is diazotized sulfanilic acid.[11] The reaction is also applied to p-cresol, p-hydroxyphenylacetic acid, p-hydroxyphen- ylpropionic acid, and p-hydroxyphenyllactic acid to produce a color which is predominantly red. Tyrosine and tyramine give a pink color which changes sharply to yellow after 30 seconds, then fades.

Phenol is quantitatively oxidized by chromic acid, while cresols and the higher phenols such as resorcinol are not affected. By making a de- termination before and after oxidation with chromic acid, total phenolic compounds are estimated, as well as phenol itself by difference. The error for 0.1 to 10 mg. per liter is about 1 per cent.

Phenolic compounds in which the *para* position is unsubstituted combine with 2,6-dibromoquinone chloroimide to form blue 2,6-dibromo- indophenols.[12] p-Chlorophenol appears to give the same reaction as phenol. o-Cresol gives a greater intensity of blue color than pure phenol. Aspartic acid gives a yellow color; resorcinol or pyrogallic acid, a red- dish color. The blue color is developed in a buffered medium at pH 9.1-9.7. Change toward a blue-green often indicates the presence of o-chlorophenol. Sulfides vary the color through yellow-green to pink. Oxidizing and reducing agents interfere. The rate of color formation varies considerably with pH. The developed color can be concentrated by direct extraction with butanol [13] or amyl alcohol.[14] In a more com- plex technic, the developed solution is acidified, the color extracted with chloroform, and this reconverted to the alkaline form by addition of alcoholic alkali.[15] Beer's law holds for samples containing up to 0.1 parts per million of phenolic bodies.

Phenol or cresols react with the nitrous acid to form p-nitrosophenol or a nitrosocresol, which condense to form colored compounds. The color formation is accelerated by the presence of mercury compounds. Excess nitric acid bleaches the color. The reagent is a solution of mercury in

---

[11] J. J. Fox and A. J. H. Gange, *J. Soc. Chem. Ind.* **39**, 260T (1920).

[12] H. D. Gibbs, *J. Biol. Chem.* **71**, 445-59 (1927); Ibid. **72**, 649-64 (1937); *J. Phys. Chem.* **31**, 1053-8 (1927); J. R. Baylis, *J. Am. Water Works Assoc.* **19**, 597-604 (1928); H. D. Gibbs, W. L. Hall, and W. M. Clark, *U. S. Public Health Repts. Suppl.* **69**, (1929); E. J. Theriault, *Ind. Eng. Chem.* **21**, 343-6 (1929); M. B. Ettinger and C. C. Ruchhoft, *Anal. Chem.* **20**, 1191-6 (1948).

[13] I. W. Tucker, *J. Assoc. Official Agr. Chem.* **25**, 779-82 (1942).

[14] Felipe Carlos Basavilbaso, *Rev. obras sanit. nación.* (Buenos Aires) **11**, No. 117, 158-65 (1947); *Anales asoc. quím. argentina* **35**, 34-54 (1947).

[15] A. W. Beshgetoor, L. M. Greene, and V. A. Stenger, *Ind. Eng. Chem., Anal. Ed.* **16**, 694-6 (1944).

nitrous and nitric acids, known as Millon's reagent,[16] a mixture of nitric and sulfuric acids,[17] or acidified sodium nitrite.[18] Using Millon's reagent, substitution in the p-position does not prevent the color reaction, although it slows down the rate of development. Not more than a trace of alcohol should be present. Hydrochloric acid prevents the color formation if present in a concentration of more than 0.33 per cent. Phenol gives a deep red, o-cresol a faint orange, m-cresol a strong yellow, and p-cresol a greenish yellow. Salicylic acid and β-naphthol interfere, as the former gives a deep red and the latter a brown. Most other similar compounds, such as thymol and guaiacol, give a yellow to orange.

The reaction with acidified nitrous acid gives greenish yellow for phenol and meta substituted phenols, orange-yellow to brownish yellow for dihydroxyphenols and naphthols. Only aniline and xylidene among common aliphatic or aromatic compounds interfere and the extraction procedure provides for them. Development of peroxides oxidizes the phenols.

Condensation of 4-aminoantipyrine with a phenol in the presence of alkaline oxidizing agents gives a reddish antipyrine dye.[19] The method is applicable to a fraction of a part per million in aqueous solution. Color develops within 2 minutes and is most sensitive in the range 0.2-2 ppm. The color gradually changes with time but not significantly within an hour. Sunlight bleaches the color. Cresols, xylenols, naphthols, etc. will interfere with determination of phenols by this reaction, the colors developed not being necessarily the same. Iron salts interfere by reaction with ferricyanide used as oxidizing agent.

Many ring compounds give the test.[20] Only those having an enol-keto structure give the reaction, and not all of that structure so react. By extraction of the dye with immiscible solvent, the sensitivity of the reaction is improved.[21] This alters the color and the wave length for

---

[16] M. Th. Koks, *Pharm. Weekblad* **68**, 557-69 (1931); Official and Tentative Methods of Analysis of the Association of Official Agricultural Chemists, 7th Edition, pp. 47-49, Association of Official Agricultural Chemists, Washington, D. C. (1950).

[17] R. W. Stoughton, *J. Biol. Chem.* **155**, 293-9 (1936); L. A. Wetlaufer, F. J. Van Natta, and H. B. Quattlebaum, *Ind. Eng. Chem., Anal. Ed.* **11**, 438-9 (1939).

[18] J. Rae, *Pharm. J.* **119**, 332 (1927); *Ibid.* **124**, 239-40 (1930); Louis Lykken, R. S. Treseder, and Victor Zahn, *Ind. Eng. Chem., Anal. Ed.* **18**, 103-9 (1946).

[19] Edgar Emerson, *J. Org. Chem.* **8**, 417-19 (1943); Edgar Emerson and Kenneth Kelley, *Ibid.* **13**, 532-4 (1948); R. W. Martin, *Anal. Chem.* **21**, 1419-20 (1949).

[20] Edgar Emerson and L. C. Beegle, *J. Org. Chem.* **8**, 433-7 (1943).

[21] M. B. Ettinger, C. C. Ruchhoft, and R. J. Lishka, *Anal. Chem.* **23**, 1783-8 (1951).

reading. Potassium ferricyanide is not extracted. The intensity of color varies with pH.

Phenol can be oxidized to the indophenol by hypochlorite in the presence of p-aminodimethylaniline.[22] Phenol reacts in anhydrous solution with titanium tetrachloride to give a red color of $C_6H_5OTiCl_3$.[23] The color is affected by other phenols, water, alcohol, and ether. Phenol and related compounds are determined turbidimetrically as the tribromo compound.[24] Alcohols, amines, aldehydes, organic bases and oils interfere. An alternative is to brominate, extract with carbon tetrachloride, and read at 284 mμ.[25]

It is an expected thing that gasolines produced by cracking will contain small amounts of phenols.[26] The color produced by the quinoid form of the α-naphthols in ammoniacal solution is a rapid and rather applicable method.[27] Large errors can arise from differences in absorption of different phenols. Another method of estimation is by absorption in the ultraviolet at 290 mμ, various alkaline phenolates varying in maxima from 288 mμ to 296 mμ but overlapping.[28] Analyses are applicable to 0.002 per cent of phenols.

The free phenol in either heat-stable or heat-reactive phenol formaldehyde resins is read in acetone solution at 14.4μ.[29] Phenols isolated from gasoline are read as the absorption of a statistical average. Mercaptans show negligible absorption at 290 mμ and do not interefer. Thiophenols show about the same absorption as phenols. At 265 mμ the thiophenols show a maximum while the phenolates show about 30 per cent as great absorption as at 290 mμ. Thus reading at 265 mμ and 290 mμ shows thiophenols if the reading at 290 mμ $\times$ 0.3 is subtracted from that at 265 mμ. The result divided by 1.25 is a rough measure of thiophenols.

[22] G. U. Houghton and R. G. Pelly, *Analyst* **62,** 117-20 (1937); M. P. Babkin, *Zavodskaya Lab.* **9,** 1244-6 (1940).

[23] G. P. Luchinskii, *Ibid.* **5,** 233-4 (1936).

[24] J. A. Shaw, *Ind. Eng. Chem., Anal. Ed.* **1,** 118-21 (1929); *Ibid.* **3,** 273-4 (1931).

[25] R. G. Simard, Ichiro Hasegawa, William Bandaruk, and C. E. Headington, *Anal. Chem.* **23,** 1384-7 (1951).

[26] Edward Field, Fred H. Dempster, and George E. Tilson, *Ind. Eng. Chem.* **32,** 489-96 (1940).

[27] R. W. Stoughton, *J. Biol. Chem.* **115,** 293-8 (1936); L. A. Wetlaufer, F. J. Van Natta, and H. B. Quattlebaum, *Ind. Eng. Chem., Anal. Ed.* **11,** 438-9 (1939); Louis Lykken, R. S. Treseder, and Victor Zahn, *Ibid.* **18,** 103-9 (1946).

[28] M. J. Murray, *Anal. Chem.* **21,** 941-5 (1949).

[29] Joseph J. Smith, Frank M. Rugg, and Harry M. Bowman, *Anal. Chem.* **24,** 497-8 (1952).

Carboxylic acids do not interfere unless phenolic, as in the case of salicylic acids. Naphthenic acids, quinolines and hydro-peroxides, do not interfere. Few oxidation products do and usually so indicate by color on exposure. Reproducibility to ±1 per cent is usual.

Phenols extracted into carbon tetrachloride are read in the infra-red at 2.6-2.9 microns.[30] Phenol is separated chromatographically from commercial cresylic acids [31] with accuracy to ±2 per cent.

Samples—*Urine*. To 10 ml. of ordinary urine or 20 ml. of dilute urine add a solution containing 3 per cent of silver lactate and 3 per cent of lactic acid until no further precipitation of proteins and uric acid occurs. This required 2-20 ml. Add a few drops of colloidal iron, mix, dilute to 50 ml., mix, and filter. To 25 ml. add a concentrated solution of sodium chloride in 1:99 hydrochloric acid until all the silver is precipitated. Dilute to 50 ml. and filter. Develop with phosphotungstic-phosphomolybdic acid.

Alternately, treat 20 ml. of urine with 2 ml. of 10 per cent sodium tungstate solution and 2 ml. of 1:54 sulfuric acid. Shake and filter precipitated proteins after 10 minutes. To 12 ml. of filtrate add 10 ml. of a 2.5 per cent solution of zinc chloride, and dilute to 30 ml. with a 20 per cent solution of sodium carbonate. Mix and filter to remove precipitated uric acid. Develop with phosphotungstic-phosphomolybdic acid.

The free and conjugated phenols are both present in the preceding samples. The volatile urinary phenols are phenol and *p*-cresol. The relative amounts of each are unknown.[32] To separate [33] distil 10 ml. of urine, 190 ml. of water, and 0.5 gram of sodium bicarbonate, collecting a 10-ml. sample. For conjugated phenols distil 50 ml. of the original urine.

For development with Millon's reagent, add 15 grams of powdered barium hydroxide to 50 ml. of urine. Mix and add 1 liter of a mixture of 650 ml. of ethanol and 350 ml. of ether. These precipitate tyrosine and hydroxyproteic acid together with various other substances. The urea all remains in solution. Decant after 30 minutes through a Büchner

---

[30] R. G. Simard, Ichiro Hasegawa, William Bandaruk, and C. E. Headington, *Anal. Chem.* **23**, 1384-7 (1951).

[31] R. J. Zahner and W. B. Swann, *Anal. Chem.* **23**, 1093-5 (1951).

[32] Benjamin Warshowsky and E. J. Shantz, *Anal. Chem.* **20**, 951-4 (1948); E. G. Schmidt, *J. Biol. Chem.* **145**, 533-44 (1942); *Ibid.* **179**, 211-15 (1949).

[33] Antonio Tanzella, *Sperimentale* **91**, *Sect. rend. adunanze accad. med. fis. fiorentina* 26-33 (1937).

funnel and collect the precipitate in the funnel. Transfer the precipitate to a beaker and add 25 ml. of 1:9 sulfuric acid. Mix and filter to remove barium sulfate. Add 2 ml. of 20 per cent phosphotungstic acid solution to the colored filtrate and dilute to a known volume. Mix well and filter. To an aliquot add an excess of 2 per cent quinine hydrochloride to remove an excess of phosphotungstic acid. Mix well and filter. To an aliquot of the filtrate add 50 per cent sodium hydroxide solution drop by drop until quinine is no longer precipitated. Filter and acidify an aliquot of the filtrate with 1:1 sulfuric acid.

Feces. Suspend 1 part by weight of feces in 9 parts of water. Treat 5 ml. of the 10 per cent suspension with 5 ml. of a 10 per cent solution of sodium tungstate and 5 ml. of 1:54 sulfuric acid. Shake and filter precipitated proteins after a few minutes standing. To eliminate sulfides add to 12 ml. of filtrate 10 ml. of a 2.5 per cent solution of zinc chloride and 10 ml. of a 20 per cent solution of sodium carbonate. Mix and filter. Use 16 ml. of filtrate as the final sample for development with phosphotungstic-phosphomolybdic acid. Free tyrosine is reported with the phenol and has the same significance.

Whole blood.[34] Mix 1 volume of blood with 7 volumes of water. Add 1 volume of 10 per cent sodium tungstate solution and 1 volume of 1:54 sulfuric acid. Let stand for 1 hour and filter. To 25 ml. of filtrate add 1 ml. of 2.5 per cent zinc chloride solution and 1 ml. of 10 per cent sodium carbonate solution. Mix well, let stand 1 hour and centrifuge. The precipitate can be saved for determination of uric acid (page 436). In that case decant before diluting. If the precipitate is not to be saved, dilute to 30 ml. and filter. Use 10 ml. of the clear solution as sample for development with phosphotungstic-phosphomolybdic acid or diazotized sulfanilic acid.

Plasma. Centrifuge a sample of oxalated blood until the volume of corpuscles remains constant. Carefully pipet off the plasma without disturbing the corpuscle layer. Dilute a convenient volume of the plasma with 8 volumes of water, and add 0.5 volume each of 10 per cent sodium tungstate solution and 1:54 sulfuric acid. Stopper and shake. The precipitated proteins may be filtered off immediately. Pour the plasma onto the filter, slowly at first to allow the wetting of the filter paper before any filtrate has passed through. If the filtrate is turbid, the analysis can be saved by adding a few drops of 1:36 sulfuric acid to the mixture. The filtrate should be perfectly clear, and only faintly acid. It is suitable

---

[34] Cf. Fernando Marcolongo, *Arch. sci. med.* '63, 262-71 (1937); Wilhelm Deichmann and Lawrence J. Schafer, *Am. J. Clin. Path.* 12, 129-43 (1942).

for the determination of all constituents included in the system of blood analysis. The tendency is for phenol to be low in the filtrate. Use 10 ml. of filtrate as sample for development with phosphotungstic-phosphomolybdic acid.

Corpuscles. Remove the plasma that remains above the corpuscle layer as completely as possible. Insert a blood pipet into the corpuscle layer and remove a convenient volume. Lake it with 5 volumes of water. Add 2 volumes each of 10 per cent sodium tungstate solution and 1:54 sulfuric acid. Stopper, shake, and filter. Develop 10 ml. with phosphotungstic-phosphomolybdic acid.

Preserved serum. Phenolic preservatives in serum may be determined. To 1 ml. of serum add 125 ml. of water, 4 ml. of 1:3 sulfuric acid, 4 ml. of a 12 per cent solution of silicotungstic acid to precipitate substances which cause foaming, and a fragment of hot pumice. Bring to boiling slowly and distil about 100 ml. Add 100 ml. more of water to the distillation flask and distil over nearly 200 ml. Dilute to 200 ml. and mix. Test qualitatively with Millon's reagent to distinguish the preservative used. Phenol gives a deep red, *o*-cresol a faint orange, *m*-cresol a strong yellow, and *p*-cresol a greenish yellow color. Develop 10 ml. with phosphotungstic-phosphomolybdic acid.

For development with Millon's reagent, dilute 0.5 ml. to 275 ml. and mix with 25 ml. of 1:1 sulfuric acid. Distil 200 ml. from an all-glass still and filter the distillate.

Spinal fluid. Mix 10 ml. of sample and 13 ml. of water. Add 1 ml. of 10 per cent sodium tungstate solution and mix. Add 1 ml. of 1:54 sulfuric acid and mix. Continue as for whole blood starting at "Let stand for 1 hour and filter."

Tissue. Triturate 1 gram of tissue with sand in a mortar until a homogeneous pulp is produced. Treat this as described for whole blood starting at "Add 1 volume of 10 per cent sodium tungstate solution . . ."

Alternatively,[35] mix a sample with 10 ml. of water and an appropriate amount of sand and grind. Dilute to about 40 ml., add 20 ml. of 10 per cent sodium tungstate solution, and mix. Add 20 ml. of 1:54 sulfuric acid and mix. Filter and steam-distil a known volume to which has been added 2 ml. of 1:1 sulfuric acid per 25 ml. After collecting about 270 ml. of distillate add 2 ml. of 4 per cent sodium hydroxide solution and evaporate to under 10 ml. Filter and wash to 20 ml. Use this as sample for development with diazotized *p*-nitroaniline as volatile phenols.

---

[35] Wilhelm Deichmann and Eugene W. Scott, *Ind. Eng. Chem., Anal. Ed.* **8**, 423-4 (1936).

Air.[36] Collect the phenol by absorption in an extraction thimble. Disintegrate the thimble in water and decant or filter. Evaporate to 150 ml. and add about 0.5 gram of copper sulfate pentahydrate. Make acid to Congo red with phosphoric acid and distil 10 ml. Develop with phosphotungstic-phosphomolybdic acid.

Alternatively,[37] absorb the phenols from 2 liters of air in 15 ml. of 0.4 per cent sodium hydroxide solution. Neutralize 10 ml. of the sample with glacial acetic acid and develop with diazotized *p*-nitroaniline solution.

Water. Dilute the sample to about 1 mg. of phenolic compounds per liter. To a 250-ml. portion of the sample add 3 ml. of concentrated sulfuric acid. Distil in duplicate. Return the distillates to their respective flasks. To the sample to be used for correction add 10 ml. of a saturated solution of chromium trioxide in concentrated sulfuric acid. To the sample which is to give total phenols add 10 ml. of concentrated sulfuric acid. Connect the flasks to condensers and apply heat to bring the contents to boiling in 40-45 minutes. As soon as the boiling point is reached, remove the flame. Let the flasks stand hot for 30 minutes, then apply a full flame and collect 225-ml. portions of distillate. The distillate from the second sample contains phenol plus all other phenolic compounds originally present. The distillate from the oxidized sample contains no phenol, but all the related compounds. The difference between the two as determined by diazotized salicylic acid gives the amount of phenol alone. Use 50 ml. of each distillate for the determination.

For development with 2,6-dibromoquinone chloroimide, add 0.7 ml. of 10 per cent phosphoric acid to 500 ml. of sample. If aniline is present, substitute sulfuric acid. If hydrogen sulfide is present, add 5 ml. of 10 per cent cupric sulfate pentahydrate solution. Rapidly distil 400 ml. from an all-glass still. Add 50 ml. of distilled water to the distillation flask and distil over 50 ml. more. If the amount of phenolic material exceeds 0.1 part per million, take an aliquot which on dilution will approximate that level.

Coke-oven wastes.[38] *Dilute samples.* Make an appropriate sample acid to methyl orange with 1:35 sulfuric acid. Add about 4 drops of 10 per cent cadmium chloride solution, make alkaline with 4.2 per cent sodium bicarbonate solution, and add about 4 drops in excess. Shake with ether which has been washed with 10 per cent sodium hydroxide

[36] Wilhelm Liesegang, *Gesundh.-Ing.* **61**, 320-2 (1938).

[37] V. P. Maevskaya, *Zavodskaya Lab.* **8**, 812-15 (1939).

[38] Joseph A. Shaw, *Anal. Chem.* **23**, 1788-92 (1951).

solution, then with water, and finally with water acid to methyl orange. As extractant approximate 25, 15, and 15 per cent of the sample volume. Discard the aqueous layer and shake the combined ether extracts with 10, 10, and 10 ml. of 10 per cent sodium hydroxide solution. Discard the ether and heat to drive off that dissolved in the alkaline extracts. Dilute with water to 50 ml. and proceed as for less-dilute samples.

Less-dilute samples. Make 10 ml. of sample just acid to methyl orange by dropwise addition of 1:1 sulfuric acid. Steam-distil with nitrogen or compressed air through an 8-inch spiral condenser. Pass water-washed gas at 1-2 cubic feet per hour which should deliver 1-2 drops of condensate per second. Collect 25 ml. of distillate and develop with 4-aminoantipyrine.

Sewage. Concentrate the sample solution by making 1 liter strongly alkaline with 10 ml. of 30 per cent potassium hydroxide solution and evaporating to about 50 ml. Transfer the residue quantitatively, including precipitated salts, make strongly acid with 10 to 20 ml. of concentrated sulfuric acid, cooling under the tap, and dilute to about 150 ml. Distil 100 ml. Develop with Millon's reagent.

Samples insoluble in acetic acid-potassium acetate buffer but soluble in octane or other solvents. As prepared diluent, extract 1 liter of octane twice with 100-ml. portions of 10 per cent potassium hydroxide solution. Wash with 10 ml. of water and filter. Other solvents, such as benzene, ether, etc., similarly purified, are suitable. As sample for 0-100 mg. per 100 ml., use 50 ml.; for 50-200 mg. per 100 ml., use 10 ml.; for 200-1000 mg. per 100 ml., use 5 ml. Dilute to 50 ml. with the prepared diluent.

Add 10 ml. of 10 per cent potassium hydroxide solution and shake mechanically for 5 minutes. Separate the aqueous layer quantitatively and again extract with 5 ml. of the alkali solution. Finally, wash the sample by shaking 2 minutes with 5 ml. of water. Chill the combined extracts and dilute to 100 ml. with glacial acetic acid. Use an appropriate aliquot diluted to 5 ml. with a buffer which is a 4:1 mixture of glacial acetic acid and 7.5 per cent potassium hydroxide solution. Develop with nitrous acid.

Aniline and xylidene present. To a sample containing about 15 mg. of phenols in 100 ml. of octane, add 10 ml. of 1:20 sulfuric acid and shake mechanically for 5 minutes. Remove the extract and wash the solvent layer with 10 ml. of water for 1 minute. Remove and repeat the acid and aqueous extractions. Proceed with extraction, starting at ''Add 10 ml. of 10 per cent potassium hydroxide solution and shake.''

Samples soluble in acetic acid-potassium acetate buffer. These include cresylic acids, alcohols, naphthenic acids, glycerols, phenyl ethers, ketones, and aqueous solutions. As sample for this containing up to 0.4 per cent of phenol, use 2 grams; for 0.3-0.8 per cent, use 1 gram; for 0.6-1.6 per cent, use 0.5 gram; for 1.5-4 per cent, use 0.2 gram; and for 3-8 per cent, use 0.1 gram. Dilute to 100 ml. with the buffer described for dilution after extraction.

Commercial cresol. Dissolve a 2.5-gram sample in 10 ml. of 10 per cent sodium hydroxide solution and dilute to 250 ml. for determination with Millon's reagent.

For reading in the ultraviolet, use 0.2 gram for 2.5-10 per cent; 0.05 gram for 10-50 per cent. Dilute to 25 ml. with isooctane and extract with 25 ml. of 10 per cent sodium hydroxide solution. Dilute 1 ml. of the extract to 25 ml. with water for reading.

Saponified cresols, coal-tar dips and disinfectants, phenols in petroleum solvents. Dilute a 5-gram sample to 250 ml. with water. If there is an insoluble layer adjust the water level to 250 ml. Use the aqueous solution for development with Millon's reagent.

Phenol containing salicylates. Mix 10 grams of sample with 50 ml. of kerosene and extract thrice with 100-ml. portions of water. Filter the combined aqueous extracts, dilute to 500 ml., and develop an aliquot with Millon's reagent.

Glycerine. Dilute the glycerine sample to one-tenth its original concentration and determine with Millon's reagent.

Gasoline. Dissolve the specified sample in isooctane and extract according to Table 2. After extraction and separation as specified, separate and dilute 1 ml. of the indicated volume to 25 ml. for reading in the ultraviolet.

TABLE 2. PHENOL EXTRACTION FROM GASOLINE

Approximate Concentration in Percentage	Sample	Volume of Isooctane	Volume of 10 Per Cent Sodium Hydroxide Solution	Final Dilution for Reading
0.001-0.005	15 ml.	100	5	25
0.005-0.02	15 ml.	25	5	25
0.02-0.1	15 ml.	15	15	25
0.1-0.5	15 ml.	15	15	125
0.5-2.5	15 ml.	5	25	125
2.5-10	0.2 gram	25	25	25
10-50	0.05 gram	25	25	25
50-100	0.1 gram	25	25	125

Separation from cresylic acid. Prepare a column as shown in Figure 13. The column is 250 × 18 mm. i.d. Grind 19 grams of 100-mesh silicic acid containing 22 per cent of water with 10 ml. of water so that it remains as a fine powder. Add 30 ml. of cyclohexane to form a mobile slurry and pour on a wad of glass wool in the bottom of the column. Add more cyclohexane to the column and apply a pressure of 5 pounds psi of nitrogen to force the cyclohexane through the column. This will

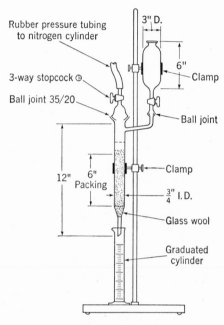

FIG. 13. Chromatographic column for isolation
of phenols

pack the silicic acid to about 150 mm. Release the pressure when the cyclohexane approaches the surface of the silicic acid, repeating if necessary to get the desired height. Place glass wool on the top of the column and at no time during use let the surface be disturbed or the liquid level fall below its surface. To do the latter will require repacking. Cyclohexane leaches ultraviolet-light-sensitive material from the column if allowed to remain dormant for 2 hours, but this is flushed out with 100 ml. of cyclohexane. The column flows at about 130 ml. per hour.

To standardize add a solution containing about 2 mg. each of phenol and *m*-cresol to the column. Percolate with 200 ml. of cyclohexane, collecting as fractions 0-50 ml., 5-ml. fractions up to 150 ml., 150-200 ml., 200-205 ml. Using the last fraction as the blank and checking against pure solvent, make readings in the ultraviolet. Plotting the data will give a point around 80 ml. where the cresol has all passed with the phenol not yet started.

Dissolve a sample expected to contain about 2 mg. of phenol in 5 ml. of cyclohexane. Add to the column by removal of the ball joint. Apply 5 pounds pressure of nitrogen until this just passes into the packing. Collect the 5 ml. of solvent which comes through. Add solvent to fill the upper portion of the column and reapply pressure until the solvent approaches the packing surface. Release the pressure and repeat until 200 ml. of percolate are collected as determined by the standardization, typically 0-70 ml., 5-ml. fractions to 95 ml., 95-195 ml., and 195-200 ml. Discard the first fraction containing cresols, etc. Read the other fractions in the ultraviolet against the final 5 ml. as a blank. Alternatively develop the phenol in the fractions by conventional methods. There are no interfering substances present.

Procedure—*By phosphotungstic-phosphomolybdic acid.* To prepare the reagent,[39] transfer to a 1500-ml. flask 100 grams of sodium tungstate, 25 grams of sodium molybdate, and 700 ml. of water. Add 50 ml. of 85 per cent phosphoric acid and 100 ml. of concentrated hydrochloric acid. Attach to a reflux condenser by means of a stopper wrapped in tinfoil and boil gently for 10 hours. Add 150 grams of lithium sulfate, 50 ml. of water, and a few drops of liquid bromine. Boil without the condenser attached for about 15 minutes to remove excess bromine. Cool, dilute to 1 liter, and filter. The filtrate should not have a greenish tint, as this indicates the presence of reduction products. Protect well against dust, as organic materials will have a slight reducing action. The addition of lithium prevents the formation of insoluble sodium salts, the main source of turbidity in the final colored solution. Larger amounts of this reagent can be used than would be possible with the lithium absent, without causing turbidity. Bromine is added to counteract the effect of possible reducing substances originally present.

Free phenols. To the sample add 5 ml. of reagent and 15 ml. of a 20 per cent solution of sodium carbonate. Dilute to 50 ml. with water which has been warmed to 30-35°, let stand for 20 minutes, and read at 520 mμ against a reagent blank.

Free and conjugated phenols. To the sample add 10 drops of con-

---

[39] Otto Folin and Vintilla Ciocalteu, *J. Biol. Chem.* **73**, 627-50 (1927).

centrated hydrochloric acid. Heat rapidly to boiling over a free flame, with provision for condensation, and place in a boiling water bath for 10 minutes. Cool and add 10 ml. of reagent and 25 ml. of a 20 per cent solution of sodium carbonate. Dilute to 100 ml. and mix. After 20 minutes read at 520 mμ against a reagent blank.

Conjugated phenols. Subtract the free phenol from the free and conjugated phenols to obtain conjugated phenols by difference.

With phosphomolybdic acid. Lubricating oils. For phenols up to 0.4 per cent, use 8.5 grams; for 0.3-0.6 per cent, use 3 grams; for 0.5-1 per cent, use 2 grams. Add the sample to a separatory funnel followed by 4 ml. of a filtered fresh solution of 1.2 grams of phosphomolybdic acid per 100 ml. of n-amyl alcohol. Mix and add 8 ml. of a mixture of 25 ml. of concentrated ammonium hydroxide, 50 ml. of ethylene glycol, and 50 ml. of *n*-amyl alcohol. Swirl and add 2 ml. of saturated aqueous potassium chloride to expedite breakage of the emulsion. Shake for 15-20 seconds and let the layers separate. Read a portion of the lower layer at 700 mμ against a similar sample carried through with phenol-free oil. The time of reading should be exactly 10 minutes after the ammonia was added.

With diazotized p-nitroaniline. Total phenols. Prepare the reagent by dissolving 1.5 grams of *p*-nitroaniline base in 400 ml. of 1:9 hydrochloric acid and dilute to 500 ml. Before use, diazotize 25 ml. of this solution with 0.75 ml. of a 10 per cent solution of sodium nitrite.

To 10 ml. of sample add 1 ml. of a 1 per cent solution of gum acacia, 1 ml. of a 50 per cent solution of sodium acetate, and 1 ml. of diazotized nitroaniline reagent. After 1 minute add 2 ml. of a 20 per cent solution of anhydrous sodium carbonate and dilute to a known volume. Read at 470 mμ after 2-4 minutes against a reagent blank.

Conjugated phenols. To the sample add 1 ml. of concentrated hydrochloric acid and heat for 10 minutes in a boiling water bath. Cool and neutralize with 10 per cent sodium hydroxide solution. To a second sample add the same amounts of acid and base. Continue the determination as for free phenols from ". . . add 1 ml. of a 1 per cent solution of gum acacia. . . ." The difference between the heated and the unheated samples gives the value for conjugated phenols.

With diazotized sulfanilic acid. Macro. To 50 ml. of sample add 4 ml. of an 8 per cent solution of recrystallized sulfanilic acid. Add 2 ml. of a freshly prepared solution containing 8 per cent by weight of sodium nitrite. Mix, add 5 ml. of a 10 per cent solution of sodium hydroxide, and mix. Read against a reagent blank.

Micro. As reagent, chill 1.5 ml. of 1 per cent sulfanilic acid solution and add 1.5 ml. of chilled 0.5 per cent sodium nitrite solution. Continue to cool for 5 minutes and add 6 ml. more of the sodium nitrite solution. After 5 minutes dilute to 50 ml. with ice-cold water and store in an ice bath. It is ready for use 15 minutes later.

Mix 5 ml. of 1.1 per cent solution of sodium carbonate and 2 ml. of reagent. Add 1 ml. of sample solution exactly 1 minute after the reagent began to mix with the alkali. Mix as before. Read against a reagent blank after 2 minutes but before 7 minutes elapse.

With 2,6-dibromoquinone chloroimide. As buffer dilute a solution containing 3.1 grams of boric acid, 3.5 grams of potassium chloride, and 32 ml. of 4 per cent sodium hydroxide solution, to 1 liter. To check, dilute 5 ml. to 100 ml. with water and, if the pH is not 9.4, make appropriate additions to the more concentrated buffer.

As a reagent stock, stable up to 1 week, filter a 0.4 per cent solution of ethanolic 2,6-dibromoquinone chloroimide and refrigerate. For immediate use dilute 4.5 ml. to 100 ml. with water.

Mix 300 ml. of sample at below 26° with 15 ml. of buffer and add 5 ml. of reagent. After 18-24 hours, if the intensity of color is appropriate, read at 610-630 mμ against a reagent blank. To intensify by concentration, shake with 75 ml. of *n*-butanol. Filter the turbidity from the butanol layer and read at 670 mμ against a reagent blank. To check against variation in color intensity developed, run one standard at the same time. The main sources of this variation are in deterioration of the reagent and in temperature of development. If the nature of the phenolic bodies is unknown also read at 670 mμ and report in terms of a phenol standard.

Accelerated reaction. Carry out as previously but have all solutions at 37° before adding the reagent. Incubate at 37° and read the aqueous solution or, after 1 hour, cool to 25° before extraction with butanol.

With Millon's reagent. As reagent treat 2 ml. of mercury with 20 ml. of concentrated nitric acid under a hood. After the first violent reaction, shake to subdivide the mercury and promote reaction. After about 10 minutes, even though undissolved mercury remains, add 35 ml. of water and, if basic salt separates, dissolve the salt in 1:4 nitric acid. Add 10 per cent sodium hydroxide solution dropwise with mixing until the curdy precipitate which forms after each drop disperses to give a permanent turbidity. Add 5 ml. of 1:4 nitric acid and mix well. Do not use after the first day.

Dilute 5 ml. of sample to about 50 ml., add one drop of 0.05 per cent aqueous methyl orange and neutralize with 1:4 nitric acid, and dilute to 200 ml. Place 2 ml. of diluted sample in each of 2 tubes and 5 ml. of 0.025 per cent phenol in 2 other tubes. Flow 5 ml. of reagent down the side of each tube, mix, and heat exactly 30 minutes in boiling water. Cool at once for 10 minutes in cold water and add 5 ml. of 1:4 nitric acid. Mix and add 2 ml. of 1:50 dilution of commercial 37 per cent formaldehyde solution to one of each pair of tubes. This destroys the phenol. Dilute all to 25 ml. with water, mix well, and let stand overnight. The tubes to which formaldehyde was added will be yellow; the others, orange to red.

Transfer 20 ml. from each phenol tube, add 5 ml. of 1:4 nitric acid, and dilute to 100 ml. These are the red phenol standard and the yellow phenol blank. Transfer each to burets. Transfer 10 ml. of each sample solution to Nessler tubes. Add phenol standard to the yellow sample blank and the same volume of phenol blank to the unknown until a match is obtained. Obtain this match promptly or formaldehyde in the phenol blank will reduce the color of the phenol standard.

With nitrous acid. To a 5-ml. aliquot in acetic acid-potassium acetate buffer, add dropwise 5 drops of concentrated sulfuric acid followed by 2 drops of saturated aqueous sodium nitrite solution. Mix and after 30 minutes add, with cooling, a mixture of 45 per cent of anhydrous isopropanol, 30 per cent of concentrated ammonium hydroxide, and 25 per cent of water, until 50 ml. is reached. Let stand at least 1 hour, preferably overnight, and read at 420 mμ. Correct for a sample blank from which the nitrite was omitted, for the nitrite blank, and the solvent without sample or blank.

With 4-aminoantipyrine. Dilute an appropriate aliquot of sample nearly to 500 ml. Adjust the pH to 10 $\pm$ 0.2 by adding 1:1.5 ammonium hydroxide. This will usually require about 1.6 ml. Add 1 ml. of 3 per cent aqueous 4-aminoantipyrine and mix. Add 2 ml. of 10 per cent potassium ferricyanide solution and mix. If the color is deeper than would correspond to 0.2 ppm. of phenol read at 510 mμ. If not that deep extract with 15, 10, and 5 ml. of chloroform. Combine the extracts which, allowing for loss of chloroform by solubility, are under 25 ml. and dilute to that volume. Filter and read at 460 mμ against a reagent blank.

In the ultraviolet. The sample should be in 0.4 per cent sodium hydroxide solution. Read at 290 mμ against the concentration of sodium hydroxide present. If the optical density is not between 0.3 and 0.9, repeat with more sample or dilute further with 0.4 per cent sodium hydroxide solution. Calculate on the basis of the approximate average estimation coefficient of the mixed phenols found in gasoline as extracted by 0.4 per cent sodium hydroxide solution.

o-CHLOROPHENOL

In the absence of interfering phenolic bodies, determined by 2,6-dibromoquinone chloroimide and read in buffered aqueous solution at 650-670 mμ or in butanol at 680-700 mμ. Details are given under phenol (page 118).

p-CHLOROPHENOL

In the absence of interfering phenolic bodies, determine by 2,6-dibromoquinone chloroimide and read in buffered aqueous solution at 600-620 mμ or in butanol at 670 mμ. Details are given under phenol (page 118).

2,4-DICHLOROPHENOL

Develop the red color with 4-aminoantipyrine as described for G-4 (page 153).

o-CRESOL

In the absence of other phenolic bodies determine by 2,6-dibromoquinone chloroimide and read in buffered aqueous solution at 600 mμ or in butanol at 660 mμ. Details are given under phenol (page 118). Substitution in the ortho position displaces the absorption toward longer wave lengths.[40] o-Cresol and m-cresol in p-cresol are read in the infra red, the ortho at 13.37μ, the meta at 12.92μ.[41] o-Cresol is determined by diazotized sulfanilic acid.[42] Many other phenols interfere, and conversely the method is used for determination of many other phenolic bodies. Apply the micro method given under phenol (page 118) and read 2 minutes after adding the sample to the reagent mixture.

Procedure—*In the infra red.* Dissolve a 1-gram sample in 10 ml. of cyclohexane and read at 13.37μ and 12.92μ. Calculate as

$$\text{percentage ortho} = 100 \times 1.54 \times A_{13.37}\mu/\text{Sample}$$
$$\text{percentage meta} = 100 \times 2.90 \times A_{12.92}\mu/\text{Sample}$$

[40] K. Gardner, *Analyst* 77, 160-1 (1952).
[41] O. E. Knapp, H. S. Moe, and R. B. Bernstein, *Anal. Chem.* 22, 1408-10 (1950).
[42] Milton T. Hanke and Karl K. Koessler, *J. Biol. Chem.* 50, 235-69 (1927).

Tetrabromo-o-cresol

Tetrabromo-o-cresol reacts with 4-aminoantipyrine as described for G-4 (page 153) to give first a green color which within 1 hour changes to red and is stable for 12 hours.

m-Cresol

In the absence of interfering phenolic bodies determine by 2,6-dibromoquinone chloroimide and read in buffered aqueous solution at 610-620 mμ or in butanol at 660-670 mμ. Details are given under phenol (page 118). In the absence of other phenols, m-cresol is determined by diazotized sulfanilic acid according to the technic described under phenol (page 117). The violet color of m-cresol and p-cresol when converted to the nitrosocresols shows the widest spread at 492 mμ.[43]

Procedure—*As the nitrosocresols.* Prepare a buffer containing 80 ml. of glacial acetic acid, 15 ml. of 10 per cent potassium hydroxide solution, and 5 ml. of water. Dilute a 10-mg. sample of mixed cresols containing 0.7-1.2 mg. of p-cresol with the buffer to 5 ml. Add 5 drops of concentrated sulfuric acid and mix. Add 2 drops of saturated aqueous solution of sodium nitrite and mix. After 30 minutes chill in ice and add a mixture of 45 per cent of absolute ethanol or isopropanol, 30 per cent of concentrated ammonium hydroxide, and 25 per cent of water, to 50 ml. with further cooling. After standing overnight read at 492 mμ against a reagent blank. Compare with a calibration curve prepared with varying relative proportions of the two cresols.

p-Cresol

Determine by the diazotized sulfanilic acid procedure for phenol (page 117) but read within 2 minutes. Determine as the nitroso compound [44] as described for phenol (page 119). Dilute the sample to 5 ml. with 4:1 glacial acetic acid-7.5 per cent potassium hydroxide solution before development. Read at 494 mμ. m-Cresol gives negligible interference which can be corrected from curves but the o-compound must be absent.

Mixed Cresylic Acids

Determine mixed cresylic acid by nitrous acid as described under

[43] Sidney A. Savitt, Alan M. Goldberg, and Donald F. Othmer, *Anal. Chem.* 21, 516-18 (1949).
[44] Ibid.

phenol (page 119). An alternative is to treat with sodium hypochlorite and dilute ammonium hydroxide to form the blue indophenol [45] or to determine with phosphotungstic-phosphomolybdic acid [46] as described for phenol (page 116).

5-Methyl-2-isopropyl-1-phenol, Thymol

Determine as described for phenol with 2,6-dibromoquinone chloroimide (page 118) but read at 575 mμ.

o-tert-Butylphenol

The reaction of phenols with iodine as described for catechol in the presence of resorcinol is applicable to o-tert-butylphenol in the absence of o-phenylphenol.[47] The color is extracted with toluene for reading. The reaction is carried out at pH 12-12.5. Accuracy is to ± 1 per cent.

Procedure—Dissolve a sample containing no more than 10 mg. of total phenols, no more than 0.5 mg. of o-tert-butylphenol, and no o-phenylphenol in 1 per cent sodium hydroxide solution. Add 5 ml. of 5.3 per cent sodium carbonate solution and 10 ml. of 1.27 per cent iodine solution. After 1 minute add 10 ml. of 1:120 hydrochloric acid to stop the reaction. Add 2.5 per cent sodium thiosulfate solution until decolorized to starch indicator. Extract the color by shaking with 50 ml. of toluene for 30 seconds. Filter the toluene and read at 490 mμ against a reagent blank.

p-tert-Butylphenol

Determine, in the absence of interfering phenols, by diazotized p-nitroaniline as described under phenol (page 117). Make the final solution strongly alkaline with sodium hydroxide solution to develop a stable red color.

Alkyl Phenols

The method of formation of the nitrosocompound with nitrous acid was developed for alkyl phenols, although it is applicable to simpler phenols. For details of sample preparation and procedure see phenols (page 119).

45 G. E. Mapstone, *Australian Chem. Inst. J. and Proc.* **15**, 9-12 (1948).

46 T. S. Harrison, *J. Soc. Chem. Ind.* **63**, 312-13 (1944).

47 Hobart H. Willard and A. L. Wooten, *Anal. Chem.* **22**, 423-4 (1950).

α-PHENYLETHYL PHENOLS

By reading mixed α-phenylethyl phenols in the ultraviolet, it is feasible to determine less than 1 per cent of the ortho or para isomer in the other.[48]

Procedure—Dilute the sample to approximately 0.005 per cent in cyclohexane. Read in 1 cm. quartz cells at 273 mμ and 285 mμ for comparison against curves of known mixtures. The optimum wave length for the ortho isomer is 273 mμ; for the para, 285 mμ.

1-HYDROXY-2-METHOXY-4-ALLYLBENZENE, EUGENOL AND 1-HYDROXY-2-METHOXY-4-PROPENYLBENZENE, ISOEUGENOL

The maximum absorption by eugenol is at 279 mμ. Other appropriate wave lengths are 254 mμ and 282 mμ. The maximum for isoeugenol is at 256 mμ.[49]

Procedure—Read at 254 and 282 mμ. In the absence of other materials absorbing at those wave lengths the values are as follows:

$$\text{Molar concentration of eugenol} = (13{,}200 \ A^{282} - 4640 \ A^{254}) / (480 \cdot 4640 - 13{,}200 \cdot 2650)$$

$$\text{Molar concentration of isoeugenol} = (480 \ A^{282}) / (480 \cdot 4640 - 13{,}200 \cdot 2650)$$

In these the molar absorbencies used which require checking with the specific instrument are as follows:

$$\text{Eugenol } 254 \text{ m}\mu = 480$$
$$\text{Eugenol } 282 \text{ m}\mu = 2650$$
$$\text{Isoeugenol } 254 \text{ m}\mu = 13{,}200$$
$$\text{Isoeugenol } 282 \text{ m}\mu = 4640$$

o-PHENYLPHENOL

Follow the procedure described for *o-tert*-butylphenol (page 122) but use a sample containing about 2.5 mg. of *o*-phenylphenol and read at 450 mμ. Accuracy is to ± 1 per cent. *o*-Phenylphenol in hexane is read in the ultraviolet at 235 mμ. In alkaline ethanol it gives a blue-violet

---

[48] Harold Hart, *Anal. Chem.* 24, 1500-1 (1952).
[49] V. C. Vespe and D. F. Boltz, *Anal. Chem.* 24, 664-6 (1952).

fluorescence.[50] Alternatively develop with 4-aminopyrine as described for G-4 (page 153).

DIMETHYLPHENOLS

Determine by nitrous acid as described under phenol (page 119). The maximum absorption is at 405 mμ for the 3,5-compound, 420 mμ for the 2,5-compound, 425 mμ for the 2,3-compound, and 450 mμ for the 2,4-dimethylphenol.

2,4,6-TRIMETHYLPHENOL

Determine by nitrous acid as described under phenol (page 119).

o-NITROPHENOL

o-Nitrophenol in p-nitrophenol is determined by reduction to the amine, roughly separated from p-aminophenol, and fused to form a fluorescent compound.[51] This will detect 0.005 per cent in the original sample.

Procedure—Reflux 1.3 grams of crude nitrophenol for 15 minutes with 150 ml. of 1:5 hydrochloric acid and 5 grams of zinc dust. Cool, filter residual zinc, and wash with 10, 10, and 10 ml. of water. Add 15 ml. of concentrated ammonium hydroxide, then 1:15 ammonium hydroxide dropwise until alkaline to Congo red. Precipitation of zinc hydroxide indicates too much ammonium hydroxide. Cool to room temperature and extract with 25, 25, and 25 ml. of ether. This extracts the o-aminophenol with very little p-aminophenol. Wash the combined ether extracts with 5 ml. and 5 ml. of ether and evaporate the washed extracts to dryness rapidly on a steam bath. Mix the residue at once with 5 grams of benzoic acid and heat at 155-160° until melted and hold for 15 minutes. Cool and treat the residue successively with concentrated ammonium hydroxide and water until dissolved. Extract the blue solution so formed with 25 and 25 ml. of benzene. Extract the combined benzene extracts with 10 ml. portions of 1 per cent sodium hydroxide until no more blue color is removed. Wash the benzene extract with 10-ml. portions of water until neutral to litmus. Read the fluorescence against natural standards.

---

[50] H. E. Cox, *Analyst* **70**, 373 (1945).

[51] William Seaman, A. R. Norton, and O. E. Sundberg, *Ind. Eng. Chem., Anal Ed.* **12**, 403-5 (1940).

p-NITROPHENOL

p-Nitrophenol in parathion is determined by extraction with alkali and reading as sodium p-nitrophenoxide.[52] The latter technic is appropriate for up to 0.2 per cent contamination.

Sample—*Parathion.* Dissolve 0.6-0.9 grams of sample in 100 ml. of ethyl ether. Extract successively with 20-ml. portions of chilled 1 per cent sodium carbonate solution until the ether layer is colorless. Four extractions will usually suffice. Use the combined alkaline extracts as sample. The parathion remains in the ether layer. The aqueous layer contains p-nitrophenol present as an impurity.

Dusts. Extract a weighed sample with 150 ml. of ethyl ether in a Soxhlet for 1 hour. Proceed with the ether extract as for parathion starting at "Extract successively with. . . ."

Procedure—*Extracts.* Add 20 ml. of 4 per cent sodium hydroxide solution to the combined aqueous extracts and dilute to 200 ml. with water. Read at 400 mμ against a reagent blank. If necessary for reading, further dilute the solution with 0.4 per cent sodium hydroxide solution.

Liquid parathion preparations. To a sample containing about 0.5 mg. of p-nitrophenol add 25 ml. of a buffer containing 12 ml. of 25 per cent dimethylamine solution and 6 ml. of 1:11 hydrochloric acid diluted to 100 ml. Use 9:1 isopropanol-benzene to dilute to 100 ml. Read within 1 hour at 405 mμ as p-nitrophenol. During that time less than 0.1 per cent of the parathion will hydrolyze.

HYDROXYPHENYLACETIC ACID

In the absence of other phenolic bodies, determine by diazotized sulfanilic acid as described for phenol (page 117). Read 4-5 minutes after addition of the reagent.

HYDROXYPHENYLPROPIONIC ACID

In the absence of other phenolic bodies, determine by diazotized sulfanilic acid as described for phenol (page 117). Read 4-5 minutes after addition of the reagent.

---

[52] J. A. A. Ketelaar and J. E. Hellingman, *Anal. Chem.* **23**, 646-50 (1951); Kathryn O'Keeffe and P. R. Averell, *Ibid.* **23**, 1167-9 (1951).

Hydroxyphenyllactic Acid

In the absence of other phenolic bodies, determine by diazotized sulfanilic acid as described for phenol (page 117). Read 4-5 minutes after addition of the reagent.

o-Dihydroxybenzene, Catechol, Pyrocatechol

The reaction of catechol, o-dihydroxybenzene, with iodine in the presence of resorcinol gives a dark, insoluble precipitate which dissolved in acetone is suitable for colorimetric estimation.[53] Interferences are discussed under determination of resorcinol.

Catechol and related compounds produce a violet color with ferrous sulfate in the presence of sodium potassium tartrate.[54] The reaction is due to two hydroxyl groups in the o-position, as catechol, protocatechuic acid, pyrogallol, gallotannic acid, and gallic acid produce the violet color. The ratios between them as to color intensities are not always molecular. Phenol, hydroquinone, resorcinol, phloroglucinol, salicylic acid, m-hydroxybenzoic acid, β-resorcylic acid, and guaiacol do not produce the color. The pH range in which the violet color is produced varies with the particular compound. On the acid side of this range the color changes to a greenish yellow; on the basic side, to orange. This change begins to be apparent for catechol outside of pH 7-10.3.

To insure the maximum intensity of the violet color it is advisable to work with solutions having a pH value at least 1 unit above the lower limit. To effect this result ammonum acetate and, in some cases, ammonium hydroxide are added. If the sample does not contain any considerable amount of acid or alkali, the addition of ammonium acetate should result in a pH of about 7.6. A little ammonium hydroxide will bring the pH value up to 8.

Catechol is determined by osmium tetroxide according to a technic described under gallic acid (page 411). As an alternative, develop with phosphotungstic acid as described for p-aminophenol (Vol IV). Catechol gives a pale yellow color with ammoniacal cadmium sulfate readable at 0.005-0.08 mg. per ml.[55]

---

[53] Hobart H. Willard and A. L. Wooten, *Anal. Chem.* **22**, 670-1 (1950).

[54] C. Ainsworth Mitchell, *Analyst* **48**, 2-15 (1923); A. L. Kursanov and M. N. Zaprometov, *Biokhimiya* **14**, 467-75 (1949).

[55] D. N. Vaskevich and Ts. A. Gol'dina, *J. Applied Chem.* (USSR) **24**, 1214-16 (1951).

Procedure—*With iodine.* Dilute a neutral sample containing not over 0.75 mg. of catechol to 15 ml. and add 10 ml. of an acetic acid-sodium acetate buffer for pH 5.7. Add 10 ml. of 0.05 per cent resorcinol solution and complete as described for resorcinol (page 128) starting with "Add 15 ml. of 1.27 per cent iodine solution. . . ."

With ferrous tartrate. The method given here is applicable to several phenols beside catechol. Therefore, a method of determining the optimum pH, whatever the sample, is given. To test whether an ammonium acetate buffer is sufficient add 2 ml. of a fresh solution containing 0.1 per cent of ferrous sulfate and 0.5 per cent of sodium potassium tartrate to 1 ml. of the solution. Then add 5 ml. of a 10 per cent ammonium acetate solution. If the color is orange add 1:50 hydrochloric acid until a maximum violet color is produced. If the color is greenish yellow or only faintly violet, add 1:60 ammonium hydroxide until a maximum violet color is produced. Note the amount of acid or base added and add the same amount in the procedure.

To 1 ml. of sample add 2 ml. of a fresh solution containing 0.1 per cent of ferrous sulfate and 0.5 per cent of sodium potassium tartrate. Add 10 ml. of a 10 per cent solution of ammonium acetate. This buffers the pH at about 7.6 after dilution. A previous test of the pH may indicate the desirability of adding a known amount of standard acid or alkali at this point. Dilute to 100 ml. and read against a sample blank.

m-DIHYDROXYBENZENE, RESORCINOL

When resorcinol is estimated volumetrically by iodine in the presence of catechol, a dark, insoluble precipitate is found.[56] After destruction of excess iodine the precipitate dissolves in acetone to give a blue suitable for colorimetric estimation.[57] The reaction is applied for either resorcinol or catechol. The color body is formed from one mole of each, but for complete reaction in 1 minute it is necessary to have at least twice the concentration of the added dihydroxybenzene. A large excess of iodine is essential to completion of the reaction. Acidification will bleach the color and liberate free iodine. Excess thiosulfate bleaches the color.

An amount of hydroquinone equal to the resorcinol does not interfere; a large excess does. There is no interference by 50 times the amount of *o*-cresol, *m*-cresol, *p*-cresol, phenol, *o*-phenylphenol, *p*-phenylphenol, *o-tert*-butylphenol, *p-tert*-butylphenol, *p-tert*-amylphenol, salicylic alde-

[56] Hobart H. Willard and A. L. Wooten, *Anal. Chem.* 22, 585-6 (1950).
[57] Hobart H. Willard and A. L. Wooten, *Ibid.* 22, 670-1 (1950).

hyde, p-hydroxybenzaldehyde, m-hydroxybenzoic acid, p-hydroxybenzoic acid, salicylic acid, p-aminophenol, m-aminophenol, o-aminophenol, o-nitrophenol, and m-nitrophenol.

When developed with phosphotungstic-phosphomolybdic acid according to the technic for phenol (page 116), resorcinol is determined. Resorcinol develops a bright yellow with ammoniacal cadmium sulfate over a period of 15 hours.[58]. It is read at 0.005-0.08 mg. per ml. It is also read in the ultraviolet in the absence of other polyhydric alcohols and related compounds.[59]

Sample—*Hair dyes. Sulfated surface-active agent absent.* Make a 5-ml. sample, containing 0.03-0.06 gram of resorcinol, acid with 1:1 hydrochloric acid and dilute to about 15 ml. with water. Extract with 25, 25, and 25 ml. of chloroform. Wash the combined chloroform extracts with 5 ml. of water and wash the separated water extract with 5 ml. of chloroform. Discard the chloroform and add the water wash to the original solution. Extract the acid aqueous solution with 5 successive 25-ml. portions of water-saturated ether. Discard the acid-aqueous solution extracted and combine the ether extracts. Add 25 ml. of 1:1000 hydrochloric acid to the ether extracts and evaporate to loss of all the ether. Cool the aqueous-acid solution, filter through cotton, and dilute to 100 ml. with 1:120 hydrochloric acid for reading in the ultraviolet.

Sulfated surface-active agent present. Mix 5 ml. of sample, containing 0.03-0.06 gram of resorcinol, with 2 ml. of concentrated hydrochloric acid. Reflux with a few silicon carbide chips for 30 minutes and transfer to a separatory funnel with 25 ml. of chloroform and 8 ml. of water. Proceed as for surface-active agents absent from "Extract with 25, 25, and 25 ml. of chloroform."

Procedure—*By iodine.* Dilute a neutral sample containing not over 0.75 mg. of resorcinol to 15 ml. Add 10 ml. of an acetic acid-sodium acetate buffer for pH 5.7, then 10 ml. of 0.05 per cent catechol solution. Add 15 ml. of 1.27 per cent iodine solution and let stand for 1 minute. Add 1 per cent starch indicator containing 2 per cent of potassium iodide and titrate the excess iodine with sodium thiosulfate solution. Add 50 ml. of acetone, dilute to 100 ml., and read at 725 mμ against a reagent blank.

[58] D. N. Vaskevich and Ts. A. Gol'dina, *J. Applied Chem.* (USSR) **24**, 1214-16 (1951).

[59] S. H. Newburger and J. H. Jones, *J. Assoc. Official Agr. Chem.* **34**, 787-92 (1951).

In the ultraviolet. Dilute 10 ml. of the sample containing resorcinol to 100 ml. with 1:120 hydrochloric acid and mix. Read at 273 mμ against a blank of 1:120 hydrochloric acid.

p-DIHYDROXYBENZENE, HYDROQUINONE

Hydroquinone in ether gives a violet color with nitric acid when made alkaline.[60] There is no interference by resorcinol, guaiacol, naphthol, pyrogallol, benzoquinone, and naphthoquinones. An alternative is to develop in styrene monometer with phosphotungstic acid or [61] in general as described for *p*-aminophenol (Vol. IV). Another technic is to treat with excess of a ferric chloride solution at a buffered acidity. The hydroquinone reduces this quantitatively to ferrous ion. Then add sodium pyrophosphate solution to sequester the excess ferric ion. Read the ferrous ion with *o*-phenanthroline (Vol. II, pages 314-16). Hydroquinone gives a brownish yellow with ammoniacal cadmium sulfate after about 5 minutes.[62] It is read at 0.005-0.08 mg. per ml.

Sample—*Styrene monomer.* Extract 1 ml. of sample with 20, 10, and 10 ml. of water. Dilute the aqueous hydroquinone extract to 50 ml. for development with phosphotungstic acid.

Procedure—*By nitric acid.* Mix 10 ml. of sample in ether with 5 ml. of 1:1 nitric acid. Shake and drain off the acid layer from the yellow ether layer. Add cracked ice to the separated acid layer. Wash the ether layer with 10 ml. of 5 per cent sodium hydroxide solution until colorless and add to the acid previously separated. Wash the ether with 10 ml. of water and add to the previous aqueous layers. Make the combined aqueous layers alkaline and dilute to 50 ml. for reading against a reagent blank.

By phosphotungstic acid. To 50 ml. of sample, add 2 ml. of reagent prepared by refluxing 10 grams of sodium tungstate dihydrate, 8 ml. of 85 per cent orthophosphoric acid, and 90 ml. of water for 90 minutes. Add 4 ml. of 10 per cent sodium carbonate solution and read after 15 minutes against a reagent blank.

---

[60] Baidyanath Ghosh and Annada Bhattacharya, *J. Proc. Inst. Chemists* (India) **18**, 154-7 (1946).

[61] S. M. A. Whettem, *Analyst* **74**, 185-8 (1949).

[62] D. N. Vaskevich and Ts. A. Gol'dina, *J. Applied Chem.* **24**, 1214-16 (1951).

p-tert-Butyl Catechol

The amount of *p-tert*-butyl catechol in butadiene is read at 279 mμ with accuracy to 10 ppm.[63] A colorimetric method with ferric chloride has also been developed but not published. The ultraviolet reading is not suitable for recycle butadiene from copolymer plants due to possible accumulation of other materials absorbing in the same range.

Procedure—Weigh about 30 grams of sample from a weighed metal bomb into a flask cooled in acetone-dry ice. Remove the flask from the cooling bath and allow the butadiene to evaporate in a hood. Take up the phenolic residue in four successive 20-ml. portions of water. Filter, dilute to 100 ml., and read at 279 mμ. With K the calculated absorption for 1000 ppm. in aqueous solution, A the observed value, and W the weight of sample, ppm. $= 100\ AK/W$.

l-a-3,4-Dihydroxy-*a*-(Methylaminomethyl) Benzyl Alcohol, Epinephrine, Adrenaline

Epinephrine, the active principle of the suprarenal gland, is a phenol, an alcohol, and a secondary amine. Various oxidizing agents produce colors from orange to red or brown with it.[64] Even at a level of 1 ppm., epinephrine reduces fresh manganese dioxide to a lower oxide and itself forms a red color. This is stable for several hours and is not destroyed by ammonium sulfate, magnesium sulfate, sodium chloride, neutral lead acetate, and many other neutral salts. Alternative oxidizing agents are mercuric chloride,[65] mercuric nitrate,[66] iodate,[67] iodine,[68] ferric chlo-

---

[63] G. G. Campbell and Shirley A. Tacker, *Anal. Chem.* 24, 1090-2 (1952).

[64] Wilbur L. Scoville, *J. Ind. Eng. Chem.* 12, 769-71 (1920).

[65] G. Comessatti, *Deut. med. Wochschr.* 35, 576-8 (1909); *Berl. klin. Wochschr.* 46, 356-8 (1909); A. Ingier and G. Schmorl, *Deut. Arch, klin. Med.* 104, 123-67 (1911); Georges Deniges, *Bull. soc. pharm. Bordeaux* 56, 185 (1918); O. Bailly, *J. pharm. chim.* 30, 404-5 (1925).

[66] Andrée Vinet, *Bull. soc. chim. biol.* 21, 678-88 (1939); P. Bouvet, *Ibid.* 21, 695-712 (1939).

[67] Wilbur L. Scoville, *J. Ind. Eng. Chem.* 12, 769-71 (1920); Th. Konschegg and J. Monsauni, *Z. klin. Med.* 131, 99-111 (1936).

[68] J. E. Abelons, A. Sonlie and G. Tonjan, *Compt. rend. soc. biol.* 55, 301-2 (1905); S. Fränkel and Rudolph Allers, *Biochem. Z.* 18, 40-3 (1909); Georges Weller, *Bull. soc. chim. biol.* 15, 1308-16 (1933); Léon Binet and Georges Weller, *Compt. rend. soc. biol.* 115, 598-9 (1934); John L. D'Silva, *Biochem. J.* 31, 2171-7 (1937); Knud. A. Jackerott, *Dansk. Tids. Farm.* 15, 217-35 (1941); D. Barkovič, and V. Fintić, *Farm. Glasnik* 7, 341-7 (1951).

ride,[69] and persulfate.[70] In these oxidations, extracts free from epinephrine give no color. The red color is greatest at 37.5°. It does not develop so rapidly in gland extracts as in pure solutions. Ethanol must be evaporated *in vacuo* at a pH above 5 and temperature not over 30°, as it lowers the color developed. The only general interfering substances other than bases allied to epinephrine are *p*-methylaminophenol sulfate and *p*-anisidine. With mercuric chloride, dihydroxyphenylalanine interferes by giving a similar color, but this can be largely overcome by use of a filter corresponding to wave length 420 mμ. Mercuric chloride also gives some turbidity from precipitation of mercurous chloride and a small proportion of mercury or mercurous hydroxide. Such turbidity can be removed by centrifuging. Use of mercuric nitrate avoids both of these difficulties, but the kinetics of the reaction is less favorable. With this salt, the color developed is affected by pH, the time of standing, and the concentration of reagent. Proteins reduce the color intensity. The average error varies from ±3 per cent for extracts to ±10 per cent for fresh beef suprarenal gland.

The maximum by adrenaline is at 540 mμ. The fluorescence of *l*-arterenol, α-(aminomethyl)-3,4-dihydroxybenzyl alcohol, a derivative of protocatechuyl alcohol, is only one-tenth as great and slightly toward the violet. Adrenaline becomes fluorescent by a two-step oxidation.[71] Results are accurate to ±2 per cent. Ferrous solution develops a similar red-blue color at pH 8-8.5.[72]

The pH must be closely controlled and the initial blue given time to convert over. At least 0.6 mole of iron per mole of epinephrine is required. The reaction is general for adjacent diphenols such as pyrocatechol and pyrogallol. Ascorbic acid interfers slightly. Local anesthetics such as procaine do not.[73] The product of oxidation is adrenachrome or when iodate is used 2-iodoadrenochrome is present.[74] Oxidation with iodine gives a mixture. The absorption maximum for adrenochrome is at 485 mμ, for the iodo derivative higher. By reading

[69] Italo Sansoni, *Officina* 3, 323-34 (1930); Jacques Mercier, *Compt. rend. soc. biol.* 138, 935-6 (1944).

[70] A. J. Ewins, *J. Physiol.* 40, 317-26 (1910); James H. Barker, Cyril J. Eastland and Norman Evers, *Biochem. J.* 26, 2129-43 (1932).

[71] J. H. Heller, R. B. Setlow, and E. Mylon, *Am. J. Physiol.* 161, 268-77 (1950); *Ibid.* 166, 304-13 (1951); *Science* 112, 88-9 (1950).

[72] G. Vogeler, *Arch. exptl. Path. Pharmakol.* 194, 281-3 (1940); J. Roy Doty, *Anal. Chem.* 20, 1166-8 (1948).

[73] Jan Gustafson, *Svensk Farm. Tid.* 54, 653-62, 677-83 (1950).

[74] Inge Ehrlén, *Farm. Revy* 47, 321-6 (1918).

at 525 mμ the presence of a mixture is immaterial. Potassium ferricyanide, silver oxide, and ceric sulfate also give adrenochrome on oxidation.

Ephinephrine as adrenochrome in alkaline solution forms adrenolutine which is read fluorimetrically in the ultraviolet.[75] Propynaline, 3,4-$(HO)_2C_6H_3CHOHCH_2NHCH(CH_3)_2$, gives 70 per cent as much fluorescence, arterenol about 11 per cent, and catechol, m-synephrine, and neosynephrine none. The formation of adrenochrome depends on pH.[76] At pH4, l-adrenaline is completely oxidized by iodine within 2 minutes while l-noradrenaline is less than 10 per cent oxidized. At pH 6 in the absence of an inhibitor both are completely oxidized in 2 minutes. The fluorescence of adrenaline in strongly alkaline solution is also read without oxidation.[77]

The blue of epinephrine with phospho-18-tungstic acid, Folin's uric acid reagent, is almost exactly 3 times that of an equal weight of uric acid.[78] The amount of uric acid in extracts of blood and tissue is so slight that this reagent may be used for examination of gland extracts. The reaction is sensitive to 0.3 ppm. and properly applied is accurate to ±5 per cent. The color due to epinephrine is not quite as bright as that from uric acid. There is no interference by tyrosine, phenylalanine, histamine, thyroxine, tryptophane, l-histidine, yeast nucleic acid, glutathione, zinc sulfate, boric acid, antipyrine, procaine, and cocaine. Color is given by cysteine hydrochloride and many other easily oxidizable substances. Ascorbic acid gives a blue-violet but can be removed with lead acetate. Metabisulfite must be removed by acidification and aeration at a low temperature. Phosphotungstic-phosphomolybdic acid, is also applied, as well as ammonium molybdate.[79]

The similar reaction of epinephrine as a reducing agent with areseno-

[75] Alf. Lund, *Acta Pharmacol. et Toxicol.* **5**, 231-47 (1949); *Ibid.* **6**, 137-46 (1950).

[76] U. S. von Uhler and Ulla Hamberg, *Acta Physiol. Scand.* **19**, 74-84 (1949).

[77] Gunther Lehmann and Hans F. Michaelis, *Klin. Wochschr.* **20**, 949-50 (1941); S. Annersten, A. Grönwall, and E. Köiw, *Scand. J. Clin. and Lab. Invest.* **1**, 60-9 (1949).

[78] Otto Folin, W. B. Cannon and W. Denis, *J. Biol. Chem.* **13**, 477-83 (1912-13); Hans von Euler, Dagmar Burström and H. Hellström, *Svensk Kem. Tids.* **44**, 288-90 (1932); M. I. Shapiro, *Farm. Zhur.* **1934**, 131-4; Cesare Giordano and Pietro Zeglio, *Arch. sci. med.* **64**, 325-32 (1937); G. F. Somers and G. B. West, *Quart. J. Pharmacol.* **17**, 308-14 (1944); Sachchidananda Banerjee, *J. Biol. Chem.* **159**, 327-31 (1945); Naresh Chandra Ghosh, Chandicharan Deb, and Sachchidananda Banerjee, *Ibid.* **192**, 867-74 (1951).

[79] L. Rae, *Pharm. J.* **125**, 451 (1930); James H. Barker, Cyril J. Eastland and Norman Evers, *Biochem. J.* **26**, 2129-43 (1932).

molybdic acid is suitable for colorimeteric estimation.[80] Reduction is also given under the specified conditions by trioses, glyceraldehyde, dihydroxyacetone, and glycolaldehyde. Hexoses, pentoses, phenols, cresols, uric acid, and resorcinol do not reduce the reagent. Reduced glutathione as found in blood gives the reaction but may be sorbed on alumina cream at pH 4. Beer's law does not apply exactly.

Other methods of development of color include use of an enzyme from *dolichos lablab* meal,[81] reaction at the phenolic groups with o-iodoxybenzoate,[82] and reaction with 4-nitro-2-chloro-1-diazophenyl a-napthalenesulfonate.[83] Other materials for diazotizing and coupling include [84] o-methoxyaniline, p-nitroaniline,[85] and o-chloro-p-nitroaniline. An apple green fluorescence in alkaline solution when excited by ultraviolet is also read.[86]

Adrenaline and noradrenaline are successfully separated by paper chromatography.[87,88] The sample is applied containing 0.005-0.05 mg. of test substance, and chromatographed for 22 hours with a mixture of butanol and acetic acid. After location on a test strip the sections are removed, extracted, and developed.

Sample—*Fresh suprarenal gland.* The amount of adrenaline in the cortical and medullary parts of the gland is quite different. Equal parts of each can be taken as sample or the medullary can be separated from

[80] John C. Whitehorn, *J. Biol. Chem.* **56**, 751-64 (1923); *Ibid.* **108**, 633-43 (1935); Frank H. Shaw, *Biochem. J.* **32**, 19-25 (1938); W. R. Bloor and S. S. Bullen, *J. Biol. Chem.* **138**, 727-39 (1941).

[81] Kamala Bhagvat, *Indian J. Med. Research* **25**, 911-16 (1938).

[82] C. Robert Moodey and George A. Emerson, *Univ. Calif. Pub. Pharmacol.* **1**, 235-47 (1939); George A. Emerson and B. E. Abreu, *Ibid.* **1**, 283-90 (1940).

[83] W. Schuler, P. Heinrich, and E. Lazarus, *Helv. Physiol. et Pharmacol. Acta* **7**, C22-3 (1949).

[84] W. Schuler and P. Heinrich, *Experientia* **1**, 235 (1945).

[85] E. Sinodinos and R. Vuillaume, *Bull. soc. chim. biol.* **32**, 409-14 (1950).

[86] E. F. von Hueber, *Klin. Wochschr.* **19**, 664-5 (1940); L. Kajala and H. Savolainen, *Nord. Med.* **12**, 3562 (1941); Kowad S. Jorgensen, *Acta Pharmacol. Toxicol.* (Copenhagen) **1**, 225-54 (1945); Pertil von Porat, *Acta Med. Scand.* **123**, 317-39 (1946); G. B. West, *J. Physiol.* (London) **106**, 418-25 (1947); Aimo Pekkarinsen, *Acta Physiol. Scand.* **16**, Suppl. 54, 11 pp. (1948); Inge Ehrlén, *Farm. Revy* **47**, 242-50 (1948), *Ibid.* **48**, 485-96 (1949); Alf Lund, *Acta Pharmacol. et Toxicol.* **5**, 1218 (1949); Svante Annersten, Anders Grönwall, and Erich Köiw, *Nature* **163**, 136-7 (1949); J. H. Heller, R. B. Setlow, and E. Mylon, *Am. J. Physiol.* **166**, 304-13 (1951).

[87] W. O. James and Natalie Kilbey, *J. Pharm. Pharmacol.* **3**, 22-6 (1951).

[88] For general details of paper chromatography see nucleic acids, page 451.

the cortical part by dissection. Weigh 8 grams of mixed gland, 2 grams of medullary, or 10 grams of cortical portion and grind with silica. Mix with a solution of 4 per cent trichloroacetic acid and 2 per cent metaphosphoric acid. Let stand a half-hour for extraction of adrenaline. Centrifuge and wash the mixed-acid solution, adding the wash liquid to the main extract. Centrifuge and wash a second time. Dilute the extract and washings to 100 ml. and mix for development with mercuric chloride or mercuric nitrate.

For development with manganese grind the weighed sample in a mortar with a small amount of quartz sand. Add 10 parts of 1:50 acetic acid and a small crystal of thymol. Let stand for 18 hours and filter. Add 5 parts of 1:50 acetic acid to the residue and heat for 15 minutes in a water bath at 70°. Filter and wash the residue on the filter with 5 parts of 1:50 acetic acid. If the combined extracts are colored, add an equal volume of saturated ammonium sulfate solution free from sulfites, and mix. Filter and dilute with 1:50 acetic acid to a volume at which the epinephrine amounts to about 10 ppm. Dilute a portion of this to about 1 ppm. of epinephrine.

Powdered extract. Add 1 gram of suprarenal powder to 1 ml. of 1:35 sulfuric acid and 5 ml. of distilled water. Shake frequently for 15 minutes and dilute to 100 ml. with water. Let stand 15 minutes longer with shaking and filter for the development of aliquots with mercuric chloride.

For development with manganese dioxide, weigh 1 gram of dried sample and treat as for fresh gland, starting at "Mix with a solution of 4 per cent . . ."

Injectable gland extract. This contains chloride ion present as isotonic chloride and some protein decomposition products, both of which should be removed. To 10 ml. of extract add sufficient of the solution of 4 per cent trichloroacetic acid and 2 per cent metaphosphoric acid to precipitate protein matter. Add enough 3.4 per cent silver nitrate solution to precipitate chloride. Dilute to 20 ml., shake, and centrifuge for development with mercuric chloride or mercuric nitrate.

Tissue. Grind fresh or dried tissue with sand and water. Add an equal volume of 10 per cent trichloroacetic acid solution to precipitate proteins. Let stand to coagulate, filter, and wash. Add solid potassium acetate to the filtrate and washings until the pH is raised to about 4 and dilute to a known volume such that about 0.1 mg. of epinephrine per ml. is present for development with iodine.

Blood, plasma, or serum. Mix a 5-ml. sample with 5 ml. of 1.6 per cent solution of sodium acetate. Filter 1 gram of chromatographic aluminum oxide in a 7-mm. column. Wash the column with 5 ml. of the sodium acetate solution. Elute the epinephrine with 5 ml. of 1.2 per cent acetic acid and wash with 10 ml. of water. Add 0.1 gram of manganese dioxide which oxidizes the epinephrine to adrenochrome. Filter and develop the solution fluorescently as adrenolutine.

Serum. Mix 5 ml. of serum with 5 ml. of ethanol and dry in a thin layer at 38°. Powder, transfer to a Soxhlet extractor, and extract with 30 ml. of absolute ethanol. To liberate the adrenaline mix a 2-ml. aliquot of this extract with 4 ml. of 1:50 acetic acid and store at 38° for 3 days. The sample is suitable for development with iodate.

Blood. Add 10 ml. of freshly withdrawn blood to about 50 ml. of 3 per cent trichloracetic acid solution and mix. Dilute to 100 ml. with the trichloroacetic acid solution, mix, and let stand for 15 minutes or more. Filter. Make 3 small indentations in the stem of a 20 ×200 mm. calcium chloride tube, about 7 mm. below the bulb. Close the stem between these and the bulb with cotton or glass wool. Fit the tube to a suction flask with a T in the line to the flask so that the rate of filtration can readily be controlled.

Add 20 grams of fine granular silicic acid or precipitated silica to 60 ml. of 1:1 sulfuric acid and heat to boiling over a free flame with constant swirling. Boil for 10-15 minutes and let stand to cool. Decant the supernatant liquid and wash the silicic acid 10-12 times with 100 ml. portions of water. Filter on a Büchner funnel and dry. Put 5 ml. of this in the prepared bulb.

Dissolve 5 grams of anhydrous sodium sulfite in 50 ml. of water, and centrifuge. Just before use pipet 5 ml. of this into 35 ml. of 1:1 sulfuric acid. Wash the silicic acid with this reagent until the washings are alkaline or neutral to bromothymol blue.

Measure 50 ml. of sample into a flask. Add 3 drops of bromothymol blue indicator solution and add 0.4 per cent sodium hydroxide solution to a green or blue color. Add 1 ml. of phosphate buffer solution containing 17.4 per cent of dipotassium phosphate and 6.0 per cent of monopotassium phosphate and mix. Filter the diluted sample through the prepared silicic acid at a rate of 3 drops per second. Wash the silicic acid 3 times with 8 ml. portions of freshly boiled and cooled water. The epinephrine has now been sorbed by the silicic acid. Do not draw air through the silicic acid.

Put a clean, dry tube in the suction flask as receiver. Add 4 ml. of 1:50 sulfuric acid to the silicic acid, swirl to suspend the silicic acid, and filter by suction into the receiver. Dilute the filtrate to 5 ml. for development with arsenomolybdate.

Procedure—*With manganese dioxide.* As reagent dissolve 3 grams of potassium permanganate in 24 ml. of water, add 8 ml. of lactic acid, and mix well. Add 1 ml. of this suspension to 10 ml. of sample containing approximately 1 ppm. of epinephrine in 1:50 acetic acid. Mix and, after 5 minutes, add 1 drop of 3 per cent hydrogen peroxide solution to remove excess manganese dioxide. Read against a reagent blank.

With mercuric chloride. Add 2 ml. of sample solution to 1 gram of crystallized sodium acetate in 8 ml. of water and mix. Add 3 drops of 5 per cent mercuric chloride solution and mix. The maximum red color develops within 3 minutes. Read against a reagent blank.

Alternatively, transfer 1 ml. of prepared extract from fresh or dried glands, or 5 ml. of centrifugate from the injectable gland extract. Add 0.5 ml. of a 50 per cent solution of sodium acetate trihydrate and 3 drops of a 5 per cent solution of mercuric chloride. Dilute to 10 ml., mix, and let stand in a water bath at 35° for an hour. Centrifuge to separate precipitated mercury compounds and read photometrically at once.

With iodate. To 20 ml. of distilled water and 5 ml. of a 1 per cent solution of potassium iodate, add 0.25 ml. of 1:10 hydrochloric acid. Heat to 38° and add 0.5 ml. of the sample solution. After 15 minutes at that temperature read against a reagent blank at the same temperature.

With iodine. To 10 ml. of extract containing about 0.1 mg. of epinephrine per ml., add 1 ml. of 7 per cent solution of disodium phosphate dodecahydrate. Next add 5 ml. of 1.25 per cent iodine solution. After 15 minutes at room temperature add a few drops of starch paste and remove excess iodine by titration with sodium thiosulfate solution. Dilute to 50 ml. and read the red solution against a reagent blank. The development of a uniform color is closely related to pH control.

With ferric chloride. To 5 ml. of sample extract, containing about 1 mg. of epinephrine per ml., add 5 ml. of 40 per cent sodium acetate solution and 4 drops of 1 per cent ferric chloride hexahydrate solution. Mix and read. The pH must be controlled at 1.3-4.8.

With persulfate. As reagent, dissolve 0.2 gram of potassium persulfate, 1 gram of sodium chloride, 0.239 gram of disodium phosphate dodecahydrate, and 0.937 gram of monosodium phosphate dihydrate in water, and dilute to 100 ml. This has a pH of 5.5 and is stable if kept cool and dark. At room temperature the pH falls in a few weeks due to decomposition of persulfate with liberation of sulfuric acid. Adjust the pH of the sample to 5.4 with methyl red as an external indicator. To 1 ml. of the adjusted extract add 1 ml. of reagent and read after 30 minutes against a reagent blank.

With ferrous salt. Borate absent. As reagent dissolve 1.5 grams of ferrous sulfate heptahydrate in 200 ml. of water to which 1 ml. of 1:10 hydrochloric acid and 1 gram of sodium bisulfite have been added. As fresh reagent daily add 0.5 gram of sodium citrate dihydrate to 10 ml. of this solution.

As a buffer add 42 grams of sodium bicarbonate and 50 grams of potassium bicarbonate to about 180 ml. of distilled water. Solution will not be complete. To another 180 ml. of distilled water add 37.5 grams of aminoacetic acid and 17 ml. of concentrated ammonium hydroxide. Mix and dilute to 500 ml., when solution will be complete.

Measure out an aliquot of sample to contain not over 0.5 mg. of epinphrine. If not already present add 20 mg. of sodium bisulfite and dilute to 10 ml. Add 0.1 ml. of the reagent and 1 ml. of buffer. After 10 minutes read at 530 mμ against water as the blank. The color is constant for hours.

Borate present. Measure out a sample solution to contain not over 0.5 mg. of epinephrine, not over 60 mg. of boric acid, and 20 mg. of sodium bisulfite. Dilute to 5 ml. and add 4 ml. of 15 per cent mannitol solution. Add 0.1 ml. of the reagent and 2 ml. of buffer. Read after 10 minutes at 530 mμ as above.

With phospho-18-*tungstic acid.* Treat 0.5 ml. of sample solution containing 5 per cent of trichloroacetic acid and not over 0.004 mg. each of ascorbic acid and epinephrine in each of two tubes. Cool one to 15° for 5 minutes and add 0.5 ml. of a 10 per cent solution of sodium bicarbonate very slowly. Mix gently. To the second tube add 0.5 ml. of 10 per cent sodium bicarbonate solution and 0.75 ml. of 5 per cent sodium hydroxide solution. Shake. Store for 30 minutes at 30°. In the first tube ascorbic acid, cysteine, and part of the glutathione are destroyed. In the second epinephrine, ascorbic acid, and cysteine are destroyed without affecting uric acid, ergothioneine, and the glutathione not destroyed by sodium bicarbonate.

After 5 minutes add 0.25 ml. of phospho-18-tungstic acid reagent (page 437) to each and 0.75 ml. of 5 per cent sodium hydroxide to the first tube. Read the blue color after 90 seconds. The difference between the two tubes is epinephrine.

With arsenomolybdate. As reagent dissolve 60 grams of crystallized sodium molybdate and 10 grams of crystallized sodium arsenate in about 250 ml. of water and filter. Wash the filter twice and add 5 ml. of saturated bromine-water to the filtrate. Dilute to 500 ml. For use mix 100 ml. of reagent with 100 ml. of concentrated sulfuric acid. If sulfurous acid is not to be added in the procedure remove excess bromine by blowing air through the solution.

Transfer 5 ml. of the sample solution in 1:50 sulfuric acid to a test tube. To another tube, add 2 ml. of the arsenomolybdic acid reagent. Heat this reagent in boiling water for 5-10 minutes. During this period stopper the tube lightly with an improvised air condenser. Pipet 5 ml. of fresh 1.2 per cent sodium sulfite reagent in 1:1 sulfuric acid into the sample tube, mix quickly, and pour into the tube of hot reagent. Pour back into the original tube once to rinse it and again into the heated tube. Accurate and rapid manipulation is essential as the tube must be heated exactly 3 minutes after the sample is added. After heating for 3 minutes transfer to a beaker of cold water. After 15 minutes or longer dilute to 25 ml. and read against a reagent blank.

By mercuric nitrate. For color development use 2 ml. of prepared extract from fresh or dried glands or 2 ml. of centrifugate from the injectable gland extract. Separately use 2 ml. of standard solution containing 0.001 mg. of adrenaline per ml. Add successively to empty tubes with mixing: 9.5 ml. of 12.5 per cent sodium acetate trihydrate solution, 0.5 ml. of 1:360 sulfuric acid, 2 ml. of sample or standard, and 3 drops of mercuric nitrate reagent containing 1.5 grams of mercury per 100 ml. The final liquid should be clear and should have a neutral pH because of the buffer solutions present. Compare after 5 minutes.

Fluorescently as adrenolutine. Transfer 8 ml. of the oxidized solution to each of two cuvets. To one add 0.84 ml. of 20 per cent sodium hydroxide solution to convert it to adrenolutine. Air oxidizes this further within 2-3 minutes to a nonfluorescent compound. After 5 minutes add 0.16 ml. of 1 per cent ascorbic acid solution. This is the blank. To the other add 1 ml. of a mixture of 5 parts of 20 per cent sodium hydroxide solution and 1 part of 1 per cent ascorbic acid solution. The ascorbic acid protects the adrenolutine formed from oxidation by air. Read the fluorescence of both in ultraviolet light against a quinine bisulfate standard.

As adrenochrome. Mix two 1-ml. samples and 1 ml. of acetate buffer for pH 4 and pH 6 respectively. Add 0.2 ml. of 1.25 per cent iodine solution to each and mix. After 3 minutes add 1 per cent sodium thiosulfate solution until the excess iodine is decolorized. After 5 minutes read each at 540 mμ. That at pH 4 is adrenaline; that at pH 6 includes noradrenaline.

Direct fluorescence. Plasma. Mix 4.5 ml. of plasma with 1.5 ml. of protective solution containing 1 per cent of sodium citrate and 3 per cent of sodium thiosulfate. Centrifuge and separate the supernatant layer. Saturate this with air by shaking for 5 minutes. To 1 ml., add 2 ml. of 10 per cent sodium hydroxide solution free from carbonate and mix with a rod without introducing air bubbles. Read the fluorescence against a standard until a maximum is reached. Add 0.1 ml. of 40 per cent formaldehyde to destroy the fluorescence of the adrenaline, keep in the dark for 5 minutes, and read the background fluorescence. Add 0.1 ml. of adrenaline solution containing 0.005 mg., mix, and read the maximum fluorescence. Then the result is 1.36 × (first reading − second reading)/(third reading − second reading).

l-α(Aminomethyl)-3,4-Dihydroxybenzyl Alcohol, *l*-Arterenol, *l*-Norepinephrine, *l*-Noradrenaline

The amount of arterenol in adrenaline is estimated from its color with sodium 1,2-naphthoquinone-4-sulfonate and quaternary ammonium compounds.[89] Amino acids interfere but dihydroxyphenylalanine, known as Dopa, and 3-hydroxytyramine do not. Another method determines arterenol in the presence of adrenaline by a difference in the rate at which they react with iodine to form the characteristic red color.[90] The method for adrenaline by oxidation to a fluorescent compound (this page) is applicable to artenol at 365 mμ in the absence of adrenaline.[91]

Sample—*Adrenaline.* Dissolve 0.02 gram of adrenaline in 0.1 per cent borax solution and make up to 10 ml. with the same solution. Develop with sodium 1,2-naphthoquinone-4-sulfonate.

Procedure—*With sodium 1,2-naphthoquinone-4-sulfonate.* Mix 0.5 ml. of sample with 1 ml. of borate buffer for pH 9.6 (Vol. I, page 175), and 0.5 ml. of 0.5 per cent solution of sodium 1,2-naphthoquinone-4-sulfonate. After 45 minutes add 0.15 ml. of a 1 per cent solution of alkyl dimethyl-ammonium chlorides and mix. Add 10 ml. of an 85:15 mixture of toluene and ethylene dichloride. Shake at intervals for 45 minutes and read the solvent layer at 540 mμ against the solvent.

[89] M. E. Auerbach and Eleanor Angell, *Science* **109**, 537-8 (1949).
[90] N. S. von Euler and Ulla Hamberg, *Science* **110**, 561 (1949).
[91] J. H. Heller, R. B. Setlow, and E. Mylon, *Science* **112**, 88-9 (1950).

With iodine. Two equal portions of sample containing 0.02-0.2 mg. are required. To the first add 1 ml. of acetate buffer for pH 4 and 0.2 ml. of 1.25 per cent iodine solution. After exactly 90 seconds remove the excess iodine with sodium thiosulfate solution. Read at 529 mμ within 5 minutes against a blank to which iodine was not added.

Treat the second sample with 1 ml. of acetate buffer for pH 6 and 0.2 ml. of 1.25 per cent iodine solution. After exactly 180 seconds remove the excess iodine with thiosulfate solution and read as before. For calculation of results:

a = 90 second reading at pH 4.

b = 180 second reading at pH 6.

m = 100/reading for 0.1 mg. of adrenalin after 90 second treatment at pH 4.

n = 100/reading for 0.1 mg. of noradrenaline after 180 second treatment at pH 6.

p = relative amount of noradrenaline oxidized in 90 second treatment at pH 4.

$$\text{Noradrenalin} = n(b - a)/1 - p$$
$$\text{Adrenalin} = M[a - p(b - a)/1 - p]$$

l-m-HYDROXY-*a*-(METHYLAMINOMETHYL) BENZYL ALCOHOL PHENYLEPHRINE, NEO-SYNEPHRINE

Phenylephrine is $HOC_6H_4CH(OH)CH_2NHCH_3 \cdot HCl$. It couples with diazotized p-nitroaniline to give an appropriate color development. There is no interference by penicillin, tetracaine, procaine, chlorobutanol, and quaternary ammonium compounds. Esters of p-hydroxybenzoic acid do not react. Sulfathiazole and sulfamylon must be removed.

It is also determined by reaction with a mercury salt, followed by diazotization.[92] The method is used to determine the purity of therapeutic preparations in which this compound may have deteriorated by oxidation. The method is accurate to ±3 per cent.

Sample—*Solutions, tablets, concentrates.* Dissolve and dilute if required, to give a solution containing approximately 0.5 mg. of phenylephrine hydrochloride which may contain 0.5 mg. of tetracaine hydrochloride per ml. Filter if necessary. To 1 ml. of clear solution add

---

[92] Robert I. Ellin and Albert A. Kondritzer, *J. Am. Pharm. Assoc.* **41**, 71-4 (1952).

3 ml. of 15 per cent mercuric sulfate in 1:7 sulfuric acid. Mix and immerse in boiling water for 10 minutes, then cool to room temperature. Develop with nitrous acid.

Procedure—*By coupling.* Dilute a solution of sample in water or dilute ethanol to a content of 0.025 mg. of test substance per 5-ml. sample. Add 1 ml. of 5 per cent solution of borax.

As diazo reagent dissolve 30 mg. of *p*-nitroaniline in 2 ml. of 1:1 hydrochloric acid by warming. Chill in ice and add 0.5 ml. of 7 per cent prechilled sodium nitrite solution. After 2 minutes add 100 ml. of ice water and 1 ml. of 4 per cent sulfamic acid. Mix, store in an ice bath, and use in less than 3 hours. Add 0.5 ml. of the diazo reagent to the sample, mix, and let stand for 10 minutes. Add 1 ml. of 10 per cent sodium hydroxide solution, dilute to 10 ml., and mix. Read at 495 mμ against a reagent blank.

By nitrous acid. To the sample solution add 3ml. of 0.1 per cent sodium nitrite solution and dilute to 10 ml. After 15 minutes read at 495 mμ. If glycols are present, a precipitate may form during the heating stage of preparation of the sample. This is avoided by allowing the 10 ml. of colored sample solution containing both the mercuric sulfate and sodium nitrite, to stand at 30° for 30 minutes before reading.

3,4-DIHYDROXY-α-METHYLAMINOACETOPHENONE, ADRENALONE

A complex reaction with iodine is applicable to estimation of adrenalone [93] with accuracy to ± 1 per cent.

Procedure—Dilute a sample solution containing 0.2-1 mg. of test substance to 5 ml. with water. Add 3 ml. of a reagent containing per 100 ml. 4 grams of anhydrous sodium acetate, 30 ml. of 1:120 hydrochloric acid, and 10 ml. of 1.27 per cent iodine solution. After 1 minute add 2 ml. of 1.2 per cent sodium thiosulfate solution and mix. After 60 minutes heat for exactly 2 minutes at 100°, cool, and read at 470 mμ against a reagent blank, correcting for a sample blank.

1,3,5-TRIHYDROXYBENZENE, PHLOROGLUCINOL

Phloroglucinol is determined by the reaction product with iodine in the presence of catechol. Follow the instructions for resorcinol (page 128) but buffer at pH 6.

---

[93] István Gyenes, *Magyar Kém. Folyoirat.* **56**, 190-5 (1950).

1,2,3-Trihydroxybenzene, Pyrogallol

Pyrogallol is determined by osmium tetroxide by a method described under gallic acid (page 411). Alternatively, develop with phosphotungstic acid as described for p-aminophenol (Vol. IV).

4,4'-Isopropylidenediphenol

Determine by 4-aminoantipyrine as described for G-4 (page 153).

4,4'-Isopropylidenebis(2-chlorophenol)

Determine by 4-aminoantipyrine as described for G-4 (page 153).

Hydroxybenzanilide, Salicylanilide

Salicylanilide, $C_6H_5NHCOC_6H_5OH$, is classified with phenols because it is determined by its phenolic properties and by the color with ferric chloride. Alternatively, develop with 4-aminoantipyrine as described for G-4 (page 153).

Sample—*Varnish. Phenolic fungicides other than pentachlorophenol absent.* Swirl a 3-gram sample with 40 ml. of absolute ether, or with benzene if it is precipitated by ether, and add 20 ml. of 2.5 per cent aqueous sodium hydroxide. Shake vigorously and draw off the aqueous layer. Repeat twice more, using ether the third time in any event. Filter the aqueous layer through a wet paper and combine the solvent extracts. Wash the solvent with four 20-ml. portions of 2.5 per cent sodium hydroxide solution and filter these extracts. Wash the paper and heat the combined aqueous extracts to evaporate dissolved ether. Cool at approximately 80 ml. and dilute to 100 ml. with water.

Acidify 50 ml. with 1:1 hydrochloric acid to approximately pH 1. The fungicides extracted from the varnish are precipitated. Take the precipitate up in ether and wash the aqueous solution thrice with 20-ml. portions of ether. Wash the combined ether extracts with 5 ml. of water and discard the aqueous layers.

Extract the fungicides from the ether with successive 20-ml. portions of 0.4 per cent sodium hydroxide solution and filter through a wet paper. Wash the paper with water and heat the combined extracts and washings to drive off ether. Evaporate to dryness on a steam bath. Dry at 110° for 1 hour. Dissolve the residue in 25 ml. of water by warming. Cool and dilute to 50 ml. for estimation of salicylanilide with ferric chloride and pentachlorophenol with nitric acid.

Other phenolic fungicides present. Proceed as before until the sample is in 2.5 per cent sodium hydroxide solution and ". . . filter these extracts." Acidify that sample to pH 1 with 1:1 hydrochloric acid and dilute to 100 ml. After 12 hours adjust to 25° ± 1° and filter through an inorganic filter. Transfer the precipitate with the filtrate; use no water. The loss in the filtrate is 3 mg. to be compensated in the final calculation. Other phenolic fungicides are removed in the filtrate.

Dissolve the wet residue from the filter by several passages of 100 ml. of 0.4 per cent sodium hydroxide solution. Finally wash the filter with water and complete from "Evaporate to dryness on a steam bath."

Procedure—*With ferric chloride.* Dilute a sample containing about 5 mg. of salicylanilide to 75 ml. and acidify to nearly pH 5 with 1:1 hydrochloric acid, finally adjusting with 1:120 hydrochloric acid and a glass electrode. Filter after 1 hour, rinse the paper with water, and add 2 ml. of 1 per cent ferric chloride in 6 per cent acetic acid. Dilute to 100 ml. and read at 525 mμ against water as the blank.

Sesamol

Sesamol is a phenol and an oxygen cycle, $CH_2O_2C_6H_3OH$. It is isolated as in free or bound form and read by the color in alkaline solution. Correction is applied for sesamolin present. The latter is sesamol combined with samol to give $CH_2O_2C_6H_3OC_{13}H_{13}O_4$. Sesamin, $C_{20}H_{18}O_6$, contains the same methylenedioxyphenyl group as the other two members.[94]

Sample—*Sesame oil.* Dissolve in 1:4 chloroform-isooctane and dilute to 100 ml. with the same solvent.

Sesamin concentrate. Dissolve 0.25 gram in the chloroform-isooctane mixture.

Procedure—*Free sesamol.* As reagent dissolve 10 grams of potassium hydroxide in 80 ml. of water and dilute to 100 ml. with absolute ethanol. Mix 50 ml. of sample solution with 10 ml. of this reagent and shake for 3 minutes. Centrifuge for 10 minutes to separate the layers. Filter the lower layer for the determination and reserve the solvent layer for the bound sesamol.

[94] Pierre Budowski, R. T. O'Connor, and E. T. Field, *J. Am. Oil Chem. Soc.* **27**, 307-10 (1950); *Ibid.* **28**, 51-4 (1951); Carlos Suarez C., R. T. O'Connor, E. T. Field, and W. G. Bickford, *Anal. Chem.* **24**, 668-71 (1952).

To 50 ml. of sulfuric acid, specific gravity 1.37 at 15°, add 1 ml. of 2 per cent furfural in ethanol and 0.6 ml. of the alkaline extract. Mix by inversion and read between 50 and 75 minutes later at 518 mμ against a blank in which ethanol replaces the furfural reagent.

Bound sesamol. Filter the solvent extract to remove turbidity. To 50 ml. of sulfuric acid, specific gravity 1.37 at 15°, add 1 ml. of 2 per cent furfural in ethanol, then 2 ml. of the solvent solution of bound sesamol. Shake mechanically for 30 minutes. Separate and, when clear, read the acid layer at 518 mμ between 50 and 75 minutes after shaking was started against a blank in which ethanol replaces the furfural reagent. To convert sesamol to sesamolin multiply by 2.68. If sesamin is to be determined (page 182) reserve a portion of the sample in solvent.

Sesamolin

See sesamol where it is determined as bound sesamol.

α-Naphthol

Determine α-naphthol as extracted from dyestuffs submitted for certification by extraction and coupling with diazotized *p*-nitroaniline.[95] α-Naphthol is determined as an impurity in β-naphthol by means of the greater affinity of the former for diazo compounds.[96] α-Naphthol reacts with *p*-nitrodiazobenzene to give a blue color in alkaline solution, while β-naphthol produces no color under the same conditions.

In the absence of interfering phenolic bodies, determine α-naphthol by 2,6-dibromoquinone chloroimide and read in buffered aqueous solution at 580-600 mμ or in butanol at 660-670 mμ. Details are given under phenol (page 118). Aqueous alkaline standards are unstable. Use a neutral alcoholic solution. Recovery in distillation of a sample is less satisfactory than with phenol. Alternatively, develop with phosphotungstic acid as described for *p*-aminophenol (Vol. IV).

Samples—*Food, Drug, and Cosmetic Orange 1.* Extract 2 grains in a Soxhlet with ether for 4 hours. Wash the ether extract and ether washings of the extraction flask with 20 ml. of water. Extract the ether layer with six 30-ml. portions of 0.4 per cent sodium hydroxide solution. Use 100 ml. of this alkaline extract as sample.

[95] Lee S. Harrow, *J. Assocn. Official Agr. Chem.* **34**, 127-30 (1951).
[96] John Prochazka, *Ind. Eng. Chem.* **15**, 944-5 (1923).

Procedure—*With diazotized p-nitroaniline.* Chill a solution of 20 mg. of *p*-nitroaniline in 2 ml. of concentrated hydrochloric acid diluted to 200 ml. with water by addition of 100 grams of crushed ice. When at 5-10° add 2 ml. of 10 per cent sodium nitrite solution and stir for 10-15 minutes. Add a few drops of 10 per cent sulfamic acid solution and stir until there is no reaction with starch-iodide paper.

Cool the extract under 10° with crushed ice and add the diazotized reagent slowly with stirring. After stirring for 15 minutes heat to 90° on a steam bath and add 1:1 hydrochloric acid until litmus turns red. Cool to room temperature and extract with 20-ml. portions of chloroform so long as color is removed. Wash the combined chloroform extracts with 30 ml. of 0.4 per cent sodium hydroxide solution. Filter the chloro-from extract through cotton, dilute to 500 ml. with chloroform, and read at 490 mμ.

By p-nitrodiazobenzene. Dissolve 1.44 grams of sample in 50 ml. of ethanol. Add 3 ml. of a solution of *p*-nitrodiazobenzene, of which 100 ml. are equivalent to 1 gram of nitrite. Prepare this solution according to the usual methods of diazotizing. It should contain only a very slight excess of nitrous acid, and an excess of 30 to 50 per cent of hydrochloric acid over the theoretical amount. To the β-naphthol solution add 0.03 gram of sodium nitrite. If the original naphthol mixture contained less than 0.5 per cent of the α-compound, the latter will be completely precipitated, together with a small amount of the β-form, as the *p*-nitroazobenzene compound. Let stand for 30 minutes, dilute with 60 ml. of boiling water, filter hot, and wash the precipitate with hot water. All the uncombined β-naphthol passes into the filtrate with some impure azo compound of the α-naphthol. Wash the precipitate from the filter and boil with 50 ml. of 0.5 per cent sodium hydroxide solution. Filter hot and dilute to 100 ml. with 0.5 per cent sodium hydroxide solution. Read within 30 minutes.

4-AMINO-2-METHYL-1-NAPHTHOL

The synthetic product, 4-amino-2-methyl-1-naphthol is reacted in alkaline solution with sodium pentacyanoammine ferroate to give an intense blue color which is compared with natural standards.[97] Aliphatic amines and secondary or tertiary aromatic amines do not interfere in this reaction. If sodium bisulfite exceeds five times the amount of test substance,

---

[97] Amel R. Menotti, *Ind. Eng. Chem., Anal. Ed.* **14**, 601-2 (1942).

it slows color development and gives lower final intensity. The oxidation product, 2-methyl-1,4-naphthoquinone, gives no color with this reagent. Other primary aromatic amines give blue colors, aromatic and aliphatic nitroso compounds give green, and hydrazine and its derivatives give red to yellow.

Samples—*Ampoules of 4-amino-2-methyl-1-naphthol.* Dilute to about 1 mg. per ml. for use.

Powdered mixtures containing 4-amino-2-methyl-1-naphthol. Extract the sample with distilled water containing 0.1 per cent of sodium bisulfite to inhibit decomposition of the drug. Dilute the clear extract so that it contains about 1 mg. of test substance per ml.

Procedure—To prepare the sodium pentacyanoammine ferroate, shake 10 grams of finely ground sodium nitroprusside with 30 ml. of concentrated ammonium hydroxide to dissolve, and store overnight at 0-10°. Filter the crystals which form, wash with ethanol, and finally with absolute methanol. Dry over sulfuric acid *in vacuo*. Another crop of lower purity can be precipitated from the mother liquor with ethanol. As working reagent, dissolve 0.25 gram of sodium pentacyanoammine ferroate and 0.5 gram of anhydrous sodium carbonate in 25 ml. of water. It is stable for about 1 week.

As standard dissolve 60.53 mg. of pure 4-amino-2-methyl-1-naphthol hydrochloride and 50 mg. of sodium bisulfite in 50 ml. of water and store in a dark glass-stoppered bottle. It is stable for 4-6 hours. Transfer a 1-ml. aliquot of sample solution and 1 ml. of the standard solution. Add 1 ml. of reagent to each, mix, and let stand in the dark for 15 minutes. Dilute each to 50 ml. with water, mix, and compare. If there is a variance of more than 10 per cent in aminonaphthol content, carry out a second determination after adjusting the concentration of the standard to approximately that of the unknown.

β-NAPHTHOL

β-Naphthol reacts with malic acid to give a product which is estimated fluorimetrically.[98] Aging with the reagent for 24 hours prior to heating intensifies the color sixfold. The presence of an equal amount of α-naphthol introduces a positive error of the order of 5 per cent. Un-

---

[98] Elmer Leininger and Sidney Katz, *Anal. Chem.* **21**, 1375-7 (1949).

combined β-naphthol in coal tar colors is determined by coupling with diazotized p-nitroaniline.[99]

Sample—*Dyestuff. Soluble in water.* Acidify a solution of 2 grams in 250 ml. of water by addition of 5 ml. of 1:5 sulfuric acid. Extract with six 30-ml. portions of isopropyl ether. Wash the combined extracts with 20 ml. of 1:120 hydrochloric acid and discard the washings. Extract with six 30-ml. portions of 0.4 per cent sodium hydroxide solution. Combine these extracts as the sample.

Soluble in isopropyl ether. Dissolve a 2-gram sample in 250 ml. of isopropyl ether, warming as necessary. Extract with six 30-ml. portions of 0.4 per cent sodium hydroxide solution. Wash the combined extracts with 30 ml. of isopropyl ether, discard the washings, and use the extract as sample.

Insoluble in water or isopropyl ether. Extract a 10-gram sample with isopropyl ether for 10 hours in a Soxhlet. Extract the isopropyl ether, including solvent washings of the extraction flask, with six 30-ml. portions of 0.4 per cent sodium hydroxide solution. Wash the combined alkaline extracts with 30 ml. of isopropyl ether. Dilute the washed extract to 500 ml. and use 100 ml. as sample.

Procedure—*With malic acid.* Evaporate a solution containing 0.001-0.015 mg. of β-naphthol to dryness in a vacuum desiccator. Add 1 ml. of reagent containing 1 gram of malic acid per 100 ml. of 91.5-92.5 per cent sulfuric acid. This is 100 ml. of concentrated sulfuric acid with 7 ml. of water. The reagent keeps for 10 days in a refrigerator. Wet the dried sample thoroughly and let stand at room temperature for 24 hours. Heat at 35-40° for 10 minutes. Transfer quantitatively to a 100-ml. volumetric flask, dilute to volume at 25° ± 11.5° with water, and read the fluorescence at 365 mμ at the same temperature. Use secondary yellow and blue filters. Set 0 with water and 100 with 0.2 per cent sodium salicylate.

By diazotized p-nitroaniline. Follow the technic for α-naphthol to ". . . to 90° on a steam bath." Omit the neutralization and proceed from "Cool to room temperature. . . ."

COUMARIN

Coumarin with the structure $C_6H_4CH:CHC=O$ is a simple result of

$$\vert\underline{\hspace{2em}} O \underline{\hspace{1em}}\vert$$

[99] Lee S. Harrow, *J. Assocn. Official Agr. Chem.* **34**, 127-30 (1951).

ring closure of coumaric acid o-$HOC_6H_4CH:CHCOOH$. Melilotic acid is similar in that the double bond has been hydrogenated. After separation from interfering substances the red color with diazotized p-nitroaniline is suitable for estimation of coumarin.[100] Thus it has been applied to sweet clover and to vanilla extracts. Colorimetric values agree with those obtained by titration. o-Coumaric acid does not distil and addition of sodium acetate prevents melilotic acid from distilling. Unless glucosides of plants are hydrolyzed to release bound coumarin, results will be low, often by 50 per cent. That is related to the stage of development of the plant.

Coumarin is converted to salicylic acid by fusion with potassium hydroxide. Salicylic acid is then estimated by the purple color of ferric salicylate in chloroform.[101] Interference by vanillin, saccharin, and salicylic acid is prevented by extracting coumarin from ammoniacal solution with ether. Coumarin and saccharin may be found together in food products, especially in soft drinks.

Sample—*Vanilla extract.* The apparatus consists of a 1-liter, long-necked, round-bottom flask with a steam inlet to the bottom, leading at the outlet through a trap to an efficient condenser. The receiver at the base of the condenser is a 1-liter suction flask connected with a manometer and suction pump. The flask containing the extract is heated by immersion in boiling water in a 4-liter beaker.

Transfer 12.5 ml. of vanilla extract to the flask and add 0.5 gram of potassium sulfate. Dilute to about 100 ml. Heat by boiling the water about the flask and pass in dry steam. When distillate starts to go over, without reduction of pressure, apply suction as rapidly as possible without boiling over until the pressure is reduced to 140 mm. Distil until the flask is dry. This gives about 95 per cent recovery. Add 100 ml. of water to the flask and repeat the distillation. Recovery of as much as 30 mg. now approximates 100 per cent. Dilute the distillate and rinsings of the condenser to 1 liter for determination of aliquots with diazotized p-nitroaniline.

Alternatively, remove the alcohol from a sample of extract. The resi-

---

[100] J. S. Clayton and R. K. Larmour, *Can. J. Research* **C13**, 89-100 (1935); T. M. Stevenson and J. S. Clayton, *Ibid.* **C14**, 153-65 (1936); Ira J. Duncan and R. B. Dustman, *Ind. Eng. Chem., Anal. Ed.* **9**, 416-18, 471-4 (1937); Willard L. Roberts and Karl Paul Link, *Ind. Eng. Chem., Anal. Ed.* **9**, 438-41 (1937); J. Ansel Anderson, *Dept. Trade and Commerce, Can., Grain Research Lab., Winnipeg, Ann. Rept.* **13**, 35-6 (1939).

[101] J. R. Dean, *J. Ind. Eng. Chem.* **7**, 519 (1915).

due after an alcohol determination may be used. Make alkaline with 5 ml. of 1:3 ammonium hydroxide. Extract the coumarin with 15 ml. of ether. Vanillin, salicylic acid, and saccharin are insoluble in ether in the presence of excess ammonium hydroxide. Evaporate the ether. Add 5 drops of a 50 per cent solution of potassium hydroxide, evaporate to dryness with care, and fuse at the lowest possible temperature, avoiding charring. Dissolve the residue in about 5 ml. of water. Acidify with 1:10 sulfuric acid, add 5 ml. of chloroform, and shake. Remove the chloroform containing the salicylic acid derived from the coumarin and filter through cotton. Wash the cotton with another 5 ml. of chloroform added in several small portions. Develop an aliquot of the solution with ferric chloride.

Imitation vanilla flavors.[102] Dilute a 2-ml. sample to about 80 ml. with water. Add 5 ml. of a solution containing 5 per cent each of neutral and basic lead acetate. Dilute to 250 ml., mix, and filter, discarding the filtrate until clear. Add 0.2 gram of anhydrous sodium oxalate to the clear filtrate, agitate until dissolved, and let stand for at least 5 minutes. Filter, discarding the filtrate until clear and use an aliquot for development with diazotized *p*-nitroaniline.

Clover. Using a sharp cork borer, cut 8 discs 6-7 mm. in diameter from the center of a 8 leaflets. Put 4 discs in an incubation tube containing 0.1 gram of 70-mesh sand and thoroughly dry the 4 other discs at 105° C. for determination of the dry weight of the sample used.

Add 0.1 ml. of water to the sample in the incubation tube, grind with a glass rod having an enlarged end, and stopper with a cork fitted over the handle of this glass pestle. Incubate for 1 hour at 40° to hydrolyze coumarin esters or glucosides. Add 4 drops of ethanol and grind. Add about 1 ml. of ethyl ether and grind. Filter through paper and a pad of dry asbestos in a small glass Büchner funnel, using a 10-ml. test tube as receiver. Add 4 drops of ethanol, grind, add ether, grind, and decant through the filter as before. Repeat this operation twice more, then wash the pestle, the outer edge of the test tube used as mortar, and the funnel with a small jet of ether. The total filtrate should be about 4 ml. Evaporate the ether by placing the tube in a water bath at 45°. Dilute the small amount of ethanol and water remaining in the test tube to 10 ml. with 1:720 sulfuric acid. Mix, warm to about 70°, shake, cool, and filter with suction through a filter prepared as before. Use this as sample for development of aliquots with diazotized *p*-nitroaniline.

Sweet clover stems and leaves. Heat just to boiling 1 gram of air-

---

[102] Anon, *J. Assn. Official Agr. Chem.* **34**, 73-4 (1951).

dried, ground stems and leaves of sweet clover with 25 ml. of ethanol. Shake for 30 minutes, dilute to 50 ml. with water, and shake for another 30 minutes. Let the solution settle for an hour and take 5 ml. as sample. Dilute to about 40 ml. for development of aliquots with diazotized *p*-nitroaniline.

Sweet clover seed. Grind 1 gram and prepare the sample as described for stems and leaves.

Wheat. Extract 1 pound with ether in a Soxhlet for 3 hours. Evaporate the ether and add 20 ml. of 1:720 sulfuric acid. Steam-distil the extract and develop the distillate with diazotized *p*-nitroaniline. The results read the degree of melitot taint.

Procedure—*With diazotized p-nitroaniline.* As reagent, dissolve 3.5 grams of *p*-nitroaniline in 45 ml. of concentrated hydrochloric acid, dilute to 500 ml., and filter. Store at 0-3°. For use chill 5 ml. at 0° for at least 5 minutes. Add 10 ml. of chilled 5 per cent sodium nitrite solution, which if protected from light will keep a month at 0-3°. Mix and store at 0° for 5 minutes. Dilute to 100 ml. with water at 0° and let stand 15 minutes before use. It must be renewed after 24 hours.

Melilotic acid must be determined separately and can then be applied as a correction. Add 1 ml. of 2 per cent sodium hydroxide solution to a 4-ml. aliquot of the sample solution, mix, and heat for 5 minutes at 85°. Cool, add 1 ml. of 1:72 sulfuric acid, mix, and let stand for 10 minutes. This brings about closure of the coumarin ring. Add 1 ml. of diazonium solution and mix. Add 0.5 ml. of 20 per cent sodium hydroxide solution in small drops, mixing well after each drop. Dilute to 10 ml., mix, and immediately read the melilotic acid present at 490 mμ against a coumarin standard curve.

To determine both melilotic acid and coumarin, dilute a 1-4 ml. sample with 1:720 sulfuric acid. Add 1 ml. of 7 per cent sodium carbonate solution, mix, and heat for 5 minutes at 85°. Cool and add 1 ml. of diazonium solution drop by drop, mixing after each drop. Dilute to 10 ml., mix, and read immediately against a coumarin standard curve.

The corrected coumarin value is that obtained less 0.9 of the melilotic acid value determined.

With ferric chloride. Add 1 ml. of 0.05 per cent ferric chloride solution to the salicylic acid in chloroform. Shake and read at 530 mμ against a reagent blank.

3,3'-Methylenebis(4-hydroxycoumarin), Dicumarol

As with so many other phenolic substances, dicumarol is separated and determined with phosphotungstic-phosphomolybdic acid.[103] It is also readable in the ultraviolet.

Sample—*Serum or plasma*. Mix 4 ml. of sample, 15 ml. of benzene, and 0.25 ml. of 1:24 sulfuric acid. Shake mechanically for 30 minutes, then centrifuge. Mix a 10-ml. aliquot of the benzene layer with 5 ml. of a buffer containing 0.7 per cent of glycine adjusted to pH 9.7 by addition of 5 per cent sodium hydroxide solution. Shake as before for 30 minutes, centrifuge, and remove the benzene layer to waste. Extract traces of benzene with 10 ml. of ether and use the aqueous alkaline layer.

Procedure—*By phosphotungstic-phosphomolybdic acid reagent*. Develop an aliquot of sample with phosphotungstic-phosphomolybdic acid (page 116).

In the ultraviolet. Read at 313 mμ.

8-Hydroxyquinoline and Derivatives

Since 8-hydroxyquinoline is determined by its phenolic properties, it is here classified as a phenol. The intense color resulting with ferric chloride is used for its estimation.[104] The same reaction is applicable to many derivatives. The most satisfactory solvent is 2-methoxyethanol, methyl Cellosolve. It is suitable for 8-hydroxyquinoline, 5-chloro-8-hydroxyquinoline, 5-chloro-7-iodo-8-hydroxyquinoline, and 5,7-diiodo-8-hydroxyquinoline, but not for insoluble 8-hydroxyquinoline-5-sulfonic acid or 7-iodo-8-hydroxyquinoline-5-sulfonic acid. The color in that solvent is insensitive to small amounts of moisture. Excess iron increases the color intensity. A pH below 1 destroys part or all of the color. At room temperature the color is stable for at least 24 hours. The color is proportional to the molar concentration.

Samples—*8-Hydroxyquinoline or a derivative*. Dissolve in methyl Cellosolve and dilute to about 0.05-0.5 mg. per ml. with that solvent.

Mixtures. Dissolve as 8-hydroxyquinoline and develop according to the procedure. Pour the developed sample into 25 ml. of 1:10 hydro-

[103] Saul Reseman and Howard Green, *J. Lab. Clin. Med.* **37**, 321-4 (1951).

[104] Carl Grabbe, *Arch. Exptl. Path. Pharmakol.* **137**, 96-115 (1928); Fresenius, *Suddent. Apoth. Ztg.* **79**, 68 (1939).

chloric acid. Extract with five 5-ml. portions of ethylene dichloride. Evaporate the extracts to dryness at room temperature in a stream of air. Take up the residue in 1 ml. of methyl Cellosolve, develop, and read as 8-hydroxyquinoline. Subtract the value obtained from the total as 8-hydroxyquinoline, which has been left behind in acid extraction. The direct reading after extraction is the derivative which multiplied by a suitable factor or read against an appropriate curve is the amount present.

Urine. Free 8-hydroxyquinoline. Add sodium bicarbonate if necessary to bring the pH above 7. Extract 50 ml. with five 10-ml. aliquots of ethylene dichloride. Centrifuge to break the usual emulsions. Filter the clarified extracts through a dry paper and evaporate at room temperature in a blast of air. Take up the residue in 1 ml. of methyl Cellosolve and develop, if necessary separating 8-hydroxyquinoline and its derivatives.

Conjugated 8-hydroxyquinoline. These are not extracted with ethylene dichloride. Extract with 8 portions of 25-ml. each of butanol, centrifuge to break emulsions, and filter. Evaporate *in vacuo* and take up in 5 ml. of methyl Cellosolve. Dilute to 10 ml. with the solvent for development of an aliquot. The color develops slowly over 8 hours as it must await hydrolysis of the conjugate by the acid.

Procedure—Mix 1 ml. of sample in methyl Cellosolve containing 0.05-0.5 mg. of the compound with 0.5 ml. of a ferric chloride reagent containing 1 mg. of ferric iron per ml. in 1:1000 hydrochloric acid. Dilute to 5 ml. with methyl Cellosolve, mix, and read at 650 mμ against a reagent blank.

Bis(2-hydroxy-5-chlorophenyl)methane

The bischlorophenols are determinable by their reaction to form 2,6-dibromoindophenol.[105] The pH must be controlled for maximum intensity at 9-10, preferably 9.8. At higher pH levels within the range the stability is better. This is also determinable by the reaction for phenols with 4-aminoantipyrine (page 119).[106]

Sample—Weigh a sample containing 25 mg. of test substance and add 1 per cent sodium hydroxide solution to a volume of 100 ml. Shake

---

[105] Arnold J. Singer and Emanuel R. Stern, *Anal. Chem.* **23**, 1511-12 (1951).
[106] S. Gottlieb and P. B. Marsh, *Ind. Eng. Chem., Anal. Ed.* **18**, 16-19 (1946).

occasionally for 30 minutes and filter. Develop an aliquot with 2,6-dibromoquinone chloroimide.

Procedure—To 1 ml. of sample solution containing about 0.02 mg. of test substance per ml., add 4 ml. of 1 per cent sodium hydroxide solution and 10 ml. of a buffer containing 1.24 per cent of boric acid, 1.49 per cent of potassium chloride, and 0.16 per cent of sodium hydroxide solution. Add 0.04 ml. of 0.032 per cent solution of 2,6-dibromoquinone chloroimide. After 15 minutes add 3 ml. of 1 per cent sodium hydroxide solution and dilute to 100 ml. Read at 580 mμ against a sample blank.

2,2′-Dihydroxy-5,5′-dichlorodiphenylmethane, 2,2′Methylenebis(4-chlorophenol), G-4

2,2′-Methylenebis(4-chlorophenol) is a mildew preventative conveniently determined with 4-aminoantipyrine.[107] Condensation occurs in the presence of alkaline oxidizing agents to form a red dye.

Determination of small amounts of G-4 is by oxidation with alkaline potassium permanganate, removal of excess permanganate with sodium nitrite, and estimation of silver chloride nephelometrically.[108] All alkalisoluble organo-halogen compounds so react if easily oxidized.

Sample—*Fabric.* To a 1-gram sample add 50 ml. of a 0.25 per cent sodium carbonate solution and heat at gentle boiling for 5 minutes. Decant and extract similarly twice more. Dilute nearly to 200 ml. with 0.25 per cent sodium carbonate solution with solution used to further rinse the sample. Cool, filter a portion, and use an aliquot for determination by 4-aminoantipyrine or as silver chloride.

Procedure—*By 4-aminoantipyrine.* To 2 ml. add 0.5 ml. of 2 per cent 4-aminoantipyrine solution, and dilute to 25 ml. with 0.025 per cent sodium carbonate solution. Add 0.25 ml. of 8 per cent potassium ferricyanide, shake vigorously, and after 5 minutes read at 505 mμ.

By permanganate. To 25 ml. of solution in 0.025 per cent sodium carbonate add 15 ml. of 10 per cent sodium hydroxide solution. Add 25 ml. of saturated potassium permanganate solution. If the purple color

---

[107] *Ibid.*

[108] David M. Jenkins, Kennetth L. Waters, and George D. Beal, *Ind. Eng. Chem.*, *Anal. Ed.* **18**, 609-10 (1946).

does not persist, add more. Boil gently for 10 minutes and cool. Add 10 ml. of concentrated nitric acid. Reduce the excess permanganate with 10 per cent sodium nitrite solution. Add 0.5 per cent phenolphthalein indicator solution in ethanol followed by sufficient 10 per cent sodium hydroxide solution to give a pink color. Add 10 ml. of 1:4 nitric acid, cool, and add 4 ml. of 1.27 per cent silver nitrate solution. Dilute to 200 ml. with water and mix. After 10 minutes read at 525 mμ. Subtract a sample blank representing inorganic chloride and a reagent blank.

2,2'-METHYLENEBIS(3,4,6-TRICHLORO)PHENOL, HEXACHLOROPHENE, G-11

Determine by the 2,6-dibromoindophenol reaction as described for bis (2-hydroxy-5-chlorophnyl) methane (page 153) but read at 680 mμ. Alternatively develop with 4-aminoantipyrine (page 153). The latter method is not applicable to soaps.[109]

Hexachlorophene is determined in soap by reaction with ferric chloride.[110] The method is applicable to any soap that does not form a precipitate with ferric chloride and that will give a finely dispersed barium soap. Phenolic perfumes and abietic acid in the amounts usually encountered do not interfere. The sequestrant, ethylene diamine tetraacetic acid does not interfere, but 0.05 per cent of nitritotriacetic acid gives a positive error of 2 per cent. When large amounts of glycerol are present, this may introduce a positive error of 6 per cent of the glycerol content. The method in general is accurate to about ±5 per cent.

Sample—*Milled sodium soaps.* To 5 grams of soap containing less than 50 per cent of water, or 4 grams if the soap is made only from coconut oil, add 55-60 ml. of ethanol, a few marble-chips, and heat until the soap is all dissolved. Add 30 ml. of a 10 per cent solution of barium bromide in methanol while the soap solution is still at the incipient boiling point. Mix, cool to room temperature, dilute to 100 ml. and mix. Filter and use the filtrate as sample.

Liquid potassium soaps. Dissolve 5 grams in 45 ml. of ethanol. Add 30 ml. of a 10 per cent solution of barium bromide in methanol, diluted to 50 ml. with ethanol. Mix, filter, and use the filtrate as sample.

Procedure—To a 5-ml. aliquot add 15 ml. of ethanol and 1 ml. of

[109] Chester A. Snell, Private communication.
[110] Harry L. Larson, *J. Am. Oil Chemists' Soc.* **28**, 301-4 (1951).

a 2.5 per cent ferric chloride solution with stirring, at 25°. Let stand for 3 minutes at this temperature and read at 550 mμ.

4,4'-(2,3-Dimethyltetramethylene)dipyrocatechol, Nordihydroguaiaretic acid

Nordihydroguaiaretic acid, familiarly known as NDGA, is an important antioxidant for fats and oils. Therefore, its determination in small amounts becomes important. Since it a complex tetrahydroxyphenol, it is natural, in the absence of interfering phenols, to use some of the phenol-reactive reagents. The reaction with 2,6-dibromoquinonechloroimide to form a 2,6-dibromoindophenol is greatly affected by light, and oxidizing or reducing agents. Another applicable reaction is that with ferric chloride and 2,2'-bipyridine.[111] This is dependent on time for control of the color intensity developed. Solutions of ammonium molybdate develop a stable light-resistant orange color at once with alcoholic solutions of NDGA.[112] The method is sensitive to a concentration of 0.025 mg. per ml. This reaction is general for o-dihydroxybenzene compounds such as tannic acid, gallic acid, pyrogallol, and catechol. Therefore for accurate work correction may be required, depending on the source of the sample. Flavanols do not give the reaction. Compounds which do not have orthophenolic groups do not react.

This fat antioxidant is determined along with propyl gallate, tocopherols, and butylated hydroxyanisole by a technic described under propyl gallate (page 157).

Sample—*Creosote bush leaves.* Extract 5 grams of ground air-dried sample with ethanol in a Soxhlet for 4 hours. The extraction is 95 per cent complete in 90 minutes. Evaporate the solution to about 50 ml. and let it stand for 2-3 hours. Filter the alcohol-insoluble, wash with cold ethanol, and dilute the filtrate and washings to 200 ml. with ethanol. Dilute 5 ml. to 50 ml. with ethanol and use 5 ml. aliquots of this dilution for the determination. Unless corrected for water-insoluble tannins, results may be expected to read about 0.15-0.25 per cent higher than the true value.

Procedure—Transfer two 5-ml. samples containing 0.25-2.5 mg. of NDGA. Add 10 ml. of distilled water to one to serve as a blank, and

---

[111] A. Emmerie and C. Engel, *Rec. trav. chim.* **58**, 283-9 (1939); W. O. Lundberg and H. O. Halvorson, *Proc. Inst. Food Tech.* **1945**, 115-25.

[112] Peter C. Dinsberg, Luke B. Shires, and Clayton W. Botken, *Anal. Chem.* **21**, 1392-96 (1949).

10 ml. of 1 per cent ammonium molybdate solution to the other. An orange color develops at once. Read at 500 mμ against a reagent blank. The result will include water-insoluble forms of tannic acid. To correct, separately determine tannic acid in the sample. Prepare a buffer for pH 4.8 (Vol. 1, page 176). This is necessary because the reaction is only specific for tannic acid and tannins in the pH range 4.1 to 5.5 Then to 5 ml. of sample solution mixed with 5 ml. of this buffer, add 2 ml. of a reagent containing equal volumes of fresh 0.1 per cent ferrous sulfate heptahydrate solution and 0.5 per cent sodium potassium tartrate. A violet color develops rapidly with tannins. Read at 550 mμ and take the value from a curve prepared from tannic acid. Subtract half the concentration of tannic acid so obtained from the guaiaretic acid, half because tannic acid gives only half the intensity of color with the molybdic acid reagent.

PROPYL GALLATE

The antioxidants used in food products, propyl gallate, butylated hydroxyanisole, nordihydroguariaretic acid, and tocopherols must be considered together. The trend has been toward the use of mixtures. Fortunately, not all the possible multiple combinations are used.

The purple color with ferrous tartrate and gallic acid is specific for trihydroxyphenols.[113] The effect of pH is controlled by buffers at pH 7.[114] The complex with gallic acid has a maximum at 0.2-1 mg. per 100 ml. and 540 mμ[115] The reaction with propyl gallate is analogous to that with gallic acid.[116]

Tocopherols are estimated by the reaction of ferric ion and 1,1'-bipyridine.[117] This reaction has been applied to such reducing substances as propyl gallate, nordihydroguaiaretic acid, and butylated hydroxyanisole.[118] In view of the overlapping nature of these reactions, extraction by differential solubility is desirable. It was found that at 72 per cent ethanol the tocopherols were not extracted to a practical degree while the others were quantitative. Since mixtures of propyl gallate and nordihydroguaiaretic acid are not usual mixtures in the U. S. or Canada

[113] C. A. Mitchell, *Analyst* **48**, 2-15 (1923).

[114] S. Glasstone, *Ibid.* **50**, 49-53 (1925).

[115] K. F. Mattil and L. J. Filer, Jr., *Ind. Eng. Chem., Anal. Ed.* **16**, 427-9 (1944).

[116] J. H. Mahon and R. A. Chapman, *Anal. Chem.* **23**, 1116-20 (1951).

[117] A. Emmerie and C. Engel, *Rev. trav. chim.* **57**, 1351-5 (1938).

[118] H. R. Kraybill, L. R. Dugan, Jr., B. W. Beadle, F. C. Vibrans, VeNona Swartz, and Helen Rezabek, *J. Am. Oil Chem. Soc.* **26**, 449-53 (1949).

that offers a further practical method of separation. Then the propyl gallate may either be in the aqueous layer or, if absent, the nordihydroguaiaretic acid and butylated anisole separated in the 72 per cent ethanol layer with the tocopherols not extracted.

If the solution is too acid, color formation is incomplete, if alkaline the purple tends to fade. Gallic acid, tannic acid, and other gallates give the identical reaction. They are not used as antioxidants. Gum guaiacum in lard or shortening is extracted with 72 per cent ethanol and reducing substances give a color like that of the reagents with butylated hydroxyanisole or nordihydroguaiaretic acid. A qualitative blue color of the ferric chloride reagent with the 72 per cent ethanol extract indicates this gum to be present.

Sample—Dissolve 50 grams of fat in petroleum ether of the highest quality and after warming as necessary to dissolve, dilute to 250 ml. with the solvent.

Propyl gallate. Extract 50 ml. of sample solution with three 20-ml. portions of aqueous 1.67 per cent ammonium acetate solution by repeated inversion in a separatory funnel, followed by extraction with 15 ml. of water. The combined extracts on dilution to 80 ml. contain 1.25 per cent of ammonium acetate.

Butylated hydroxyanisole. After aqueous extraction of propyl gallate, if present, extract the residual solution with three successive 25-ml. aliquots of 72 per cent ethanol by inversion, complete by similar extraction with 60 ml. of 72 per cent ethanol. Dilute the combined extracts to 150 ml. or 200 ml. with 72 per cent ethanol.

Nordihydroguaiaretic acid. Propyl gallate must not have been extracted with ammonium acetate buffer as it will have removed this test substance. Extract as described for butylated hydroxyanisole and dilute in the same way.

Tocopherols. Use the petroleum ether solution from which, if present, propyl gallate, butylated hydroxyanisole, and nordihydroguaiaretic acid have been extracted. It still retains the tocopherols.

Procedure—*Propyl gallate.* Dilute three aliquots of sample to 20 ml. with 1.25 per cent ammonium acetate solution. As reagent dissolve 0.1 per cent of ferrous sulfate septahydrate and 0.5 per cent potassium sodium tartrate, Rochelle salt, in water. Add 4 ml. of water and 1 ml. of reagent to each sample aliquot. Mix and read at 540 mμ against a reagent blank. If emulsification occurs during aqueous extraction, add

2 ml. of 1-octanol before extraction. Then extract with the ammonium acetate in 5 per cent ethanol.

Butylated hydroxyanisole. Dilute 1-5 ml. of aliquots of the sample to 5 ml. with 72 per cent ethanol in flasks impervious to light. As reagent ml. with 72 per cent ethanol in flasks impervious to light. As reagent dissolve 0.2 per cent of ferric chloride hexahydrate in absolute ethanol distilled from 0.1 per cent of potassium permanganate and 0.1 per cent of potassium hydroxide. Successively add 3 ml. of absolute ethanol, 2 ml. of fresh ferric chloride reagent, and 2 ml. of 0.2 per cent solution of 1,1'-bipyridine in absolute ethanol. Swirl and after 30 minutes read at 515 mμ against a reagent blank.

Nordihydroguaiaretic acid. Develop exactly as described for butylated hydroxyanisole but read after 3 minutes.

Butylated hydroxyanisole and nordihydroguaiaretic acid. When both are present they are in the extract with 72 per cent ethanol. Read according to the procedure after 1 minute and 30 minutes. The first represents 90 per cent of the nordihydroguaiaretic acid and 10 per cent of the butylated hydroxyanisole. That after 30 minutes represents all of both. Therefore this, with L the observed absorbency at the indicated time, N the absorbency of nordihydroguaiaretic acid, and B the absorbency of butylated hydroxyanisole, gives the following equations.

$$L_1 = 0.1B + 0.9N$$
$$L_{30} = B + N$$

Tocopherols. The fat present has a depressing effect on the color developed with ferric chloride and 1,1'-bipyridine and therefore requires the use of an internal standard. Dilute to 250 ml. the extracted petroleum ether sample and the washings with petroleum ether of extraction equipment used. Place 3 aliquots varying in content of tocopherols from 1 to 8 ml. in duplicate in a series of six 125-ml. actinic separatory funnels. To one set of 3 funnels add 2 ml. of petroleum ether containing 0.015 mg. of *d,a*-tocopherol per ml. Dilute each sample, with and without added standard, to 10 ml. with petroleum ether. Add 2 ml. of fresh 0.2 per cent solution of ferric chloride hexahydrate in absolute ethanol. Old solutions give high blanks. Add 2 ml. of 0.5 per cent solution of 1,1'-bipyridine in absolute ethanol and mix. At this stage the mixture is homogeneous. Six minutes after adding the ferric chloride reagent, add 14 ml. of 86 per cent ethanol, rapidly. The resulting 96 per cent ethanol is insoluble and separates leaving the fat in the petroleum ether layer. After 3 minutes more, withdraw the ethanolic layer to read it at 515 mμ exactly 10 minutes after the ferric chloride reagent was added. The blank for reading is petroleum ether ex fat treated in the same way.

Then with S the absorbency due to tocopherol in the fat and ST that due to tocopherol plus 0.03 mg. of d,a-tocopherol the tocopherol per aliquot is $30S/(ST - S)$. Results in the range 0.02-0.12 mg. per aliquot are most accurate. This method is the least accurate of those presented. Carotenoids if present cause high results.

BUTYLATED HYDROXYANISOLE

The 2,6-dichloroquinonechloroimide reagent is highly specific for butylated hydroxyanisole among antioxidants added to lard or shortening.[119] Maximum color formation occurs at pH 9.4. Under appropriately controlled conditions the maximum blue is developed in 15 minutes and stable for 5 hours. When read at 620 mμ, only gum guaiacum of the commercial inhibitors interferes seriously. The color from 3-*tert*-butyl-4-hydroxyanisole is 52 times as great as for 2-*tert*-butyl-4-hydroxyanisole. Therefore, the method is only applicable to batches of known ratio of the two forms. The determination in the presence of propyl gallate, tocopherols, and dihydroguariaretic acid is given under propyl gallate.

Procedure—*Development with 2,6-dichloroquinone chloroimide.* Dissolve 10 grams of fat in 50 ml. of low-boiling petroleum ether. Extract by shaking 3 minutes with 3 successive 25-ml. portions of 72 per cent ethanol. Extract for 1 minute with 60 ml. of 72 per cent ethanol. Dilute the combined extracts to an appropriate volume with 72 per cent ethanol and filter. To 12 ml., or an aliquot diluted to 12 ml. with 72 per cent ethanol, add 2 ml. of fresh 0.01 per cent solution of 2,6-dichloroquinone-chloroimide in absolute ethanol and 2 ml. of 2 per cent aqueous sodium tetraborate pentahydrate. Mix and read after 15 minutes at 620 mμ against a reagent blank.

GOSSYPOL

Aniline and gossypol react to form dianilinogossypol which is soluble in petroleum ether and suitable for reading around 445 mμ.[120] Results are obtained within 2 hours.

Treatment of gossypol extracts in ether or chloroform with antimony

---

[119] J. H. Mahon and R. A. Chapman, *Anal. Chem.* **23**, 1120-3 (1951).

[120] C. M. Lyman, B. R. Holland, and T. Hale, *Ind. Eng. Chem., Anal. Ed.* **15**, 489-91 (1943); F. H. Smith, *Ibid.* **18**, 41-5 (1946).

trichloride gives a red product with an absorption maximum at 510-520 mμ.[121] Interfering substances react more slowly permitting determination with reasonable accuracy. Gossypol bound up in pigment form must be released by acid hydrolysis.[122] The color is stable for at least 30 minutes, in this being unlike the better known reactions of this reagent with vitamin A and carotene. The reaction is given only by compounds of closely related structure. Accuracy is ±1 per cent.

Procedure—*With aniline. Cottonseed oil.* For this specially prepared iron-free Super-cel is necessary, as iron destroys gossypol. Boil 100 grams of Super-cel with 650 ml. of 1:11 hydrochloric acid for about 15 minutes, filter on a Büchner funnel, and wash well with water. Redisperse in a fresh portion of acid and repeat. Finally dry for storage.

Prepare a 2 mμ layer of the iron-free diatomaceous earth on a Hirsch funnel by applying it dispersed in low-boiling petroleum ether under suction and evaporate the bulk of the petroleum ether. Filter some oil sample and discard. Filter the crude cottonseed oil for use.

Dilute a 5-ml. sample to 100 ml. with low-boiling petroleum ether. Dilute 3 ml. of this diluted sample to 6 ml. with petroleum ether and add 0.5 ml. of redistilled, water-white aniline. Warm in water at 60-65° for 40 minutes and when removed add 10 ml. of petroleum ether at once. Cool, dilute to volume, and mix. Read at 440 mμ against a reagent blank. If the color is too deep for reading dilute the blank and developed sample further with petroleum ether. For calculation assume the specific gravity of 0.925 for the sample. The color is stable for 40 hours.

Alternatively, extract a 2-gram sample wrapped in filter paper with 60 ml. of peroxide-free ether in a unit surrounded by vapor of boiling solvent. To the solvent also add 2.5 per cent of ethanol and about 1 per cent of water. After 72 hours extraction, add 5 ml. of *n*-butanol and evaporate the ether *in vacuo* on a water bath. Take up the residue in *n*-butanol and dilute to 25 ml. For development add 2 ml. of freshly redistilled aniline to a 5-ml. aliquot and dilute to 25 ml. with *n*-butanol. Read at 440 mμ after 20 minutes.

Cottonseed meal. Prepare 30 per cent ethanol by dilution of 384 ml.

[121] Charlotte H. Boatner, *Oil and Soap* **21**, 10-15 (1944); Charlotte H. Boatner, Maizie Caravella, and Lillian Kyame, *Ind. Eng. Chem., Anal. Ed.* **16**, 566-72 (1944); Catherine M. Hall, Leah E. Castillon, Wilma A. Guice, and Charlotte H. Boatner, *J. Am. Oil Chemists Soc.* **25**, 457-61 (1948).

[122] Charlotte H. Boatner, Maizie Caravella, and Carolyn S. Samuels, *J. Am. Chem. Soc.* **66**, 838-9 (1944).

of 95 per cent ethanol with water to 1 liter and 72 per cent ethanol by similar dilution of 830 ml. of 95 per cent ethanol.

Add 20 ml. of 30 per cent ethanol to a 2-gram sample in a Waring blender and let stand for 10 minutes. Rotate by hand occasionally. Add 55 ml. of 72 per cent ethanol to make the final mixture 60 per cent. Add 15 ml. of peroxide-free ether and blend for 5 minutes. Stop and rinse down the sides by swirling once during this operation.

Transfer the contents after swirling to suspend the particles. Rinse the cap and jar with a wash bottle containing 100 ml. of 72 per cent ethanol to 7 ml. of ether. Collect this for later use as washings.

Insert a filter tube in a 2-holed rubber stopper in the top of a filter jar. A tube for suction occupies the other hole. Place a porcelain disc in the tube and with vacuum prepare an asbestos filter on it. On this prepare a 2-mm. layer of iron-free Super-cel applied from suspension in 72 per cent ethanol. Place a 100-ml. volumetric flask in the jar as receiver, containing 5 ml. of ether to replace that lost in evaporation. Transfer the first solution to the filter with suction. Wash this in with the second solution. Wash both with the alcohol-ether from the wash bottle and dilute to volume with this mixture. A haze will indicate the loss of too much ether in filtration.

As a blank dilute a 5-ml. aliquot to 25 ml. with the ethanol-ether mixture. Use another 5-ml. aliquot as sample. Add 0.5 ml. of freshly distilled water-white aniline and heat in water at 65° for 40 minutes. Add 10 ml. of the ethanol-ether mixture at once and, when cool, dilute to volume. Read at 445 mμ against the blank.

Cottonseed. Add a mixture of 20 ml. of 30 per cent ethanol and 55 ml. of 72 per cent ethanol to a 0.25-gram sample, the premixing avoiding formation of a stick paste. Add 15 ml. of peroxide-free ether and complete as for cottonseed meal starting ". . . and blend for 5 minutes."

With antimony trichloride. As reagent wash about 30 grams of finely ground antimony trichloride with a small volume of chloroform. Then add 100 ml. to the washed crystals, warm, shake vigorously, and let cool. Use the clear supernatant liquid.

Cottonseed. Add 25 ml. of chloroform to 0.25 gram of finely ground cottonseed. Shake occasionally for 24 hours. Filter a portion without evaporation and shake 5 ml. with 0.5 ml. of concentrated hydrochloric acid. Let this stand for 24 hours. To 1 ml. add 1 drop of acetic anhydride and 5 ml. of chloroform saturated with antimony trichloride. Read within 10-40 minutes at 520 mμ against a reagent blank.

Cottonseed Meal. Use about 0.5 gram as sample and follow the technic for cottonseed.

2-METHYL-3-HYDROXY-γ-PYRONE, MALTOL

Maltol gives characteristic phenol reactions such as that with ferric chloride.[123]

Sample—*Malt coffee.* Grind 50 grams to a fineness approximating 0.5 mm. Digest a 10-gram portion with 5 ml. of water for 1 hour. Add 3 ml. of water, 15 grams of sand, and 1.5 grams of activated carbon. Extract for 5 hours in a Soxhlet apparatus with carbon tetrachloride.

Procedure—Shake the carbon tetrachloride extract with 100 ml. of water containing 3 drops of 10 per cent ferric chloride solution and 2 ml. of 1:10 hydrochloric acid. Read against a reagent blank.

---

[123] T. Merl, *Z. Untersuch. Lebensm.* **60**, 216-17 (1930).

CHAPTER 5

QUINONES [1]

THE oxidation-reduction reactions of quinones often convert them to color bodies. Alternatively the alkaline salts are often colored. Coupling as hydrazones with nitro hydrazines is another technic for development of color. Fluorescence is rather usual for quinones and therefore often used for their estimation.

2,3,5,6-TETRACHLORO-1,4-BENZOQUINONE

A solution of this insecticide in anhydrous acetone gives a yellow color when anhydrous diethylamine is added.[2]

2-METHYL-3-PHYTYL-1,4-NAPHTHOQUINONE, VITAMIN K

There are various structures, both natural and synthetic, having the properties attributed to vitamin K. All are quinones or easily oxidized to quinones. Vitamin K or phylloquinone occurs in green plants, and vitamin K_2 occurs in bacteria. The synthetic products which are those used prophylactically and therapeutically, are either 2-methyl-1,4-naphthoquinone, vitamin K_3, or structures closely related thereto which are covered as a separate topic.

Quinone-like substances, whose standard oxidation-reduction potentials, Eo, are less than 0.5 volt can be assayed by catalytic reduction of the quinone to hydroquinone and reoxidation of the latter in butanol solution with 2,6-dichloroindophenol. This is a dye stable against air oxidation, which acts as its own indicator.[3] By this method diminution in the color of indophenol is a measure of the quinone present originally. Use of phenosafranine as an additional indicator is advantageous.

Tocopherylquinones can form and cause interference. This is avoided by working under nitrogen at reduced pressures in the absence of light.

---

[1] See Chapter 1 for details of organization, condensation, etc.

[2] H. P. Burchfield and G. L. McNew, *Phytopathology* **38**, 299-306 (1948).

[3] N. R. Trenner and F. A. Bacher, *J. Biol. Chem.* **137**, 745-55 (1941); John V. Scudi and Rudolf P. Buhs, *Ibid.* **141**, 451-64 (1941); *Ibid.* **143**, 665-9 (1942).

Hydroquinone can be used as an anti-oxidant, but if a sample contains tocopherylquinones before the concentrate is prepared, other means of removing the interfering substance must be resorted to. The method is the most sensitive as well as the most complicated method for vitamin K.

Sodium diethyl dithiocarbamate and alcoholic alkali react with vitamin K to give a cobalt blue for estimation.[4] A reddish brown with sodium methylate has also been used.[5]

The hydrazone formed by vitamin K_1 with 2,4-dinitrophenylhydrazine on heating in acid solution is extractable from ammonia solution as a green color in amyl alcohol.[6] The reaction is also applied without extraction to the 2-methyl-1,4-naphthoquinone.

Samples—*Extraction.* Dehydrate samples by refluxing for 3 hours with alcohol. Remove solids by filtration and extract them in the dark for 48-96 hours in a Soxhlet apparatus with petroleum ether boiling at 60-80°. All steps carried out in the procedure should be done in the absence of light. Evaporate the combined alcohol and petroleum-ether extracts to dryness *in vacuo* under nitrogen. Take up the residue in a minimum known volume of petroleum ether and check the acidity. Organic acids present will give erroneous results, as reduction does not proceed smoothly in acid solution. To test this, mix an aliquot of the petroleum ether-solution with indophenol reagent. A diminution in the blue color indicates that the sample is acidic.

Shake a 10-ml. aliquot of the petroleum-ether solution of the sample with an equal volume of cold half-saturated barium hydroxide solution. Wash the ether layer with 5 ml. of water and then with 5 ml. of 1:1 alcohol-water solution. Extract the washes with 10 ml. of petroleum ether and dry the combined petroleum-ether extracts over anhydrous sodium sulfate. Evaporate the extract to dryness *in vacuo* under nitrogen, take up the residue in petroleum ether, and dilute to 0.0025-0.015 mg. of vitamin K_1 per ml. for development with 2,6-dichloroindophenol.

4 Filadelfo Irreverre and M. X. Sullivan, *Science* **94**, 497-8 (1941).

5 H. Dam, A. Geiger, J. Glavind, P. Karrer, W. Karrer, E. Rothschild, and H. Salomon, *Helv. Chim. Acta.* **22**, 310-13 (1939); H. Erhard Fernholz, S. Ansbacher, and Mildred L. Moore, *J. Am. Chem. Soc.* **61**, 1613-14 (1939); H. J. Almquist and A. A. Klose, *Ibid.* **61**, 1610-11 (1939).

6 Eugenio E. Vonesch, *Anales farm. bioquim.* (Buenos Aires) **12**, 109-16 (1941); *Rev. farm.* (Buenos Aires) **84**, 115-21 (1942); Mario Ruiz Armstrong *Anales quim. farm.* (Chile) **1943**, 48-52; Henrique Tastalki, *Rev. quim. farm.* (Rio de Janiero) **10**, No. 9, 9-16 (1945); D. V. S. Reddy and V. Grinivasan, *Current Sci.* (India) **17**, 22-3 (1948).

If at this stage the sample is colored carry out a preliminary reduction in the apparatus shown in Figure 14. Thus such samples as blood, urine, cod-liver oil, and peanut oil do not require concentration but require preliminary reduction. Some concentrates will be sufficiently colorless not to require the preliminary reduction.

Place 10 ml. of sample solution containing less than 2 grams of solids or oil and 5 ml. of methanol in C. Add 10-15 mg. of powdered phenosafranine and a piece of Raney nickel [7] about the size of a pea. Pass hydrogen through a methanol wash to prevent evaporation losses and then through stopcock 12 and inlet 13 at a rate to keep the catalyst in motion. Stopcock 14 serves as a vent and is trapped like cock 4 in Figure 15. Appearance of the color of safranine indicates complete reduction. When reduction is complete add to chamber D 15 ml. of a solution containing 50 grams of potassium hydroxide in 25 ml. of water, diluted to 100 ml. with methanol. Bubble nitrogen from 17 through this for about 10 minutes to eliminate air—any air leakage vitiates the results. Add the alkali through 15 and mix with hydrogen through 12. The vitamin is in the alkaline phase as the potassium salt.

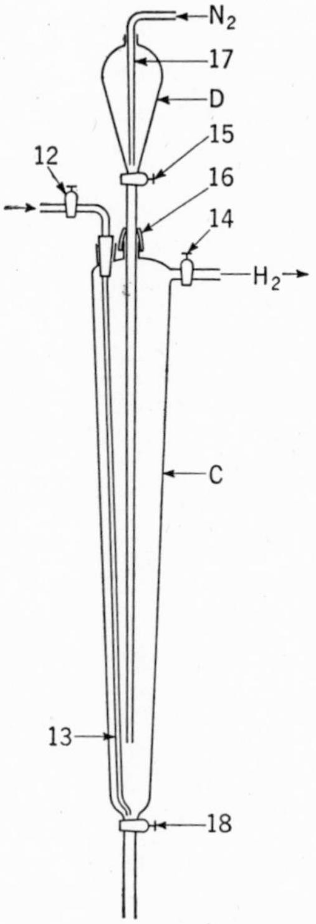

Shut off the hydrogen at 12 and let the phases separate. Remove chamber D through 16 and apply an aspirator to remove the petroleum ether containing neutral fats and petroleum-ether soluble chromogens. After removal of that solvent, add 30 ml. of air-free water to hydrolyze the potassium salt of the vitamin. Mix for 5 minutes and add 30 ml. of air-free petroleum ether through 15 to extract the vitamin hydroquinone. Mix for 10 minutes with hydrogen, let the phases

FIG. 14. Apparatus for the separation of the vitamin K hydroquinones from colored extracts by means of the reductive Claisen's alkali treatment (*Scudi and Buhs*)

separate, and draw off the lower aqueous alkaline layer through 18. Wash the petroleum-ether layer in the apparatus with 30 ml. of air-free water and draw off the washings at 18. Run the petroleum ether containing the vitamin hydroquinone into a graduated cylinder and dry it with

---

[7] Lloyd W. Covert and Homer Adkins, *J. Am. Chem. Soc.* **54**, 4116-7 (1932).

sodium sulfate. Some air exposure in measuring the volume turns some safranine pink, but the sodium sulfate takes that up. Transfer to butanol and evaporate the petroleum ether *in vacuo*. Develop with 2,6-dichlorindophenol.

Procedure—*With 2,6-dichloroindophenol*. The special apparatus required is shown in Figure 15. Prepare a stock reagent by shaking 0.05 gram of 2,6-dichloroindophenol for 15-20 minutes with 100 ml. of butanol. Filter with suction and store in a dark bottle in the refrigerator. It is

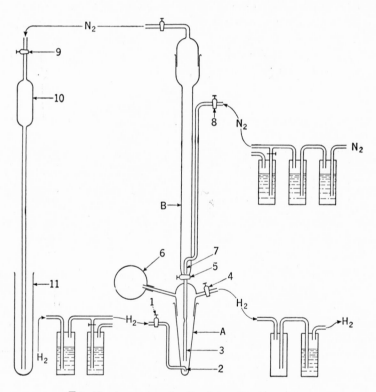

Fig. 15. Apparatus for the determination of the K vitamins

stable for at least 3 months. As a diluent for this dissolve 0.5 gram of potassium acetate in 50 ml. of water and dilute to a liter with neutral *n*-butanol. For use dilute 1 ml. of the stock reagent to 50 ml. with the diluent. The absorption of 10 ml. diluted with 5 ml. of the butanol diluent should be 85 per cent at 660 mμ with pure n-butanol as 100 per cent. Adjust such dilution to give exactly 15 per cent transmittance, which is to say 85 per cent absorption.

For use clean the apparatus with acetone and dry by vacuum. Place a cotton plug in the delivery tube 3. In the lower chamber, place a tiny piece of Raney nickel to act as catalyst, 10 ml. of sample solution, and 10-15 mg. of powdered phenosafranine as indicator. Close cock 1 and open 8, 5, and 4 to replace the air in tube 3 with nitrogen. Close 8 and 5 and open 1 and 4.

Pass commercial hydrogen through a spiral tower containing butanol to prevent evaporation losses and provided with a water seal blow-off to prevent excessive pressures. Admit hydrogen through inlet 2 at a rate brisk enough to keep the catalyst in motion. While the reduction is going on, squeeze rubber bulb 6 occasionally to expel the air in it. When all the quinone has been reduced, the phenosafranine will lose its pink color. Allow the reduction to continue another 5-10 minutes.

While the reduction is in progress, pipet 10 ml. of standard indophenol reagent into the upper chamber, and remove the air in this indophenol solution with a stream of nitrogen which has been passed through a spiral tower containing alkaline hydrosulfite to remove traces of oxygen and through a butanol tower to saturate the gas. Have a butanol blow-off tower attached to the gas train for safety purposes. Admit the nitrogen through inlet 7, bubble through the indophenol solution for 10 minutes, and through the uncalibrated pipet 10 into the colorimeter tube 11.

When reduction is completed, close stop-cocks 1, 4, and 8. Using the rubber bulb 6, force the contents of the lower chamber through the cotton plug in delivery tube 3 and into the upper chamber, meanwhile opening cock 5. When the volume in the upper chamber reaches 15 ml., close cock 5 and admit nitrogen through cock 8 for 1-2 minutes to mix the contents of the upper chamber. Then close cocks 8 and 9.

Leaving cock 9 closed, place a deflated rubber bulb on the end of the pipet. Withdraw the contents of the upper chamber by inserting the nitrogen-filled pipet into the chamber and slowly opening cock 9. After the solution has been drawn up, close cock 9 and remove the rubber bulb. Place the stem of the pipet in the nitrogen-filled colorimeter tube and run the solution in without splashing. Take readings at 600 mμ exactly 3 minutes after the hydroquinone and indophenol are mixed. Read against a reference curve prepared with crystalline 2-methyl-1,4-

naphthoquinone which multiplied by 2.615 is converted stoichiometrically to vitamin K_1.

Even after reduction, extraneous substances may reduce the reagent slowly. If necessary read at intervals and extrapolate to zero time for a more accurate value.

With 2,4-Dinitrophenylhydrazine. Dilute a sample containing 0.005-0.03 mg. of test substance to 2 ml. Not more than 1:1 ethanol is permissible. Add 1 ml. of a 0.04 per cent solution of 2,4-dinitrophenylhydrazine in 1:5 hydrochloric acid. Heat in boiling water for 45 minutes and cool. Add 2 ml. of 8 per cent sodium-hydroxide solution and 1 ml. of amyl alcohol. Heat in a boiling water bath for 2 minutes and cool. Dilute to 10 ml. with ethanol and read at 620 mμ against a water blank.

2-METHYL-1,4-NAPHTHOQUINONE, MENADIONE, VITAMIN K_3

The reaction with 2,4-dinitrophenylhydrazine to form a colored hydrazone with vitamin K_1 is also applicable to vitamin K_3 to give a blue color in sodium hydroxide solution,[8] accurate to ± 2.6 per cent. The reaction of phenylhydrazine with a quinone is parallel and given not only by vitamin K_3 but also by naphthoquinone, 2-methyl-naphthoquinone, 2-bromonaphthoquinone, 2-methylnaphthohydroquinone and its diesters, and juglone.[9]

The synthetic vitamin, 2-methyl-1,4-napthoquinone gives a suitable color reaction with cyanoacetic acid ethyl ester.[10] It also reacts with p-carboxyphenylhydrazine in ethanol for reading as a red color at 470 mμ.[11] This can be extracted with amyl alcohol. A modification uses hydrazine phenylsulfonic acid.

The color from condensation of 2-methyl-1,4-naphthoquinone with diethyl malonate in alkaline solution is used.[12] Condensation with cysteine in alkaline solution is also effective.[13] The same reaction is given by the monosulfonate. A color is developed by refluxing with sodium

[8] Armando Novelli, *Science* **93**, 358 (1941); Amel R. Menotti, *Ind. Eng. Chem., Anal. Ed.* **14**, 418-20 (1942); I. F. Canepa and R. F. Banfi, *Rev. farm.* **88**, 453-60 (1946); William R. Collins and Ernst R. Kirch, *J. Am. Pharm. Assoc.* **35**, 215-17 (1946); E. E. van Koetsveld, *Rec. trav. chim.* **69**, 1217-22 (1950).

[9] Donato Greco and Roberto Argenziano, *Boll. soc. ital. biol. sper.* **19**, 171-3 (1944).

[10] I. L. Pinder and I. H. Singer, *Analyst* **65**, 7-13 (1940); M. Kofler, *Helv. Chim. Acta* **28**, 702-13 (1945).

[11] José C. Conticello, *Rev. facultadad cienc. quim.* **19**, 29-40 (1946).

[12] L. M. Kul'berg and Z. V. Ivanova, *Biokhimiya* **10**, 483-90 (1945).

[13] John V. Scudi and Rudolf P. Buhs, *J. Biol. Chem.* **144**, 599-606 (1942).

hydroxide [14] solution or by heating with hydrochloric acid.[15] The same reactions are given by 2-methyl-1,4-naphthohydroquinone diacetate.

Menadione condenses with o-phenylenediamine in glacial acetic acid to give a compound which shows an intense blue fluorescence in alcoholic solution.[16] This is detectable below 20 mg. per liter. 2-Methyl-1,4-naphthohydroquinone gives the same product. There is no interference by p-benzoquinone, toluquinone, 1,4-naphthoquinone, 2-methyl-3-hydroxy-1, 4-naphthoquinone, or 2-methyl-3-chloro-1,4-naphthoquinone. Fluorescence with 2-ethyl-1,4-naphthoquinone develops more slowly than with the methyl derivative and even more slowly with 2,5-dimethyl-1,4-naphthoquinone. The corresponding 2,6-dimethyl compound develops almost as rapidly as the monomethyl compound.

Procedure—*With 2,4-dinitrophenylhydrazine.* Dilute a sample of not over 1 ml. containing 0.005-0.03 mg. of vitamin K_3 to 2 ml. with water. Add 1 ml. of 0.04 per cent solution of 2,4-dinitrophenylhydrazine in 1:5 hydrochloric acid. Heat in boiling water for 45 minutes and cool. Dilute to 10 ml. with 1:30 ammonium hydroxide and read at 635 mμ against a reagent blank.

With cyanoacetic acid ester. Dry an ether extract of sample at room temperature cautiously, as the test substance is volatile. Take it up in 47.5 per cent ethanol. To a 10 ml. aliquot containing 0.01-0.05 mg. add 3 drops each of cyanoacetic acid ester and 1:3 ammonium hydroxide. Shake for 2 minutes and read after 10 minutes at 570 mμ against a reagent blank with a sample blank from which cyanoacetic-acid ester was omitted if the sample is of biological origin.

By diethyl malonate. To 2 ml. of neutral sample containing 0.02-0.1 mg. of 2-methyl-1,4-naphthoquinone in ethanol add 1 ml. of 1 per cent diethyl malonate in ethanol and 0.2 ml. of 1 per cent aqueous sodium hydroxide. If this produces a protein precipitate add 10 per cent sodium hydroxide solution dropwise until the precipitate is dissolved. Dilute to 5 ml. with water and read against a reagent blank.

By cysteine. Mix 10 ml. of sample, 4 ml. of a solution containing 0.25 mg. of cysteine per ml. and 1 ml. of 4 per cent sodium hydroxide solution. After 15 minutes read at 405 mμ.

By alkali. Reflux 9 ml. of an ethanol solution of the sample with

[14] G. Carrara, L. Braidotti, and C. Guidarini, *Chimica e industria* (Italy) **22**, 317-21 (1940); Cf. Dora Bianchi Colucci, *Ann. chim. applicata* **36**, 97-101 (1946).

[15] J. A. de Almeida Baltazar, *J. farm.* (Lisbon) **9**, 57-8 (1950).

[16] M. Kofler, *Helv. Chim. Acta* **28**, 702-13 (1945).

1 ml. of 4 per cent sodium hydroxide solution for 5 minutes. Cool and read.

By acid. Mix 0.5 ml. of a sample in ethanol containing about 0.25 mg. of menadione with 1 ml. of concentrated hydrochloric acid. Heat in boiling water for 5 minutes, add another ml. of acid, and heat for 10 minutes longer. Cool, take up in ethanol, and dilute to 20 ml. with that solvent. Read against a reagent blank.

2-METHYL-1,4-NAPHTHOHYDROQUINONE DIACETATE, MENADIOL DIACETATE

Determine by refluxing with alkali as described for 2-methyl-1,4-naphthoquinone. Results may be low, perhaps resulting from incomplete saponification.

2-METHYL-1,4-NAPHTHOQUINONE BIS(DIETHYLGLYCOCOL ESTER)

The foregoing vitamin K factor gives a color with hydroxylamine in alkaline solution [17] which is accurate to ±2 per cent.

Procedure—Dilute a sample containing 0.01-1 mg. with water to 10 ml. Add 3 drops of 20 per cent sodium hydroxide solution and 2 drops of a 40 per cent solution of hydroxylamine hydrochloride. Add 3 more drops of the sodium hydroxide solution and mix. Heat in boiling water for exactly 15 minutes, chill in water for 10 minutes, and read against a reagent blank.

5-HYDROXY-α-NAPHTHOQUINONE, JUGLONE

This naphthoquinone is read in ammoniacal solution.[18]

Sample—*Plants.* Disintegrate a 5-gram sample by grinding with sand and water. Add 5 ml. of saturated stannous chloride in 1:20 hydrochloric acid and filter. Wash and dilute to 100 ml. with water. Precipitate the tin from 50 ml. with excess of hydrogen sulfide. Filter and add 2 ml. of concentrated hydrochloric acid to the filtrate. Pass nitrogen through the filtrate until the hydrogen sulfide is removed. Dilute to 50 ml.

Procedure—Mix 10 ml. of the sample solution with 3 ml. of concen-

---

[17] István Gyenes, *Magyar Kém. Folyoirat.* **56**, 190-5 (1950).
[18] G. Petrosini and T. Eschina, *Boll. soc. ital. biol. sper.* **24**, 846-7 (1948).

trated ammonium hydroxide and dilute to 100 ml. Read within 10 minutes against a reagent blank.

2,3-DICHLORO-1,4-NAPHTHOQUINONE

A solution of 2,3-dichloro-1,4-naphthoquinone in acetone gives a red color with 10 per cent dimethylamine in acetone suitable for direct reading.[19]

BENZIL, DIBENZOYL

Benzil is determined in fabrics treated with it as a miticide. The most satisfactory reaction is that with *m*-diethylaminophenol to a blue-red dyestuff with a yellow-red fluorescence.[20] Polyvinyl alcohol gives some interference, corrected by the fluorescence of an undeveloped blank. The reaction is carried on in neutralized ethanol. Alkalinity greatly decreases the fluorescence.

Sample—*Cloth*. Extract 3-5 grams of 1-cm. squares, in a Soxhlet with ethanol for 2 hours. Let the extract stand overnight before filtering out the turbidity. Dilute with ethanol to contain 0.01-0.04 mg. of benzil per ml.

Procedure—Mix a 1-ml. sample with 1 ml. of 5 per cent *m*-diethylaminophenol in ethanol. Heat at 100° for 90 minutes, dissolve the melt in ethanol, and dilute to 100 ml. Read in a fluorimeter against a reference standard of 0.00004 per cent fluorescein. Klett filters 597 and 351 are appropriate.

1,8-DIHYDROXY-9-ANTHRANOL, ANTHRALIN

Anthralin is read in benzene solution and corrected for any danthron present.[21]

Procedure—Dissolve a sample containing about 1 mg. of anthralin in benzene and dilute to 100 ml. Read at 358 mμ and 432 mμ against benzene. Calculate on the basis

$$\text{Anthralin} = (5.4\,D_{358} - D_{432})/2440$$

---

[19] H. P. Burchfield and G. L. McNew, *Phytopathology* **38**, 665-9 (1948).

[20] Samuel Sass and Jerome Goldenson, *Anal. Chem.* **23**, 540-1 (1951).

[21] M. E. Auerbach, *J. Am. Pharm. Assoc.* **34**, 310-11 (1945).

1,8-Dihydroxy-9,10-anthraquinone, Danthron

Danthron is read in benzene solution and corrected for any anthralin present.

Procedure—Dissolve a sample containing about 1 mg. of danthron in benzene and dilute to 100 ml. Read at 432 mμ and 358 mμ against benzene. Calculate on the basis

$$\text{Danthron} = (35\,D_{432} - D_{358})/15,600$$

1,3,8-Trihydroxy-6-methylanthraquinone, Emodin

Emodin and similar anthraquinone compounds give a red color in alkaline solution.[22] Although active principles other than emodin are present in the bark of *frangula* and *cascara sagrada,* and only the related compounds in senna extracts, they can be estimated in terms of emodin. Inactive substances extracted by the alkaline solution give a yellow color. If visual comparison is made by electric light, this difference in color between the yellowish red of the sample and the purer red of the standard is not apparent.

Emodin and the related alkaloids of *Cascara sagrada* are chromatographed to purify a fraction originally present as free anthraquinones and another originally present in combined form.[23] These are then read at 440 mμ in chloroform.

Fluorescence in alkaline solution under ultraviolet light is due to the anthraquinone derivatives and specific for drugs containing emodin.[24] They are also hydrolyzed to aglycones, oxidized with 3 per cent hydrogen peroxide, and read as the bright red color.[25]

Samples—*Fluid extract.* Mix 5 ml. of sample with shredded filter paper and dry at 56°. Reflux for 1 hour with 250 ml. of chloroform. Decant and wash the residue with two 10-ml. portions of chloroform. The chloroform solution contains the free anthraquinones.

---

[22] J. Warin, *J. pharm. chim.* **21**, 253-63 (1905); Bernard V. Christensen and Ismail A. Abdel-Latif, *J. Am. Pharm. Assoc., Sci. Ed.* **38**, 589-93 (1949).

[23] Melvin R. Gibson and Arthur E. Schwarting, *J. Am. Pharm. Assoc., Sci. Ed.* **36**, 269-71 (1947).

[24] Bernard V. Christensen and Ismail A. Abdel-Latif, *Ibid.* **38**, 487-9, 589-93, 652-5 (1949).

[25] W. Kussmaul and B. Becker, *Helv. Chim. Acta* **30**, 59-63 (1947).

Reflux the partially extracted material for 2.5 hours with 250 ml. of chloroform, and 50 ml. of 1:3 sulfuric acid. Decant and wash the residue with three 20-ml. portions of chloroform. Separate the chloroform and aqueous layer. The chloroform layer contains anthraquinones originally present in glycosidal forms, referred to as the combined anthraquinones.

Pass these solutions individually through chromatographic columns packed with a mixture of 1 part of Westvaco Adsorptive Magnesia #2641 and 2 parts of Celite. The anthraquinones form a bright red layer at the top of the column followed by a yellow layer. The red layer cannot be eluted. Dry the column and remove the red layer. Treat the dry red powder with 1:2.5 hydrochloric acid to dissolve the magnesia and thus free the sorbed anthraquinones. Shake this mixture with 25-ml. portions of chloroform until the total extracts amount to 250 ml. An aliquot is read directly.

Powdered extract or bark. Weigh out a 5-gram sample. Proceed as for fluid extract starting at "Reflux for 1 hour with 250 ml. of chloroform" for reading in chloroform.

For reading in alkaline solution, extract 0.5 gram of powdered extract or bark with 50 ml. of a 2 per cent solution of sodium hydroxide. Let the mixture stand for 24 hours, shaking from time to time. Filter and dilute 10 ml. of the colored filtrate to 100 ml. for reading.

Cascara sagrada. It is necessary to hydrolyze the substances present in order to free the alkaloids. Heat 0.5 gram of powdered bark with 50 ml. of 1:50 sulfuric acid for 2 hours at 100°. Cool and extract with ether until all the colored material is present in the ether extract. Combine the ether extracts and shake with 60 ml. of a 2 per cent solution of sodium hydroxide until the ether is decolorized. Separate the alkaline solution and dilute 10 ml. to 100 ml. for direct reading.

Senna leaves. Add 75 ml. of fresh 10 per cent alcoholic potassium hydroxide solution to a 10-gram sample of senna leaves which has been previously dried at 110° for 3 hours. Reflux for 30 minutes, using glass beads to avoid bumping. Filter with suction and wash the residue with 15- and 15-ml. portions of warm ethanol. Dilute the filtrate to 100 ml. with ethanol. Mix and remove a 25-ml. portion. Add 25 ml. of water and about 10 ml. of 1:5 hydrochloric acid to bring the pH of the mixture to 2.

Shake with 30 ml. of ether and then with five 20-ml. portions. Wash the combined extracts with 5 ml. of 1:5 hydrochloric acid and 10 ml. of

water. Extract the aqueous washings with 15 ml. of ether and add to
the total ether extract. Add 10 ml. of concentrated ammonia solution to
30 ml. of ether extract and shake gently. Let stand, then shake vigorously and centrifuge until the ammonia layer separates completely from
the ether layer.

Procedure—*Aqueous alkaline solutions.* Read at 670 mμ.
Chloroform solutions. Dilute an appropriate aliquot to 100 ml. and
read at 440 mμ against chloroform.
By fluorescence. Read the solution in ammonium hydroxide by fluorescence.

1,8-Dihydroxy-3-hydroxymethylanthraquinone, Aloe-emodin

Aloe emodin is an ingredient of Curacao aloes, directly extractable
with alcohol-free chloroform for reading at 450 mμ[26]

Procedure—*Aloes.* Extract a 5-gram sample in a Soxhlet for 1 hour
with 75 ml. of alcohol-free chloroform. Dilute to 100 ml. with chloroform
and read at 450 mμ.

5,7,2′,4′-Tetrahydroxy-3-flavonol, Morin

The general reactions of rutin (page 249) apply to this structure,
much like a hydrolytic product of rutin.

5,7,3′,4′-Tetrahydroxy-3-flavonol, Quercitin

The general reactions of rutin (page 249) apply to this hydroyltic
product.

5,8-Dimethoxy-2-methyl-4,5′-furo-6,7-chromone, Khellin

The citron yellow of khellin with sulfuric acid is suitable for reading.[27]
The intensity of color developed with visnegin, 5-methoxy-2-methylfuran-
ochromone, is about half that from khellin. The direct absorption maxi-

---

[26] K. G. Stone and N. Howell Furman, *Anal. Chem.* **19**, 105-7 (1947).
[27] I. R. Fahrny, N. Badran, and M. F. Messeid, *J. Pharm. Pharmacol.* **1**, 529-37
(1949).

mum is at 216 mμ, that of khellinin which is khellol glucoside is at 246 mμ.[28] The absorption varies with the solvent.

Procedure—Mix 2.5 ml. of sample solution containing 0.02-0.4 mg. of khellin per ml. with 10 ml. of 1:2.6 sulfuric acid. After 5 minutes read against 1:2.6 sulfuric acid.

---

[28] M. S. El Ridi, Ahmed M. Hossein, and Karam Samaan, *Acta Pharm. Intern.* 1, 251-6 (1950).

CHAPTER 6

OXYGEN CYCLES, OXIDES, AND PEROXIDES [1]

INSOFAR as the members of this chapter are oxidizing agents, they are often determined by oxidation of ferrous ion to ferric ion, or by liberation of iodine. Conventional inorganic methods are then applicable. Others are reduced and determined as more conventional materials, benzoyl peroxide as nitrated benzoic acid.

ORGANIC PEROXIDES

Organic peroxides may be present in oxidized fats and oils,[2] in biological media,[3] in gasoline, rubber, etc. The usual technic is to cause them to react to oxidize ferrous iron to ferric iron as described in Vol. II, pp. 881-2, where the latter is determined as thiocyanate. If the fat peroxide is extracted into benzene and made miscible with the aqueous reagents by addition of methanol, the reaction is more sensitive.[4] An alternative is liberation of iodine from hydriotic acid.

ASCARIDOLE

Ascaridole is a complex peroxide. American worm-seed oil or chenopodium contains about 60-75 per cent ascaridole.[5] The method depends upon colorimetric determination of iodine liberated when the ascaridole reacts with an acid solution of potassium iodide, or on the oxidation of ferrous ion to ferric ion.[6] In that sense it is the general method for organic peroxides.

Procedure—*With potassium iodide.* Dissolve 2.5 grams of sample in enough 90 per cent acetic acid to make 50 ml. Mix 3 ml. of 50 per cent

---

[1] See Chapter 1 for details of organization, condensation, etc.

[2] H. Erdmann and F. Seelich, *Z. anal. Chem.* **128**, 303-12 (1948); G. Loftus Hills and C. C. Thiel, *J. Dairy Research* **14**, 340-53 (1946).

[3] F. Dubouloz, M. F. Monge-Hedde, and J. Fonderai, *Bull. soc. chim. France* 1947, 900-1.

[4] G. Howard Smith, *J. Sci. Food Agr.* **3**, 26-31 (1952).

[5] T. Tusting Cocking and F. C. Hyams, *Analyst* **55**, 180-6 (1930).

[6] J. Cardoso do Vale, *Noticias farm.* (Portugal) **14**, 391-6 (1948).

potassium iodide solution, 5 ml. of concentrated hydrochloric acid, and 10 ml. of glacial acetic acid, and chill to about −3°. Add 5 ml. of sample, stopper quickly, and allow to stand 5 minutes in a cool place. Read against a reagent blank.

With ferrous sulfate. Prepare the reagent of equal volumes of saturated aqueous ferrous sulfate and concentrated hydrochloric acid. Dilute the oil sample with a suitable amount of turpentine oil, then add 0.6 ml. of it to 6 ml. of reagent. A red-brown color forms which is proportional to the ascaridole content. Add 4.5 ml. of chloroform, shake, and read the chloroform phase against chloroform.

4-ALLYL-1,2-METHYLENEDIOXYBENZENE, SAFROLE

The ultraviolet absorption of safrole at 285 mμ is appropriate for its estimation.[7] Suitable solvents are anhydrous chloroform or hexane, or 9.5 per cent aqueous ethanol. The method will detect 0.004 per cent of safrole in soap. Other perfume constituents absorbing in that range must be known to be absent.

Sample—*Soap.* Weigh a sample estimated to contain 4 mg. of safrole and dissolve in 20 ml. of ethanol and such amount of water as is necessary. Add 20 per cent aqueous silver nitrate at approximately 5 ml. per gram of soap with swirling to cause precipitation. Steam-distil through an all-glass apparatus with a steam-trap, delivering the condensate through an adapter into a flask. Collect 200 ml. in about 20 minutes.

Procedure—Read the distillate at 285 mμ.

BENZOYL PEROXIDE

For its estimation, benzoyl peroxide is converted to dinitrobenzoic acid and reduced to the diamine.[8]

Sample—*Flour.* Mix 50 grams of flour, about 40 glass beads about 6 mm. in diameter, 0.1 gram of powdered iron, and 100 ml. of ether.

---

[7] R. O. Herzog and A. Hillmer, *Ber.* **64B**, 1288-306 (1931); Mme. Ramart-Lucas and P. Amagat, *Bull. soc. chim.* **51**, 108-26 (1932); R. F. Patterson and J. Hilbert, *J. Am. Chem. Soc.* **65**, 1862-9 (1943); Norman H. Ishler, Emanuel Borker, and Catherine R. Gerber, *Anal. Chem.* **22**, 458-69 (1950).

[8] Official and Tentative Methods of the Association of Official Agricultural Chemists, 7th Ed., pp. 205-6, Association of Official Agricultural Chemists, Washington, D. C. (1950).

After a few minutes, shake and add dropwise 2.5 ml. of concentrated hydrochloric acid. After about 30 minutes rinse down the sides with ether and let stand overnight. Shake well, let the flour settle for a few minutes, and decant the ether through a 100-mm. Büchner funnel with its filter paper wet with ether. Shake the residue with 50 ml. of ether and treat as before. Repeat twice more, transferring all of the flour to the funnel on the last washing.

Extract the combined ether extracts with 20 ml. of 5 per cent sodium bicarbonate solution without vigorous shaking. Separate and extract with 20, 10, and 10 ml. more of the bicarbonate solution. Discard the ether layer. Shake the alkaline extract with 0.3 gram of Nuchar W and filter. Wash the flask and filter with 25 ml. of water from a wash bottle.

Add 2 ml. of 1:1 sulfuric acid dropwise, swirling gently to reduce foaming. Transfer to a separatory funnel, using 12 ml. of ether for washing in. Extract with frequent release of pressure, separate, and extract twice more. Add 2 ml. of 10 per cent sodium hydroxide solution to these combined ether extracts in a 50-ml. test tube, and shake. Add a 1×200 mm. piece of copper wire and evaporate the ether slowly on a steam bath. Remove the wire, evaporate nearly to dryness, and add 0.5 ml. of 30 per cent hydrogen peroxide dropwise. After foaming subsides, add 0.5 ml. more. Evaporate to dryness, breaking the crust which forms. Wash down the sides of the tube in adding 4 ml. of a 1:1 mixture of concentrated sulfuric acid and fuming nitric acid. Heat 20 minutes at 100° with occasional rotation, and cool. Add 6 ml. of water with cooling, followed slowly by 5 ml. of concentrated ammonium hydroxide. More rapidly add 10 ml. more of concentrated ammonium hydroxide with cooling, then 2 ml. of 6 per cent hydrazine hydrochloride solution. Mix and heat at 65° for about 5 minutes. Cool, filter, and within 30 minutes read the intensity at 510 mμ.

Benzophenone oxide, Dibenzopyrone, Xanthone

In the use of benzophenone oxide as an insecticide the necessity arises for determining it on fruit. It is extracted by toluene, a 0.4-2 mg. aliquot reduced to xanthydrol with sodium amalgam and methanol, and transferred to aqueous hydrochloric acid for photometric estimation.[9] The solvent also removes the wax from fruit an advantage in obtaining complete removal of xanthone. The concentrated acid is required to

---

[9] C. C. Cassil and J. W. Hansen, *Ind. Eng. Chem.*, *Anal. Ed.* **16**, 35-7 (1944).

convert xanthydrol to the yellow chloride. Lead arsenate interferes but decomposition products of the test substance do not. Over the range of 0.2-0.5 mg. results are accurate to 3.3 per cent.

Sample—*Apples.* To purify toluene, add 50 ml. of concentrated sulfuric acid per liter, mix well, and let stand for 24 hours. Separate the upper layer and distil, discarding the first milky portion of distillate. Weigh 20-25 apples from different parts of the tree in a tared glass jar and calculate the surface area. Add 100-250 ml. of toluene according to the size of the apples and quantity of xanthone expected, and shake mechanically for 5 minutes. Filter and use up to 10 ml. of filtrate as an aliquot for color development.

Procedure—As amalgam melt 9 grams of sodium under 20 ml. of toluene. Add 750 grams of mercury, dropwise at first, later somewhat more rapidly. Toluene should remain over the amalgam when it is transferred to an air-tight bottle.

Dilute a portion of sample solution in toluene containing about 400 mg. of xanthone to 20 ml. with toluene in a flask with a ground-glass joint. Add 10 ml. of absolute methanol and about 1 ml. of the amalgam. Reflux for 30 minutes and cool before disconnecting the reflux. Add 20 ml. of water and shake vigorously to extract excess methanol. Decant, leaving the amalgam and a portion of the aqueous layer behind. Pipet 5 ml. of the toluene layer, which may be slightly turbid, into 10 ml. of concentrated hydrochloric acid and swirl gently for a minute to extract the xanthydrol. If turbidity appears at this point it is due to excessive amounts of apple wax. Read the acid layer at 424 mμ. The xanthydrol is stable in toluene for 12 hours. The final color in hydrochloric acid is stable for at least 24 hours.

5-Hydroxy-2-(hydroxymethyl)-4-pyrone, Kojic Acid

Kojic acid is produced by fermentation with *Aspergillus oryzae* to the extent of 10-40 per cent from maltose, sucrose, glucose, inulin, fructose, and xylose, and from 1 to 6 per cent from mannose, arabinose and galactose. Small amounts are formed from sorbitol, dulcitol, glycerol, glycero-β-phosphate, inositol, and gluconic acid. Kojic acid is not formed from α-methyl glucoside, rhamnose, fatty acids, ketonic acids, aldehydes, ketones, monohydric alcohols, ketonic alcohols, amino acids, lactose, glyceric aldehyde, dihydroxyacetone, mannitol, erythritol, ethylene glycol, saccharic acid, glyceric acid, or various monohydroxy acids. The red color with ferric chloride is used to follow quantitatively the formation of kojic acid in the early stages of incubation, or in cases where the amount formed is small.[10]

Sample—*Cultures.* Dissolve in water 5 grams of the sugar or alcohol to be used as substrate, 0.05 grams of ammonium sulfate, 0.1 gram of monopotassium phosphate, 0.01 gram of magnesium sulfate, and 0.01 gram of calcium chloride. Dilute to 100 ml. and inoculate with spores of *Aspergillus oryzae.* Incubate at 29-31° and sample at intervals. At the end of 20 days, filter and acidify with sulfuric acid. The initial pH value of this solution is about 4.5, and the final pH value about 2.2 whenever a considerable growth of the mold occurs. This pH range probably approaches the optimum for the formation of kojic acid.

Procedure—To an aliquot of the liquid culture, with or without dilution, add an equal volume of 0.05 per cent ferric chloride hexahydrate solution. Read against a reagent blank.

ROTENONE

Both rotenone and deguelin in acetone give a red color with potassium hydroxide and nitrite.[11] Therefore deguelin must be absent for estimation of rotenone alone. Other interferences are *iso*rotenone, *l*-elliptone, and dihydrorotenone. Tephrosine, *iso*tephrosine, toxicarol, dehydrorotenone, rotenonone, dehydroguelin, nicotine, and pyrethrins do not react. The reagents give an intense yellow. The concentration of nitrite must be rigidly controlled. Some interfering colors are extractable with ether. The color is also developed with nitrate in acid solution.[12] Rotenone, deguelin, and alliptone in acetone exhibit a maximum

[10] Hideo Katagari and Kakuo Kitahara, *Bull. Agr. Chem. Soc. Japan* **5**, 38-47 (1929).

[11] C. R. Gross and C. M. Smith, *J. Assoc. Official Agr. Chemists* **17**, 336-9 (1934); Lyle D. Goodhue, *Ibid.* **19**, 118-20 (1936); S. Schonberg, *Compt. rend. 17th Congr. chim. ind., Paris*, Sept.-Oct. **1937**, 947-52; *Rev. soc. brasil. quim.* **8**, 180-5 (1939); Howard A. Jones, *Ind. Eng. Chem., Anal. Ed.* **11**, 429-31 (1939); H. D. Anderson and A. L. Moxon, *Proc. S. Dakota Acad. Sci.* **21**, 60-4 (1941); Merriam A. Jones, *J. Assoc. Official Agr. Chemists* **28**, 352-9 (1945); *Ibid.* **29**, 127-9 (1946); N. V. Subba Rao, and A. G. Pollard, *J. Sci. Food Agr.* **1**, 367-71 (1950).

[12] Theodore Meyer, *Rev. trav. chim.* **55**, 954-8 (1936); Theodore M. Meyer and A. Rachmad, *Ibid.* **66**, 312-16 (1947).

in the ultraviolet at 360 mμ. That for toxicarol is at 400 mμ [13] reading in the infra red at 11.02μ is accurate for rotenone in the presence of dihydrorotenone.[14] Using a solution at 7 grams per liter and a single cell length accuracy to ±2 per cent is attained.

The reaction with thymol in the presence of hydrochloric acid and hydrogen peroxide is used for estimation.[15] There is no interference by the usual hydrocarbon solvents, provided a similar amount is present in the solutions used to prepare the standard curve. Isorotenone reacts. Acetylrotenone reacts more slowly than rotenone.

Sample—Extract with or dissolve in acetone and dilute to 0.005-0.25 mg. per ml. with the same solvent for development with nitrite. For development with thymol dissolve the rotenone extract in chloroform to give a dilution of 0.05-2.5 mg. of rotenone per ml.

Derris root. Shake 1 gram of 80-mesh sample with 50 ml. of acetone at intervals for an hour. Cool to below 10° and filter, minimizing evaporation. Dilute 10 ml. of filtrate with acetone to 100° for reading in the ultraviolet.

Procedure—*By alkaline nitrite.* As reagent mix 1 volume of 40 per cent aqueous potassium hydroxide with 7 volumes of 0.1 per cent sodium nitrite in highly purified ethanol, preferably refluxed with zinc and alkali and distilled. Mix 2 ml. of sample in acetone with 2 ml. of reagent. After 5 minutes at 30° add 5 ml. of 1:4 sulfuric acid. Shake and, after 5 minutes at 30°, read at 540 mμ against water. Alternatively, extract with chloroform and read at 560 mμ against chloroform.

By acid nitrate. Mix 0.2 ml. of sample in 40 per cent acetone with 5 ml. of concentrated sulfuric acid containing 0.1 mg. of sodium nitrate per ml. Read at 530 mμ against a reagent blank.

By thymol. To 10 ml. of sample in chloroform add 10 ml. of a solution of 10 grams of thymol per 100 ml. of chloroform. Mix and add 2 ml. of a reagent made by adding 2.5 ml. of 3 per cent hydrogen peroxide to 100 ml. of concentrated hydrochloric acid. Shake for one minute and read.

In the ultraviolet. Read at 360 mμ against acetone.

---

[13] Caleb Pagán, Arnaud J. Loustelot, and Richard H. Hageman, *Federal Expt. Sta. Puerto Rico, U. S. Dept. Agr.* (Mayaguez) *Rept.* **1947,** 10-11; Caleb Pagán and A. J. Loustelot, *J. Agr. Research* **77,** 271-7 (1948).

[14] H. L. Cupples, *Anal. Chem.* **24,** 1657 (1952).

[15] H. D. Rogers and J. A. Calamari, *Ind. Eng. Chem., Anal. Ed.* **8,** 135 (1936).

DEGUELIN

The red color of rotenone in acetone with nitrite and potassium hydroxide is also given by deguelin.

SESAMIN

Sesamin is a substituted bicyclodihydrofuran present in sesame oil which is recovered by extraction or molecular distillation. It is determined by the yellow color on treatment with a strong mixture of hydrogen peroxide and perchloric acid.[16] Purified sesamin for use as a standard is recovered from the oil diluted with petroleum ether by extraction with 90 per cent acetic acid or by sorption [17] on charcoal or clay, from which it is eluted with solvents.

A solution of sesamin is obtained as part of the determination of sesamol (page 144) for reading in the ultraviolet.

Sample—*Oil*. Dilute a 0.5-gram sample containing 0.25-1.75 per cent of sesamin to 10 ml. with refined kerosene. This is for determination with hydrogen peroxide and perchloric acid.

Procedure—*By hydrogen peroxide and perchloric acid*. Prepare the very corrosive reagent at 15-20° not more than 10 minutes before use. For this, add, with shaking, 2 ml. of 30 per cent hydrogen peroxide to 4 ml. of 70-72 per cent perchloric acid. To 1 ml. of sample solution in a dry tube add the 6 ml. of reagent and close quickly. Shake vigorously for 30 seconds and centrifuge for 2 minutes to clear the emulsion. The aqueous layer on the bottom shows a color which ranges from faint yellow to dark greenish yellow, depending upon the sesamin present. Read at 460 mμ against a water blank exactly 5 minutes after adding the reagent.

In the ultraviolet. Dilute the solvent solution of bound sesamol (page 144) with the same solvent if necessary and read at 225, 288, and 320 mμ.

Sesamin $= 4.541 K_{288} - 0.953\%$ sesamolin $- 2.271 (K_{255} + K_{320})$.

---

[16] Martin Jacobson, Fred Acree, Jr., and H. L. Haller, *Ind. Eng. Chem., Anal. Ed.* **16**, 166-7 (1944).

[17] P. Honig, *Chem. Weekblad.* **22**, 509-12 (1925).

Hexahydro-3a,7a-dimethyl-3,7-epoxyisobenzofurane-1,3-dione, Cantharidin

Cantharidin is the anhydride of cantharidic acid. It condenses with formaldehyde on heating with sulfuric acid to give a brown to black color which can be used for estimation.[18] The method is applicable to extracts and with less accuracy to the solid.

Sample—Extract cantharidin from a weighed sample of the natural cantharides with hot chloroform. Filter and evaporate the extract to dryness on the water bath. Extract fatty substances from the residue with carbon bisulfide. Take up the residue with a volume of glacial acetic acid such as to give about 0.5 mg. of cantharidin per ml.

Procedure—To 1 ml. of sample add 0.2 ml. of 1:3 formaldehyde solution and 5 ml. of concentrated sulfuric acid. Heat in a boiling water bath for 5 minutes. Read against a reagent blank.

Piperonyl Butoxide

Piperonyl butoxide is determined by the blue color developed with tannic acid in phosphoric and glacial acetic acids.[19] The reaction is also given by 3,4-methylenedioxy-6-propylbenzyl alcohol, as well as ethers and certain esters of this alcohol, but not by safrole, isosafrole, dihydrosafrole, piperonal, piperonyl cyclonene, sesamin, and other compounds having the methylenedioxy phenyl group. Pyrethrum extract causes a reduction in the intensity of color. DDT, chlordane, crude benzene hexachloride, and chlorinated camphene do not interfere, but solvents such as alkylated naphthalenes, cyclohexanone, and acetone cause interference. When the nature and amount of interfering material are known, correction can usually be made by using a standard incorporating the same proportion of interfering material. The method is accurate to about ± 3 per cent.

Sample—*Pyrethrum extract.* If the amount of pyrethrins present is unknown, saponify both sample and standard. For this evaporate at not over 60°. Reflux the residue with 10 ml. of 2 per cent sodium hydroxide

---

[18] Georges Deniges, *Bull. soc. pharm. Bordeaux* 72, 85-8 (1934).

[19] Howard A. Jones, H. J. Ackermann, and Marion E. Webster, *J. Assoc. Official Agr. Chemists* 35, 771-80 (1952).

for 2 hours, cool, and neutralize. Extract the butoxide with hexane. Saponification causes some reduction in color.

Wheat germ. Extract with hexane, evaporate the solvent from the extract and separate the butoxide from interfering materials by saponification of the oil with alcoholic alkali. Dilute with water and extract the butoxide with hexane.

Flour. Extract with redistilled benzene and treat the extract with a small proportion of activated carbon and fuller's earth.

Paraffin. Dissolve in hexane, extract the solution with 85-90 per cent methanol, dilute the extract with water, and extract the butoxide from the aqueous methanol with hexane.

Procedure—Dissolve a sample containing 25-75 mg. of piperonyl butoxide in deodorized kerosene and dilute to 100 ml. with this solvent. Prepare a standard containing 50 mg. of piperonyl butoxide per 100 ml. of purified kerosene, containing the same amount of interfering substance as that present in the sample.

To prepare the reagent first shake 20 grams of USP tannic acid mechanically with 100 ml. of ethyl acetate for an hour. Filter by suction and wash the residue with three 5-ml. portions of ethyl acetate. To the combined filtrate and washings add 2 grams of decolorizing carbon and shake mechanically for a half-hour. Filter and wash to give a volume of filtrate of about 125 ml. Add the filtrate dropwise to 5 times its volume of dry toluene to precipitate purified tannic acid. Filter by suction and wash thoroughly with dry toluene. Dry *in vacuo* and keep in a tightly-toppered bottle. For use, dissolve 0.025 gram of specially purified tannic acid in 20 ml. of glacial acetic acid with shaking. When solution is complete, add 80 ml. of 85 per cent phosphoric acid and mix. Prepare this reagent solution fresh daily.

To 0.1 ml. of the sample, to 0.1 ml. of standard, and to 0.1 ml. of kerosene blank, add 5 ml. of the tannic acid reagent. Place the tubes of solutions to which reagent has been added in boiling water for 5 minutes, then let cool. Read the sample against a standard and a blank at 625-635 mμ. The color is stable for several hours.

CHAPTER 7

PENTOSES [1]

CHAPTER 5 included alcohols up to and including hexahydric types. The simple sugars which are the subject of this chapter are polyhydric alcohols having other functional groups, a logical extension from the other alcohols. In the case of pentoses this is a ring of 5 carbons and one oxygen, which breaks down to a furfural ring on drastic treatment.

Development of the furfural is then by the usual aldehyde reactions. Other reagents applicable to more or less all sugars are picric acid, orcinol with ferric ion and strong sulfuric acid.

XYLOSE

When xylose is refluxed with 13 per cent hydrochloric acid, it decomposes to furfural which as a mateer of practical convenience is either extracted into xylene [2] or distilled.[3] Dehydration to furfural with phosphoric acid at 170° is an alternative. The color can be read in the ultraviolet or developed with aniline,[4] xylidene,[5] or benzidine.[6] Methyl pentoses, such as fucose or rhamnose, and hexoses, do not interfere. They form methyl furfural which does not react. The conversion is not quantitative; therefore conditions are necessarily strictly controlled. The reaction is also given by other pentoses such as arabinose, lyxose, and ribose, and by galacturonic acid. The degree of conversion varies with different sugars, but is reproducible for each. Amounts of 0.5-5 mg. are determinable to ±2 per cent. Glucose and galactose are correspondingly converted to 5-hydroxymethyl furfural but in much lower yield. Rham-

---

[1] See Chapter 1 for details of organization, condensation, etc.

[2] Richard E. Reeves and Jackson Monro, *Ind. Eng. Chem., Anal Ed.* **12**, 551-3 (1940).

[3] Sonia Dunstan and A. E. Gillam, *J. Chem. Soc.* **1949**, S 140-4.

[4] Guy E. Youngbird and George W. Pucher, *J. Biol. Chem.* **61**, 741-6 (1924); Ira J. Duncan, *Ind. Eng. Chem., Anal. Ed.* **15**, 162-4 (1943); Francois Duffan, *Bull. soc. chim. biol.* **28**, 873-7 (1946).

[5] Kunihiko Suminokura and Z. Nakahara, *Trans. Totteri Soc. Agr. Sci.* **1**, 158-9 (1928); Kunihiko Suminokura, *J. Biochem. (Japan)* **14**, 343-59 (1931).

[6] R. A. McCance, *Biochem. J.* **20**, 1111-3 (1926).

nose or *d*-allomethylose do not give serious interference at a level where they equal no more than 50 per cent of the xylose. Hexoses are conveniently extracted with ethanol.[7] The pentoses can be developed directly by aniline acetate in the presence of hexoses and uronic acids.[8]

Xylose is conveniently read by the color developed with picric acid. Arabinose, mannose, fructose, galactose, rhamnose, maltose, lactose, and glucose interfere. The intensity of color can be read in terms of a glucose or maltose standard and the result multiplied by 0.934 for conversion to xylose. Details are given under mannose (page 213).

Xylose gives a yellow with diphenylamine.[9] Other pentoses interfere. At 1 mg. per ml. there is no color with glycine, cystine, arginine, lysine, tyrosine, creatine, histidine, aspartic acid, uric acid, leucine, cholesterol, and lecithin.

A qualitative reagent [10] for pentoses containing orcinol, ferric ion, and hydrochloric acid gives a greenish blue color. This has been developed to quantitative application.[11]

This reaction with 1 per cent of orcinol in 1:4 sulfuric acid is given by glucose, mannose, galactose, fructose, sorbose, xylose, arabinose, rhamnose, alkali-metal glyconates, mannitol, glucosamine, dextran, yeast mannan, yeast nucleic acid,[12] and many more substances. If heated for 10 minutes, the absorption for arabinose, xylose, and ribose is 1:1.4:1.5. By heating at 104° for 30 minutes more than double the color is developed and each of the pentoses gives equal color intensity.[13]

There is a general reaction for sugars in which they are treated with strong sulfuric acid, usually about 80-90 per cent. The colorless mixture has a strong absorption around 320-330 mμ which is brought into the visible range on reaction with cysteine.[14] The concentration of acid necessary for stability varies with the sugar. That from xylose and other pentoses decomposes readily at 4:1 sulfuric acid-water but is stable at 8:1. Thus in the absence of desoxypentoses, methyl pentoses, and hexu-

---

7 Willard L. McRary and Marion C. Slattery, *Arch. Biochem.* **6,** 151-6 (1945).

8 M. V. Tracey, *Biochem. J.* **47,** 433-6 (1950).

9 K. Slavik and C. Michalec, *Chem. Listy* **43,** 235-8 (1949).

10 M. Bial, *Deut. med. Wochschr.* **29,** 253, 477 (1902).

11 Vanda V. Meibaum, *Z. physiol. Chem.* **258,** 117-20 (1939); *Biokhimiya* **10,** 353-9 (1945); Allan H. Brown, *Arch. Biochem.* **11,** 269-78 (1946); M. L. McRary and M. C. Slattery, *Ibid.* **6,** 151-6 (1945); H. F. Drury, *Ibid.* **19,** 455 (1946); Harry G. Albaum and W. W. Umbreit, *J. Biol. Chem.* **167,** 369-76 (1947).

12 Erik Vasseur, *Acta Chem. Scand.* **2,** 693-701 (1948).

13 T. Vályi-Nagy, *Z. Vitamin-Hormon-u. Fermentforsch.* **1,** 279-88 (1947).

14 Zacharias Dische, *J. Biol. Chem.* **181,** 379-92 (1949).

ronic acids in significant amounts the pentoses blank out hexoses by determination by the increment $D_{390} - D_{420}$ read about 20 minutes after adding the cysteine. Other pentoses interfere, giving values about half that for xylose.

Another reaction for reading xylose, and other pentoses is that with carbazole.[15] Other sugars give it, but modifications avoid undue interference. Hexoses must be absent. Similar reagents are indole, diphenylamine, and sulfhydryls. Thus it is related to the immediately preceding method.

The reaction is not only applicable to xylose as such but in many cases to its derivatives. Specifically it is satisfactory for this or other pentoses with adenosine, guanosine, adenylic acid, guanylic acid, yeast nucleic acid, streptococcus nucleic acid, thymus nucleic acid, etc. Uridine, uridylic acid, and cytidin tend to give low results. Therefore, bromination is applied to eliminate unsaturated bonds. Then the products are more readily hydrolyzed. Unless this is done, quantitative results are not obtainable with pyrimidine nucleotides due to incomplete hydrolysis of the pyrimidine-pentose linkages. Dihydrouridine phosphoric acid and dihydrocytidine phosphoric acid are readily hydrolyzed.[16] Desoxyribose and desoxyguanosine are markedly attacked by bromine. Hence this reaction is not applicable; that with diphenylamine as described for fructose (page 212) is more appropriate. Purines and pyrimidines do not interfere. Bromine is not necessary with purine nucleotides and nucleosides. Samples must be free from polysaccharides, simple sugars, uronic acids, most ketones and aldehydes, nitrates and nitrites.

The reaction of carbohydrates with anthrone is applicable to d-xylose.[17] Very nearly the same color intensity is developed with arabinose and ribose.

Sample—Set up an all-glass distillation apparatus as shown in Figure 16. Place 1 ml. of sample containing 0.1-0.5 per cent of the sugar in the distillation tube and add 5 ml. of 85 per cent phosphoric acid. Pass steam through and heat as rapidly as possible with a microburner. Maintain at 165-175°. Dilute the distillate of furfural to a known volume for reading in the ultraviolet.

Alternatively, dissolve a sample containing 0.5-1 mg. of pentoses in 10 ml. of 13 per cent hydrochloric acid prepared by dilution of 37 ml.

[15] Samuel Gurin and Dorothy B. Hood, *Ibid.* **139**, 775-85 (1941).

[16] P. A. Levene and Erik Jorpes, *Ibid.* **81**, 575-80 (1929).

[17] Robert Roy Bridges, *Anal. Chem.* **24**, 2004-5 (1952).

of concentrated acid to 100 ml. Reflux with 25 ml. of redistilled xylene
for 2.5 hours. Let cool and decant the xylene layer. Dry it with anhydrous sodium acetate. If the xylene solution is brown, due to decomposition of accompanying hexoses, distil a 20-ml. aliquot *in vacuo*. When the
distillation flask is dry, add 3 ml. more of xylene and distil this. Make
the distillate up to 25 ml. The pentoses are present as furfural for
development with aniline acetate.

Samples containing nucleosides and nucleotides. Add 1:7 acetic acid
to a 5-ml. sample until acid to litmus. Add 2 ml. of saturated aqueous
uranyl acetate, then 0.5 ml. of 1 per cent solution of anhydrous disodium
phosphate. Dilute to 50 ml. with water, and mix. When filtered and

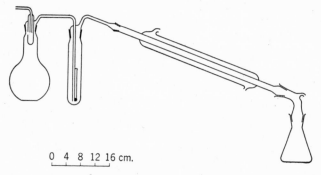

0 4 8 12 16 cm.

Fɪɢ. 16. Apparatus for steam distillation of furfural from pentoses

developed with orcein and ferric ion, this gives the pentose present as
such.

Prepare another sample replacing the uranyl acetate solution with
2 ml. of water. When developed, this includes pentoses present as
nucleotides. Then by difference this gives that amount present as
nucleotides.

Nucleic acids. Dissolve about 4 mg. of nucleic acid in 2 ml. of 0.4
per cent sodium hydroxide solution. Neutralize the alkali with 1:360
sulfuric acid and chill in an ice-water mixture. Treat with excess of
saturated bromine water and allow to stand in the ice bath for 5 minutes.
Aerate to remove excess bromine. Dilute to 10 ml. with water. Use
a 1-ml. aliquot of this for determination of the xylose by carbazole.

Procedure—*In the ultraviolet.* Read an aqueous distillate at 278.5
mμ against water.

As furfural by aniline acetate. As reagent dissolve 1 ml. of aniline

0.002-0.02 mg. of furfural with 2.5 of xylidine and 12.5 ml. of glacial acetic acid. The color will develop completely in 30 minutes. Read and interpret in terms of a furfural standard. The value for xylose is furfural times 1.605. The corresponding value for arabinose is furfural times 1.802.

As furfural by xylidine. Mix 10 ml. of sample distillate containing 0.002-0.02 mg. of furfural with 2.5 ml. of xylidine and 12.5 ml. of glacial acetic acid. The color will develop completely in 30 minutes. Read and interpret in terms of a furfural standard. The value for xylose is furfural times 1.605. The corresponding value for arabinose is furfural times 1.802.

As furfural by benzidine. Prepare a benzidine reagent containing 0.5 gram of benzidine in a mixture of 50 ml. of absolute ethanol and 50 ml. of glacial acetic acid. Add 4 ml. of this to 2 ml. of the sample solution containing about 2 mg. of furfural in benzene. Read between 30 minutes and 2 hours after adding the reagent.

With orcein and ferric ion. As reagent, just before use dissolve 0.01 gram of orcinol in 1 ml. of a 0.1 per cent solution of ferric chloride in concentrated hydrochloric acid. Mix this with 1 ml. of sample containing 0.01-0.02 mg. of the pentose. Heat in boiling water for 20 minutes, cool, and dilute to 4 ml. with water. Read at 610 mμ. By suitable preparation of the sample this includes or excludes pentoses from nucleosides and nucleotides.

With cysteine. Add, with cooling under running water, 4 ml. of concentrated sulfuric acid to 1 ml. of solution containing 0.01-0.5 mg. of xylose. Shake vigorously and place in a cold water bath. When the mixture has cooled to room temperature, the decomposition of the sugar ceases and the reaction mixture is colorless. Add 0.1 ml. of 3 per cent solution of cysteine hydrochloride. Read after 20 minutes at 390 mμ and 425 mμ against a reagent blank. Interpret in terms of the difference in reading at the two wave lengths.

By carbazole. As xylose. Prepare a mixture of 8 parts of sulfuric acid with 1 part of water. Chill 10 ml. in an ice bath. Layer above it 1 ml. of sample solution containing 0.05-0.2 mg. of xylose. Chill and mix while in the ice bath to avoid appreciable rise in temperature. Remove and add 0.3 ml. of a 0.5 per cent solution of carbazole in absolute ethanol. Mix and heat in boiling water for 10 minutes. Chill in ice and read at 520 mμ against a reagent blank.

Directly with aniline acetate. As reagent mix 100 ml. of glacial acetic acid, 10 ml. of 5 per cent aqueous oxalic acid, 24 ml. of water, and 16 ml.

of colorless aniline. Keep dark and use within a week. To 6 ml. of reagent add a sample containing 0.01-0.05 mg. of xylose and dilute to 8 ml. with water. Keep in the dark for 24 hours and read at 622 mμ.

By anthrone. To 2 ml. of sample solution containing 0.00002-0.0002 mg. of xylose add as a separate lower layer 4 ml. of a 4-hour old 0.05 per cent solution of anthrone in concentrated sulfuric acid. Quickly mix by oscillating for 10 seconds which in mixing will raise the temperature to about 95°. Chill in ice for 5 minutes, let come to room temperature, and read within 45 minutes at 620 mμ.

ARABINOSE, PECTINOSE, PECTIN SUGAR

As another pentose, arabinose is in general determined by the methods used for xylose. It can be decomposed to furfural and then determined in the way there described. It is developed directly with aniline acetate. Like so many sugars, it is read by the color developed with picric acid (page 213). It is developed with orcinol, cysteine, carbazole, or anthrone etc., as described for xylose.

LYXOSE

See comments on arabinose.

RIBOSE

Ribose is a pentose recovered from nucleosides. It is estimated by ferric chloride and orcinol.[18] The details as given include preliminary separation of fractions for development by other technics. The color with anthrone described above for xylose is also applicable to d-ribose within 90 minutes after mixing.

Sample—*Tissue.* Add 35 grams of well-minced tissue to 300 ml. of 10 per cent trichloroacetic acid solution. Store on ice for 1 hour mixing frequently, filter, and neutralize to phenolphthalein. Reserve 105 ml. of this for determination of purines in the nucleotides. Uranium acetate will precipitate the nucleotides without affecting nucleosides or purines.[19] Acidify the protein-free filtrate with 5 drops of glacial acetic acid per 100 ml. and add about 0.4 ml. of 8 per cent uranyl acetate solution, the

---

[18] Stanley E. Kerr and Krikor Seraidarian, *J. Biol. Chem.* **159**, 211-25 (1945).
[19] Stanley E. Kerr and M. E. Blish, *Ibid.* **98**, 193 (1932); Stanley E. Kerr, *Ibid.* **132**, 147-59 1940).

minimum amount to provide a slight excess. Centrifuge and wash the precipitate, the combined liquids being a sample for study of nucleosides and purines. Dissolve the precipitate with 2 ml. of 1:2.6 sulfuric acid for each 100 ml. of tissue extract.

Purines. Add an equal volume of 1:360 sulfuric acid to the filtrate and washings from the uranium precipitate. Add 0.34 per cent silver nitrate solution until the purines are precipitated. After sedimentation separate by centrifuging, definitely within an hour. Wash and centrifuge. Combine the centrifugate and washing for determination of nucleosides. Wash again and discard this washing.

Nucleosides. Having separated the acid silver precipitate of purines, make the solution alkaline to phenol red with 4 per cent sodium hydroxide solution. The resulting alkaline silver precipitate contains the nucleosides, some silver oxide, and any residual uranium. Wash this precipitate and centrifuge, and repeat. Discard the washings.

Recovery of ribose. Disperse the silver precipitates in 15 ml. of 1:24 hydrochloric acid and heat in boiling water for 30 minutes. Filter hot through asbestos in a Gooch crucible. Wash the residual silver chloride 5 times with 1:24 hydrochloric acid at 100°. Dilute the cooled filtrate to 35 ml. with 1:24 hydrochloric acid. The uranium cannot be precipitated before determination of the ribose. Unless the amount is excessive, it does not interfere.

Procedure--To a quantity of the sample solution containing 0.02-0.05 mg. of ribose add 0.3 ml. of 1:10 hydrochloric acid and dilute to 5 ml. Add 5 ml. of concentrated hydrochloric acid containing 0.02 per cent of ferric chloride. Follow with 0.3 ml. of 10 per cent orcinol and mix. Immerse in boiling water for 20 minutes, cool, and dilute to 15 ml. Read against a reagent blank.

DESOXYRIBOSE

Determine by the carbazole reagent [20] as described under xylose (page 189).

RHAMNOSE

Rhamnose is a methyl pentose which on acid hydrolysis yields methyl furfural. The latter does not react to form a colored compound with

[20] Zacharias Dische, *Proc. Soc. Exp. Biol. and Med.* **55,** 217-18 (1944); P. K. Stumpf, *J. Biol. Chem.* **169** 367-71 (1947).

aniline or benzidine as does furfural from pentoses. It does form a colored compound with phloroglucinol suitable for estimation.[21] Results are accurate to ±4 per cent. The error introduced by traces of hydroxy-methylfurfural from hexoses is unimportant. If unsubstituted pentoses are present, the total of pentoses and methyl pentoses is read with phloroglucinol and the pentose as determined with aniline or xylidene is subtracted.[22]

When rhamnose is treated with sulfuric acid of the order of 80-90 per cent acid the reaction product can be developed with cysteine.[23] By controlling acid concentration, temperature and time, the reaction will determine 0.002-0.01 mg. of rhamnose in the presence of other sugars except methyl pentoses. For this the time of heating is particularly important, so much so that at some shorter heating periods other sugars give a greater intensity of color than rhamnose. The color from pentoses, hexoses, and hexuronic acids is pink while that from rhamnose is greenish yellow. The reaction product of methyl pentoses and of desoxyribose with 2.5:1 sulfuric acid-water is completely stable but becomes unstable at 1.6:1.

Other methods for rhamnose are more general. It is read by picric acid as described under mannose. It gives a yellow with diphenylamine as discussed under xylose.

Procedure—*As methyl furfural.* The sample must be available in a solution diluted to contain about 1 mg. of rhamnose per ml. Mix 3 ml. of sample with 6 ml. of 1:1 hydrochloric acid. Reflux in a boiling water bath for 2 hours. Cool and add 4 ml. of benzene. Shake vigorously for 3 minutes and let stand for 20 minutes. Clear the benzene layer of black humic matter by spinning the tube.

Add 4 ml. of 0.25 per cent phloroglucinol solution in 95 per cent ethanol to 2 ml. of sample in benzene. Shake, add 0.65 ml. of concentrated hydrochloric acid, and shake again. A deep yellow color will develop for a period of about 3 minutes. Read within one-half to one hour after adding the hydrochloric acid.

By cysteine. To 1 ml. of aqueous solution containing 0.05 mg. or more of a rhamnose, add, with cooling in ice, 45 ml. of a mixture of

---

[21] Robert A. McCance, *Biochem. J.* 23, 1172-4 (1927).

[22] Alfred Torricelli, *Mitt. Lebensm. Hyg.* 36, 251-73 (1945).

[23] Zacharias Dische and Landrum B. Shettles, *J. Biol. Chem.* 175, 595-603 (1948); Zacharias Dische, Landrum B. Shettles, and Martha Osnos, *Arch. Biochem.* 22, 169-84 (1949).

6 parts of sulfuric acid with 1 part of water. Warm to 20-22°, place in boiling water for exactly 10 minutes, and cool in tap water. Add 0.1 ml. of 3 per cent aqueous cysteine hydrochloric solution with shaking. A greenish yellow color appears which is stable for 24 hours. Read at 396 mµ and 430 mµ against a reagent blank. Interpret in terms of the difference between those two readings. Color from other sugars will be substantially the same at the two wave lengths and therefore cancels out.

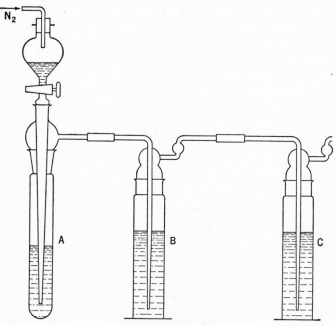

Fɪɢ. 17. Apparatus for fucose estimation

Fᴜᴄᴏsᴇ

Fucose is quantitatively oxidized with periodic acid [24] and read colorimetrically after development with nitroprusside.[25] As a methylpentose fucose gives the same reactions as rhamnose.

Sample—*Seaweed.* Reflux a 0.2-gram sample with 5 ml. of 1:70 sulfuric acid for 3 hours. Neutralize to litmus with sodium bicarbonate.

[24] M. C. Cameron, A. G. Ross, and E. G. V. Percival, *J. Soc. Chem. Ind.* **67**, 161-5 (1948).

[25] W. A. P. Black, W. J. Cornhill, E. T. DeWar, E. G. V. Percival, and A. G. Ross, *Ibid.* **69**, 317-20 (1950).

Add the following in as exact amounts as possible: 0.5 gram of sodium bicarbonate, 0.2 gram of alanine, 14 ml. of $0.1N$ sodium arsenite solution, and 0.5 ml. of white mineral oil.

As absorber for the aldehyde saturate sodium carbonate solution with sulfur dioxide and dilute to one-tenth strength. In one absorber dilute 4 ml. to 25 ml., in another 1 ml. to 20 ml. Use the apparatus shown in Figure 17. Add 7 ml. of 11.4 per cent periodic acid dihydrate to the tap funnel. Add it about 1 ml. at a time to the sample, stopping each time until foaming from evolution of carbon dioxide has ceased. About 2 minutes after the final addition start bubbling nitrogen through the solution at a rate stepped up gradually to 800 ml. per minute. Continue for 2.5 hours.

Combine the contents of the absorbers and add starch indicator. Titrate out the excess bisulfite with iodine solution and discharge the blue with a drop of 2.5 per cent sodium thiosulfate solution. Dilute to 100 ml. for the development of aliquots.

Procedure—To an aliquot diluted to 6 ml. with the same menstruum add 0.5 ml. of fresh 4 per cent sodium nitroprusside solution and 1.5 ml. of 33 per cent piperazine solution. Shake for 1 minute and read with a yellow filter, correcting for a reagent blank.

CHAPTER 8

HEXOSES AND HEPTOSES [1]

HEXOSES give many of the reactions common to other sugars. These are reduction of alkaline ferricyanide for reading directly or as Prussian blue, reduction to molybdenum or tungsten blue by many technics, caramelization, color with picric acid, colors with nitro compounds, anthrone, etc. Specific reactions include that of fructose with resorcinol and ferric ion.

GLUCOSE, DEXTROSE

Many of the reactions of glucose are generally applicable to other aldohexoses and to ketohexoses. Therefore this topic necessarily includes many reactions, of which nearly all are applicable to other sugars.

Glucose reduces alkaline ferricyanide. Results can be read in terms of the yellow of excess ferricyanide,[2] since ferrocyanide is colorless in acid solution. For greater sensitivity the ferrocyanide is converted to Prussian blue.[3] In recent technics sodium lauryl sulfate replaces gum

---

[1] See Chapter 1 for details of organization, condensation, etc.

[2] J. A. Hawkins and D. D. Van Slyke, *J. Biol. Chem.* **81**, 459 (1929); W. Z. Hassid, *Ind. Eng. Chem., Anal. Ed.* **8**, 138-40 (1936); *Ibid.* **9**, 228-9 (1937); A. J. L. Terwen, *Deut. Arch. klin. Med.* **180**, 27-31 (1937); W. T. Forsee, Jr., *Ind. Eng. Chem., Anal. Ed.* **10**, 411-12 (1938); S. A. Morell, *Ibid.* **13**, 249-51 (1941); Otto Schales and Selma S. Schales, *Arch. Biochem.* **8**, 285-92 (1945); F. Rappaport and F. Eichhorn, *Am. J. Clin. Path* **20**, 295-6 (1950).

[3] Otto Folin, *J. Biol. Chem.* **77**, 421-30 (1928); *Ibid.* **81**, 231-6 (1929); Otto Folin and H. Malmros, *Ibid.* **83**, 115-20 (1929); William S. Hoffman, *Ibid.* **120**, 51-5 (1937); Leonard F. Jourdonais, *J. Lab. Clin. Med.* **23**, 847-52 (1938); Niels C. Klenshoj and Roger S. Hubbard, *Ibid.* **25**, 1102-6 (1940); S. M. Horvath and C. A. Kuehr, *J. Biol. Chem.* **140**, 869-77 (1941); R. F. Milton, *Analyst* **67**, 183-4 (1942); Roger M. Reinecke, *J. Biol. Chem.* **143**, 351-5 (1942); Cecilia M. Kortuem, *Am. J. Clin. Path. Tech. Sect.* **8**, 70-4 (1944); E. Romo Aldama and F. Fernandez de la Calle, *Rev. españ. fisiol.*, **2**, 203-9 (1946); R. Wolff and Emile de Lavergne, *Compt. rend. soc. biol.* **141**, 926-8 (1947); James T. Park and Marvin J. Johnson, *J. Biol. Chem.* **181**, 149-51 (1949); Maurice Herbain, *Bull. soc. chim. biol.* **31**, 1104-13 (1949); George R. Kingsley and John G. Reinhold, *J. Lab. Clin. Med.* **34**, 713-19 (1949); C. Scandura, C. Ardy, and A. Muratorio, *Arch. "E. Marigliano" patol e clin.* **5**, 53-9 (1950); M. Plumel, *Ann. biol. clin.* (Paris) **9**, 307-17 (1951); Ko Ito, *J. Japan. Biochem. Soc.* **23**, 29-32 (1951).

ghatti as a stabilizer. Addition of ammonia and lithium tartrate [4] or of polyvinylpyrrolidone or dilute "Tween" solution [5] to the ferric reagent stabilizes the Prussian blue dispersion. Glucose and other sugars are determined photometrically by their reaction with ferricyanides.[6] Unless reducing substances other than glucose are thoroughly removed, the method will give high values. Other dispersing agents are used to avoid flocculation of the Prussian blue. Glucose is estimated in the presence of fructose by determining both with ferricyanide and subtraction of the fructose as determined by a method applicable to ketoses rather than aldoses.

There are a series of methods of determination in which glucose is used for reduction of a form of organic copper salt solution such as copper tartrate. This reduced cuprous oxide is then developed in various ways. The simplest, chemically, but not the most important or most accurate is to reduce Fehling's solution, separate the cuprous oxide, dissolve and read as the copper-ammonia complex.[7]

The more desirable technics reduce complex salts with the cuprous oxide to give molybdenum blue or tungsten blue. Thus addition of phosphomolybdate solution to the reduced copper solution discharges the blue of excess copper and at the same time produces a blue proportional to the amount of cuprous oxide present from reduction of copper.[8] The color is not affected by creatinine nor uric acid up to 50 mg. per 100 ml. A rough measurement is even made by the color of the unreduced copper without further treatment.[9]

The solution should be read promptly after development of color. There is danger of reoxidation of the precipitated cuprous oxide unless exposure to air is reduced to a minimum.

[4] A. D. Marenzi and F. Villalonga, *Rev. soc. argentina biol.* **15**, 246-55 (1939).

[5] Pierre Fonty, *Ann. biol. clin.* (Paris) **8**, 312-15 (1950).

[6] A. Saifer, F. Valenstein, and J. P. Hughes, *J. Lab. Clin. Med.* **26**, 1969-77 (1941).

[7] Ernest Komm, *Münch. med. Wochschr.* **72**, 1602-3 (1925); *Z. angew, Chem.* **38**, 1094-6 (1925); K. Seiler, *Pharm. Acta. Helv.* **4**, 65-8 (1929); Ed. Lasausse, P. Kermarec, and I. Frocrain, *J. pharm. chim.* **24**, 461-6 (1936); M. I. Kulenok, *Gigiena i. Sanit.* 1949, No. 1, 34-6.

[8] Otto Folin and Hsien Wu, *J. Biol. Chem.* **38**, 81-110 (1919); *Ibid.* **41**, 367-74 (1920); Otto Folin, *Ibid.* **67**, 357-70 (1926); *Ibid.* **82**, 83-93 (1929); Stanley R. Benedict, *Ibid.* **68**, 759-67 (1926); *Ibid.* **76**, 457-70 (1928); W. S. Hoffman, *Ibid.* **120**, 51-5 (1937); Mauricio Klurfan, *Semana méd.* (Buenos Aires) 1942, II, 736-40; B. D. Polis and Maxine Sortwell, *Arch. Biochem.* **11**, 229-33 (1946); A. Sols, *Rev. españ. fisiol.* **5**, 149-54 (1949).

[9] Albertos Justinianos, *Praktika Akad. Athenon.* **12**, 265-7 (1937); Salah El-Dewi, *Brit. Med. J.* 1949, I, 899-900.

The arsenotungstate reagent is an alternative to the phosphomolybdate.[10] Another uses ammonium molybdate [11] buffered by potassium dihydrogen phosphate. Others are phosphotungstophosphomolybdic acid [12] and arsenomolybdate.[13] The latter uses a copper reagent with a carbonate-bicarbonate buffer. The copper concentration is too high for colorimetric use and correspondingly requires excess tartrate to keep the copper in solution. By reducing the copper and tartrate content a more appropriate reagent for colorimetry is obtained.[14] There is substantially no self-reduction.

All monosaccharides give these reactions. Disaccharides and raffinose barely react. High concentrations of maltose interfere. The intensity of color increases for glucose up to about 4 hours at 100°. A 30-minute heating period is most desirable in the presence of disaccharides and trisaccharides. Less heating time reduces the sensitivity; longer heating increases interference from disaccharides. Results agree with the Munson and Walker method. Other forms determine excess copper after reduction is complete. These include recording as the bicarbonate [15] or the ammonia complex.[16]

Deproteinizing with zinc sulfate in which barium hydroxide [17] replaces the earlier sodium hydroxide is advantageous in that no salts are left.

A basic reaction for carbohydrates is the red color with picric acid and sodium carbonate.[18] Strong colors may interfere. Polyphenols, aldehydes, ketones, purine bases, etc. interfere by reducing alkaline picrate solutions. The color is due to a salt of picramic acid. Glycogen, if present in the sample, must first be hydrolyzed with sulfuric acid.

[10] Stanley R. Benedict, *J. Biol. Chem.* **64**, 207-13 (1925); R. B. Gibson, *Proc. Soc. Exptl. Biol. Med.* **27**, 480-3 (1930); Norton Nelson, *J. Biol. Chem.* **153**, 375-80 (1944); Hermann Frank and Ernest Kirberger, *Biochem. Z.* **320**, 359-67 (1950); J. Lon Pope, *Am. J. Clin. Path.* **20**, 801-5 (1950).

[11] G. Harvey Benham and John E. Despaul, *Anal. Chem.* **20**, 944-5 (1946).

[12] M. Fiorentino and G. Giannettasio, *Diagnostica tec. lab.* (*Napoli*)*Riv. mens.* **10**, 401-12 (1939); Georg Hausdorf, *Pharmazie* **2**, 257-61 (1947).

[13] Norton Nelson, *J. Biol. Chem.* **153**, 375-80 (1944); M. Somogyi, *Ibid.* **160**, 61-73 (1945).

[14] Michael Somogyi, *J. Biol. Chem.* **195**, 19-23 (1952).

[15] I. Fabian, *Biochem. Z.* **179**, 59-61 (1926).

[16] E. M. Emmert, *J. Assoc. Official Agr. Chem.* **15**, 327-9 (1932).

[17] Michael Somogyi, *J. Biol. Chem.* **160**, 69-73 (1945).

[18] C. D. Braun, *J. prakt. Chem.* **96**, 411-14 (1865); *Z. anal. Chem.* **4**, 185-8 (1865); George Johnson, *Brit. Med. J.* 504-7 (1883); José F. Escarza, *Rev. asoc. bioquím.* **10**, 36-7 (1944); Nicola Cappuccio, *Rass. med.* **28**, 197-8 (1951).

Changes in color are produced by changes of concentration, temperature, and alkalinity. Deviations from Beer's law therefore occur unless conditions are closely controlled. Potassium bichromate is an appropriate standard for comparison.[19]

The red color of reducing sugars with 2,4-dinitrosalicyclic acid in alkaline solution is employed for their determination.[20] The reagent is almost completely specific for reducing sugars. Color is permanent for one hour.

The red-violet with m-dinitrobenzene in alkaline solution is a variant of this method [21] as are also those with o-dinitrobenzene [22] or 2,4-dinitrophenolate.[23] Fructose gives the same effect as glucose. The method with 2,4-dinitrophenolate appears with fructose (page 212). Another variation is to react glucose with formaldehyde to form formose and use it for reduction of 2,4-dinitro-1-naphthol-7-sulfonic acid.

If solutions containing 0.005-0.02 per cent of glucose are mixed with twice their volume of concentrated sulfuric acid, a violet to red coloration results.[24] The color is given only by hexoses, free or as polysaccharides. Chlorides must have been removed.

A very simple method is based on the yellow to brown color developed when sugars are heated in alkaline solutions.[25] The alkali may be sodium hydroxide or sodium carbonate and is dependent to a marked degree on the concentration of alkali used. Proteins or acetone bodies do not affect the color.

---

[19] Nagahide Goya and Ryuichi Yokoyama, *Igaku to Seibutsugaku* 23, 68-71 (1952).

[20] James B. Sumner and V. A. Graham, *J. Biol. Chem.* 47, 5-9 (1921); James B. Sumner, *Ibid.* 62, 287-90 (1924); *Ibid.* 65, 393-5 (1925); Dorothea Klemme and Charles F. Poe, *J. Bact.* 32, 1-9 (1936); James B. Sumner and Eleanor B. Sisler, *Arch. Biochem.* 4, 333-6 (1944); Rachel S. Leech and Norma Woodford, *J. Lab. Clin. Med.* 33, 644-50 (1948); Rolf Brodersen and Henry T. Ricketts, *Ibid.* 34, 1447-56 (1949).

[21] Mario Banco, *Boll. soc. ital. biol. sper.* 17, 354-5 (1942).

[22] M. Peronnet and J. Hugonnet, *Ann. pharm. franc.* 9, 397-407 (1951).

[23] Charles F. Poe and Frank G. Edson, *Ind. Eng. Chem., Anal. Ed.* 4, 300-2 (1932); Frank G. Edson and Charles F. Poe, *J. Assoc. Official Agr. Chemists* 31, 769-75 (1949).

[24] Bruno Mendel and Milly Bauch, *Klin. Wochschr.* 5, 1329-30 (1926); Juan A. Sanchez, *Semana méd.* (*Buenos Aires*) 1935, II, 914-17; Juan A. Sanchez and R. C. D'Alessio, *J. pharm. chim.* 23, 377-87 (1936); J. Peltzer, *Chem.-Ztg.* 64, 122-4 (1940); *Ibid.* 65, 331-2 (1941); M. Bianco, *Boll. soc. ital. biol. sper.* 16, 302-4 (1941); Michele Ragno, *Diagnostica tec. lab.* (Napoli) *Riv. mens.* 8, 81-8 (1937).

[25] Herbert Habs, *Münch med. Wochschr.* 80, 1101-2 (1933); Michael Somogyi, *J. Lab. Clin. Med.* 26, 1220-3 (1941).

The reaction of pentoses with sulfuric acid and carbazole is applicable to glucose.[26] For details see the method given under xylose (page 189) but read at 540 mμ. Other hexoses also so react. Amino acids in general do not interfere, but proteins containing much tryptophan do. As applied to mixtures of sugars, there is some inaccuracy due to different intensities of color development.

The decomposition of sugars with sulfuric acid followed by development with cysteine is applicable to glucose and other hexoses. It has been discussed in more detail under xylose. The product from glucose is stable at 4:1 sulfuric acid-water but becomes unstable at 2.5:1.[27]

Glucose and other hexoses are converted by strong acids to 5-hyroxy-methylfurfural which is determinable by colors formed with aniline, xylidene, etc. The reaction only proceeds to about 12 per cent and is therefore not as satisfactory as for determining pentoses and methyl pentoses. The furfural derivative formed is also read directly at 278.5 mμ.

Anthrone in reasonably concentrated sulfuric acid solution gives a blue-green with all mono-, di- and polysaccharides.[28] It also reacts positively with dextrins, dextrans, glycogen, gums, glucosides, acetates of the saccharides, and salts of mannosidostreptomycin and dihydromanosido-streptomycin. The only nonsugar which reacts is furfural. The reaction is applicable to blood sugar.[29]

Glucose reduces sodium biselenite and can be read as the colloidal dispersion of selenium. Details are given under maltose (page 217). The color of glucose is developed with a-naphthol in the presence of a large excess of sulfuric acid.[30] The absorption curve of a-naphthol-sulfuric acid differs somewhat for different monosaccharides.

---

[26] Samuel Gurin and Dorothy B. Hood, *J. Biol Chem.* **131**, 211-23 (1939); *Ibid.* **139**, 775-85 (1941); Tikasuke Yamomoto, *J. Biochem.* (Japan) **32**, 161-73 (1940).

[27] Zacharias Dische, *J. Biol. Chem.* **181**, 379-92 (1949).

[28] Roman Dreywood, *Ind. Eng. Chem., Anal. Ed.* **18**, 499 (1946); E. E. Morse, *Ibid.* **19**, 1012-3 (1947); D. L. Morris, *Science* **107**, 254-8 (1948); Frederick J. Viles, Jr. and Leslie Silverman, *Anal. Chem.* **21**, 950-4 (1949); Sam Seifter, Seymour Dayton, B. Novic, and Edward Muntwyler, *Arch. Biochem.* **25**, 191-200 (1950); W. Fay Durham, Walter Lyon Bloom, George T. Lewis, and Emanuel E. Mandel, *U. S. Pub. Health Repts.* **65**, 670-4 (1950).

[29] K. Motegi, *J. Japan. Biochem. Soc.* **21**, 40-1 (1949).

[30] Robert Frailong, *Bull. assoc. chim. sucr. dist.* **27**, 1188-90 (1910); Forschbach and Severin, *Zentr. ges. Physiol. Path. Stoffw.* **6**, 177-84 (1911); Alois Dolinek, *Listy Cykrovar.* **49**, 595-8 (1931); Paul Ujsághy, *Biochem. Z.* **298**, 141-9 (1938); Kazuo Yamahuzi and Tadasi Yosida, *Ibid.* **301**, 61-4 (1939); A. W. Devor, *Proc. S. Dakota Acad. Sci.* **26**, 75-6 (1946-7).

A proprietary tablet for estimation of glucose [31] against a series of standards contains 1 part of anhydrous cupric sulfate, 10 parts of monohydrated citric acid, and 20 parts of powdered sodium hydroxide. A 5-grain tablet used with 0.5 ml. of urine is sensitive to 0.075 per cent of glucose. It also reacts to fructose at 0.125 per cent and to arabinose at 0.135 per cent. Chloroform, uric acid, creatinine and albumin do not interfere.

Saccharides are estimated in serum by their color with tryptophan in the presence of sulfuric acid.[32] The maximum differs for different sugars, 500 mμ for galactose and mannose, 460 mμ for glucose, 520 mμ for fructose, below 400 mμ for glucuronic acid, glucosamine, and hemoglobin.

For the determination of glucose in wheat meals and flour, the most suitable method involves caramelization.[33] Color developed is proportional to the sugar present. Sucrose, raffinose, starch, dextrin, mannitol, and sorbitol do not develop. Maltose, fructose, mannose, and arabinose caramelize like glucose.

Glucose, and other hexoses, give a blue with diphenylamine which is accurate to ±1.5 per cent in the presence of pentoses. This is suitable for determination of sugars in flour.[34]

Glucose in the aldehyde form is oxidized by sodium hypochlorite but the cyclic lactal form is not. By preheating an alkaline solution of glucose at 100° for several minutes conversion to the aldehyde form is complete.[35] When cool determine the excess of oxidizing agent by excess Fast Green FCF.

Among other methods applicable to glucose is formation of the osazone with phenylhydrazine hydrochloride.[36] This technic is somewhat long but permits the estimation in the presence of other reducing agents.

[31] Jonas Kamlet, U. S. 2,418,033 (1947).

[32] M. R. Shetlar, Janeal V. Foster, and Mark R. Everett, *Proc. Soc. Exptl. Biol. Med.* 67, 125-30 (1948).

[33] Ernst A. Schmidt, *Muhlenlab.* 8, 121-32 (1938); *Mehl. u. Brot.* 38, No. 20, 1-3 (1938).

[34] Elisabeth Tornow, *Z. Untersuch. Lebensm.* 83, 132-41 (1942).

[35] H. T. Gordon, *Anal. Chem.* 23, 1853-8 (1951).

[36] G. Rodillon, *Bull. biol. pharm.* 3, 242-4 (1929); E. Herzfeld, *Biochem. Z.* 256, 127-33 (1932); V. S. Butkevich and M. S. Gaevskaya, *Compt. rend. acad. sci. (USSR)* 3, 313-16 (1935).

[37] B. Glassman, *Z. physiol. Chem.* 150, 16-43 (1925); Ibid. 162, 145-7 (1926); B. Glassman and A. Zwilling, *Ibid.* 180, 124-6 (1929).

Others are reduction of 1,5-nitroanthraquinone sulfonate [37] and reaction with resorcinol at 100°.

Reducing sugars convert the colorless solution of triphenyltetrazolium chloride to a red precipitate of triphenylformazan.[38] This is dissolved by pyridine for estimation. The reaction is given by lactose, fructose, glucose, and of course invert sugar. Therefore each will interfere with the others.

Sample—*Blood. Free sugar.* Mix 4 ml. of a solution containing 3 per cent of sodium tungstate and 2 per cent of sodium sulfate. Add 0.1 ml. of blood, mix, and let stand for 15 minutes. Add 1 ml. of a solution containing 2 grams of sodium sulfate and 12 ml. of 1:54 sulfuric acid per 100 ml. Stir and centrifuge for 5 minutes. Develop with ferricyanide.

To clarify blood for development as molybdenum blue, prepare 5 per cent zinc sulfate heptahydrate solution. Then prepare 4.75 per cent barium hydroxide octahydrate solution. Adjust the latter so that 4.7-4.8 ml. gives a pink to phenolphthalein with 5 ml. of the zinc sulfate solution diluted to 25 ml. Add 1 volume of blood to 15 volumes of water, mix, and add 2 volumes of the barium hydroxide solution. Mix and after the mixture turns brown, add 2 volumes of 5 per cent zinc sulfate solution. Mix and, after a few minutes, filter.

When blood is to be read with picric acid, pipet 2 ml. of oxalated blood into 5 ml. of water. Add 15 ml. of a saturated aqueous solution of picric acid and mix. Add 2 drops of ethanol to break the foam. Dilute to 25 ml., shake, and filter.

For determination with *o*-dinitrobenzene, centrifuge blood containing fluoride, with or without oxalate.

Protein sugar.[39] Some glucose is combined with proteins and removed in defacation. To include it dilute 1 ml. of blood or serum with 4 ml. of water. Add 1.5 ml. of 1:4 sulfuric acid and autoclave at 120° for 15 minutes. Cool and neutralize by dropwise addition of 30 per cent sodium hydroxide. Dilute to 8 ml. with water and defacate according to the method to be used for development. Subtract the free sugar from the result to get that bound as a protein complex.

Corpuscles. Mix 1 ml. of corpuscles with 5 ml. of water. Add 2 ml. of 10 per cent zinc sulfate solution and mix. Add 2 ml. of 4.75 per cent

[38] A. M. Mattson and C. O. Jensen, *Anal. Chem.* **22**, 182-5 (1950).

[39] Lucas Desimone and Carlos B. Brodersen, *Rev. asoc. bioquim. argentina* **3**, No. 9, 21-3 (1938).

barium hydroxide solution and shake. Filter through a dry paper after 10 minutes and develop as molybdenum blue.

Plasma or serum. Add 1 ml. of plasma or serum to 8 ml. of water. Add 0.5 ml. of 10 per cent zinc sulfate solution and mix. Add 0.5 ml. of 4.75 per cent barium hydroxide solution, and mix. Shake, let stand 10 minutes, and filter through a dry paper. Develop as molybdenum blue.

Urine. Add 5 ml. of approximately 0.45 per cent oxalic acid solution and 5 ml. of water to 10 ml. of urine. Mix, shake for 2 minutes with about 1.5 grams of Lloyd's reagent, and filter. Dilute 5 ml. of filtrate in such a way as to give a solution containing 0.1-0.2 mg. of glucose per ml. Develop with ferricyanide as Prussian blue or as molybdenum blue.

When urine is to be read with picric acid, dilute so that the specific gravity is not greater than 1.03. Add 1 gram of acid-washed boneblack to 15 ml. of sample. Shake for 10 minutes and filter. Mix 1 ml. of the filtrate and 2 ml. of saturated aqueous picric acid solution for development as alkaline picrate.

Spinal fluid. Dilute 20 ml. of 10 per cent sodium tungstate solution to 800 ml. Add 20 ml. of 1:54 sulfuric acid and dilute to 1 liter. Mix 10 ml. of this solution with 0.1 ml. of spinal fluid. Centrifuge and develop with ferricyanide or as molybdenum blue. Alternatively, develop directly with *o*-dinitrobenzene.

Saliva. To 0.2 ml. of saliva add 4 ml. of reagent containing 0.3 per cent of sodium cyanide, 0.3 per cent of sodium tungstate, and 2 per cent of sodium sulfate. Mix, let stand for 20 minutes, and add 1 ml. of a solution composed of 2 per cent of anhydrous sodium sulfate in 1:300 sulfuric acid. Mix, let stand for 10 minutes, and centrifuge. Develop with ferricyanide as Prussian blue.

Milk. To 25 ml. of sample add 5 ml. of 15 per cent potassium ferrocyanide solution and 5 ml. of 30 per cent zinc sulfate heptahydrate solution. Precipitate calcium with ammonium oxalate, dilute to 50 ml., shake, and filter. Develop with sulfuric acid.

Glucose solution. If the solution is not clear and colorless, saturate with basic lead acetate. Filter and delead by adding a slight excess of disodium phosphate. Mix 1 ml. of the solution, diluted to contain 0.02-0.32 mg. of glucose per ml. with 2 ml. of saturated aqueous solution of picric acid and read as alkaline pictrate.

Food. Transfer 1-10 grams to a mortar. Add sufficient water to total 100 grams plus the solid content of the sample. Triturate and centrifuge or filter. Treat this solution as described for a glucose solution. If sucrose is also present, invert and determine by difference (page 216). Both are as alkaline pictrate.

Fruits and vegetables. Grind the sample in a food chopper. Weigh a sample to contain not less than 0.05 grams of soluble sugars and grind with sand, adding a known volume of water, until extraction is complete. Saturate the more or less cloudy liquid with dry picric acid. Filter and read glucose as alkaline pictrate. If sucrose is also present determine it after inversion.

Plants. Plunge a representative sample of about 50 grams into boiling ethanol. Add 0.2 gram of calcium carbonate to prevent hydrolysis by acids present in the sample. Allowing for the moisture in the sample, dilute to 70-75 per cent ethanol. Filter and wash with 75 per cent ethanol. Dry the solid material at 70° and pulverize to pass an 80-mesh screen. Extract the powder in a Soxhlet extractor with the alcoholic filtrate until the percolate is colorless. Dilute the alcoholic solution of sugars to 1-10 mg. of sugar per ml. The extracted residue so obtained may be used for estimation of starch and reserve polysaccharides.

Evaporate a 10-ml. aliquot at a low temperature until the ethanol is removed. As a clarifying agent stir 110 grams of mercuric oxide into 80 ml. of concentrated nitric acid, heat to boiling, and let cool. Dilute to 1 liter and store in the dark.

Dilute the sample to 30 ml. and add 5 ml. of mercuric nitrate reagent. Add solid sodium bicarbonate in small portions until it no longer foams. Then continue to add until just alkaline to litmus. Filter, wash the paper with 10 ml. of 5 per cent sodium bicarbonate solution, and dilute to 250 ml. To 50 ml. add 0.5 gram of zinc dust, then a drop of concentrated hydrochloric acid. Agitate and set aside for 15 minutes. Filter and test the filtrate to insure the absence of mercury. To 1 ml. of solution add 2 ml. of saturated aqueous picric acid and read as alkaline picrate.

Green or quick-dried plant material. Extract with hot 80 per cent ethanol and evaporate the ethanol to give an aqueous sugar solution. This must be clarified to water-white. For this purpose evaporate a sample containing 5-35 mg. of glucose or other reducing sugar to about 10 ml. Cool and add 5 ml. of saturated aqueous neutral lead acetate. Precipitate excess lead with 10 ml. of saturated aqueous disodium phosphate. Add 0.3 gram of activated carbon and shake at intervals for 30 minutes. Filter on a Büchner funnel precoated with talc. Wash with distilled water and dilute to 100 ml. for estimation of an aliquot with ferricyanide for direct reading. With suitable supplemental treatment this sample is also appropriate for estimation of total sugars.

Plant juice. Heat in boiling water to destroy enzymatic activity. Then treat as the extract from plant material from "For this purpose evaporate a sample. . . ."

For development as molybdenum blue, dilute 2 ml. of sample, usually highly colored, to 10 ml. Add 2 ml. of saturated neutral lead acetate solution, mix, and centrifuge. Add 10 per cent disodium phosphate solution until the sample turns blue with bromothymol blue on a spot plate. Centrifuge and decant. Wash the precipitate and dilute the clear solution to a known volume for development of an alequot as molybdenum blue.

Chocolates. Heating chocolate pastes at 50-120° causes some glucose to form from the sucrose present. Extract 5 grams of chocolate or fondant with warm water and dilute to 100 ml. Treat a suitable aliquot of this as directed for plant juices for development as molybdenum blue. The final solution should not contain more than 20 mg. of glucose per 100 ml.

Procedure—*By ferricyanide. Direct reading.* As concentrated reagent prepare a solution of 0.18 per cent of potassium ferricyanide and 3 per cent of sodium carbonate. For use as fresh dilute reagent, dilute 65 ml. to 100 ml. with water.

To 1 ml. of sample solution add 2 ml. of dilute reagent. Mix and immerse in boiling water for exactly 5 minutes. Cool under the tap and dilute to 8 ml. Mix by inversion and read at 420 mμ. The comparison curve shows greater absorption the less the glucose content.

As Prussian blue. Dilute a sample containing 0.53 per cent of sodium cyanide and 1 ml. of 0.05 per cent potassium ferricyanide solution. Mix and heat in boiling water for 15 minutes. Cool and add 5 ml. of a solution containing 0.15 per cent of ferric ammonium sulfate and 0.1 per cent of sodium lauryl sulfate (Duponol ME) in 1:720 sulfuric acid. After 15 minutes read at 690 mμ against a reagent blank.

As molybdenum blue by phosphomolybdate. As copper reagent, dissolve 15 grams of anhydrous sodium carbonate, 2 grams of sodium potassium tartrate, and 3 grams of alanine in about 300 ml. of warm water. Dissolve 3 grams of copper sulfate pentahydrate in about 50 ml. of water. Add the copper solution to the other solution with shaking. Cool and dilute to 500 ml. For use add 1 drop of a 1 per cent solution of sodium bisulfite per ml. not more than 2 days before use.

As phosphomolybdic acid reagent, weigh 150 grams of molybdic acid and 75 grams of anhydrous sodium carbonate. Add water in small portions until about 500 ml. have been added. Shake and heat to boiling until nearly all of the molybdic acid has been dissolved. Filter off the insoluble residue and wash it with hot water until the filtrate totals about 600 ml. Add 300 ml. of 85 per cent phosphoric acid, cool, and dilute to 1 liter.

To 2 ml. of the copper reagent add 2 ml. of sample. Shake gently and heat in boiling water for 6 minutes. Cool in cold water for 2 minutes. Add 2 ml. of the phosphomolybdic acid reagent and mix well. After 1 minute dilute to 25 ml., mix, and read within 10 minutes.

By arsenomolybdate. As arsenomolybdate reagent dissolve 25 grams of ammonium molybdate in 450 ml. of water, add 21 ml. of concentrated sulfuric acid, and mix. Add 3 grams of sodium arsenate dissolved in 25 ml. of water, mix, and incubate at 37° for 24-48 hours.

The copper reagent contains 0.4 per cent of copper sulfate pentahydrate, 2.4 per cent of sodium carbonate, 1.6 per cent of sodium bicarbonate, 1.2 per cent of sodium potassium tartrate, and 1.8 per cent of anhydrous sodium sulfate. To prepare this dissolve the sodium carbonate and sodium potassium tartrate in about 250 ml. of water. Add the copper sulfate as 10 per cent solution with stirring followed by the bicarbonate. Dissolve the sodium sulfate in about 500 ml. of water and boil to expel oxygen. Cool, mix, and dilute to 1 liter with water. Store for a week to permit cuprous oxide and impurities to settle and filter.

To 1 ml. of sample, add 1 ml. of fresh copper reagent. Mix, heat for 10 minutes in boiling water, and cool in cold water. Add 1 ml. of arsenomolybdate reagent to dissolve the cuprous oxide. Color develops rapidly. Dilute to 25 ml., mix, and read at 500-520 mμ against a reagent blank. The wave length is a compromise. At 660 mμ the sensitivity is quadrupled.

As tungsten blue. As the alkaline copper tartrate reagent, dissolve 16 grams of anhydrous sodium carbonate in 160 ml. of water. Add 3 grams of tartaric acid and, when dissolved, 1.8 grams of copper sulfate pentahydrate. Mix and dilute to 400 ml.

As arsenophosphotungstic acid reagent, dissolve 100 grams of sodium tungstate in about 600 ml. of water. Add 50 grams of arsenic oxide, 25 ml. of 85 per cent phosphoric acid, and 20 ml. of concentrated hydrochloric acid. Boil for 20 minutes, cool, and dilute nearly to 1 liter. Add 50 ml. of 40 per cent formaldehyde solution and complete the dilution.

To 2 ml. of clear sample solution, add 2 ml. of the alkaline copper tartrate reagent. Mix and heat for 6 minutes in boiling water. Cool and add 2 ml. of arsenophosphotungstic acid reagent. Mix by agitating slightly until evolution of gas has ceased. Dilute to 10 ml., mix, and read against a reagent blank.

By ammonium molybdate. Mix 5 ml. of 0.27 per cent potassium dihydrogen phosphate solution and 10 ml. of 7.5 per cent ammonium molybdate solution. Add an amount of sample containing 1-10 mg. of glucose and dilute to 25 ml. Mix, and autoclave for exactly 30 minutes at 100°, using open steam. Cool at once in ice water to room temperature to stop the reaction, and read the color at 650 mμ against a reagent blank.

By copper complexes. Mix 2 ml. of clear sample with 1 ml. of Fehling's solution. Heat in boiling water for one-half minute, or until reduction appears to be complete. Cool and centrifuge. The cuprous oxide precipitate is deposited on the bottom of the tube. Decant the supernatant blue solution. Suspend the cuprous oxide precipitate in 5 ml. of water and centrifuge. Decant and repeat. Dissolve the residue of cuprous oxide in 0.3 ml. of 1:160 nitric acid with shaking. Add 0.6 ml. of concentrated ammonium hydroxide and dilute to 2 ml. for reading at 620 mμ.

As alkaline picrate. To the prepared sample containing picric acid add 1 ml. of 20 per cent sodium carbonate solution. Mix well and stopper lightly with a tin foil-covered stopper. Heat in boiling water for 30 minutes. When cool dilute to 10 ml. and read at 530 mμ.

By sodium carbonate. Mix 0.5 ml. of sample with 5 ml. of 10 per cent sodium carbonate solution and place in boiling water for 8 minutes. Read against a reagent blank.

By dinitrosalicylic acid. As reagent, dissolve 255 grams of Rochelle salt in 500 ml. of water. Add 8.8 grams of dinitrosalicylic acid, 588 ml. of 5 per cent sodium hydroxide solution, 7 grams of phenol, and 7 grams of sodium metabisulfite. Cool and dilute to 2 liters. To 10 ml. of reagent add 0.1 ml. of sample, stir, and heat for 3 minutes in boiling water. Cool to room temperature and read at 540 mμ against a reagent blank.

By sulfuric acid. Add 10 ml. of sample to 20 ml. of 70 per cent sulfuric acid. Shake and read against a reagent blank.

Alternatively dilute a chloride-free sample containing 0.01 mg. of glucose to 3 ml. Add 6 ml. of concentrated sulfuric acid slowly with stirring and plunge in boiling water for 3 minutes. Cool quickly and read against a blank.

By a-naphthol. Add to 10 ml. of sample, 0.5 ml. of 20 per cent solution of α-naphthol in ethanol. Shake and add 5 ml. of concentrated sulfuric acid carefully. Cool after 3 minutes and read at 570 mμ against a reagent blank.

By anthrone. Mix 5 ml. of sample with 10 ml. of 0.2 per cent anthrone in 95 per cent sulfuric acid by adding the latter from a buret. After 15 minutes read at 620 mμ against a reagent blank.

By caramelization. Flour. Make a thin paste of 10 grams of flour and 50 ml. of water at 29° and allow to stand at 29° for 1 hour with frequent shaking. Filter this mixture and collect about half as filtrate. Refilter this portion on the same filter. Shake the filtrate and to a 15-ml. aliquot add 5 ml. of 4 per cent sodium hydroxide solution. Keep in boiling water for 5 minutes, cool for 5 minutes, and read against a blank.

By diphenylamine. Flour. Wet a 5-gram sample with 10 ml. of water and add 40 ml. more of water. Keep a 28° for 1 hour with frequent stirring and filter. Add 1 ml. of 1:3 hydrochloric acid to 10 ml. of filtrate and heat in boiling water for 5 minutes. Filter out proteins.

As reagent dissolve 0.1 gram of diphenylamine in 4 ml. of 95 per cent ethanol and dilute to 10 ml. with 1:3 hydrochloric acid. To 11 ml. of sample solution add 2 ml. of this reagent and heat in boiling water for 5 minutes. Cool and read.

By triphenyltetrazolium chloride. Adjust a 10-ml. sample containing 1.5-19 mg. of glucose to 25°. Add 10 ml. of 4 per cent sodium hydroxide solution and mix. After 6 minutes at 25° add 2 ml. of a 0.5 per cent aqueous solution of 2,3,5-triphenyltetrazolium chloride and maintain at 25° for exactly 30 minutes. Add 10 ml. of pyridine containing 15 ml. of concentrated hydrochloric acid per 100 ml. of the pyridine. Read at 490 mμ against a reagent blank.

By o-dinitrobenzene. Mix 1 volume of sample with 4 volumes of ethanol. Add successively 1.5 ml. of water, 2.5 ml. of ethanol, 0.5 ml. of 5 per cent sodium hydroxide solution, and 0.5 ml. of 1 per cent solution of o-dinitrobenzene in ethanol. Cover the sample loosely and heat at 100° for 2 minutes. Cool, dilute to 15 ml., and read at 640 mμ.

FRUCTOSE, LEVULOSE

Fructose is estimated by the cherry-red color produced with resorcinol and ferric ion in acid solution.[40] By alkaline hydrolysis, sucrose is esti-

---

[40] San-Yin Wong, *Lingnan Sci. J.* **8**, 619-23 (1929); A. Castiglioni, *Ann. chim. applicata* **22**, 570-4 (1932); Joseph H. Roe, *J. Biol. Chem.* **107**, 15-22 (1934).

mated from the fructose liberated. The method is accurate to ± 1 per cent. Glucose up to 3 mg. per ml. or galactose up to 5 mg. per ml. does not affect the color. Above that quantity corrections must be applied by development of a suitable correction curve. A green color is given by furfural and by 10 mg. of xylose per ml.

By proper control of conditions, levulose is determined in the presence of glucose by reduction of the phosphotungstate-phosphomolybdate reagent to molybdenum blue.[41] The total sugar present must be known as glucose gives some reduction. Results do not conform exactly to Beer's law.

In acid solutions fructose gives a blue color with ammonium molybdate.[42] This can be carried out in acetic acid solution but if a carbohydrate is present in substantial amount, gives high results. Nitric acid in such amount that carbohydrates or sucrose are not appreciably hydrolyzed avoids this. The estimation is satisfactory in the presence of 70-80 per cent as much d-glucose, 80-90 per cent as much galactose, 60-70 per cent as much mannose, 80-90 per cent as much arabinose, or 80-90 per cent as much of a mixture of these sugars. The determination can be made in the presence of 80 per cent as much of a mixture of glucose and sucrose.

Fructose gives a reddish purple color with sodium tauroglycocholate.[43] For 0.05-0.5 mg. per ml. of blood, the error is ±5 per cent.

Fructose and skatole react in warm hydrochloric acid to give a red color.[44] However, when diluted with water, the reaction is inhibited [45] and ethanol saturated with hydrogen chloride must be used instead of hydrochloric acid. Interfering colors are avoided by delaying the addition of the ethanol as diluent. Glucose gives less than 1.25 per cent as much color as fructose.

When fructose is heated with hydrochloric acid and diphenylamine, a blue color is produced.[46] The reaction is not specific as large concen-

[41] D. T. Englis and James W. Miles, *Anal. Chem.* **21**, 583-4 (1949).

[42] Leslie D. Scott, *J. Lab. Clin. Med.* **19**, 523-39 (1934).

[43] H. Bredereck, *Ber.* **64B**, 1730-2 (1931); Leslie D. Scott, *Biochem. J.* **29**, 1012-6 (1935).

[44] R. C. Jordan and J. Pryde, *Biochem. J.* **32**, 279-81 (1938).

[45] Roger M. Reinecke, *J. Biol. Chem.* **42**, 487-90 (1942).

[46] S. van Creveld, *Klin. Wochschr.* **6**, 697-8 (1927); Paul Radt, *Biochem. Z.* **198**, 195-203 (1928); Hermann Steinitz and Ilse von Riesen, *Ibid.* **252**, 201-4 (1932); Freda K. Herbert, *Biochem. J.* **32**, 815-19 (1938); A. C. Corcoran and Irvine H. Page, *J. Biol. Chem.* **127**, 606-8 (1939); Richard W. Martin, *Z. physiol. Chem.* **259**, 62-74 (1939); W. J. van Dorp, *Acta Brevia Klin. Wochschr.* **18**, 723-4 (1939); *Neerland. Physiol. Pharmacol., Microbiol.* **10**, 81-3 (1940).

trations of glucose, trichloroacetic acid, and several other materials give a blue or greenish blue color. The method is accurate to ±3 per cent.

Fructose gives a yellow color or a yellow precipitate with orcein in phosphoric acid solution, which changes to an orange solution on addition of alkali.[47] Glucose, maltose, lactose, galactose, and arabinose do not interfere. Sucrose is hydrolyzed by the phosphoric acid and does interfere. Substitution of sulfuric acid gives a cherry red with glucose, intense lemon-yellow with fructose, blue-red with galactose, and deep red with mannose.[48]

Fructose reduces selenites in acid solution to give a colloidal dispersion of selenium which separate readily.[49] The acid solution hydrolyzes sucrose of which the fructose then reacts. Fructose also reacts in alkaline solution, under which conditions glucose, maltose, galactose, and lactose also reduce the selenite.

Fructose or glucose are estimated in food products by heating with 2,4-dinitrophenolate and Rochelle salt.[50] The method is primarily applicable to solutions containing 1-10 per cent of fructose or glucose. rather than to very dilute solutions. Sucrose does not interfere. Fructose has exactly the same reducing value as glucose. While six minutes of heating is ample, this may be lengthened up to 25 minutes without affecting the results. No change in color occurs on standing for 20 minutes after the color is developed. The method is equally applicable to lactose. Results agree closely with the Munson and Walker method and are obtained much more quickly.

Fructose is read by the color developed with picric acid. Mannose, galactose, rhamnose, arabinose, maltose, lactose, xylose, and glucose interfere. The intensity of color is identical with that of a glucose or mannose standard. Details are given under manose (page 213).

When fructose is heated in solution with metabenzaminosemicarbazide, cryogenin, and hydrochloric acid, a bluish violet color is developed.[51] Glucose gives a reddish brown which can scarcely be detected unless the concentration is very high. A color is given by 1 per cent solutions of mannose, galactose, l-arabinose, l-lactose, d-ribose, maltose, lactose, and

[47] L. Loewe, *Proc. Soc. Exptl. Biol. Med.* **13**, 71-2 (1916).

[48] J. Brückner, *Z. physiol. Chem.* **277**, 181-91 (1943).

[49] Elizabeth Tornow, *Z. ges. Getreidew.* **27**, 42-5 (1940).

[50] Charles F. Poe and Frank G. Edson, *Ind. Eng. Chem., Anal. Ed.* **4**, 300-2 (1932).

[51] Kichinosuke Yamada, *Japan J. Med. Sci.* II, *Biochem.* **2**, 93-105 (1933); Hiro'o Okamura, *Ibid.* **3**, 9-14 (1935); *Ibid.* **4**, 11-13 (1938).

sucrose, but not by 1 per cent solutions of uric acid, creatinine, alanine, histidine, and urea. Fructose is also developed with phenylhydrazine.

The method of estimation of glucose by triphenyltetrazolium chloride (page 207) is equally applicable to fructose in the absence of gucose and lactose. The sample should contain 0.3-3 mg. of fructose.

Samples—*Solutions.* Dilute to a concentration of about 1 mg. per ml. and develop with resorcinol.

Blood. Mix 1 ml. of blood and 7 ml. of water. After a few minutes add 1 ml. of a 10 per cent solution of zinc sulfate heptahydrate. Mix and add 1 ml. of 2 per cent sodium hydroxide solution. Mix, filter, and develop with resorcinol.

For development with sodium taurocholate, dilute 5 ml. of whole blood with water to nearly 30 ml. Add 5 ml. of a 10 per cent zinc sulfate solution and 5 ml. of 2 per cent barium hydroxide solution. Mix well after each addition. Dilute to 40 ml. and mix. Place in a water bath at 80-85° for 5 minutes, making sure that the water in the bath completely covers the solution in the tube. Remove, cool in running water, and filter, stirring the gelatinous precipitate on the filter paper carefully, to free the last few ml. of solution.

For development with skatole, prepare a dilute tungstic acid solution by adding 2 ml. of 1:56 sulfuric acid and 2 ml. of 10 per cent sodium tungstate to 96 ml. of water with shaking. Add 0.05 ml. of blood to 5 ml. of the dilute tungstic acid and mix. Centrifuge after 15 minutes and decant.

For development with diphenylamine, add 1 ml. of defibrinated blood or serum to 1 ml. of 1:8 hydrochloric acid in a test tube. Add 2 ml. of 5 per cent mercuric chloride, shake thoroughly, and filter.

For development with cryogenin, mix 1 ml. of blood with 1 ml. of water and 0.5 ml. of a solution containing 12.8 grams of cadmium chloride, and 75 ml. of 1:2 hydrochloric acid per 100 ml. After a few minutes add 0.5 ml. of 16 per cent sodium hydroxide solution and mix. Let stand for 10 minutes and centrifuge. The supernatant liquid is perfectly clear and protein-free. If necessary, dilute the sample to fall in the range of 0.01-0.03 mg. of fructose per ml.

Urine. Add 1 per cent of acetic acid to a urine sample and decolorize with acid-washed activated carbon. Develop with resorcinol.

Food products. Ordinary sirups, jellies, jams, fruit juices, etc., need only be diluted to a fructose or glucose concentration in the desired range. The natural color does not interfere. With very high coloring matter any of the usual methods of removal of excess color are used. such as clarification with neutral lead acetate, alumina cream, fuller's earth, decolorizing carbon or dry basic lead acetate, without interfering with accuracy.

Procedure—*With resorcinol.* Mix 2 ml. of sample with 2 ml. of a 0.1 per cent solution of resorcinol in ethanol and 6 ml. of concentrated hydrochloric acid containing 0.75 mg. of ferric chloride per 100 ml. Heat in a water bath for 8 minutes at 80°. Cool and read at 480 mμ against a reagent blank.

By phosphotungstate-phosphomolybdate. Transfer a 15-ml. sample of solution containing 1-80 mg. of levulose to a 100-ml. flask. Add 5 ml. of the phosphotungstate-phosphomolybdate reagent (page 116) and, after 4 minutes, 10 ml. of 20 per cent trisodium phosphate dodecahydrate solution. Heat in boiling water for 10 minutes, cool, and dilute to volume with water. Read at 650 mμ against a reagent blank and obtain the results from a calibration curve. For this determine the total sugars as by copper reduction. Assume the reading is due to levulose and read from the curve. Subtract that value from the total sugars and apply a correction from a corresponding curve as if the balance were glucose.

By ammonium molybdate. To 1 ml. of the sample solution containing 3-50 mg. of fructose per ml. add 10 ml. of 4 per cent ammonium molybdate solution. Add 0.25 ml. of 1:3 nitric acid, stopper lightly, and heat for 2.5 minutes at 65°. Cool in ice water for 3 minutes and read against a reagent blank.

By sodium tauroglycocholate. Carefully boil 20 ml. of clear filtrate and 3 drops of 1 per cent acetic acid with a few silica chips until reduced to about 1.5 ml. Add 3 ml. of a 2.25 per cent solution of sodium tauroglycocholate in ethanol. Add 7 to 10 ml. of absolute ethanol and evaporate to dryness on a water bath. Leave the tube in the water bath for a minute or two after evaporation is complete, to make sure that the last traces of ethanol are driven off.

Remove, cool, and add 10 ml. of concentrated hydrochloric acid. Mix well and stopper securely. Place in a water bath at 40° for one-half hour with occasional shaking. Cool in running water, filter, discarding the first 2 or 3 ml. which is usually slightly cloudy, and read against a reagent blank.

By skatole. Prepare ethanolic hydrogen chloride by bubbling hydrogen chloride through iced 95 per cent ethanol until it is 10 N. Add 4 ml. of this to 2 ml. of the sample, cover, and heat for 30 minutes at 60°.

Place in cold water for 3 minutes and add 0.1 ml. of 1 per cent skatole in ethanol. After 5 minutes dilute to 10 ml. with ethanol and 10 minutes later read at 520 mμ against a reagent blank.

By diphenylamine. As reagent dissolve 1 gram of diphenylamine in 100 ml. of a 6:4 mixture of ethanol and concentrated hydrochloric acid. Add 1 ml. of sample to 3 ml. of reagent, heat in boiling water for 15 minutes, and cool. Dilute to an appropriate volume with ethanol and read at 610 mμ against a reagent blank.

By orcein. To 1 ml. of sample add 0.4 ml. of a 0.2 per cent aqueous solution of orcein, and 1 ml. of 85 per cent phosphoric acid. Heat to boiling over a free flame, then heat in boiling water for 10 minutes. Dilute to 10 ml. with 20 per cent sodium hydroxide solution and read while still warm.

By sodium biselenite. Mix 5 ml. of sample solution containing 0.01-0.25 per cent of fructose with 4 ml. of a 1 per cent sodium biselenite solution and 1 ml. of 1:3 hydrochloric acid. Place in boiling water for 5 minutes and cool in cold water for 0.5 minute. Read the colloidal dispersion of selenium at once.

By 2,4-dinitrophenolate. As reagent, dissolve 8 grams of sodium, 2,4-dinitrophenolate and 2.5 grams of phenol in 200 ml. of 5 per cent sodium hydroxide solution. Dissolve 100 grams of sodium potassium tartrate in 700 of water. Mix the two solutions and dilute to 1 liter.

Mix 1 ml. of sample solution with 3 ml. of the reagent and heat in boiling water for 6 minutes. Cool for 3 minutes in running water and read within 20 minutes against a reagent blank. All reducing sugars are determined in terms of fructose.

By cryogenin. Mix 1 ml. of protein-free sample and 1 ml. of a solution of 2 per cent solution of cryogenin in 2:1 hydrochloric acid. This reagent keeps only a few days. Add a drop or two of a 0.1 per cent solution of ferric sulfate in 10 per cent sodium chloride solution. Mix and heat in a boiling water bath for exactly 15 minutes. Cool quickly and read at once against a reagent blank. To report the glucose subtract the value for fructose from that for total glucose and fructose by the ferricyanide method (page 204), as determined on another portion of the filtrate from the sample.

MANNOSE

Mannose is an aldehyde hexose read by the color developed with picric acid.[52] Fructose, galactose, rhamnose, arabinose, xylose, maltose,

---

[52] R. Okey, *J. Biol. Chem.* **38**, 33-42 (1919); J. J. Wilaman and F. R. Davison, *J. Agr. Research* **28**, 479-88 (1924).

lactose, and glucose interfere. The intensity of color is identical with that of a glucose standard. Salts increase the color developed.

Procedure—Mix 1 ml. of sample solution containing 0.2-3 mg. of the sugar with 2 ml. of a saturated aqueous solution of picric acid and 1 ml. of a 20 per cent solution of sodium carbonate. Stopper lightly with a tinfoil-covered stopper and heat in boiling water for 30 minutes. When cool, dilute to 10 ml. and read against a reagent blank. It is convenient to read in terms of a glucose curve. Results on mixed sugars are only approximate as some give different intensities of color with the reagent.

GALACTOSE

Galactose is an aldehyde hexose read by the color developed with picric acid. Mannose, rhamnose, arabinose, maltose, lactose, xylose, and glucose interfere. The concentration read in terms of either glucose or mannose is multiplied by 1.132 to get the value. Details are given under mannose.

Galactose reduces sodium biselenite and can be read as the colloidal dispersion of selenium. Details are given under maltose (page 217).

d-ALTRO-*d*-FRUCTOHEPTOSE, SEDOHEPTULOSE

Sedoheptulose is a naturally occurring heptose found in many plants. The stable bluish-green color which the compound gives with a hydrochloric acid solution of orcinol and ferric chloride [53] is used for its determination, after extraction with amyl alcohol.[54] Free pentoses, uronic acids, and large quantities of hexoses interfere. The method is accurate to about ±2 per cent.

Sample—*Plant material.* Centrifuge 0.05-0.2 gram of fresh plant material containing 1-2 per cent of sedoheptulose for a half-minute with 2-4 ml. of chloroform. Transfer to a mortar and allow the chloroform to evaporate at room temperature. Triturate the plant material with 1 gram of quartz sand until finely comminuted. Add water in small portions and centrifuge for 10-15 minutes. Decant by suction through an asbestos mat. Stir the plant material with water, again centrifuge for 10-15 minutes, and filter. Repeat once more. Wash to a total volume of 40-45 ml. and dilute to 50 ml.

---

[53] M. Bial, *Deutsch. med. Wochenschr.* 28, 253 (1902); *Ibid.* 29, 477 (1903).
[54] Arnold Nordal and Rolf Klevstrand, *Anal. Chim. Acta* 4, 411-21 (1950).

Procedure—Prepare the reagent by dissolving 1 gram of orcinol and 0.08 ml. of 15 per cent ferric chloride solubilized with hydrochloric acid in 5 ml. of concentrated hydrochloric acid. Dilute to 500 ml. with concentrated hydrochloric acid. To 1 ml. of sample solution containing 0.01-0.05 mg. of sedoheptulose, add 2 ml. of orcinol-hydrochloric acid reagent.

Boil the solution of sample and reagent in a water bath, for exactly 15 minutes. Cool under running water for 60 seconds and add 5 ml. of furfural-free amyl alcohol. Add 10 ml. of water and shake. After separation of the layers, filter the amyl alcohol extract. Read against a blank at 610 mμ.

FERMENTABLE SUGARS

Fermentable sugars are determined by the reducing sugars with and without fermentation.[55]

Procedure—*Plasma or serum*. Mix 1 ml. with 1 ml. of water and add 1 ml. of 2 per cent yeast emulsion. Incubate at 32° for 18 hours and centrifuge. Mix 1 ml. with 3.5 ml. of water and add 0.5 ml. of 44:56 sulfuric acid. Autoclave at 120 pounds pressure for 30 minutes. When cool, neutralize with 2 per cent sodium hydroxide solution. Add 1.5 ml. of 10 per cent sodium tungstate solution and 1.5 ml. of 1:56 sulfuric acid. Dilute to 10 ml. and filter as a sample for determination of reducing sugars. Subtract the value from total sugars as separately determined.

---

55 Reishi Ohta, *J. Biochem.* (Japan) **25**, 1-9 (1937).

CHAPTER 9

POLYSACCHARIDES [1]

The polysaccharides on hydrolysis yield glucose or fructose. Therefore, when they can be separated from pentoses and hexoses they are often hydrolyzed and determined by usual methods for hexoses. The reaction with anthrone in sulfuric acid is often used. Others have specific reactions such as that of alkali and methylamine with a 1,4-glucosidic linkage.

SUCROSE

Small amounts of sucrose are estimated by the blue color with anthrone in strong sulfuric acid.[2] Accuracy to ±2 per cent is obtainable. Typical samples are those of the sugar factory containing about 0.2 mg. of sucrose per ml. Greater permanence of the reagent is attained by not predissolving in sulfuric acid.

It is also hydrolyzed with acid and read with orcinol.[3] The alkaline picrate reaction applies after hydrolysis. An alternative is to estimate the fructose with resorcinol after hydrolysis.

Procedure—*By anthrone.* To 2 ml. of sample solution, containing the equivalent of less than 40 mg. of glucose per ml., add 0.5 ml. of 2 per cent anthrone in ethyl acetate. Carefully layer 5 ml. of concentrated sulfuric acid below this. Swirl gently until the anthrone dissolves indicating hydrolysis of the ethyl acetate. Swirl more vigorously to mix thoroughly. Read after 10 minutes at 620 mμ against water and correct for a reagent blank.

By orcinol. To 1 ml. of sample solution add 10 ml. of a 2 per cent solution of orcinol in 66 per cent sulfuric acid. Heat in boiling water for 12 minutes, cool, and dilute to 50 ml. with water. Read against a reagent blank.

---

[1] See Chapter 1 for details of organization, condensation, etc.

[2] E. E. Morse, *Ind. Eng. Chem., Anal. Ed.* **19**, 1012-13 (1947); D. L. Morris, *Science* **107**, 254-8 (1948); Frederick J. Viles, Jr., and Leslie Silverman, *Anal. Chem.* **21**, 950-3 (1949); Frank A. Loewns, *Ibid.* **24**, 219 (1952).

[3] J. Tillmans and K. Philippi, *Biochem. Z.* **215**, 36-60 (1929).

By picrate. *Sucrose solution.* Saturate with basic lead acetate. Filter and delead with a slight excess of disodium phosphate. Mix 2 ml. of a saturated aqueous solution of picric acid and 1 ml. of sample containing about 0.08 mg. of sucrose per ml. Heat in boiling water for 10 minutes to complete inversion of the sucrose. Read as the alkaline pictrate. If gluclose is also present, determine without inversion and subtract to get the value for sucrose.

By resorcinol. Dilute to 2 mg. of sucrose per ml. or less. Heat 5 ml. of the diluted sample in 5 ml. of 20 per cent sodium hydroxide solution in boiling water for 10 minutes. Add saturated bromine-water until any color is removed. Heat again for 1 minute and if color returns again remove it with bromine-water. When the color has been completely removed, add 2 ml. of a 5 per cent solution of urea to destroy hypobromite. Cool, add a few drops of phenolphthalein solution and neutralize with 1:1 hydrochloric acid. Dilute to 25 ml. and mix well.

Determine fructose in 2 ml. of this solution by the method described for fructose (page 211) which includes any free fructose originally present as well as that from hydrolysis of sucrose. Also determine free fructose on the original solution. The total fructose less the free fructose gives the combined fructose. Multiply the result obtained for combined fructose by 2 to get the sucrose content.

MALTOSE

The production of molybdenum blue (Vol. II, pp. 660-668) has been used for estimation of glucose.[4] As modified it is applicable to maltose alone or in mixture with glucose.[5] The color before hydrolysis is that due to glucose and after hydrolysis is the original glucose plus that due to hydrolysis of the maltose. Naturally, this requires no color from maltose before hydrolysis and no destruction of glucose during hydrolysis of the maltose. Before the hydrolysis sucrose does not interfere but maltose does show some color. Correction must be applied. After hydrolysis of maltose the glucose approximates 100 per cent. Unduly high acid concentration causes destruction of glucose. Partially hydrolyzed starch such as dextrines must be removed prior to the determination. Partial reduction of Fehling solution is also applicable.[6]

---

[4] G. Harvey Benham and J. E. Despaul, *Anal. Chem.* **20**, 933-5 (1948).

[5] G. Harvey Benham and Virginia E. Petzing, *Ibid.* **21**, 991-3 (1949).

[6] Erich Thomae, *Suddeut. Apoth.-Ztg.* **86**, No. 2, 39-40 (1946).

Another difference method consists of determination of glucose and maltose with ammonium phosphomolybdate and the reducing sugars alone with 3,5-dinitrosalicylic acid.[7]

Maltose reduces sodium biselenide to selenium in alkaline solution. The colloidal selenium is readable as a measure of the maltose content.[8] The same reaction is given by glucose, fructose, or galactose. Each may be determined or, since their intensities are similar, the total sugar present. Lactose interferes.

The reactions by reduction of ferricyanide, discussed in detail under glucose apply to maltose.[9] Caramelization of maltose by heat and dilute alkali is also applicable.[10]

Procedure—*By ammonium molybdate.* Dilute a 0.5-gram sample of glucose and maltose to 100 ml. Dilute 50 ml. of this to 100 ml. as the unhydrolyzed sample. Mix 2 ml. of this with 5 ml. of 2.72 per cent potassium dihydrogen phosphate solution and 10 ml. of 7.5 per cent ammonium molybdate solution. Dilute to 25 ml. and heat in an autoclave at 100° for exactly 30 minutes to develop the color. Cool, dilute to 25 ml., and read at 650 mμ. For the direct reading hydrolyze the remaining 50 ml. of the sample solution with 3 ml. of 1:2 hydrochloric acid at 15 pounds pressure for 1 hour. Cool, neutralize with 0.4 per cent sodium hydroxide to methyl red, and dilute to 100 ml. Treat this for development of color starting at "Mix 2 ml. of this with 5 ml. . . ." The indicator does not interfere. This is reading A.

Then with maltose = M

$$A - B = 0.0743 M + 0.00088$$

And with glucose = G

$$A = 0.0840 (G + M) - 0.0245$$

By sodium biselenite. Mix 5 ml. of sample solution containing 0.01-0.25 per cent of maltose with 5 ml. of 5 per cent sodium hydroxide solution. Add 2 ml. of 1 per cent sodium biselenite solution. Heat in boiling water for 5 minutes and cool for 0.5 minute under the tap. Read against a reagent blank.

---

[7] H. Rüggeberg, *Mikrochemie ver. Mikrochim. Acta* **36/37**, 916-23 (1951).

[8] Elizabeth Tornow, *Z. ges. Getreidew.* **27**, 42-5 (1940); *Ibid.* **28**, 132-7 (1941).

[9] R. M. Sandstedt, *Cereal Chem.* **14**, 603-4 (1937); *Ibid.* 767-8 (1937).

[10] E. A. Schmidt, *Mehl u. Brot.* **38**, No. 20, 1-3 (1938).

Lactose gives a color reaction with alkali and methylamine at a 1,4-glucosidic linkage.[11] Results correspond to Beer's law over the range 0.25-3 mg. Interference is given by monosaccharides, cellobiose, sugar phosphates, calcium, and barium.

Lactose on hydrolysis is estimated by molybdenum blue [12] as described in detail under glucose (page 204). Lactose gives a red-brown color on heating with potassium hydroxide. The method is reasonably accurate as applied to fat- and protein-free serum. Other sugar reaction which it gives are with picric acid, sodium 2,4-dinitrophenolate, and that with sulfuric acid. These methods are usually unsatisfactory for lactose determination in complex mixtures.[13]

The method of estimation of glucose by triphenyltetrazolium chloride (page 207) is equally applicable to lactose in the absence of glucose and fructose. For lactose the sample should contain 3-30 mg. of the sugar.

Procedure—*By methylamine.* As reagent mix 2 volumes of 1.6 per cent methylamine solution and 1 volume of 21.6 per cent sodium hydroxide solution. Mix a sample with 0.3 ml. of reagent, dilute to 5 ml., and close loosely with a stopper carrying a capillary. Bubble nitrogen through, first purifying by passing over hot copper. After 10-15 minutes, stop the passage of gas, withdraw the capillary to above the liquid, seat the stopper and close with a clamp. Incubate at 55° for 30 ± 0.5 minutes and cool in tap water. Read at 540 mμ at 2-15 minutes.

By potassium hydroxide. Milk serum. Heat 3 ml. of fat- and protein-free milk serum (page 202) with 3 ml. of a 5 per cent potassium hydroxide solution for 1 minute in boiling water. Cool to 15° and read against a blank of unheated milk serum.

Inulin is a somewhat starchy carbohydrate which is probably a trihexose. When hydrolyzed with acid, it gives only fructose. Hydrolysis by concentrated hydrochloric acid is complete in 8 minutes at 80°.[14]

---

11 W. R. Fearon, *Analyst* **67**, 130-2 (1942); F. H. Malpress and A. B. Morrison, *Biochem. J.* **45**, 455-9 (1949).

12 Paul B. Larsen and I. A. Gould, *J. Dairy Sci.* **34**, 16-20 (1951).

13 S. J. Foley, *Biol. Rev.* **24**, 332 (1949); F. H. Malpress and A. B. Morrison, *Biochem. J.* **46**, 307-12 (1950).

14 Kurt Steinitz, *J. Biol. Chem.* **126**, 589-93 (1938).

It follows that after hydrolysis substantially all of the methods for fructose will apply if glucose is not present from other sources. Thus it is determined with resorcinol and ferric ion,[15] with resorcinol and thiourea,[16] with diphenylamine, [17] and even by the somewhat classical ferricyanide methods after hydrolysis. The reorcinol-thiourea reaction is reproducible to ±4.2 per cent. The diphenylamine reagent is more sensitive if in acetic acid solution.[18]

The reaction of inulin with skatole [19] has been applied to fructose [20] and to that produced by hydrolysis of inulin.[21] Results are reproducible with an accuracy of ±1.7 per cent.

Since inulin is not fermentable, a method of estimation in the presence of glucose is to ferment out the latter, then proceed to hydrolyze the inulin. Another is to determine glucose by ferricyanide, and inulin plus glucose by another method.[22]

Sample—*Urine*. Use a trichloroacetic acid filtrate. Develop with resorcinol and ferric ion.

Alternatively mix 1 ml. of urine with 5 ml. of water. Add 2 ml. of 10 per cent zinc sulfate septahydrate solution and 2 ml. of 2 per cent sodium hydroxide solution. Filter and develop an aliquot with thiourea and resorcinol.

For development with diphenylamine dissolve as reagent 3.467 grams of hydrated cadmium sulfate in water, add 17 ml. of 1:35 sulfuric acid, and dilute to 100 ml. Mix 1 ml. of sample, 2 ml. of reagent, and 4 ml. of 4 per cent sodium hydroxide solution. Shake for a few seconds and

[15] B. Hatz and L. Szeczenyl-Nagy, *Biochem. Z.* **306**, 71-3 (1940) ; Acme Higashi and Laurence Peters, *J. Lab. Clin. Med.* **35**, 475-82 (1950).

[16] Joseph H. Roe, Jerome H. Epstein, and Norman P. Goldstein, *J. Biol. Chem.* **178**, 839-45 (1949) ; George Ross and Ruben Mokotoff, *J. Biol. Chem.* **190**, 659-63 (1951).

[17] Alf. S. Alving, Jack Rubin, and Benjamin F. Miller, *J. Biol. Chem.* **127**, 609-16 (1939) ; A. C. Corcoran and Irvine H. Page, *Ibid.* **127**, 601-6 (1939) ; Alf S. Alving, Jack Flox, Isidore Pitesky, and Benjamin F. Miller, *J. Lab. Clin. Med.* **27**, 115-18 (1941) ; M. Gukelberger and E. Sanz, *Z. ges, exptl. Med.* **110**, 97-103 (1942) ; Kaj Røjel, *Acta Med. Scand.* **112**, 338-52 (1942) ; J. Maxwell Little, *J. Biol. Chem.* **180**, 747-54 (1949) ; Ejgil Bojesen, *Acta Med. Scand.* **142**, Suppl. 266, 275, 82 (1952).

[18] Harold E. Harrison, *Proc. Soc. Exptl. Biol. Med.* **49**, 111-14 (1942).

[19] R. C. Jordan and J. Pryde, *Biochem. J.* **32**, 279-81 (1938).

[20] R. M. Reinecke, *J. Biol. Chem.* **142**, 487-90 (1942).

[21] Helen Ranney and D. J. McCune, *J. Biol. Chem.* **150**, 311-13 (1943).

[22] P. Krubhøffer, *Acta Physiol. Scand.* **1**, 1-15 (1946).

occasionally for 10 minutes. Centrifuge and filter through cotton. Mix 4 ml. with 1 ml. of 16 per cent sodium hydroxide solution. Stopper loosely, heat in boiling water for 10 minutes, and cool.

Plasma. Mix 1 ml. of heparinized plasma with 15 ml. of water. Complete as for the second method for urine from "Add 2 ml. of 10 per cent . . . ." Alternatively use the third method for urine.

Blood. Mix 0.5 ml. of blood, 1 ml. of water, and 0.5 ml. of 10 per cent zinc sulfate septahydrate solution. Add 0.5 ml. of 2 per cent sodium hydroxide solution, mix, and filter. Develop with diphenylamine.

Tissue. Heat 0.5-2 grams of fresh tissue containing about 0.15-0.4 mg. of inulin per gram with 6 ml. of 3.4 per cent sodium hydroxide solution in boiling water for about 15 minutes with occasional stirring. Cool to room temperature, add about 2 ml. of 1:4 hydrochloric acid, and complete neutralization with 1:20 hydrochloric acid. Use litmus as an outside indicator. Add 10 ml. of 10 per cent zinc sulfate and 10 ml. of 2 per cent sodium hydroxide solution and dilute to 50 ml. Stopper, shake thoroughly, and allow to stand about 15 minutes. Filter and develop an aliquot of filtrate with resorcinol.

As the blank treat the same size sample with 6 ml. of 3.4 per cent sodium hydroxide and 3 ml. of 1:1 hydrochloric acid. Heat for 30 minutes and add 6.5 ml. of 16 per cent sodium hydroxide solution. Stir and heat 15 minutes longer. Cool and add 3 ml. of 1:1 hydrochloric acid. Continue as the sample from ". . . and complete neutralization with 1:20 hydrochloric acid."

Procedure—*With resorcinol and ferric ion.* Follow the procedure for fructose (page 211).

With resorcinol and thiourea. To 3 ml. of clear sample add 1 ml. of a reagent containing 0.1 per cent of resorcinol and 0.25 per cent of thiourea in glacial acetic acid. Add 6 ml. of concentrated hydrochloric acid. Heat at 80° for 10 minutes. Cool to room temperature under running water for two minutes in the dark and allow to stand for another 3 minutes in the dark. Read at 520 mμ against a blank prepared from the same sample.

With diphenylamine. As concentrated reagent prepare 20 per cent diphenylamine in absolute ethanol. Mix 7:5 absolute ethanol-concentrated hydrochloric acid. As fresh reagent mix 1 ml. of the diphenylamine solution with 16 ml. of the solvent. Shake 5 ml. of this reagent with 0.5 ml. of sample solution. Heat in boiling water for 30 minutes. Cool and read at 610 mμ against a reagent blank.

By skatole. Mix 2 ml. of the clear sample with 4 ml. of 95 per cent ethanol saturated with hydrogen chloride. Heat at 60° for 30 minutes and cool. Dilute to 10 ml. with ethanol and add 0.1 ml. of 1 per cent skatole solution in ethanol. After 5-7 minutes dilute to 10 ml. with ethanol. Heat 1 minute at 60° and read at 520 mμ 10-15 minutes later against a reagent blank.

PECTIN

Pectin is a polygalacturonic acid ester. Methods for its determination depend on its being broken down to a simpler structure. One method is by the reaction of hexuronic acids with carbazole.[23] Sugars react weakly, and practically do not interfere. Alcohol of high purity is essential, usually obtained by refluxing with zinc and sulfuric acid and distillation from zinc and potassium hydroxide.

Another method is to decompose to furfural by steam distillation from strongly acid solution.[24] This is then reacted with aniline and acetic acid or one of the analogous reagent combinations.

Sample—*Cotton.* Grind to pass a 20-mesh screen. Extract a 1.5-gram sample in a Soxhlet overnight with ethanol to dewax. Extract briefly with ether to remove the alcohol, and air-dry. Heat in boiling water with 50 ml. of 1:400 hydrochloric acid for 15 minutes, stirring occasionally. Centrifuge and decant the sample extract. Extract successively with 50 ml. of each of the following, but heat for only 10 minutes each: Water, twice with 0.4 per cent sodium hydroxide solution, three times with water. Add 1.75 ml. of 60 per cent acetic acid to the combined extracts and dilute to 500 ml. Filter through paper, discarding the first 50 ml., and determine with carbazole.

Urine. To 2 ml. add 20 ml. of ethanol. Centrifuge after an hour, and decant. Dry the residue at 100° until alcohol is absent, usually 30 minutes. The residue is dissolved in the method for conversion to furfural.

Blood. Mix 2 ml. of blood with 13 ml. of water and add 2 ml. of 10 per cent sodium tungstate solution. Mix and add 3 ml. of 1:70 sulfuric acid. Centrifuge after 15 minutes and use 2 ml. of the clear upper layer for development as furfural.

---

[23] S. M. Stark, Jr., *Anal. Chem.* **22**, 1158-60 (1950); Elizabeth A. McComb and R. M. McCready, *Anal. Chem.* **24**, 1630-2 (1952).

[24] C. Griebel and H. Zeglin, *Z. Untersuch. Lebensm.* **74**, 16-21 (1937); Edwin F. Bryant, Grant H. Palmer, and Glen H. Joseph, *Ind. Eng. Chem., Anal. Ed.* **16**, 74-6 (1944).

Animal tissue. To 10 grams of macerated sample add 100 ml. of water and homogenize in a blendor. Dilute an aliquot equivalent to 0.5 gram of original sample to 15 ml. with water. Mix with 2 ml. of 10 per cent sodium tungstate solution, then add 3 ml. of 1:70 sulfuric acid. Mix and after 15 minutes and centrifuge. Develop 2-ml. portions of centrifuge as furfural.

Procedure—*By carbazole.* To 2 ml. of sample immersed in ice-water add 12 ml. of concentrated sulfuric acid slowly and carefully. Heat in boiling water for 20 minutes and cool to room temperature. Add 1 ml. of 0.1 per cent carbazole in absolute ethanol. After 2 hours read at 520 mμ against a blank in which the added ethanol contained no carbazole.

As furfural. Add 5 ml. of 85 per cent phosphoric acid to the sample. Heat to 170-175° and steam-distil collecting 40 ml. of distillate. Test the next 10 ml. of distillate to be sure the furfural is all in the first 40 ml. If positive, this can be used in the determination.

To 20 ml. of the first distillate and 5 ml. of each successive 10-ml. distillate which was positive add 0.5 ml. of aniline and 4.5 ml. of glacial acetic acid. Store in the dark at 20-25° for 15 minutes and read at 500-520 mμ against a water blank.

DEXTRAN

Dextran is a neutral polyglucide prepared from sugar beet juice. It yields only glucose units on hydrolysis. After precipitation with a copper reagent the excess copper is determined by diethyldithiocarbamate.[25]

Sample—*Blood.* Dilute 0.2 ml. to 5 ml. with water and deproteinize with 5 ml. of 10 per cent trichloroacetic acid. Shake, heat at 70-80° for 5 minutes, and filter.

Procedure—As copper reagent prepare a solution containing 3 per cent of sodium citrate and 0.3 per cent of copper sulfate pentahydrate. Just before use dilute 3 ml. to 100 ml. Mix 2 ml. of 10 per cent sodium hydroxide solution, 5 ml. of deproteinized sample, and 2 ml. of reagent. Shake mechanically for 4 hours and centrifuge thoroughly. Remove 6 ml. of clear solution from the blue precipitate and add to about 75 ml. of water. Add 3 ml. of 0.2 per cent aqueous sodium diethyl dithiocar-

---

25 H. C. Hint and G. Thorsén, *Acta. Chem. Scand.* 1, 808-12 (1947).

bamate and mix. Dilute to 100 ml. and read at 470 mμ against a reagent blank.

GLYCOGEN

The red-brown color developed with the animal starch, glycogen, by iodine is used for its colorimetric estimation.[26] This color intensity varies with temperature, concentration of iodine, and source of glycogen. The glycogen is often precipitated with ethanol for separation from interfering substances. An alternative is to hydrolyze to glucose and determine.[27] The color with diphenylamine can also be used to estimate glycogen.[28]

Other methods of estimation are turbidimetrically [29] or nephelometrically.[30] There is no effect of considerable variation in pH. Electrolytes promote dispersion.

Sample—*Liver.* Shake 10 grams of finely ground sample with 25 grams of 60 per cent aqueous potassium hydroxide mechanically for 45-50 minutes. Dilute with water so that 1 ml. is equivalent to 0.1 gram of liver. Cook and filter. Mix 2 ml. of filtrate, 0.5 gram of potassium iodide, about 7 ml. of ethanol, and a few drops of phenolphthalein indicator solution. Add 1:1 hydrochloric acid dropwise until the indicator is decolorized. Centrifuge to throw down the precipitate and decant the supernatant liquid to waste. Wash the precipitate with 5 and 5 ml. of 66 per cent ethanol. Dissolve the precipitate in 5 ml. of warm water as sample for development with iodine.

Uterine mucosa. Digest a 0.125-gram sample with 0.15 ml. of 60 per cent potassium hydroxide solution and heat for 1 hour in boiling water. Add 0.3 ml. of water and 0.7 ml. of ethanol. Heat, centrifuge, and decant the supernatant layer. Wash with 2 ml. of 70 per cent ethanol, then with 2 ml. of 95 per cent ethanol. Dissolve the precipitate in 1 ml. of warm water. Add 3 drops of 1.27 per cent iodine in 2.5 per cent aqueous potassium iodide.

[26] Charles Jung, *Compt. rend. soc. phys. hist. nat.* Genève **58**, 137-40 (1940); Bernhard Zondek and Benjamin Shapiro, *Am. J. Obstet. Gynecol.* **44**, 345-7 (1942); Willem J. Van Wagtendonk, Donald K. Simonsen, and Patricia L. Hackett, *J. Biol. Chem.* **163**, 301-6 (1946); Daniel L. Morris, *Ibid.* **166**, 199-203 (1946).

[27] John P. Tully, *Analyst* **63**, 93-8 (1938).

[28] Edward G. Boettiger, *J. Cellular. Comp. Physiol.* **27**, 1-8 (1946).

[29] Tadeusz Korzbski, *Med. Dóswiadczalna i Mikrobiol.* **1**, 273-84 (1949).

[30] R. G. Hansen, W. J. Rutter, and E. M. Craine, *J. Biol. Chem.* **196**, 127-32 (1952).

Oysters. Digest 20 grams with 50 ml. of hot 60 per cent potassium hydroxide solution for 3 hours with frequent stirring. Cool, dilute to 100 ml., and filter. Add 80 ml. of ethanol to 50 ml. of filtrate. Stir and heat to boiling. Decant the supernatant liquid to waste. Dissolve the precipitate in 50 ml. of boiling water and reprecipitate as before. Dissolve the purified glycogen in hot water and dilute to 100 ml. Add 10 ml. of concentrated hydrochloric acid and digest for 3 hours on a steam bath. Cool, add phenolphthalein indicator, and make just alkaline with 60 per cent potassium hydroxide solution. Filter, wash the paper with boiling water, and dilute to 250 ml. Determine glucose on an aliquot (pages 204 to 207).

Tissue. Add 0.1 gram of tissue to 0.5 ml. of 30 per cent aqueous potassium hydroxide and add 0.8 ml. of a 1:7 mixture of 2 per cent sodium chloride solution and 95 per cent ethanol. Mix gently and heat in boiling water until bubbles appear. Refrigerate at least 3 hours to complete precipitation of polysaccharides. Centrifuge and drain. Take up the precipitate in 2 ml. of water, mix, and centrifuge. Develop an aliquot of the solution turbidimetrically.

Procedure—*By iodine.* To 5 ml. of sample solution add a drop of 5 per cent iodine in 10 per cent aqueous potassium iodide. Read at 470 mμ against a reagent blank.

By diphenylamine. As reagent dissolve 3 grams of diphenylamine in 100 ml. of glacial acetic acid. Add 60 ml. of concentrated hydrochloric acid and mix well. To 2 ml. of sample solution containing 0.005-0.08 mg. of glycogen add 5 ml. of reagent and heat in boiling water for 40 minutes. Cool and read at 635 mμ.

Nephelometrically. Dilute an aliquot containing up to 0.5 mg. of glycogen to 2 ml. with water and add 5 ml. of a reagent containing 70 ml. of 95 per cent ethanol, 10 ml. of 2 per cent sodium chloride solution, and 10 ml. of 1 per cent solution of Dreft (40 per cent sodium lauryl sulfate and 60 per cent sodium sulfate) diluted to 100 ml. Mix and after 15 minutes read in a spectrophotometer at 660 mμ, or in a nephelometer.

TOTAL SUGARS

The preparation of samples of plant tissue and plant juice for direct reading with ferricyanide is also appropriate for total sugars.

Sample—Use that prepared for glucose determination (pages 203-4).

Procedure—Determine the amount of dilute acetic acid necessary to neutralize 50 ml. to methyl red. Add it to 50 ml. of clarified sample. Add 2-4 drops of 1 per cent solution of Wallerstein's invertase and let stand overnight at room temperature. Dilute to volume and follow the procedure for reducing sugars (pages 204 to 207). Subtract a blank determined on the invertase.

SACCHAROIDS

The estimation of glucose without interference by saccharoids is accomplished by phosphomolybdic acid in the presence of a copper reagent containing bisulfite.[31] By omission of the sodium bisulfite the saccharoids are included.

Procedure—Follow that given for glucose (page 204) but omit the addition of sodium bisulfite to the copper reagent. Also determine the glucose by that procedure. The difference between the two values is saccharoids in terms of glucose.

STARCH

The estimation of starch by its color with iodine is a logical colorimetric method and has been applied [32] spectrophotometrically.[33] Beer's law does not hold for ordinary solutions of starch-iodide. The composition of the blue pigment is not well-defined, the iodine content varying with that of the liquid with which it is in contact. When the liquid is very rich in iodine, the ratio of iodine to starch becomes fixed and Beer's law then holds. Temperatures up to 70° do not affect the color.

Variation in the ratio of amylose and amylopectin which makes up the starch, giving respectively strong blue and weak violet colors with

---

[31] Stanley R. Benedict, *J. Biol. Chem.* **92**, 141-59 (1931).

[32] M. Dennstedt and F. Voigtländer, *Forsch. Ber. Lebensm.* **2**, 173-6 (1895); Helen Q. Woodard, *Ind. Eng. Chem., Anal Ed.* **6**, 331-3 (1934); Ralph H. Müller and Mary Helen McKenna, *J. Am. Chem. Soc.* **58**, 1017-20 (1936).

[33] Charles S. Hanes and Margaret Cattle, *Proc. Roy. Soc.* (London) **B 125**, 387-414 (1938); L. E. Simerl and B. L. Browning, *Ind. Eng. Chem. Anal. Ed.* **11**, 125-8 (1939); Ralph W. Kerr and O. R. Trubell, *Paper Trade J.* **117**, No. 15, 25-8 (1943); R. M. McCready and W. Z. Hassid, *J. Am. Chem. Soc.* **65**, 1154-7 (1943); John P. Nielsen, *Ind. Eng. Chem., Anal. Ed.* **15**, 176-9 (1943); John P. Nielsen and Peggy C. Gleason, *Ibid.* **17**, 131-4 (1945); F. P. Niinivaara, J. Jonna, and J. Puranen, *Suomen Kemistilehti* **23B**, 1-3 (1950); Carroll L. Hoffpauir, *J. Assoc. Official Agr. Chem.* **32**, 291-5 (1949); *Ibid.* **33**, 810-15 (1950).

iodine causes variation in the color from starches from different sources. Fortunately, that ratio is constant for starch from a given source and in many plants is like that of the potato, 20 per cent amylose and 80 per cent amylopectin. There is wide variation by garden peas whose starch is about 75 per cent amylopectin and by waxy corn starch which is practically 100 per cent amylopectin. An alternative is to approximate from Ridgeway or Munsell color charts [34] the type and intensity of color. Excess iodide affects the color; small amounts greatly increase the sensitivity, large amounts shift the color toward violet.

The general method is probably more dependable than any other. Any procedure based on starch-iodide is dependent on strictly standardized methods of preparation of the starch solutions.

By further technic [35] one can purify the starch from interfering substances. Dilute alcohol extraction removes glucosides and alkaloids. Precipitation of the starch with iodine in the presence of calcium chloride eliminates a large group of polysaccharides. The final estimation of the precipitated starch by iodine eliminates substances which may have been precipitated by iodine or sorbed on the precipitate but which do not give a color with iodine. The method therefore defines starch as limited to the substances giving a color with iodine. The only interfering substances according to definition are some of the amylohemicelluloses occurring in seeds, fruits, leaves, and stem tissues. These give the color reaction but are not hydrolyzed by takadiastase. The method is accurate to 3 per cent on 1-3 mg.

Starch is solubilized with perchloric acid and determined by its reaction with iodine.[36] This method has been applied to determination of small amounts of starch on textiles. The use of iodine solution tends to produce a grey color which is overcome by using a calcium chloride solution as solvent. [37] Like the method in which calcium chloride is not used, this must be subdivided into a single treatment method and that using a double treatment for preliminary purification of the starch. Calcium chloride solution on long heating will destroy starch unless the pH

---

[34] Stanley A. Watson and Roy L. Whistler, *Ind. Eng. Chem., Anal. Ed.* **18**, 75-6 (1946).

[35] L. B. Mendel and Hubert B. Vickery, *Carnegie Inst. Washington Yearbook*, **34**, 298-306 (1935); George W. Pucher and Hubert B. Vickery, *Ind. Eng. Chem., Anal. Ed.* **8**, 92-7 (1936).

[36] R. L. McEven, *Am. Dyestuff Reptr.* **32**, 371-3 (1943).

[37] H. Weiss, *Z. ges. Brauw.* **45**, 122-4 (1922); Hanna Eckart, *Chem. Zelle Gewebe* **12**, 243-7 (1925).

is maintained above 6. This is conveniently provided by addition of magnesium oxide.

Another modification [38] after development of the starch-iodine complex from hydriodic acid and hydrogen peroxide is to extract excess iodine with chloroform before matching. Starch is estimated in the presence of considerable glycogen as starch-iodide complex at 750 mμ [39] with accuracy to ± 1 per cent. The accuracy of determination of starch with iodine is improved by specific information as to the type of starch.[40]

Starch is hydrolyzed to glucose by enzyme action and the glucose estimated by its reaction with picric acid.[41] This can be reported as starch without serious error. The absence of sugars from the original sample is essential. Substances other than starch in complex samples may be hydrolyzed by the enzyme and introduce error. Thus pectin yields glucose on hydrolysis. An alternative is to hydrolyze and determine the glucose with phosphotungstic acid.[42] In this case the result as glucose $\times 0.92$ is the starch.

The qualitative identification of carbohydrates [43] with anthrone in strong sulfuric acid has been applied quantitatively for sucrose [44] and carbohydrates [45] as well as specifically to starch and cotton lint.[46] The resulting green color is proportional to the carbohydrate being tested. Fading of the color only begins after 3 hours. Increase of the reagent increases sensitivity but with a maximum at 0.16 per cent. Over 0.2 per cent of reagent may cause turbidity. The reagent may darken with age and gives a lesser color intensity. The color is reproducible to ± 1.5 per cent. Sugars must be preextracted because they would react with the anthrone. Proteins give no appreciable color.

Samples—*Solids. Pectin absent.* Rub 1 gram of the air-dried powdered sample with 5-10 ml. of water. Add 350 ml. of boiling water. Heat

[38] Jamshedji Jijibhoy Chinoy, *Mikrochemie* **26**, 132-42 (1939); *Indian J. Agr. Sci.* **17**, 261-8 (1947).

[39] Lucienne Legarde, *Bull. soc. chim.* **1946**, 665-9.

[40] L. E. Simerl and B. L. Brown, *Ind. Eng. Chem., Anal. Ed.* **11**, 125-8 (1939).

[41] Walter Thomas, *J. Am. Chem. Soc.* **46**, 1670-5 (1924); Walter Thomas and R. Adams Dutcher, *Ibid.* **46**, 1662-9 (1924).

[42] Andreas Hock, *Biochem. Z.* **294**, 336-41 (1937).

[43] Roman Dreywood, *Ind. Eng. Chem., Anal. Ed.* **18**, 499 (1946).

[44] E. E. Morse, *Ibid.* **19**, 1012-13 (1947).

[45] D. D. Morris, *Science* **107**, 254-5 (1948).

[46] Frederick J. Viles, Jr., and Leslie Silverman, *Anal. Chem.* **21**, 950-3 (1941); R. M. McCready, Jack Guggolz, Vernon Silviera, and H. S. Owens, *Ibid.* **22**, 1156-8 (1950).

to boiling and add 20 ml. of 1:35 sulfuric acid. Boil gently for 30 minutes, maintaining the volume at 400 ml. Filter through fine silk cloth on a Büchner funnel. Cool, dilute to 500 ml., and develop an aliquot with iodine by the general method.

Paper. Boil 3 grams of paper for 40 minutes with 150 ml. of water and 5 ml. of glacial acetic acid. This solubilizes the starch. Cool to room temperature, dilute to 203 ml., and filter for development with iodine by the general method.

Plant tissue. Pectin absent. Dry the sample as rapidly as possible in a ventilated oven at 70-80°. Circulate air over the tissue during the drying operation. Grind to pass 60 mesh. Extract a weighed sample of 2-5 grams with 75 per cent ethanol for 6 hours to remove sugars. Dry and weigh. Grind in a mortar or ball mill to pass fine silk bolting cloth.

Heat 0.2 gram of sample, 1.5 grams of sharp sand, and 5 ml. of water in boiling water for 15 minutes to gelatinize the starch, stirring vigorously from time to time. Cool to 10° and add 5 ml. of concentrated hydrochloric acid slowly with mixing. Do not let the temperature rise above 20° Centrifuge and decant the upper layer for later use.

Dilute 247 ml. of concentrated acid to 500 ml. of water. Grind the residues in the tubes with 3 ml. of the hydrochloric acid at intervals for 10 minutes and centrifuge. Decant and repeat this twice more. If a drop of the fourth extract shows a definite blue with 0.127 per cent iodine solution, repeat the extraction with acid. Finally wash the residues in the tubes with 10 ml. of water. Dilute the combined extracts, including a prior decantate, to 50 ml. and store in a refrigerator. These solutions are stable for 72 hours. Develop with iodine by the precise method.

Pectin present. Prepare as for pectin absent to "Heat 0.2 gram of sample. . . ." To a 0.2-gram sample add 0.05 gram of magnesium carbonate, 1.5 grams of sharp sand, and 5 ml. of water. Heat with occasional trituration in boiling water for 15 minutes. Add 7 ml. of 46 per cent calcium chloride solution, previously heated in the same bath. Grind in the boiling water bath at frequent intervals for 10 minutes, and centrifuge. Decant the extracts for later use. Grind the residue for one-half minute and add 3 ml. of hot water. Return to the bath. Complete the second treatment as before, using 5 ml. of calcium chloride solution. Make two more extractions in the same way. Acidify a few drops of the fourth extract with dilute hydrochloric acid and add a drop of 1 per cent iodine solution. If a blue color is obtained, carry out a fifth extraction. Finally wash the residues with 5 ml. of water and dilute the combined extracts to 50 ml. Store in a refrigerator until ready to develop by the precise method with iodine. They are not as stable as hydrochloric acid extracts.

For estimation as glucose. Prepare as for pectin-free samples through, ". . . to remove sugars." Weigh 1-4 grams which should not contain more than 0.3 gram of starch. Mix with 100 ml. of water and heat in boiling water for 40 minutes. Stir for the first 10 minutes and occasionally thereafter. Cool to 38° and add 0.1 gram of takadiastase and 2 ml. of toluene. Place in an incubator at 38° and stir gently at frequent intervals during the first few hours to prevent separation into 2 phases. The toluene will need to be replaced occasionally. At the end of 24 hours remove from the incubator and heat in boiling water for 15 minutes to render the enzyme inactive. Filter and wash the residue with water by decantation until the volume is approximately 250 ml. and dilute to that volume.

As mercuric nitrate reagent, gradually add 110 grams of mercuric oxide to 80 ml. of concentrated nitric acid with stirring. Heat to boiling and let cool. Add 30 ml. of 5 per cent sodium hydroxide solution with stirring. Dilute to 1 liter and store in the dark. Mix 30 ml. of sample with 5 ml. of this reagent. Add solid sodium bicarbonate in small portions with stirring until frothing ceases. Then add sodium bicarbonate carefully until the solution is just alkaline to litmus. Filter, wash the paper with 10 ml. of 5 per cent sodium bicarbonate solution, and dilute to 250 ml.

Mix 50 ml. of the solution with 0.5 gram of zinc dust. Add 1 drop of concentrated hydrochloric acid to precipitate mercury. The amount of sodium bicarbonate present must be sufficient to prevent precipitation of zinc carbonate. Agitate vigorously and let stand for 15 minutes. Filter through a dense filter paper. Test the filtrate with ammonium sulfide to insure the absence of mercury. Develop with picric acid.

Pectin solution. Mix 10 ml. of pectin solution with 80 ml. of a solution containing 33 per cent by weight of anhydrous calcium chloride. If alkaline to phenolphthalein, neutralize with acetic acid. Heat on a water bath for 10 minutes, cool, and dilute to 100 ml. with the same solution. Mix well and filter through a dry filter. Use this filter for development with iodine by the general method.

Brewer's grains. Triturate 10 grams of wet grains with 10 ml. of water. Add calcium chloride solution and proceed as for pectin solution. Starch in grain is also hydrolyzed to glucose by boiling with 1:20 hydrochloric acid and thus determined.[47]

---

[47] P. Beloshapko, *Spirto-Vodochna Prom.* 17, No. 1-2, 28 (1940).

Meat. Digest a 10-gram sample on a steam bath for 45 minutes with 75 ml. of 8 per cent potassium hydroxide in ethanol. Add 75 ml. of ethanol and let stand 45 minutes longer. Filter on an asbestos mat and wash with 50 per cent ethanol. Transfer the mat and starch to 50 ml. of 50 per cent ethanol containing 2.5 ml. of 1:10 hydrochloric acid and boil for 30 minutes. Filter and dilute the filtrate to 100 ml. Develop an aliquot by iodine by the general method.

Dehydrated vegetables and apples. If the sample is dehydrated, soak 10 grams for several hours with sufficient water to keep it covered, or heat at 60° for 2 hours. Add water equal to the weight of sample and rehydrating water. Disintegrate in a good blendor. If foam is present, add a few drops of amyl alcohol. Dilute 27 volumes of 72 per cent perchloric acid with 10 volumes of water and let it cool. Mix 4 grams of prepared sample with 3.7 ml. of this acid with vigorous stirring.[48] After 10 minutes with occasional stirring to solubilize the starch, dilute with water to 25 ml. or 50 ml. according to the starch content. Let settle and mix 1 ml. of the supernatant liquid with 6 ml. of water. Add a drop of phenolphthalein indicator solution and follow with 8 per cent sodium hydroxide solution to a pink color. Remove the color with 1:8 acetic acid and add 2.5 ml. in excess. Complete by the general method by iodine.

Fresh, frozen, or canned vegetables or apples. Disintegrate a 100-gram sample with 50 grams of water at low speed, add 50 ml. more of water and comminute at full speed. Break any foam with a few drops of amyl alcohol. Complete as for dehydrated vegetables and apples from "Dilute 27 volumes of 72 per cent. . . ."

Dried peas. Grind to pass a 60-80 mesh sieve. Wet 0.2 gram with a few drops of 80 per cent ethanol, add 5 ml. of water, and mix. Add 25 ml. of hot 80 per cent ethanol and mix. After 5 minutes, centrifuge and decant. Add 30 ml. of hot 80 per cent ethanol to the residue, stir, and centrifuge. Wash twice more and discard the aqueous-alcoholic solutions.

Mix the purified residue with 5 ml. of water, ice, and add with stirring 6.5 ml. of perchloric acid prepared by dilution of 270 ml. of 72 per cent grade with 100 ml. of water. Stir for 5 minutes, occasionally for 15 minutes after that, keeping chilled. Add 20 ml. of water and centrifuge. Decant and treat the residue again from "Mix the purified residue. . . ." Combine the two extracts, dilute to 100 ml., and filter. Dis-

---
[48] George W. Pucher, Charles S. Leavenworth, and Hubert Bradford Vickery, *Anal. Chem.* **20**, 850-3 (1948).

card the first 5 ml. of filtrate. Cooling can be omitted if amylose is not to be determined. Develop with anthrone.

Fresh peas. Blend 100 grams with 100 ml. of water. Extract a 5-gram sample of slurry four times with 30-ml. portions of hot 80 per cent ethanol. Add water to make the sugar-free residue up to 10 ml. Chill and add 13 ml. of the approximately 50 per cent perchloric acid described earlier. Stir occasionally for 15 minutes. Add 20 ml. of water, stir, centrifuge, and decant. Dilute the residue to 5 ml. with water, chill, add 6.5 ml. of the approximately 50 per cent perchloric acid and complete as before. Dilute the combined extracts to 100 ml., filter, and discard the first 5 ml. of filtrate. Develop with anthrone.

Sized textiles. Cut the fabric into 1-inch squares and soak 5-10 grams in 30 ml. of 42 per cent perchloric acid at room temperature for 30 minutes, with frequent stirring. To 5 ml. of this starch solution add 5 ml. of water and a couple of drops of phenolphthalein. Add 24 per cent sodium hydroxide solution until the color turns pink. Discharge the color by addition of 1:8 acetic acid, then add 2.5 ml. excess of the acid. Develop with iodine.

Starch. Boil a sample containing 1-10 mg. of starch in water, cool, and dilute to 100 ml. Filter if turbid and develop with anthrone.

Cotton. Digest a sample containing 1-10 mg. of cotton in 50 ml. of 2:3 sulfuric acid for about 30 minutes and dilute to 100 ml. with the same acid. If cloudy, filter through a washed inorganic filter and dilute 0.5 ml. to 2 ml. with water. Cool and develop with anthrone.

Starch-cotton mixtures. Boil and analyze the filtrate for starch as by the first method. Digest the residue on the filter according to the second method and analyze for cotton according to the second method.

Procedure—*By iodine. General method. Pectin absent.* As reagent saturate a 5 per cent potassium iodide solution with iodine, filter or decant from excess iodine, and dilute 20 ml. to 100 ml. Dilute 1-25 ml. of the sample solution, according to the starch content, nearly to 500 ml. with water. Add 5 ml. of the reagent and complete the dilution. Read at 640-700 mμ against the diluted reagent.

Precise method. Pectin absent. To select the sample volumes, if a drop of 0.127 per cent iodine solution gives a light blue color, use 10 ml., if an intense blue, use 5 ml. or less. Dilute to 10 ml. with the same menstruum used for extraction and add 2 drops of 0.04 per cent thymol blue solution. Cool to 10° and add 40 per cent sodium hydroxide solution dropwise with stirring, until the color is faint blue. Then add 1:5 hydrochloric acid to a yellow color and add 1 ml. of excess acid. The temperature must not rise above 25°. If the aliquot of sample is less than 5 ml., also add 2 ml. of 20 per cent sodium chloride solution. Add 0.5 ml. of approximately 46 per cent calcium chloride solution and 6-10 drops of a solution containing 12 per cent of iodine and 20 per cent of potassium iodide. This precipitates the starch as the iodide complex.

Let stand for 10 minutes. Then immerse in boiling water for 15 minutes. Cool to room temperature, break up any floating particles, and centrifuge. Draw off the supernatant liquid. Floating particles are retained and about 1 ml. will be left. Such floating particles are usually of iodine. Wash the precipitate with 2 ml. of 60 per cent ethanol. Centrifuge, remove the wash liquid, and repeat the washing.

Add 2 ml. of 1 per cent alcoholic sodium hydroxide solution to the residue. Triturate the precipitate until nearly colorless. Add a few ml. of 60 per cent ethanol and heat at 70-80° for 5 minutes. Cool, centrifuge, and decant the liquid from a residue of starch. Wash the residue twice with 2 ml. of 60 per cent ethanol. Invert the tube and let drain thoroughly.

Add 5 ml. of water to the starch residue and heat in boiling water with frequent stirring for 5 minutes. When cool add 0.5 ml. of 1:8 acetic acid, mix, and centrifuge. Decant the starch solution so prepared. Wash the residue with 3 ml. of water, and centrifuge. To the solution add 2 ml. of 1:8 acetic acid, 0.5 ml. of 10 per cent potassium iodide solution, and 5 ml. of 0.036 per cent potassium iodate solution. Dilute to 20 ml. or 50 ml. according to the intensity of color obtained. Let stand for 5 minutes and read at 610 mμ against a reagent blank.

By anthrone. Starch. Dilute 10 ml. of sample to such a volume that it will contain 0.005-0.02 mg. of starch per ml. As reagent dissolve 0.2 gram of anthrone in 100 ml. of 95 per cent sulfuric acid. Store near 0° and prepare fresh every 2 days. Chill 5 ml. of diluted sample and add 10 ml. of reagent. Mix and heat at 100° for 7.5 minutes. Cool and read at 630 mμ against a reagent blank. Compare against a glucose curve.

Amylose. Dilute 5 ml. of sugar-free starch solution containing about 5 mg. of starch to about 400 ml. Add 5 ml. of a reagent containing 0.2 per cent of iodine and 2 per cent of potassium iodide. Dilute to 500 ml. After 15 minutes read at 660 mμ against a reagent blank.

By picric acid. As reagent, add 36 grams of dry picric acid to 500 ml. of 1 per cent sodium hydroxide solution. Add 400 ml. of hot water and shake occasionally until the picric acid has completely dissolved. Cool and dilute to 1 liter. Dilute 5 ml. of the hydrolyzed sample to 10 ml. Add 10 ml. of reagent and 2 ml. of 25 per cent sodium carbonate solution. Read at 530 mμ against a reagent blank which must include the takadiastase. Results in terms of glucose can be assumed to be the value for the original starch.

PROTEIN-BOUND POLYSACCHARIDES

The reaction of a carbazole and sulfuric acid is not only applicable to solutions of polysaccharides [49] in general, but can be applied to the protein-bound fraction. When carbohydrate is reacted with tryptophan in the presence of sulfuric acid but without anthrone [50] the wave length for maximum absorption is 500 mμ for galactose, 460 mμ for glucose, and 520 mμ for fructose. Absorption of products from glucuronic acid, glucosamine, and hemoglobin is below 400 mμ, except for a weak band at 480-500 mμ for glucuronic acid. In analysis of carbohydrate precipitated by ethanol from body fluids, this reaction is affected by residual protein coprecipitated.

The effect of residual protein is overcome in the same reaction in the presence of excess tryptophan with anthrone added.[51] The reaction between the the tryptophan, carbohydrate and anthrone, shifts the maximum wave length for absorption to 500 mμ. In the presence of a large excess of tryptophan, the other amino acids do not interfere. Acetone, pyruvic acid, pyruvic aldehyde, lactic acid, uric acid, and ascorbic acid have absorption maxima with anthrone at 470-530 mμ. Glutathione, glycylglycylglycine and glycytyrosine cause enhancement of the color of tryptophan with anthrone. None affects the color of carbohydrates with anthrone in the presence of tryptophan if present in reasonable amounts.

Procedure—*Serum*. Dilute serum with 5 volumes of 0.9 per cent sodium chloride solution. Add 0.2 ml. dropwise to 10 ml. of absolute ethanol. Centrifuge and decant. Disperse the precipitate in 10 ml. of absolute ethanol. Again centrifuge and decant. Discard the decantates.

[49] Florence B. Seibert and Jane Atno, *J. Biol. Chem.* **163**, 511-22 (1946).

[50] M. R. Shetlar, J. V. Foster, and M. R. Everett, *Proc. Soc. Exptl. Biol. Med.* **67**, 125-30 (1948).

[51] M. M. Graff, E. M. Greenspan, I. R. Lehman, and J. J. Holechek, *J. Lab. Clin. Med.* **37**, 736-42 (1951) ; M. R. Shetlar, *Anal. Chem.* **24**, 1844-6 (1952).

The precipitate contains the polysaccharides without serum glucose. Drain the precipitate for at least 30 minutes and add 1 ml. of 0.1 per cent tryptophan solution. Add 2 ml. of water and chill for 15 minutes in ice. Add 6 ml. of 0.15 per cent anthrone in 95 per cent sulfuric acid, aged for 4 hours and no more than 9 days old. Stopper, mix by inversion, and heat in boiling water for 20 minutes. Cool in water for 10 minutes and read against a reagent blank at 520 mμ.

Reserve Polysaccharides

The term reserve polysaccharides is applied to substances such as the hemicelluloses present in plants and hydrolyzed by acids. It includes the starches. Hydrolysis with 1 per cent hydrochloric acid destroys some of the glucose formed by hydrolysis. Results can be obtained in terms of glucose which may be taken as reserve polysaccharides, without serious error.[52] Hydrolysis with 1 per cent sulfuric acid followed by clarification with neutral lead acetate and deleading with sodium sulfate has also been used.

Sample—Weigh a sample of 0.5 to 1.0 gram of vacuum-dried material, free from sugars (page 228). Mix with 200 ml. of water and add 1.8 ml. of concentrated hydrochloric acid. Reflux for 4 hours. When cool, render exactly neutral with 10 per cent sodium hydroxide solution and filter. Wash the filter with water and dilute the sample to 250 ml. Clarify with mercuric nitrate and complete the process exactly as for the solution resulting from hydrolysis of starch (page 229) starting at "As mercuric nitrate reagent. . . ."

Procedure—Use that for starch (page 232).

Total Available Carbohydrate

The total available carbohydrate is extracted from a sample, by treatment with enzyme. After separation of the residue of cellulose and hemicellulose this is hydrolyzed by acid to glucose and estimated by any of the usual means such as by picric acid. The method has been applied to tobacco extracts, using lead acetate to clarify the extracts and sodium carbonate to remove the residual lead.[53]

---

[52] Walter Thomas, *J. Am. Chem. Soc.* **46**, 1670-5 (1924).

[53] E. M. Dobrin, *Vsesoyuznii Inst. Tabachnoĭ Prom.* (*Krasnodar*) **104**, 23-31 (1933).

Sample—Reflux a sample containing 0.25 to 1 gram of carbohydrate with 100 ml. of water for 90 minutes. Transfer to a mortar and grind to a thin paste. Add additional water to a volume of 150-200 ml. Heat to boiling, cool to about 40°, and add 5 ml. of 1 per cent solution of takadiastase and a few ml. of toluene. Shake, stopper with cotton, and let stand for 20 hours in an incubator at 37°. When removed and cool, dilute to 250 ml., mix, and filter.

Procedure—Mix 20 ml. of the filtrate with 1.4 ml. of concentrated hydrochloric acid and heat in a boiling water bath for 1 hour without undue loss of moisture. Dextrins and maltose are hydrolyzed to monosaccharides. Cool and nearly neutralize with 10 per cent sodium hydroxide solution. Dilute to 25 ml. Develop 1 ml. of the solution with 2 ml. of saturated aqueous solution of picric acid and read at 530 mμ against a reagent blank. The results in terms of glucose may be taken as total available carbohydrate.

In calculation of results, allow for the reducing sugars added in the takadiastase, as separately determined. In general 0.5-0.7 per cent will be present in a 1 per cent solution.

HEMICELLULOSE

The concentration of hemicellulose in a sodium hydroxide solution is read as chromic sulfate after brief oxidation with boiling acid dichromate.[54]

Procedure—For up to 0.12 per cent of hemicellulose use 25 ml., for 0.12-0.3 per cent use 10 ml., for 0.3-1.2 per cent use 2 ml., and for 1.2-2.4 per cent use 1 ml. Dilute with water or sodium hydroxide solution to 25 ml. Add 5 ml. of 4.9037 per cent potassium dichromate solution and cautiously add 25 ml. of concentrated sulfuric acid. Heat to boiling for 30 seconds, cool, and dilute to 50 ml. Read at 600 mμ against water.

CARBOHYDRATES

Carbohydrates give a mahogany-brown color with indole and concentrated sulfuric aid.[55] The color also appears with alanine, acetone, casein,

---

[54] Charles J. Barton and Arthur J. Prutton, *Ind. Eng. Chem. Anal. Ed.* **16**, 429-30 (1944).

[55] Zacharias Dische and Hans Popper, *Biochem. Z.* **175**, 371-411 (1926); *Klin. Wochschr.* **5**, 1973 (1926).

and casein hydrolyzates. The reaction can be carried out in ethanol solution, using a more dilute acid than in aqueous solution. This permits the separation of polysaccharides, which are insoluble in ethanol. Glucose and galactose give the same color intensity, while fructose gives 12 per cent more color, and polysaccharides give as much color as the combined monosaccharides. Methyl glucoside and hexose diphosphoric acid give the same color as though the hexose molecule were free.

Carbohydrates in proteins are estimated without preliminary hydrolysis by the yellow to orange-red color which they develop with orcinol.[56] Glucose, maltose, lactose, fructose, xylose, arabinose, sucrose, starch, and glycogen give the reaction; glucosamine does not. Lactic acid, tartaric acid, and acetone give negative reactions. Formaldehyde and benzaldehyde give the same color as sugars.

Samples—*Tissue.* Grind 0.1-0.5 gram of fresh tissue in a mortar with 2-3 ml. of water. Add enough concentrated hydrochloric acid to make the final concentration 1:15. Stopper with glass wool and heat on a water bath with frequent shaking for 2 hours. Dilute so that the concentration of carbohydrate becomes 0.005 to 0.05 per cent and filter through quantitative paper. Develop with indole in sulfuric acid.

Blood. Mix 0.15 ml. of blood with 2-3 ml. of water. Add 1.2 ml. of 20 per cent trichloroacetic acid, dilute to 5 ml., and filter. Develop with indole in sulfuric acid.

Soy beans. Extract 45 grams of ground soy beans with 225 ml. of 5 per cent trisodium phosphate solution. Centrifuge and filter through glass wool. Render distinctly acid with 1:1 hydrochloric acid to precipitate proteins and carbohydrates. Centrifuge and wash the precipitate with ethanol until the water has been displaced. Extract the fat from the residue with ether. Boil the residue for 5 minutes with 50 ml. of water, add 15 drops of 10 per cent sodium hydroxide solution, and dilute to 150 ml. Develop this suspension with orcinol.

Beans and lentils. Shake 150 grams of ground sample for 15 minutes with 400 ml. of 10 per cent sodium chloride solution. Centrifuge and filter through glass wool. Complete as for soya beans from "Render distinctly acid with 1:1 hydrochloric acid . . . ."

Wheat or rye glutenin. Shake 100 grams of meal for 3 hours with 400 ml. of 70 per cent ethanol containing 0.2-0.3 per cent of sodium hydroxide. Centrifuge and saturate the extract with carbon dioxide.

---

[56] J. Tillmans K. Philippi, *Biochem. Z.* **215**, 36-60 (1929).

Glutenin precipitates but gliadin remains dissolved. Filter and wash the precipitate with 70 per cent ethanol. Treat as for proteins from soy beans starting at "Render distinctly acid . . . ."

Gliadin. Save the extract in separation of glutenin. Add 1:1 hydrochloric acid until neutral and pour into 4 volumes of ice-cold 1 per cent sodium chloride solution. Centrifuge and treat the precipitate as for soy bean proteins from "Render distinctly acid . . . ."

Water-soluble proteins. Shake 50 grams of meal with 250 ml. of water for 30 minutes. Centrifuge and filter. Boil the filtrate with sufficient sodium chloride to make a 10 per cent solution. Centrifuge and treat as for soy bean proteins starting at "Render distinctly acid . . . ."

Hen's eggs. Dry and powder. Extract the color and fats with ether and proceed as for soy bean proteins from "Extract 45 grams . . . ."

Procedure—*With indole in sulfuric acid.* Dilute 77.5 ml. of concentrated sulfuric acid to 100 ml. Mix 1 ml. of sample with 9 ml. of this acid and cool. The solution may be greenish yellow but must not be brown. Add 0.3 ml. of a 1 per cent solution of indole in ethanol. Mix well, heat for 10 minutes in boiling water, and cool. Read against a reagent blank.

With orcinol. To 15 ml. of 3:2 sulfuric acid add 0.5 ml. of a 2 per cent solution of orcinol. Add 1 ml. of sample solution. Mix well by shaking and heat in boiling water for 10 minutes. Let cool in air and dilute with 3:2 sulfuric acid to 50 or 100 ml. Read against a reagent blank.

COTTON

The determination of cotton by anthrone is covered under starch (page 231).

METHYL CELLULOSE

While methyl cellulose exists in a form only soluble in the presence of alkali, the important problem is in determination of the usual water-soluble form. Knowing the type present, it is determinable with anthrone to better than ±3 per cent.[57] The same reaction is given by starch, dextrose, hydroxyethylcellulose, and carboxymethylcellulose. Therefore,

[57] E. P. Samsel and R. A. DeLap, *Anal. Chem.* **23**, 1795-7 (1951).

problems of isolation of the sample in aqueous solution depend on the materials from which it is to be separated.

Procedure—To 1 ml. of sample containing 0.1-0.5 mg. of methyl cellulose, add 4 ml. of water, then 10 ml. of 0.05 per cent solution of anthrone in concentrated sulfuric acid. Mix well and after 10 minutes read at 625 mμ against a reagent blank. It has also been estimated with β-naphtholsulfonic acid.[58]

---

[58] A. Hintermaier, *Fette u. Seifen* **51**, 368-9 (1944).

CHAPTER 10

GLUCOSIDES [1]

GLUCOSIDES, also called glycosides, are determinable by hydrolysis and estimation of glucose. That locates them at this point, chapterwise, as determinable as alcohols. Many are sterol derivatives and therefore estimated by appropriate methods related to that structure.

A general method for saccharides with alkaline picrate applies as do various other alcohol, sterol, and special methods. Since there is no basis of reasonably complete classification—they are arranged alphabetically.

ADONIDIN

Determine by the method for digitoxin by picrate [2] (page 244).

CEREBROSIDES

Cerebrosides are conveniently determined by their gallactose content after hydrolysis. Appropriate reactions are those with 80 per cent sulfuric acid and carbazole,[3] or with orcinol in sulfuric acid solution.[4]

Procedure—*With carbazole.* Evaporate an alcohol-ether extract containing 0.2-0.6 mg. of cerebrosides just to dryness on a water bath at 60°. Add 0.5 ml. of water. Stir with a glass rod and add 0.5 ml. of 1:5 hydrochloric acid. Stopper and heat in boiling water for 2 hours to bring about complete hydrolysis of the cerebrosides. Cool and remove the aqueous layer, leaving the fatty acids behind. Wash the sides with 0.5 ml. of slightly acid water, taking care not to disturb the fatty acid precipitate. Dry the clear aqueous layer in a desiccator *in vacuo* over concentrated sulfuric acid and sodium hydroxide.

---

[1] See Chapter 1 for details of organization, condensation, etc.

[2] Cesco Toffoli and Olga Marelli, *Ann. chim. applicata* **34**, 136-48 (1944).

[3] Zacharias Dische, *Mikrochemie* **8**, 4-32 (1930); P. V. Edman, *J. Biol. Chem.* **143**, 219-21 (1942).

[4] J. Tillmans and K. Philippi, *Biochem. Z.* **215**, 36-60 (1929); Margrethe Sorenson and G. Haugaard, *Ibid.* **260**, 247-77 (1933); J. Brückner, *Z. physiol. Chem.* **268**, 163-70 (1941).

Extract the dried residue with 1 ml. of ice-cold ethyl acetate for 1 hour at 0°. This removes glycerine. Decant the ethyl acetate and remove the last traces in the desiccator. Add 5 ml. of ice-cold 7:3 sulfuric acid and 0.15 ml. of 0.5 per cent carbazole in absolute ethanol. Mix by shaking gently and heat for 10 minutes in boiling water. Cool and read at 430 mμ and 530 mμ against a reagent blank. The value of the ratio $E_{530}:E_{430}$ should approximate 2.35 to establish that the color read is mainly from that source. With that established, read the 530 mμ value against a galactose curve. Multiply galactose by 4.55 to give the cerebroside content.

With orcinol. Evaporate a 1-ml. alcoholic solution of cerebroside, to dryness and add 3 ml. of 1:12 sulfuric acid. Heat in an autoclave at 110° for 45 minutes or in boiling water for 60 minutes to hydrolyze to galactose. Dilute to 3 ml. and extract with 5 ml. of chloroform to remove the liberated fatty acid. To 1.5 ml. of the aqueous layer add 1 ml. of 2 per cent aqueous orcinol solution and 4 ml. of concentrated sulfuric acid. Shake thoroughly and read at 500 mμ after 3 minutes against a reagent blank. Interpret from a galactose curve and multiply by 4.55 to convert to cerebroside.

CONVALLAMARIN

Determine by the method for digitoxin by picrate (page 244).

DIGITOXIN

Digitalis contains a series of active agents such as digitoxin, digitonin, and digitalin. They are usually determined together as digitoxin. These digitalis glucosides give a red to orange color with alkaline solutions of picric acid, which is proportional to the activity of the glucosides.[5]

[5] Henk Baljet, *Schweiz. Apoth. Ztg.* 56, 71-3, 84-8 (1918); *Pharm. Weekblad* 55, 457 (1918); Arthur Knudsen and Melvin Dresbach, *J. Pharmacol. Exp. Therapeutics* 19, 268-9 (1922); *Ibid.* 20, 205-20 (1922); J. E. Machado and J. Sonol, *Rev. farm.* (*Buenos Aires*) 76, 217-20 (1930); Frederick K. Bell and John C. Krantz, Jr., *J. Pharmacol.* 83, 213-19 (1945); *Ibid.* 87, 198-202 (1946); J. Larralde, *Rev. españ. fisiol.* 3, 243-7 (1947); J. Mendes Ribeiro and A. J. Correia Ralha, *J. farm.* (*Lisbon*) 7, 61-71 (1948); Alejandro Santa-Pau Votá, Enrique Costa Novella, and Eduardo Primo Yúfera, *Farmacognosia* (Madrid) 7, 161-99 (1948); Franca Buffoni and Alberto Giotti, *Boll. soc. ital. biol. sper.* 25, 108-12 (1949); Robert A. Abrams and Marin S. Dunn, *Am. J. Pharm.* 122, 337-47 (1950); E. E. Kennedy, *J. Am. Pharm. Assoc.* 39, 25-7 (1950); Fritz Neuwald, *Ibid.* 39, 172-4 (1950); Roger Munier and Michael Mocheboeuf, *Compt. rend.* 230, 117-9 (1950).

The reaction is due to the active hydrogen of a β-γ-lactone group, and is general for most cardiac glucosides. Inert allocymarin gives the same reaction so that results are not necessarily indicative of physiological activity. Readings at 495 mμ are accurate to ±5 per cent. Tetraethyl ammonium hydroxide is preferable to sodium hydroxide as a base for the reagent. The three glycosides mentioned do not give the same color development. The color increases slowly for 20 minutes, then decreases slowly. The same reaction is given by other glucosides such as adonis, convallaria, strophanthus, ouabain, and oleandran. There is interference by scillaren, acetone, glucose, fructose, and lactose.

Digitoxin and other related glucosides give a blue color with acetic acid, sulfuric acid, and ferric chloride.[6] Accuracy is better than ±6 per cent. The reaction is positive with all esterinic nuclei.

A brilliant blue color develops on addition of strong sodium hydroxide solution to a mixture of m-dinitrobenzene and digitoxin in ethanol.[7] Results are accurate to ±2 per cent. Lactose interferes. A comparable reaction is given by 3,4-dinitrobenzoic acid[8] or 1,3,5-trinitrobenzene.[9]

Modification of the reaction with 3,5-dinitrobenzoic acid to use benzyltrimethylammonium hydroxide as the alkali alters the color to bluish red and is highly reproducible.[10]

Digitoxin contains a methylene grouping which upon reaction with sodium β-naphthoquinone-4-sulfonate produces a purple color in alkaline solution.[11] On acidification, the color changes to a stable yellow which can be measured photometrically. This color reaches maximum intensity immediately and fades only about 1 per cent after 2 hours. The reaction follows Beer's law over a concentration range of 10-40 mg. per ml. Lactose partially inhibits the purple color. Materials related to digitoxin such as Lantoside A and Lantoside C give strong positive tests; Gitoxin and Lantoside B give weakly positive tests and digitonin gives a negative test. Chloroform is used as the extracting medium because of the high

---

[6] Arthur E. James, Fritz O. Laquer, and Joseph D. McIntyre, *J. Am. Pharm. Assoc.* **36**, 1-4 (1947) ; E. Soos, *Scientia Pharm.* **16**, 1-13, 29-38 (1948).

[7] W. D. Raymond, *Analyst* **63**, 478-82 (1938) ; *Ibid.* **64**, 113-15 (1939) ; Raymond C. Anderson and K. K. Chen, *J. Am. Pharm. Assoc.* **35**, 353-5 (1946) ; Teodor Canbäck, *Svensk. Farm Tidskr.* **51**, 261-70 (1947).

[8] D. L. Kedde, *Pharm. Weekblad* **82**, 741-57 (1947).

[9] Michiya Kimura, *J. Pharm. Soc. Japan* **71**, 991-4 (1951).

[10] E. L. Pratt, *Anal. Chem.* **24**, 1324-7 (1952).

[11] Alexander T. Warren, Frank O. Howland, and Louis W. Green, *J. Am. Pharm. Assoc., Sci. Ed.* **37**, 186-8 (1948).

solubility of the digitoxin in this solvent and because it does not extract lactose.

Digitoxin and related compounds react in acetic acid with vanillin to give a red color which changes to a stable blue in proportion to the quantity of glucoside present.[12] Alcohol must be evaporated before development of the color. Another reagent is sodium nitroprusside with sodium phosphate and sodium hydroxide at pH 11.[13] Alkaline picric acid in ethanol reacts with digitoxin to give the familiar red to orange color.[14] The method is accurate to ±5 per cent.[15]

Sample—*Tablets.* Determine the total and average weight of 20 tablets and grind into a fine powder. Weigh out a sample approximately equal to the weight of 10 tablets and add 20 ml. of chloroform. Heat to boiling on a hot plate and filter on a fritted-glass filter. Wash the residue several times with warm chloroform and add these washings to the filtrate. Adjust to room temperature and dilute to 50 ml. with chloroform. Use a 10-ml. aliquot for development with sodium β-naphthoquinone-4-sulfonate. Or, evaporate to dryness and develop the residue with acid ferric chloride. For development with *m*-dinitrobenzoic acid use ethanol.

Tincture. Dilute 10 ml. of sample to 20 ml. with water and add 2.5 ml. of 10 per cent neutral lead acetate solution. Dilute to 25 ml., shake and, after coagulation is complete, filter. The residual color is slightly yellow. Mix 12.5 ml. of filtrate and 1.25 ml. of 10 per cent hydrated disodium phosphate solution. Dilute to 25 ml. filter when sedimentation is complete and develop an aliquot with picrate.

Leaves. Triturate 1.5 gram of powdered *folia digitalis* with water and make up to 151.5 grams. Shake frequently for 1 hour. Saponines interfere with quantitative extraction. Add 15 grams of 15 per cent lead acetate solution, let settle, and filter. Extract 110 grams with 25, 25, and 25 ml. of chloroform. Dry the extract with anhydrous sodium sulfate. Filter, wash with chloroform, and evaporate the filtrate to dryness. The residue is suitable for development with acid ferric chloride. Alternatively, dissolve the extracted glucosides in 5 ml. of 50 per cent ethanol and develop with picrate.

[12] Juan A. Sanchez, *Semana med.* (*Buenos Aires*) **1934**, **II**, 399-402.

[13] D. L. Kedde, *Pharm. Weekblad* **82**, 741-57 (1947).

[14] Henk Baljet, *Schweiz. Apoth. Ztg.* **56**, 71-3 (1918).

[15] F. K. Bell and J. C. Krantz, Jr., *J. Pharmacol.* **83**, 213-19 (1945); *Ibid.* **87**, 198-202 (1946).

Ampoules. Evaporate the contents and develop with acid ferric chloride or dissolve in ethanol and develop with *m*-dinitrobenzene.

Separation from aglucons. If contamination with aglucons is suspected, add a trace of cupric chloride to a known aliquot of the solution of the sample in ethanol. Filter through a column of powdered barium hydroxide. The glycosides are insoluble; the filtrate contains all the aglucons. Reading after treatment provides the necessary correction.

Evaporate under a gentle stream of air, 10 ml. of chloroform containing about 0.02 mg. of digitoxin per ml. Add 0.1 ml. of chloroform and swirl to wet all of the residue. Submerge to a depth of 1 cm. in a 100° bath. Then add 4 ml. of ethanol and 0.5 ml. of 0.2 per cent sodium hydroxide solution. Exactly 1 minute later, add 1 ml. of the reagent containing 0.024 per cent each of sodium sulfite and β-naphthoquinone-4-sulfonate. Agitate to produce a uniform solution and, after 1.5 minutes, add 0.5 ml. of acetic acid with agitation. Remove from the bath and cool under the tap. Dilute to 25 ml. with ethanol and read at 420-460 mμ against a reagent blank.

Procedure—*By acid ferric chloride.* To the residue add 3 ml. of glacial acetic acid, 0.1 ml. of 5 per cent solution of ferric chloride hexahydrate, and 0.25 ml. of concentrated sulfuric acid. When dissolved store in the dark for 2 hours and read at 530 mμ against a reagent blank.

By m-dinitrobenzene and sodium hydroxide. Adjust the ethanol content of the sample to approximate 50 per cent. To 10 ml. add 1 ml. of a 1 per cent solution of *m*-dinitrobenzene in absolute ethanol. Mix and chill to 0°. Add 2 ml. of 20 per cent sodium hydroxide solution and read at 610 mμ at 30-second intervals. Plot and extrapolate to zero time.

By dinitrobenzoic acid and benzytrimethylammonium hydroxide. Transfer 3 ml. of sample in ethanol containing about 0.45 mg. of digitoxin, to a glass-stoppered tube. Add 5 ml. of 47 per cent ethanol and 2 ml. of 1 per cent solution of 3,5-dinitrobenzoic acid in ethanol. Add 2 ml. of 40 per cent benzyl trimethylammonium hydroxide and stopper. Mix and read at 550 mμ against a reagent blank.

By 1,3,5-Trinitrobenzene. Mix successively 4 ml. of sample solution containing 0.01-0.1 mg. of alkaloid with 0.5 ml. of 0.04 per cent solution of the trinitrobenzene in methanol and 0.5 ml. of 0.4 per cent aqueous potassium hydroxide solution. After 35 minutes read at 550 mμ.

By vanillin. Evaporate the extract of sample to dryness at 100°. Add 4 drops of glacial acetic acid and 20 drops of a 0.3 per cent solution of vanillin in concentrated hydrochloric acid. Warm at 100° for 5 minutes and add 4 ml. of glacial acetic acid and 2 ml. of chloroform. Mix well and separate the supernatant liquids for reading.

By picrate. Mix 95 ml. of 1 per cent picric acid solution and 5 ml. of 10 per cent sodium hydroxide solution. Add 5 ml. of this reagent to 5 ml. of sample. Mix well, let stand for 20 minutes for the maximum development of color, and read at 495 mμ.

INDOXYL-β-D-GLYCOSIDE, 3-(β-GLUCOSIDE) INDOLE, INDICAN

When indoxyl, from hydrolysis of indican, and thymol are oxidized together a violet indolignin is produced.[16] Phenol or resorcinol react similarly to give a lower color intensity. Several mg. of tryptophan give a faint color. There is no interference from 3 per cent of glucose nor 0.1 per cent of formaldehyde. Potassium persulfate prevents interference by formation of pigments from skatole. If omitted the color is redder. The developed color is extracted into chloroform.

Indican can be hydrolyzed and the indoxyl oxidized to the blue color of indigo. This may either be oxidized with permanganate, converted to indigo red with isatin, or estimated directly by extraction.

When triketohydrindene hydrate (ninhydrin) condenses with indoxyl, water is split off and a red color developed. The compound developed is insoluble in water but soluble in organic solvents.[17]

Indoxyl derived from indican produces a red dyestuff by condensation with acenaphthequinone in acetic acid in the presence of hydrochloric acid. The dyestuff is extracted with a solvent. Extraction with amyl acetate of the product of hexylresorcinol and indican is another method.[18]

Procedure—*Serum by oxidation in solution with thymol.* Precipitate proteins from 10 ml. of serum with 10 ml. of 20 per cent trichloroacetic acid solution. Filter and to 12 ml. of filtrate add 1.2 ml. of a 5 per cent thymol solution. Add 12 ml. of a 0.2 per cent solution of ferric chloride

---

[16] A. Jolles, *Z. physiol. Chem.* **94**, 79-103 (1915); Max Rosenberg, *Münch. med. Wochschr.* **63**, 117-20 (1916); J. Broekmeyer, *Klin. Wochschr.* **11**, 1713-4 (1932); *Ibid.* **12**, 1025-6 (1933); *Nederland. Tijdschr. Geneeskunde* **76**, III, 3942-5 (1932); *Ibid.* **77**, II, 2795-8 (1933); Herman Sharlit, *J. Biol. Chem.* **99**, 537-45 (1933); Max Rosenberg, *Bol. assoc. brasil. farm.* **16**, 276-8 (1935); Arnold P. Meikeljohn and Frank P. Cohen, *J. Lab. Clin. Med.* **27**, 949-54 (1942).

[17] Taki Kumon, *Z. physiol. Chem.* **231**, 205-7 (1935).

[18] F. Böhm and G. Grüner, *Klin. Wochschr.* **15**, 1279-80 (1936).

hexahydrate in concentrated hydrochloric acid, and mix. Let stand for one-half hour. Extract with 3 ml. of chloroform and, if the color is not all removed, repeat the extraction. Combine the extracts and centrifuge if turbid. Dilute the extracts to a standard volume with chloroform and read against a reagent blank.

Urine by oxidation in solution with thymol. Dilute a 5-ml. sample, preserved with toluene rather than formaldehyde, to 100 ml. To 2 ml. of the diluted urine add 5 drops of 1 per cent potassium persulfate solution. Mix and add 0.5 ml. of a 1 per cent solution of thymol in ethanol. Mix and add 5 ml. of an acid reagent prepared by mixing 300 ml. of 40 per cent trichloroacetic acid solution with 200 ml. of concentrated hydrochloric acid. Heat in boiling water for 5 minutes. Ethyl trichloracetate settles out carrying a purple pigment. Let cool and centrifuge. Decant the supernatant liquid, leaving about 0.3 ml. over the precipitate. Dilute to 2 ml. with glacial acetic acid, stir until clear, and read at 540 mμ against a reagent blank.

In urine as indigo. Add 5 ml. of 20 per cent lead acetate solution to precipitate the color from 50 ml. of urine. Filter through a dry filter. Treat 25 ml. of the filtrate with an equal volume of concentrated hydrochloric acid containing 0.4 per cent of ferric chloride hexahydrate. After 15 minutes extract with 25 ml. of chloroform. Repeat the extraction with 10-ml. portions of chloroform until no further color is extracted. Combine the chloroform extracts and wash with several successive portions of distilled water. Evaporate the chloroform solution to less than 25 ml. and cool. Dilute to 25 ml. and read against chloroform.

In urine by triketohydrindene hydrate. To 10 ml. of urine add 0.5 ml. of 5 per cent lead acetate solution. Shake to coagulate and filter through a dry paper. To 5 ml. of the filtrate of decolorized sample add 1 ml. of 1:2 hydrochloric acid. Add 4 drops of 5 per cent triketohydrindene hydrate solution. Heat for 3 minutes on a water bath. Cool, extract the color with 5 ml. of chloroform, and read the extract against chloroform.

In urine by acenaphthequinone. Treat 20 ml. of urine with 4 ml. of a paste containing 50 per cent of basic lead acetate. Mix and filter. To 11 ml. of filtrate add 10 ml. of a saturated solution of acenaphthequinone in glacial acetic acid and 2 ml. of concentrated hydrochloric acid. Heat to boiling. Extract with 10 ml. of hexahydrotoluene and continue to extract with further small amounts of hexahydrotoluene until no more red color is extracted. Cool the combined extracts and dilute to 25 ml. with hexahydrotoluene. Read against the solvent.

NARINGENIN-5-RHAMNOSIDE, NARINGIN

The color is diethylene glycol with alkali is given by the rhamnoside, its agulone, and by hesperidin but to different intensities. Immediate color development with quercitin, rutin, phloridzin, acetin, apiin, and kaempferol permits distinction but they do interfere. Ascorbic acid also reacts. Other possible constituents of grapefruit juice do not interfere.

The red color resulting from reaction of ferric chloride and naringin is for colorimetric estimation of the latter.[19] The boric acid method for hesperidin is also applicable.[20] The initial color deepens slowly with time.

Sample—*Grapefruit rind.* Separate the albedo from the flavedo and grind in a food chopper. Weigh out 10 grams of the ground sample, add 500 ml. of hot water, and boil for 10 minutes. Strain through cheesecloth, cool, and dilute to 500 ml. for development with ferric chloride.

Procedure—*With alkali in diethylene glycol.* To 10 ml. of 90 per cent diethylene glycol add 0.2 ml. of sample. Mix and use as a blank setting of the instrument. Add 0.2 ml. of 16 per cent sodium hydroxide solution and read at 420 mμ after 5 minutes.

With ferric chloride. To 25 ml. of sample solution add 1 drop of 50 per cent ferric chloride solution and mix. Read at once.

NERIIN

Neriin, the poisonous glucoside of red oleander, gives a pink color with concentrated sulfuric acid.[21]

Sample—Extract with ether. Evaporate the ether and take up in water. Filter and evaporate.

Procedure—Dissolve the residue in 10 ml. of concentrated sulfuric acid and read after 1 hour, diluting further with sulfuric acid if necessary.

---

[19] E. M. Harvey, *Plant Physiol.* **11**, 463-5 (1936) ; E. M. Harvey and G. L. Rygg, *Ibid.* **11**, 433-5 (1936) ; G. L. Rygg and E. M. Harvey, *Ibid.* **13**, 571-86 (1938) ; J. Tamarit Torres, *Farm. nueva* **11**, 177-8 (1946).

[20] C. W. Wilson, *J. Am. Chem. Soc.* **61**, 2303-6 (1939).

[21] N. Pitchandi, *J. Proc. Inst. Chemists* (India) **20**, 27-33 (1948).

Oleandrin

Determine by the method for digitoxin by picrate (page 244). Color develops at least twice as fast as that from digitoxin.

2-Phloretin-β-glucoside, phlorizin

Phlorizin is developed with α-nitroso-β-naphthol in acid solution.[22] The color is not stable and does not conform to Beer's law.

Procedure—To 2 ml. of sample containing not over 0.5 mg. of phlorizin per ml. add a drop of 1 per cent solution of α-nitroso-β-naphthol in ethanol. Mix and add 3 drops of concentrated nitric acid. Heat to boiling, cool at once, and add 3 ml. of 1:2 ethanol-ether. Shake and read the red color of the solvent layer at once.

Ouabain, G-Strophanthin

Determine by the method for digitoxin by picrate (page 244). Color develops about twice as rapidly as with digitoxin. Alternatively use the method for digitoxin by m-dinitrobenzene [23] (page 243) or 1,3,5-trinitrobenzene (page 243). Another method of development is p-dimethyl-aminobenzaldehyde and piperidine.[24]

Procedure—Mix 1 ml. of sample in absolute ethanol containing 0.06-0.6 mg. of ouabain. Add 1 ml. of 1 per cent solution of p-dimethylamino-benzaldehyde in absolute ethanol and mix. Add 0.3 ml. of piperidine and mix. Heat at 70° for 5 hours, cool, and add 2 ml. of absolute ethanol. Mix, let stand for 30 minutes at room temperature, and read.

Salicin, Saliginin-β-D-glucopyraniside

Salicin is read colorimetrically by its violet color in alkaline solution.[25]

Procedure—Dilute a sample containing about 5 mg. of salicin to 5 ml. Add 5 ml. of concentrated hydrochloric acid and evaporate at not over 80° to 2 ml. Let cool, filter, and wash. Discard the washings.

[22] A. Lambrechts, *Compt. rend. soc. biol.* **124**, 263-4 (1937).

[23] W. D. Raymond, *Analyst* **63**, 478-82 (1938); *Ibid.* **64**, 113-15 (1939).

[24] Masaji Yamagishi, *Ann. Rept. Takeda Research Lab.* **10**, 40-2 (1951).

[25] Morris B. Jacobs and Nicholas T. Ferinacci, *Ind. Eng. Chem., Anal. Ed.* **8**, 279-81 (1936).

Dissolve the residue from the paper with five successive 1-ml. portions of 10 per cent sodium hydroxide solution and similar portions of water. Dilute to 10 ml. and read against a reagent blank.

SCILLARENE

Scillarene in A and B forms occurs in squill. Determine by the Liebermann reaction for chlosterol in blood[26] (Vol. IV).

STROPHANTHIN, K-STROPHANTHIN

The reactions of strophanthin are largely parallel to those of digitoxin. Thus it is evaluated by the same technic with alkaline picrate solution (page 244), m-dinitrobenzene[27] page 243), or 1,3,5-trinitrobenzene (page 243).

When strophanthin reacts with acetic anhydride and sulfuric acid according to the Liebermann reaction the related compounds give an olive-green color.[28] Ouabain gives a yellow to orange. The glucoside is difficultly soluble in the reaction medium and insoluble in chloroform. It must therefore be hydrolyzed previously. The olive green changes to yellow in 4-12 hours.

Sample—*Tincture.* Evaporate 20 ml. of tincture to dryness on a water bath. Take up the residue with 18 ml. of water. Mix and add 2 ml. of a filtered solution of 3 grams of crystalline lead acetate and 10 grams of lead monoxide in 70 ml. of cold distilled water. Mix well and filter. Add 1.5 grams of sodium sulfate to precipitate lead sulfate. Filter and pipet out 10 ml. of the clear, slightly colored filtrate. Add 10 ml. of 1:360 sulfuric acid and hydrolyze by heating on a water bath at 80° for 45 minutes. Extract successively with 5 ml., 2.5 ml., and 2.5 ml. of chloroform. Combine the chloroform extracts and adjust the volume to 10 ml.

Procedure—To 2 ml. of the chloroform solution add 2 ml. of acetic anhydride and mix. Add 3 drops of concentrated sulfuric acid and mix. Read after 20 minutes.

---

26 A. Leulier and M. Ferrand, *Trav. membres soc. chim. biol.* **23**, 1311-16 (1941).

27 S. K. Rasmussen, *Dansk. Tids. Farm.* **18**, 48-52 (1944).

28 Albert Leulier and Henri Griffon, *Bull. sci. pharmacol.* **36**, 408-14 (1929).

5,7,3',4'-Tetrahydroxyflavonol-3-rhamnoglucoside, Rutin, Vitamin P

Rutin is a flavone glucoside which yields quercetin, glucose, and rhamnose on acid hydrolysis. Fluorescence of rutin and boric acid is more sensitive than colorimetric methods.[29]

The reading of rutin in the ultraviolet is feasible in the absence of substantial background absorption.[30] The reaction with aluminum ion gives an appropriate yellow color.[31] A considerable excess of aluminum chloride is required. The reaction is general for flavonols such as morin, 5,7,2',4'-tetrahydroxyflavonol and quercetin, 5,7,3',4'-tetrahydroxyflavonol.[32]

Ethanol used must be highly purified. Special denatured 1G is suitable after refluxing for 10 hours with sodium hydroxide and zinc dust, and distillation. The color is substantially increased by addition of potassium acetate. There is no interference by aminophylline, phenobarbital, mannitol hexanitrate, or ascorbic acid. Accuracy to ±5 per cent recovery is obtained. The flavones give a yellow color with boric-citric acid mixture.[33] The reaction will detect 0.002 mg. The medium must be substantially anhydrous and rigidly standardized as 1 per cent of moisture cuts the color intensity in half.

Procedure—*Tablets by aluminum ion.* Powder 5-10 tablets and weigh out a sample to contain 15-20 mg. of rutin. Extract in a micro-Soxhlet for 8-10 hours with ethanol. Dilute the extract to 50 ml. Dilute an appropriate aliquot of sample in ethanol to 5 ml. with the same solvent. Add 3 ml. of a 2.41 per cent aqueous solution of aluminum chloride hexahydrate and 5 ml. of 9.81 per cent solution of potassium acetate. Mix well, let stand, and read at 415 mμ against a reagent blank.

Urine by aluminum ion. Mix 2 ml. of urine and 3 ml. of aqueous 1.33 per cent aluminum chloride. Add 0.5 ml. of 1:3 ammonium hydroxide and dilute to 10 ml. Centrifuge and decant. Break up the gel, add 10 ml. of 1 per cent aqueous potassium acetate, and mix. Dilute to

---

[29] Anthony J. Glazko, Foster Adair, Evangeline Papageorge, and George T. Lewis, *Science* **105**, 48 (1947).

[30] W. L. Porter, B. A. Brice, M. J. Copley, and J. F. Couch, *U. S. Dept. Agr. Bur. Agr. Ind. Chem.* **AIC-159**, 6 pp. (1947).

[31] W. L. Porter, D. F. Dickell, and J. F. Couch, *Arch. Biochem.* **21**, 273-8 (1949); Arthur Turner, Jr., *Anal. Chem.* **24**, 1444-5 (1952).

[32] Earl B. Dechene, *J. Am. Pharm. Assn.* **40**, 93-4 (1951).

[33] Clarence W. Wilson, L. S. Weatherby, and William Z. Bock, *Ind. Eng. Chem., Anal. Ed.* **14**, 425-6 (1942).

50 ml. and read at 415 mμ between 30 and 120 minutes later against a reagent blank.

Vegetable tissue by boric acid-nitric acid mixture. Dry at 60°, grind, and weigh out 1-5 grams. Extract in a Soxhlet with methanol and evaporate the extract to dryness on a water bath. Digest the dry extract with chloroform to remove chlorophyll, fats, resins, etc. Extraction of chlorophyll may be incomplete in which case take up in methanol, add 2 ml. of toluene, evaporate the methanol, and digest again. Take up the residue from chloroform extraction in acetone. Filter and dilute to 100 ml.

As reagent, just before use, mix equal volumes of 10 per cent citric acid in acetone with saturated boric acid in acetone. Mix a known volume of the sample in acetone with sufficient reagent to measure 10 ml. and read. Subtract from this the reading with an equal volume of sample diluted to 10 ml. with acetone, which will be a substantial value, rarely less than 20 per cent of the total.

Meal. Distribute a 2-gram sample uniformly over a 4 × 2 × 0.25 inch piece of absorbent cotton and roll along the major axis. Place on a plug of cotton in an automatic extractor and extract for 6 hours with 75 ml. of absolute ethanol. Use glass beads to prevent bumping. Cool and dilute to 250 ml. with isoamyl alcohol.

Extract 20 ml. of the solution with 25, 25, and 25 ml. of 24 per cent solution of aluminum chloride hexahydrate. The rutin is in the aqueous layer as a yellow complex, the plant pigments in the isoamyl alcohol layer. Centrifuge after each extraction and dilute the separated aqueous extracts to 250 ml.

Read the aqueous solution of the aluminum complex at 416 mμ against an aluminum chloride solution.

THEVETIN

Thevetin gives a pink with syrupy phosphoric acid.[34]

Procedure—Evaporate the sample to dryness. Add 10 ml. of 85 per cent phosphoric acid and heat for 10 minutes in boiling water. Cool and read against a reagent blank.

UZARIN

The method with *m*-dinitrobenzene described for digitoxin (page 243) is applicable to urazin.[35]

---

[34] N. Pitchandi, *J. Proc. Inst. Chemists* (India) **20**, 27-33 (1948).
[35] Teodor Canbäck, *Svensk. Farm. Tid.* **51**, 401-3 (1947).

CHAPTER 11

ALDEHYDES [1]

THE most widely used qualitative test for aldehydes with Schiff's reagent is adaptable to estimation of almost any one in the absence of others. In addition, the reactivity of an aldehyde group permits of many color bodies being built up with such reagents as hydrazines and phenols. Since aldehyde-free reagents are essential, the determinations are preceded by methods of purification of some of the common reagents.

Aldehyde-free reagents [2]—*Alcohol.* Add 3 or 4 grams of *m*-phenylenediamine hydrochloride to each liter of 95 per cent ethanol. After standing for several days, distil slowly, collecting the middle half of the distillate. Use fresh materials for each preparation. The fraction saved should give no color with Schiff's reagent in 48 hours.

Ether. Shake the ether with concentrated sulfuric acid until fresh portions produce no change in color and let stand in contact with fresh sulfuric acid overnight. Wash the ether with water. Shake with several portions of saturated solution of potassium permanganate containing 20 grams of sodium hydroxide per liter. Wash with water and treat with concentrated sulfuric acid for a short time. Wash the ether and dry over calcium chloride. Distil at 35°, dry over sodium ribbon, and redistil. Let stand over sodium ribbon for several weeks and redistil. Such a purified ether should give no color at the interface with a layer of Schiff's reagent in 30 minutes.

Acetic acid. Reflux 500 ml. of glacial acetic acid with 10 grams of chromic acid anhydride for 1 hour. Distil the acid and test the distillate with Schiff's reagent according to the procedure for estimation of aldehydes. Repeat the treatment until the acid no longer gives a color with the reagent.

Schiff's Reagent—A routine form is as follows. Mix 30 ml. of a

---

[1] See Chapter 1 for details of organization, condensation, etc.

[2] Allen W. Rowe and Edward Phelps, *J. Am. Chem. Soc.* **46**, 2078-85 (1924); G. V. Zavrov, *Zavodskaya Lab.* **4**, 764-7 (1935).

0.1 per cent aqueous fuchsin solution with 200 ml. of a saturated solution of sulfur dioxide. Shake and add 6 ml. of 1:1 sulfuric acid. Let stand for 24 hours and filter if necessary. The solution should be colorless or a faint yellow. Protection under hydrogen reduces the rate of deterioration of the reagent. The sensitivity is limited [3] by the presence of excess sulfur dioxide and obscured by yellow to brown impurities. The latter are removable with activated carbon.

For a more sensitive form, pass sulfur dioxide into 500 ml. of water containing 0.5 gram of suspended basic fuchsin until the weight has increased by 1 gram. The solution will usually still be red. Let stand overnight in a stoppered container for the excess dye to dissolve and decolorize. Dilute to 1 liter. A brown color due to impurities will be present. Add 1 gram of decolorizing carbon, shake well, and filter with minimum exposure to air. With very good dye and carbon the solution is colorless.

A somewhat different technic is as follows.[4] Bubble sulfur dioxide through 100 ml. of water for 5 minutes. Estimate the amount absorbed by the increase in weight of the solution. Add a volume containing 0.60 gram of sulfur dioxide to 0.17 gram of rosaniline hydrochloride in 50 ml. of water. Shake at intervals for 1 hour during which time most of the color will disappear. Dilute to 250 ml., decolorize with activated carbon, filter, and use at once. For less than 0.05 per cent solution of test substance the reagent must be not over 6 hours old but for more concentrated solutions it can be used after several days. Excess sulfur dioxide must be present, but the less the excess, the greater the sensitivity.

The reagent is sensitive to temperature, probably due to loss of sulfur dioxide; used above 20°, it decomposes [5]; at 25° in 30 minutes; at 60° at once. The rate of color development is also affected by temperature; at 10°, it required 16 hours; at 20°, only 6 hours. If the reagent to be used shows a residual color, treat with decolorizing carbon at the rate of 0.2 gram per 100 ml., shake, and filter.[6] Thus the final reagent should be substantially colorless at this stage.

[3] Walter C. Tobie, *Ind. Eng. Chem., Anal. Ed.* **14**, 405-6 (1942); Cf. *Food Research* **3**, 499-504 (1938); *Ibid.* **6**, 15-29 (1941),

[4] Herbert N. Alyea and Hans L. J. Bäckström, *J. Am. Chem. Soc.* **51**, 90-109 (1929).

[5] R. I. Veksler, *Zhur. Anal. Khim.* **1**, 301-10 (1946).

[6] Leon Segal, *Anal. Chem.* **23**, 1499 (1951).

ALDEHYDES IN GENERAL

A general reaction for carbonyl groups with alcoholic 2,4-dinitrophenylhydrazine is applied to aliphatic and aromatic aldehydes and ketones in general or to either in the absence of the other.[7] There is interference by nitroaromatic groups or by chalcone-type ketones. The color is wine red. The reaction is applied to determination of total aldehydes in rancid food.[8] By use of a column of alumina the 2,4-dinitrophenylhydrazones of all aldehydes and ketones are obtained in benzene solution, but the unreacted reagent is retained in the column. Volatile aldehydes are estimated along with volatile alcohols by reactions with this reagent. Total aldehydes are also determined by Schiff's reagent.[9]

Procedure—*With 2,4-dinitrophenylhydrazine.* Prepare carbonyl-free methanol by refluxing 500 ml. of CP grade with 5 grams of 2,4-dinitrophenylhydrazine and a few drops of concentrated hydrochloric acid for 2 hours. Distil and keep tightly stoppered.

Dissolve the sample in methanol to give a concentration of not over 0.001 mole of carbonyl. If alkalinity is present in the original sample carry over to very faint acidity by dropwise addition of concentrated hydrochloric acid. Mix 1 ml. of sample solution in methanol with 1 ml. of saturated 2,4-dinitrophenylhydrazine in methanol and 1 drop of concentrated hydrochloric acid. Stopper loosely and heat at 50° for 30 minutes or 100° for 5 minutes. Cool and add 5 ml. of 10 per cent potassium hydroxide in 80 per cent methanol. Read at 480 mμ against a methanol blank. Acetophenone is an appropriate standard.

Urine. Dilute 20 ml. with an equal volume of water and add 1.5 ml. of 1:3 hydrochloric acid and 3 ml. of concentrated hydrochloric acid until the distillate totals 25 ml. Let stand at about 65° for 48 hours to complete the reaction. Then add 6 drops of acetylacetone to destroy excess hydrazine by conversion to a pyrazolone, and heat at about 75° for 45 minutes.

Filter and wash the precipitate with 1:3 hydrochloric acid. The precipitate contains both osazone and hydrazone; the filtrate contains

---

[7] G. Matthiessen and H. Dahn, *Z. ges. Exptl. Med.* **113**, 336-40 (1944); Gerald L. Lappin and Leland C. Clark, *Anal. Chem.* **23**, 541-2 (1951).

[8] M. F. Pool and A. A. Klose, *J. Am. Oil Chemists' Soc.* **28**, 215-18 (1951).

[9] Official and Tentative Methods of Analyis of the Association of Official Agricultural Chemists,'' 7th Ed., p. 311, Association of Official Agricultural Chemists, Washington, D. C. (1950).

hydrazones. Extract the filtrate with three successive 15-ml. portions of ethyl acetate and discard the aqueous acid layer. Extract the precipitate with three successive 5-ml. portions of hot low-boiling petroleum ether. Combine the petroleum ether and ethyl acetate extracts and evaporate to dryness with care. This is the sample for estimation of hydrazones.

Extract the hydrazone-free precipitate with three successive 5-ml. portions of pyridine. Dilute this solution to 30 ml. for development of the color of an aliquot as alcohols.

As aldehydes, dissolve the solid residue in 8 ml. of 1 per cent ethanolic potassium hydroxide and read. Interpret the reading in terms of a calibration curve prepared with ethanol-2,4-dinitrophenylhydrazone.

As alcohols, treat a 5-ml. aliquot of prepared solution with 1 ml. of 2 per cent potassium-hydroxide solution and read. Interpret the results in terms of a calibration curve prepared with glucosazone.

Fats and oils. Dissolve a sample in benzene to contain about 0.01-0.1 micromole of aldehyde per ml. Set up a 7 × 110 mm. chromatograph tube with a capillary at the bottom and 110 mm. of 10 mm. tubing above it. As the filling mix 80-200 mesh F-20 alumina with 15 per cent of the charge hydrated in a vacuum desiccator over water. Add a 30-mm. layer of alumina. Add 10 ml. of 0.05 per cent solution of 2,4-dinitrophenyl-hydrazine in benzene and fill up with alumina to 110 mm. When the reagent has climbed to the top of the column add 5 ml. of benzene.

When all of this has entered the column add 5 ml. of sample in benzene. Start collecting the solution and add fresh benzene until 19 ml. is collected. Dilute to 25 ml. with 6 per cent potassium hydroxide solution in absolute ethanol. Mix and read at once at 435 mμ against a reagent blank. Fading is at about 0.5 per cent per minute.

Solid foods. Grind as fine as possible and stir a 2-gram sample with an appropriate volume of benzene. Proceed as for fats and oils from "Set up a 7 × 110 mm. . . . ." At the point where the benzene solution of fat or oil would be added, transfer the solid sample in benzene to the space above the chromatograph column and proceed.

With Schiff's reagent. Citrus oils. Dilute 2 grams of lemon oil or 4 grams of orange oil to 50 ml. with aldehyde-free ethanol. Mix 2 ml. of the diluted sample with 25 ml. of aldehyde-free ethanol at about 15° and add 20 ml. of Schiff's reagent cooled to the same temperature. Dilute to 50 ml. with the cooled ethanol and keep at that temperature for 15 minutes. Read against a reagent blank and interpret from a citral curve.

FORMALDEHYDE AND PARAFORMALDEHYDE

The general reaction of aldehydes to give a violet color with reduced fuchsin solution, known as Schiff's reagent, is applied as a secondary method for alcohols. The mechanism is believed to be elimination of water to form a compound of 2 molecules of fuchsin with 3 molecules of aldehyde.[10] In the absence of other aldehydes this is used to estimate any one in solution. Thus it is applied to formaldehyde or to the polymeric form of formaldehyde, known either as paraformal or paraformaldehyde. Lactose, sucrose, and menthol do not produce color. To estimate formaldehyde in the presence of higher straight-chain aldehydes, glyoxals, and their polymers, allow the developed colors to stand for 6 hours at the appropriate pH. That due to formaldehyde does not fade. Others except trioxymethylene do.[11] A specific technic is available for formaldehyde in the presence of furfuraldehyde with that time of aging[12] or in the presence of acetaldehyde with shorter aging.[13] For concentrations up to 0.002 mg. per ml., the color conforms to Beer's law. The Schiff method is applicable to free formaldehyde in the presence of acetals, formals, and other combined forms.

Formals when hydrolyzed in the presence of sulfuric acid give formaldehyde which is determined by Schiff's reagent without distillation.[14] An appropriate sample contains 0.01-0.1 mg. of formaldehyde in 5 ml. of sample.

The red compound from reaction of formaldehyde with phenylhydrazine hydrochloride in the presence of potassium ferricyanide[15] is stable for some time. Diacetyl, glyceryl aldehyde, furfural, and some sugars interfere.

When diazobenzenesulfonic acid is used with sodium amalgam, several aldehydes give a crimson color.[16] The potency of diazobenzenesulfonic

---

[10] Hugo Schiff, *Compt. rend.* **61**, 45-7 (1865); Georges Denigès, *Compt. rend.* **150**, 529-31 (1910).

[11] W. J. Blaedel and F. E. Blacet, *Ind. Eng. Chem., Anal. Ed.* **13**, 499-50 (1941).

[12] R. I. Veksler, *Zhur. Anal. Khim.* **4**, 14-20 (1949).

[13] R. I. Veksler, *Ibid.* **5**, 32-8 (1950).

[14] Carroll L. Hoffpauir, G. Warren Buckaloo, and John D. Guthrie, *Ind. Eng. Chem., Anal. Ed.* **15**, 605-6 (1943).

[15] S. B. Schryver, *Proc. Royal Soc.* (London) **82B**, 226-32 (1910); S. B. Schryver and C. C. Wood, *Analyst* **45**, 165-70 (1920); F. Láska, *Chem. Listy* **33**, 375-6 (1939); P. Desnuelle and M. Naudet, *Bull. soc. chim.* **12**, 871-4 (1945); Danzi Matukawa, *J. Biochem.* (Japan) **30**, 385-9 (1939); Morris B. Jacobs, Eleanor L. Eastman, and David L. Shepard, *J. Am. Pharm. Assoc.* **40**, 365-7 (1951).

[16] F. Penzoldt and E. Fischer, *Ber.* **16**, 657 (1883).

acid solutions decreases in 2-3 days and the solution is useless after a week. The solid shows signs of decomposition in 1-2 months. The diazonium salt acts by oxidation as is shown by its replacement by ferric sulfate and ferricyanide, iodates, bromates, and permanganates.[17] In summary, the following colors are identical: ferricyanide development in acid solution and later made basic, diazonium reagent developed either acid or basic, ferricyanide development either acid or basic. Using phenylhydrazine and ferricyanide, there is interference in the presence of over 50 mg. per ml. of methanol or 400 mg. of ethanol, and from 0.05 mg. of acetaldehyde or 4 times that amount of isobutyraldehyde or benzaldehyde. Acetone must not exceed 2.5 mg. per ml., ethylamine 20 mg. per ml., propylamine 2 mg. per ml., phenol 50 mg., formic acid 10 mg., and pentaerythritol or its diformal 50 mg. per ml. Accuracy is within ±2 per cent. Both phloroglucinol and formaldehyde give a red color.[18] The maximum intensity is obtained in 3 minutes, after which the color gradually changes to violet and then disappears.

In alkaline solution resorcinol reacts with aldehydes to give a pink color [19] with a green undertone which will detect 0.1 mg. of formaldehyde. Heating makes red predominate.[20]

The qualitative use of chromotropic acid,[21] 1,8-dihydroxynaphthalene-3,6-disulfonic acid, has been made quantitative.[22] Formaldehyde gives a purple color which conforms to Beer's law. The original method calls for heating in the presence of sulfuric acid. As little as 0.002 mg. of formaldehyde in a final 100-ml. volume can be detected.[23] However, there are many interferences. Formals and diacetyl are hydrolyzed to formaldehyde and react. By evaporation of the solution of formaldehyde with

[17] Morris Tanenbaum and Clark E. Bricker, *Anal. Chem.* **23**, 354-7 (1951).

[18] R. J. Collins and P. J. Hanzlik, *J. Biol. Chem.* **25**, 231-7 (1916); Alfred T. Shohl and Clyde L. Denny, *J. Urology* **4**, 419-37 (1920); R. C. Hoather and P. G. T. Hand, *Analyst* **65**, 29-30 (1938).

[19] A. S. Zhitkova, S. I. Kaplun, and Joseph B. Ficklen, "Estimation of Poisonous Gases and Vapors in the Air," pp. 130-2. Service to Industry, West Hartford, Conn. (1936).

[20] Harry E. Barbeheim, *Private communication*.

[21] E. Eegriwe, *Z. anal. Chem.* **110**, 22-5 (1937).

[22] John M. Boyd and Milan A. Logan, *J. Biol. Chem.* **146**, 279-87 (1942); Clark E. Bricker and Hilding R. Johnson, *Ind. Eng. Chem., Anal. Ed.* **17**, 400-2 (1945); Douglas A. MacFayden, Helen D. Watkins, and Pearl R. Anderson, *J. Biol. Chem.* **158**, 107-33 (1945); Elmars Bremanis, *Z. anal. Chem.* **130**, 44-7 (1949).

[23] Theodor Kleinert and Eugen Trepel, *Mikrochemie ver. Mikrochim. Acta* **33**, 328-32 (1948).

the reagent these interferences are volatilized and a more specific method derived.[24]

The procedure is then suitable for estimation of 1 part of formaldehyde in the presence of 20,000 parts of chloroform, carbon tetrachloride, methanol, ethanol, *n*-butanol, isobutanol, *sec*-butanol, tertiary amyl alcohol, acetone, methylethyl ketone, pyridine, and benzene. Recovery is accurate in the presence of 1000 parts of acetic acid, propionic acid, or benzyl alcohol. With acetaldehyde or benzaldehyde present, the ratio should not exceed 100:1. Only 10 parts of benzoic acid to one of formaldehyde is permissible. All of these depend on the volatility of the interfering substance. If iodine is present up to 25:1 can be reduced with excess sodium sulfite and then does not interfere. Reasonable amounts of cyclic formals such as are present in safrole and piperonal are volatilized and do not interfere. Diacetyl does not interfere. The color of formaldehyde with ferric chloride is also important.[25]

Samples—Gas. Pass the gas at the rate of 25-30 liters per hour through suitable absorbing tubes containing water. The volume of gas passed will depend on the concentration of formaldehyde vapors. A desirable end concentration is of the order of 0.001 mg. per ml. for development with Schiff's reagent.

Alternatively use the solution prepared in estimation of methanol (page 43).

Pharmaceutical tablets.[26] Weigh the tablet, add 200 ml. of water, and reflux for 30 minutes. This converts any paraformaldehyde to formaldehyde. Let cool, rinse out the condenser, dilute to 500 ml., and filter. Use an aliquot of the filtrate as sample for development with Schiff's reagent.

Meat. Add 2 ml. of a 1 per cent solution of phenylhydrazine hydrochloride to 10 ml. of water. Add 10 grams of the sample of minced meat suspected of containing 0.002 per cent of formaldehyde and heat for 5 minutes. If necessary because of the concentration, vary the size of the meat sample. Cool, filter through cotton, and use 12 ml. of filtrate as sample for development of color with phenylhydrazine but starting with the addition of potassium ferricyanide.

Urine. Add a few drops of 50 per cent sodium hydroxide solution to precipitate phosphates, shake well, and filter. The phloroglucinol method is appropriate.

[24] Clark E. Bricker and W. Aubrey Vail, *Anal. Chem.* 22, 720-2 (1950).

[25] R. Vuillaume, *Ann. fals. fraudes* 44, 287-90 (1951).

[26] Norman Evers and Charles M. Caines, *Pharm. J.* 106, 470 (1921).

Formals. Typical of this class with theoretical percentages of formaldehyde as cited are trioxane 100 per cent, pentaerythritol diformal 37.5 per cent, pentaerythritol monoformal 20.27 per cent, piperonal 20 per cent, and n-propyl formal 22.6 per cent. Dissolve a sample in water and dilute to a volume where the equivalence to formaldehyde approximates 0.05 mg. per ml. Use this as a sample by the chromotropic acid method which will hydrolyze the formal to free formaldehyde.

Crystalline formals. Dissolve a 20-40 mg. sample in 1:2 sulfuric acid and dilute to 1 liter with that acid. Heat a portion in a stoppered flask at 90° for 2 hours, and cool. Use an aliquot for development with Schiff's reagent.

Cellulose formals. To 0.1 gram of sample add 100 ml. of 1:2 sulfuric acid. Seal and incubate at 90° for 2 hours. Cool and develop the color in an aliquot by Schiff's reagent.

Milk. Use for development by ferric chloride.

Procedure—*With Schiff's reagent.* Add 10 ml. of sample to 2 ml. of Schiff's reagent. Mix as quickly as possible and after 3 minutes read at 560 mμ.

Furfural present. Dilute a sample containing less than 0.02 mg. of formaldehyde and other aldehydes to 40 ml. and add 5 ml. of 1:1 hydrochloric acid. Add 5 ml. of Schiff's reagent. Stopper, mix, and store in the dark for 6 hours at 20°. The color developed will be stable for 2-4 hours longer at that temperature. Read the intensity at 570-590 mμ as compared with a reagent blank which under some conditions will show color.[27]

Acetaldehyde present. Adjust the pH to 0.7 at which acetaldehyde gives no color.

With phenylhydrazine. Dilute a sample of not over 0.6 ml. containing not over 0.015 mg. of formaldehyde to 1 ml. with isopropanol to contain 40-50 per cent of the latter. Add 0.5 ml. of 7.5 per cent aqueous phenylhydrazine hydrochloride and let stand for 10 ± 1 minute. Add 0.3 ml. of 5 per cent aqueous potassium ferricyanide and, after 5 ± 0.5 minute, 2 ml. of 10 per cent aqueous sodium hydroxide. Dilute to 25 ml. after 4 ± 1 minute and read at 520 mμ against a reagent blank in 10 ± 3 minutes.

With phloroglucinol. To a suitable volume of sample solution add 2 ml. of a 1 per cent solution of phloroglucinol in 10 per cent sodium

---

27 Clark E. Bricker and Hilding R. Johnson, *Ind. Eng. Chem., Anal. Ed.* **17**, 400-2 (1945).

hydroxide solution. Dilute to 50 ml., mix, and read after 3 minutes against a reagent blank.

With resorcinol. Transfer 1 to 10 ml. of standard formaldehyde solution of appropriate concentration to a series of tubes. Dilute each to 20 ml. and take 20 ml. of aqueous sample in another tube. To each add 5 ml. of a reagent made by dissolving 5 grams of resorcinol in 150 ml. of a cold 33 per cent aqueous solution of sodium hydroxide. Mix and place in a cold water bath. Gradually bring to boiling and let cool. Compare the sample with the series of varying intensities of red obtained with the standards. Since the original reagent is yellow-green and the tubes show a green undertone, the series of standards method is the desirable one.

With chromotropic acid. To 100 ± 10 mg. of chromotropic acid add 1 ml. of sample containing not over 0.1 mg. of formaldehyde. Evaporate to dryness at not over 200° and heat for 5 minutes after evaporation is complete. Cool and add 5 ml. of concentrated sulfuric acid. Heat at 100° for 30 minutes, cool, and dilute to 50 ml. Read at 570 mμ against a reagent blank.

With ferric chloride. Mix 1 ml. of sample with 5 ml. of concentrated hydrochloric acid containing 0.005 per cent of ferric chloride. Heat at 40° for 10 minutes and cool for reading against a reagent blank.

ACETALDEHYDE

The familiar Schiff's reagent is used for estimation of acetaldehyde in the absence of other aldehydes. This method is suitable for estimation of such amounts as occur as contaminants in alcohol, ether, or acetic acid. Special precautions are necessary to obtain aldehyde-free alcohol and ether for use with the standards. The color produced is not proportional to the concentration of aldehyde. For this reason the standard and the unknown solution must have approximately the same concentration for the results to be dependable, or the series of standards method may be used.

The maximum absorption of fuchsin is at 538 mμ; that of the color developed with aldehydes at 560 mμ. Increase in acidity increases the wave length of the color; hence a buffer in the solution is desirable to adjust it to about pH 6. More than 40 per cent of ethanol should not be present. Accuracy to 1 per cent is attained and 1 ppm. detected.[28] Casein, serum albumin, egg albumin and some sugars must be absent.

---

[28] Sigge Hähnel, *Svensk. Kem. Tids.* **45**, 27-41 (1933); *Ibid.* **48**, 61-4 (1936).

With somewhat more detail acetaldehyde is determined by Schiff's reagent with formaldehyde present.[29]

Acetaldehyde gives a yellow to brown color with benzidine hydrochloride.[30] Formaldehyde gives the same reaction but the color develops much more slowly. The method is only suitable for the rapid estimation of relatively large amounts.

Acetaldehyde gives a yellow to brown color with m-phenylenediamine hydrochloride.[31] The rate of color development is directly associated with ethanol concentration. Furfural gives a brown color with the reagent which is 10 times as intense as that of acetaldehyde. Copper and zinc do not interfere. Ferric ion alters the yellow or reddish-brown color to olive green, but this can be prevented by addition of a trace of phosphoric acid.

A blue color is produced by reaction with piperazine hydrate and sodium nitroprusside.[12] Hydroquinone gives a brown color with acetaldehyde which has been adapted to estimation of lactic acid (page 348). A rose color with veratrol has been similarly applied (page 348). The red color of resorcinol with formaldehyde has an equivalent green with acetaldehyde.[33]

Benzene diazonium salts give an intense red with acetaldehyde or acetone.[34] The reagent is 3 drops of aniline in 5 ml. of 1:5 hydrochloric acid cooled to 0°, and 1 ml. of 10 per cent sodium nitrite solution added. Addition to acetaldehyde will detect 0.001 mg. in 5-10 minutes. When 2 ml. of sample containing acetaldehyde is refluxed with 2 ml. of 30 per cent sodium hydroxide solution and 10 ml. of diazotized 0.2 per cent sulfanilic acid solution, a magenta red is developed.[35] Diluted to 50 ml. with 30 per cent sodium hydroxide solution, it is suitable for reading at 530 mμ. Acetaldehyde in monovinyl acetate is read directly at 287 mμ over the range 0-0.6 per cent.[36] Acetaldehyde is precipitated by ammonia from vinyl chloride and determined turbidimetrically.[37] Accuracy

[29] R. I. Veksler, *Zhur. Anal. Klim.* **5**, 32-8 (1950).

[30] N. K. Smitt, *Bur. Bio.-Tech. Bull.* **No. 5**, 117-8 (1922).

[31] G. Vegezzi and P. Haller, *Mitt. Lebensm. Hyg.* **25**, 39-47 (1934).

[32] P. Desnuelle and M. Naudet, *Bull. soc. chim.* **12**, 871-4 (1945).

[33] Harry E. Barbeheim, *Private communication.*

[34] R. Berg, *Mikrochemie ver. Mikrochim. Acta* **30**, 137 (1941).

[35] Antonio Mossini, *Boll. soc. ital. biol. sper.* **16**, 374-5 (1941) .

[36] Ingvar Jullander and Kurt Brune, *Acta Chem. Scand.* **2**, 204-8 (1948).

[37] John C. Cotman, Jr. and George C. Claver, Jr., *Anal. Chem.* **23**, 1711 (1951).

to ±0.27 per cent is obtained at 1-20 ppm. Dimethylacetal may be hydrolyzed to acetaldehyde for estimation by Schiff's reagent.[38]

Another method of estimation is by distillation of acetaldehyde from a blood or tissue filtrate into a bisulfite solution [39] and subsequent color development with p-hydroxydiphenyl as for lactic acid (page 348). Ethanol gives no color. Glucose does not give a distillate from acid solution. Lactate and pyruvate do not distil from a solution of pH 6.5-7. Acetylmethylcarbinol, acetone, and 2,3-butylene glycol do not interfere. Diacetyl interferes unless destroyed by preliminary treatment with periodic acid. Paraldehyde and formaldehyde both interfere. The method will detect 0.0002-0.002 mg. per ml. of distillate with an accuracy of ±2 per cent.

Either acetaldehyde or acetone is converted to iodoform by iodine in alkaline solution. With a hydrogen discharge or tungsten lamp this is read at 347 mμ.[40] There are other maxima at 307 mμ and 274 mμ. There is interference by methyl isopropyl ketone and by mesityl oxide. Many carbonyl compounds give background absorption. The maxima are the same in chloroform, n-heptane, isooctane, and ethylene dichloride. Iodine gives no absorption.

Samples—*Alcoholic solutions.* If low in acetaldehyde dilute only to 50 per cent by volume, if somewhat higher dilute to 30 per cent by volume. It is desirable to have the acetaldehyde of the order of 15-20 mg. per liter for estimation by Schiff's reagent. The standard must have aldehyde-free ethanol added to bring it to the same alcoholic strength as the sample.

Procedure—*By Schiff's reagent.* Measure into a test tube an amount of sample to contain 0.01-0.05 mg. of acetaldehyde. Add 1 ml. of phosphate buffer to pH 6 (Vol. I, p. 176), dilute to 5 ml. with water, and add 1 ml. of reagent (page 251). Mix well, let stand for 30 minutes, and dilute to 10 ml. Read at 560 mμ against a reagent blank. If the sample contains ethanol provide for the same amount in the standard.

Formaldehyde present. Plot the rate of development separately of color with formaldehyde and acetaldehyde at pH 2.7. Determine the

[38] Elvio Cianetti, *Ann. chim. applicata* **38**, 360-3 (1948).

[39] Elmer Stotz, *J. Biol. Chem.* **148**, 585-91 (1943); W. W. Westerfeld, *J. Lab. Clin. Med.* **30**, 1076-7 (1945).

[40] Stephen Dal Nogare, T. O. Norris, and John Mitchell, Jr., *Anal. Chem.* **23**, 1473-8 (1951).

mixed aldehydes at that pH. Subtract the formaldehyde determined at pH 0.7 at which acetaldehyde gives no reaction. For development dilute the sample to 45 ml. at the appropriate pH and add 5 ml. of Schiff's reagent. The maximum coloration is reached in 15-20 minutes. Read against a reagent blank.

By benzidine. As reagent rub 6.7 grams of benzidine or a corresponding amount of the hydrochloride in a mortar with 20 ml. of water. Rinse the paste into a liter flask, add 20 ml. of 2:1 hydrochloric acid, and dilute to volume. The solution has a brown color. Treat with activated carbon, filter, and use the clear filtrate. To 5 ml. of sample solution add 5 ml. of reagent. Treat a series of standard solutions of acetaldehyde similarly. Compare after 30 minutes.

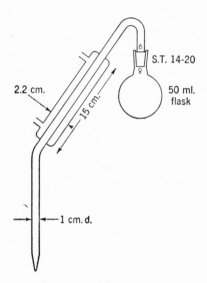

FIG. 18. Distilling unit for acetaldehyde

By m-phenylenediamine. As reagent add 0.5 ml. of 85 per cent phosphoric acid and 0.5 gram of activated carbon to 19 ml. of 10 per cent m-pheneylenediamine solution. Mix well and filter after 1-2 hours. The reagent so decolorized will remain colorless for several days.

Adjust the ethanol concentration of the sample to 40 per cent by volume. To 10 ml. of sample and to a similar standard add 1 ml. of the m-phenylenediamine reagent. Mix, let stand for 15 minutes, and compare. The period is approximately optimum for development of color in 40 per cent ethanol. If the ethanol is under 38 per cent as much as an hour may be required. In 95 per cent ethanol only 10 minutes is necessary.

With piperazine hydrate. To 1 ml. of sample solution add 1 ml. of saturated aqueous piperazine hydrate and 0.5 ml. of 4 per cent sodium nitroprusside solution. Dilute to 5 ml. and read at 570 mμ against a reagent blank.

With p-hydroxybiphenyl. Transfer a sample to the flask of the distillation apparatus shown in Figure 18. A typical sample is 8 ml. of 1:10 tungstic acid blood filtrate. At least one-quarter of the sample must be distilled. Add a quartz pebble to the flask to avoid bumping. Arrange the tip of the condenser to dip below the surface of 2 ml. of 2 per cent sodium bisulfite solution contained in a graduated cylinder which stands in an ice bath. Collect about 3 ml. over a distillation period of about 2 minutes. Lift the condenser from the solution, adjust the total volume to exactly 5 ml., and mix thoroughly.

Add 1 ml. of distillate to 0.05 ml. of 5 per cent copper sulfate solution, place in an ice bath, and add exactly 8 ml. of concentrated sulfuric acid slowly with constant shaking. As p-hydroxybiphenyl reagent dissolve 1 gram in 25 ml. of hot 8 per cent sodium hydroxide solution and dilute to 100 ml. Add 0.2 ml. of the p-hydroxybiphenyl reagent close to the surface of the liquid and disperse the precipitate evenly by gentle rotation. Allow to stand at room temperature for 1 hour or at 30° for 0.5 hour with occasional mixing. Place in boiling water for 90 seconds and upon cooling read the purple color at 560 mμ against a reagent blank.

As iodoform. Mix 10 ml. of 20 per cent iodine solution and 3.3 ml. of 20 per cent sodium hydroxide solution. Swirl and, if not orange-yellow, add more iodine solution dropwise. Add 1-5 ml. of sample solution containing up to 0.4 mg. of acetaldehyde or acetone from a pipet and mix at once. During the next 5 minutes of reaction time, if the orange-yellow is becoming discharged, restore the color with iodine solution.

At the end of the reaction, add 5 per cent sodium thiosulfate solution dropwise until the iodine color disappears. Extract with 22-24 ml. of chloroform, which will give complete extraction, and separate the extract. Wash with an equal volume of water to reduce background absorption, and dry the chloroform layer by filtering through anhydrous sodium sulfate. Wash the sodium sulfate with chloroform to dilute to 25 ml. Read at 347 mμ against chloroform.

Turbidimetrically in vinyl chloride by 2-methylindole. Transfer 1 ml. of concentrated ammonium hydroxide to a pressure bottle, add 100 grams of vinyl chloride containing not over 20 ppm. of acetaldehyde, below its boiling point, and seal with a tin-lined crown closure. This acts as a release in case of excessive pressure. Shake mechanically for 1 hour in a metal enclosure. Chill in ice water and puncture the cap under a hood.

As reagent dissolve 0.1-0.2 gram of 2-methylindole in 60 ml. of concentrated hydrochloric acid and 30 ml. of water. Use within 10 hours due to oxidation. Dilute the sample, from which vinyl chloride has evaporated, to not over 50 ml. Add 20 ml. of reagent and dilute to 100 ml. with water. After 10 minutes read turbidimetrically, subtracting a reagent blank. For 20-50 ppm. dilute to 200 ml. before reading or repeat with 50 grams of sample.

ACRYLIC ALDEHYDE, ACROLEIN

The reaction of acrylic aldehyde, acrolein, with tryptophane in strong hydrochloric acid gives an intense color with a maximum at 550 mμ.[41] The only disadvantage of substituting sulfuric acid is its heat of dilution. A blank is colorless. It will detect 0.015 mg. of acrolein. Formaldehyde gives a yellow color, glyoxal one approximating that of acrolein. Work has been mainly in ethanol. In its absence the intensity of color is reduced by about one-third. The color conforms to Beer's law over the range 0.015-0.15 mg. in the procedure given.

Acrylic aldehyde reacts with sulfuric acid and veratrol to form a red condensation product.[42] The same reaction is given by acetaldehyde, by pyruvic aldehyde, and by dihydroxyacetone. The method was originally applied to lactic acid after converting it to acetaldehyde. The determination is made with concentrations varying from 40 to 140 mg. per liter, with an average error of 1 or 2 per cent.

Acrylic aldehyde gives a yellow color with benzidine acetate solution, which is suitable for its colorimetric estimation.[43] Other aldehydes give the color with a different hue and therefore interfere. In ethanol this will detect 0.005 mg. of acrylic aldehyde.

Schiff's reagent has been applied,[44] as have also phloroglucinol, hydrogen peroxide and hydrochloric acid,[45] pyrogallol and hydrochloric acid, and phenol and sulfuric acid.[46]

Procedure—*By tryptophane.* Dilute a sample containing 0.01-0.2 mg. of acrolein to 2 ml. Add 0.5 ml. of 0.2 per cent tryptophane in 1:200 hydrochloric acid, and 1.2 ml. of water. Cool in ice and dilute to 10 ml. with ice-cold concentrated hydrochloric acid. Heat at 40° for 50 minutes, avoiding bright light which will cause fading. Read at 550 mμ

[41] Sidney J. Circle, Leonard Stone, and C. S. Boruff, *Ind. Eng. Chem., Anal. Ed.* **17**, 259-62 (1945).

[42] Erich Baer, *Arbeitsphysiol.* **1**, 130-5 (1928).

[43] A. S. Zhitkova, S. I. Kaplun, and Joseph B. Ficklen, "Estimation of Poisonous Gases and Vapors in the Air," pp. 134-5. Service to Industry, West Hartford, Conn. (1936).

[44] C. Moureu and E. Boismenu, *J. pharm. chim.* **27**, 49-54, 89-97 (1923); D. P. Senderikhina, *Gigiena i Sanit*, **12**, No. 3, 17-19 (1947).

[45] I. L. Uzdina, *Hig. Truda Tekh. Bezopastnosti* (USSR) **15**, 63-6 (1937).

[46] M. K. Berezova, *Hig. i. Sanit.* (USSR) **1940**, No. 10, 31-7.

against a reagent blank. If chilling is omitted results are only a little less consistent. If the developed color is chilled, it is stable for some hours.

By veratrol. To 0.5 ml. of sample solution and to a standard add dropwise, cooling in ice, 3 ml. of concentrated sulfuric acid which is free from nitrogen compounds. Heat for 4 minutes in boiling water. Cool quickly in ice and after 2 minutes treat with 0.1 ml. of a 0.125 per cent solution of veratrol in absolute ethanol. Compare after 20 minutes.

By benzidine. Dilute a sample containing 0.01-0.1 mg. of acrylic aldehyde to 10 ml. Add 1 ml. of a fresh 1 per cent solution of benzidine in glacial acetic acid. Mix and place in a cold water bath. Heat to boiling and discontinue heating. Let stand for 15 minutes and read the yellow color.

CROTONALDEHYDE, β-METHYLACROLEIN

The formation of a Schiff base with *m*-phenylenediamine dihydrochloride in ethanol described for cinnamic aldehyde (page 279) is applicable to crotonaldehyde with reproducibility to ±1.7 per cent.

Procedure—Add 15 ml. of the reagent to a sample containing 0.25-2.5 mg. of the aldehyde and dilute to 50 ml. with absolute ethanol. Heat, minimizing evaporation, in a water bath at 65° for 30 minutes. Cool in ice for 1 minute and read at 415 mμ against a reagent blank within 30 minutes.

PYRUVIC ALDEHYDE, METHYLGLYOXAL

Pyruvic aldehyde is precipitated by 2,4-dinitrophenylhydrazine. While some sugars are incompletely precipitated under the same conditions their osazones can be extracted with ethanol. The residue dissolves in alcoholic potassium hydroxide to give a violet color which is proportional to the amount of methylglyoxal present.[47]

The characteristically violet condensation product of pyruvic aldehyde with pyrrol in hydrochloric acid is suitable for quantitative use under controlled conditions.[48] The reaction is not given by acetaldehyde, pyruvic acid, acetone, or formaldehyde. The method is sensitive to 30 ppm.

---

[47] H. K. Barrenscheen and Miklos Dreguss, *Biochem. Z.* **233**, 305-10 (1931); Carl Neuberg and Eduard Strauss, *Arch. Biochem.* **7**, 211-30 (1945).

[48] H. K. Barrenscheen and Karl Braun, *Biochem. Z.* **233**, 296-304 (1931).

The reaction given by veratrol with acetaldehyde, acrylic aldehyde, and dihydroxyacetone is applied to estimation of pyruvic aldehyde in the absence of interfering substances.[49] Follow the procedure given for acrylic aldehyde (page 265).

Pyruvic aldehyde in concentrated sulfuric acid with chromotropic acid, 4,5-dihydroxynaphthalene-2,7-disulfonic acid, gives a soluble yellow condensation product which on irradiation at 380-510 mμ gives an intense green fluorescence.[50] The same end result is obtained with glyceraldehyde and dihydroxyacetone, probably by their conversion to pyruvic aldehyde in acid solution. Over the range of 0.001-0.002 mg. per ml. the fluorescence conforms to Beer's law. Photochemical decay necessitates rigid standardization of the time between addition of sulfuric acid and reading the fluorescence of samples and standards. The decay approximates 1 unit of fluorometer reading per 15 minutes after the first 20 minutes. Formaldehyde or diacetyl form a purple dye which absorbs at maxima of 485 and 570 mμ and so interferes. High values result from the presence of d-xylose which is converted to pyruvic aldehyde. Degradation of d-glucose to diacetyl or formaldehyde causes low results. At 1000:1 there is no interference from furfural, acetylsalicylic acid, methylethyl ketone, pyruvic acid, lactic acid, levulinic acid, acetic acid, propionic acid, acetone, acetaldehyde, *iso*butyric aldehyde, methanol, ethanol, and n-butanol. Reading is accurate to about 4 per cent.

Sample—*Blood or tissue extracts.* Mix 10 ml. of blood or extract with 40 ml. of 10 per cent trichloroacetic acid. After standing for 1 hour filter through heavy paper. The filtrate must be water-clear. Dilute an aliquot of the filtrate with 8 per cent trichloroacetic acid to a suitable concentration for estimation with 2,4-dinitrophenylhydrazine.

Procedure—*By 2,4-dinitrophenylhydrazine.* Put 5 ml. of sample and 5 ml. of fresh standard solution containing 0.02 mg. of pyruvic aldehyde per ml., in pointed centrifuge tubes. The standard must have the same menstruum as the sample. Thus for a trichloroacetic acid filtrate it would be 8 per cent trichloroacetic acid solution. Add 1 ml. of a fresh hot 1 per cent solution of 2,4-dinitrophenylhydrazine in 1:5 hydrochloric acid to each. After 2 hours centrifuge for 10 minutes. Wash the precipitates 3 times with 5 ml. of hot 1:10 hydrochloric acid. Follow this by washings with 1:10 hydrochloric acid containing successively 30 per cent, 50

[49] Erich Baer, *Arbeitsphysiol.* 1, 130-5 (1928).
[50] Barbara J. Thornton and John C. Speck, Jr., *Anal. Chem.* 22, 899-902 (1950).

per cent, and then 75 per cent of ethanol. Continue with the latter until the washings are colorless.

Dissolve the precipitates in 5-ml. portions of 5 per cent alcoholic potassium hydroxide. Dilute the standard to 100 ml. and the sample to a proper volume to give a similar color and compare.

By pyrrol. To 1 ml. of sample add 2 drops of freshly distilled colorless pyrrol and mix. Add 2 drops of concentrated hydrochloric acid and mix. Add 10 per cent acetic acid until distinctly acid and then dilute to 5 ml. with saturated alcoholic zinc acetate solution. Compare with a similar color produced from a standard of known concentration, containing the same deproteinizing agents or other ingredients as the sample.

Fluorometrically. To 1 ml. of sample containing 0.0005-0.002 mg. of pyruvic aldehyde add 1 ml. of fresh 2 per cent chromotropic acid solution. Similarly treat standards and a blank. Chill each in ice water and add 10 ml. of ice-cold concentrated sulfuric acid with swirling to cool. When all are so prepared, transfer to a 50° bath for 5 minutes of swirling. Quickly bring to room temperature in cold water and dilute to 25 ml. with concentrated sulfuric acid. Compare the fluorescence of the unknown with the standards employing a blue primary and yellow secondary filter such as the Coleman PC-2 and B-2.

CITRAL, GERANIAL

The major method of determination is by metaphenylenediamine, perhaps because it is the official AOAC method.[51] Due to its aldehyde properties, citral gives a yellow color with the reagent. Other compounds present in lemon and orange oils and extracts sometimes interfere by producing a blue when either the reagent or the oil is not fresh. The blue may be caused by the oxidation of terpenes. Adding oxalic acid as a reducing agent overcomes the interference. It is probable that the method, with or without the use of oxalic acid, merely gives a somewhat low figure for total aldehydes, rather than a true figure for citral. An advantage is that the alcohol used does not have to be free from aldehyde. The reaction with Schiff's reagent is also applicable.

[51] C. E. Parker and R. S. Hiltner, *J. Biol. Chem.* **130**, 149-66 (1939); John Bailey and Christopher K. Beebe, *Ind. Eng. Chem., Anal. Ed.* **13**, 834-6 (1941); "Official and Tentative Methods of Analysis of the Association of Official Agricultural Chemists," 7th ed., pp. 311-12, Association of Official Agricultural Chemists, Washington, D. C. (1950).

Samples—*Lemon Oil.* Dilute about 0.5 gram of lemon oil to 50 ml. with ethanol and mix. Determine by metaphenylenediamine.

Orange Oil. Dilute about 4 grams of orange oil to 50 ml. with ethanol and mix. Determine by metapheylenediamine.

Lemon Extract. Dilute about 10 grams of lemon extract to 50 ml. with ethanol and mix. Determine by metaphenylenediamine.

Orange Extract. Weigh exactly 50 ml. of orange extract and determine by metaphenylenediamine.

Emulsion flavors. Weigh a 10-gram sample and dilute to 50 ml. with ethanol. Develop the color as usual and centrifuge a 20-ml. portion to obtain a clear solution for reading.

Procedure—*By metaphenylenediamine.* As reagent dissolve 1 gram of colorless metaphenylenediamine hydrochloride in about 45 ml. of 85 per cent ethanol. Similarly dissolve about 1 gram of crystalline oxalic acid in about 45 ml. of 85 per cent ethanol. Mix, add 2 or 3 grams of fuller's earth, dilute to 100 ml. with 85 per cent ethanol, shake, let settle, and decant on to a double filter. The filtrate should be clear and practically colorless. It is stable for about 2 days.

Mix 5 ml. of sample with 10 ml. of the reagent and dilute to 50 ml. with ethanol. Read at 420 mμ against a reagent blank. Except for colorless samples, also do a sample blank.

By Schiff's reagent. To 2 ml. of sample containing about 2 mg. of citral, add 25 ml. of 95 per cent aldehyde-free ethanol cooled to 14-16°. Add 20 ml. of Schiff's reagent (page 251) cooled to the same temperature. Dilute to 50 ml. with the cold aldehyde-free alcohol. Stopper, mix, and place in a bath at 14-16° for 15 minutes. Read at 560 mμ against a reagent blank. The blank should show only a faint pink color on standing 20 minutes in the cold bath.

HIGHER FATTY ALDEHYDES

Higher fatty aldehydes and certain derivatives are determined by reaction with fuchsin-sulfurous acid.[52] The acetals and carboxymethoximes of palmitaldehyde and stearaldehyde also react, except that synthetic acetals do not give the colored complex at low temperatures. With these compounds the reaction must be carried out at 37°; at this temperature the maximum is reached in 18 hours. Formaldehyde, heptalde-

---

[52] R. Feulgen and H. Grünberg, *Z. physiol. Chem.* **257**, 161-72 (1939); Marjorie Anchel and Heinrich Waelsch, *J. Biol. Chem.* **152**, 501-9 (1944).

hyde, glyceraldehyde, glyceraldehyde phosphoric acid, and methylglyoxal give no reaction.

Sample—*Muscle*. Mince, suspend 1 gram in 10 ml. of acetone, and shake for an hour. Decant off the solution and repeat the extraction. Evaporate the combined extract to dryness *in vacuo* and dissolve in 5 ml. of glacial acetic acid.

Brain. Mince and extract 100 mg. with 5 ml. of boiling ethanol. Centrifuge, decant, and repeat the extraction. Extract 10 times with 2-ml. portions of boiling ether in the same way. Evaporate the combined extracts *in vacuo* and dissolve the residue in 10 ml. of glacial acetic acid.

Nerve. Let 20 mg. stand for 1 hour in acetone, remove, and grind with sand. Wash the sand-tissue mixture into a centrifuge tube with 5 ml. of ethanol and boil for a few seconds. Centrifuge and repeat the extraction 10 times with 2-ml. portions of boiling ether. Evaporate the combined extracts *in vacuo* and dissolve the residue in 3 ml. of glacial acetic acid.

Procedure—To a 1-ml. portion or other suitable aliquot of sample of acetic-acid solution, add 3 drops of 6 per cent mercuric chloride solution and 10 ml. of reagent containing 1 gram of fuchsin, 100 ml. of 1:11 hydrochloric acid, and 5 grams of sodium bisulfite per liter. Add 1 ml. of 1:11 hydrochloric acid. Mix, stopper, and warm at 37° for 18-24 hours. Cool, extract with 10 ml. of capryl alcohol freshly distilled over sodium, centrifuge the extract, and read at 530 mμ against capryl alcohol.

ALDEHYDES IN FATS AND OILS AS A MEASURE OF RANCIDITY

Rancidity of fats and oils in its earlier stages is accompanied by aldehyde formation. Extreme oxidation of fats is not measured by this method as it is apparently due to formation of condensation products with a reduction in aldehydes. At that stage, measurement of relative rancidity becomes unimportant.

It is usual to apply the reagent in a 2-phase system as by agitating the fat in nonpolar solvent with the aqueous reagent. Thus the Schiff reagent applied [53] and in a modified form [54] gives the measurement of aldehyde content in quantitatively reproducible figures on an arbitrary scale. While several aldehydes such as butyric aldehyde, heptaldehyde,

---

[53] T. von Fellenberg, *Mitt. Lebensm. Hyg.* **15**, 198-208 (1924); Inichof and Schoschine, *Bull. Russe*, **64**, 159-73 (1926).

[54] Helge Schibsted, *Ind. Eng. Chem., Anal. Ed.* **4**, 204-8 (1932).

cinnamic aldehyde and vanillin do not give the color, it is believed that the high molecular weight aldehydes formed in incipient stages of rancidity do. An alternative to the arbitrary standard is to read the color in isoamyl alcohol at 530 mμ.[55]

The development of rancidity is quantitatively estimated colorimetrically by phloroglucinol, a modified Kreis reaction.[56] The substance in rancid fat which gives the reaction is epihydrinaldehyde.[57] The reaction is sensitive to 10 mg. of this aldehyde in 100 ml. of oil. The development of color is a linear function of time. It increases with temperature and is decreased by the presence of water. The lower limit at which the color can be read is about 0.014 per cent of epihydrinaldehyde.

The intensity of the red color in Lovibond units follows Beer's law. The color is fully developed in 20 minutes and should be read at once. With fresh oils the values are all under 5 red units for a 20-mm. layer. A rancid odor is first noted when a Kreis number of 6.6 is reached. A fresh linseed oil gives a yellow-green color. The method is not suitable for application to strongly oxidized and rancid oils because part of the color remains in the ether layer. The course of the reaction is such that these cannot be diluted for estimation. With aromatic oils the reaction is not quantitative. Aside from reading the color with Lovibond glasses, a standard of 0.005 per cent methyl red in 1:1 ethanol and concentrated hydrochloric acid has been used.[58]

Samples—Prepare a special grade of petroleum ether. For this use a grade boiling at 30-100° and shake 4-5 times with one-eighth of its volume of concentrated sulfuric acid. The last acid used should turn only a faint yellow. Reflux with 5 per cent of its volume of 50 per cent sodium hydroxide solution for 2 hours. Separate the petroleum ether and distil over 100 grams of calcium oxide. Collect the fraction boiling at 50-100° for use.

Fat or oil. The weight of fat or oil required may vary over a wide range according to the expected degree of rancidity. Dissolve a weighed sample in the special petroleum ether and dilute to a concentration vary-

55 Walter Mangold, *Vorratspflege u. Lebensmittelforsch.* **4**, 297-303 (1941).

56 H. Kreis, *Chem.-Ztg.* **26**, 1014 (1902); Johs M. Aas, *Fettchem. Umschau* **41**, 113-5 (1934); Magnus Pyke, *Analyst* **60**, 515-9 (1935); N. Drozdov and N. Materanskaya, *Myasnaya Ind.* (USSR) **22**, 30-2 (1951).

57 W. C. Powick, *J. Agr. Research* **26**, 326 (1923).

58 H. Werner, H. Smalfuss and A. Gehrike, *Margarine-Ind.* **29**, 4-8 (1936).

ing from 0.05 to 10 grams per 100 ml. If necessary, filter before diluting to volume. Estimate with Schiff's reagent.

Butter.[59] Dissolve 1 gram of butter in 10 ml. of petroleum ether and estimate with Schiff's reagent.

Procedure—*With Schiff's reagent.* As a special form of reagent, dissolve 20 grams of anhydrous rosaniline hydrochloride in 600 ml. of absolute ethanol by shaking. Dilute to 1 liter with absolute ethanol. Let stand for several days to separate a dark sediment of organic impurities and salt. Pipet 500 ml. of the clear supernatant layer into a liter volumetric flask. Add 133 ml. of 0.64 per cent aqueous sulfur dioxide solution or its equivalent, previously standardized volumetrically with iodine and thiosulfate. Dilute to volume with distilled water.

Prepare an arbitrary artificial color standard from cresol red at pH 8.3. As a buffer dissolve 7.5477 grams of sodium borate decahydrate, 7.5044 grams of boric acid and 1.7696 grams of sodium chloride in distilled water, and dilute to 1 liter. Dissolve 0.1 gram of anhydrous cresol red in a portion of this buffer and dilute to 100 ml. with the buffer. Pipet 5 ml. into a 500-ml. flask and dilute to volume with the buffer. This color standard is assigned an arbitrary value of 100.

Pipet 25 ml. of the solution of sample in petroleum ether into a test tube. Add 5 ml. of the rosaniline reagent. Close the tube with a rubber stopper covered with tinfoil. Place in a holder attached to a vertical disc and rotate at 30 rpm. for 4 minutes. The color obtained is much higher than by vigorous shaking. Let stand for a few minutes and pipet about 20 ml. of the petroleum ether layer into a clean test tube. Stopper with a foil-covered stopper and let stand for 2 hours. Compare with the cresol red standard by balancing. If the color value of one of the comparison solutions differs from that of the other by more than 100 per cent, repeat the determination with a different dilution of the sample.

Calculate to a basis of 0.1 gram of fat per 100 ml. of solution to give the "fat aldehyde value" by following formula:

$$A = \frac{100 \times R_s \times 0.1}{R_t \times P}$$

in which A = fat aldehyde value

R_s = reading of color standard in mm.

R_t = reading of test solution in mm.

P = grams of fat per 100 ml. of solution.

---

[59] G. S. Inihov and A. F. Shoshin, *Trans. Vologda Dairy Institute* (*Russian*) *Bull.* **64**, 161-74 (1926).

Typical Values—Some values reported which will be of assistance in examining occasional samples are as follows:

Sample	Organoleptic Report	Fat Aldehyde Value
Olive oil, fresh	good	14.3
Olive oil, old	rancid	71.0
Cottonseed oil, fresh	good	20.0
Cottonseed oil, old	rancid	132.0
Corn oil, fresh	good	5.5
Corn oil, old	rancid	104.0
Butter oil, fresh	good	0.5
Butter oil, exposed to air..........	tallowy	10.3
Suet, fresh	good	5.0
Suet, old	tallowy	360.0

With phloroglucinol. Prepare a 1 per cent solution of phloroglucinol in acetone. This keeps indefinitely in a dark bottle. Mix 1 gram of oil with 9 grams of this solution. Add 1 ml. of concentrated sulfuric acid and mix. Put in a water bath at 10° for 15 minutes. Read the color with the Lovibond tintometer in terms of red glasses. If the oil sample has been extracted with ether, a precipitate may form. In that case filter through dry paper into the tintometer cell. Interpret the results either in terms of known standards of epihydrinaldehyde or oils of known degree of rancidity.

Alternatively, shake 1 volume of sample and 1 volume of concentrated hydrochloric acid for one-half minute. Add one volume of a 0.5 per cent solution of phloroglucinol in 95 per cent ethanol. Again shake for one-half minute and add 3 volumes of ether. Shake well, venting the pressure developed, and let stand for 10-20 minutes. Separation should occur within 5 minutes. The upper layer retains the color of the oil and consists of the oil with 2 volumes of ether. The lower layer shows the red of the reaction and consists of 1 volume of alcohol, 1 volume of ether, and 1 volume of aqueous hydrochloric acid. Read the color of the lower layer in a thickness of 20 mm. with the Lovibond Tintometer. If the color reads more than 10 units, dilute the colored solution with water and calculate as a linear function.

FURFURAL

Furfural produces a red color with aniline acetate or xylidene acetate.[60] Increase of temperature accelerates both color development and the subsequent fading, the effect being accentuated at low concentrations. A suitable compromise is 25° and 20 minutes. Aniline sulfate [61] and aniline hydrochloride are also used under appropriate conditions. Methyl furfural and hydroxymethylfurfural give yellow to orange colors which do not interfere. The red color is transient in the presence of mineral acid, and very sensitive to sunlight.

The color produced by xylidene has about 1.8 times the intensity of that from aniline and develops more rapidly, but unfortunately is limited in applicability by the rarity of pure xylidene isomers. Addition of ethanol increases the sensitivity. The minimum transmittance is at 500-518 mμ. Excess acetic acid improves the stability of the color and slightly raises the wave length of maximum absorption. Excess aniline increases the intensity of color but decreases its stability. Sodium chloride increases stability of color and slightly decreases its intensity. Over the range of 0.03-0.1 mg. per 100 ml. results conform to Beer's law.[62] Results by this method are lower than by phloroglucinol because the latter also reports methyl furfural and hydroxymethylfurfural as furfural. Since the reaction is not given by acetaldehyde, it is used for estimation of furfural in spirits.

The reaction with p-bromoaniline is applicable in xylene with the reagent in acetic acid.[63] An appropriate range is 0.0004-0.0006 mg. per ml. of sample. This is closely allied to the aniline acetate reagent, the color from which is unstable in this reagent.

The color of furfural with Schiff's reagent develops immediately at 18° while that of formaldehyde develops slowly, permitting estimation of the first if formaldehyde in the sample taken is below 0.13 mg. per ml.[64] The intensity of color developed below pH 2.7 decreases so that

[60] G. de Chalmot, *Am. Chem. J.* **15**, 276-85 (1893); *Ibid.* **16**, 218-29 (1894); L. M. Tolman and T. C. Trescott, *J. Am. Chem. Soc.* **28**, 1619-30 (1906); R. A. Stillings and B. L. Browning, *Ind. Eng. Chem., Anal. Ed.* **12**, 499-502 (1940); Ira J. Duncan, *Ibid.* **15**, 162-4 (1943); G. A. Adams and A. E. Castagne, *Can. J. Research* **26B**, 314-24 (1948); I. M. Korenman, F. S. Frum, and A. A. Russkilsh, *Zavodskaya Lab.* **16**, 3-7 (1950).

[61] Erich Haupt, Theodor Kleinert, and Elfriede Stach, *Mitt. chem. Forsch-Inst. Ind. Österr.* **1**, 97-9 (1947).

[62] G. A. Adams and A. E. Castagne, *Can. J. Research* **26B**, 314-24 (1948); Cf. H. Riffart and H. Keller, *Z. Untersuch. Lebensm.* **68**, 113-38 (1934).

[63] Eugene W. Rice and Joseph H. Roe, *J. Biol. Chem.* **188**, 463-9 (1951); Eugene W. Rice, *Anal. Chem.* **23**, 1501-2 (1951).

[64] R. I. Veksler, *Zhur. Anal. Khim.* **4**, 14-20 (1949).

none forms at pH 0.7. The color conforms to Beer's law over most of the range.

Furfural gives a blue color with orcinol in acetic acid.[65] The color is intensified by a trace of iron. At 0.01 mg. per ml. the method is accurate to about 1 per cent. The color with acetophenone is also suitable for giving acuracy to ±0.5 per cent.[66]

Furfuraldehyde forms a Schiff base with m-phenylenediamine dihydrochloride in ethanol as described for cinnamic aldehyde (page 279) and crotonaldehyde but read at a different wave length. Furfural gives a reddish violet color with benzidine.[67] The color is completely destroyed by water but is developed in benzene. The method is only applicable when no coloring matter is extracted from the aqueous sample by benzene. Arabinose gives a similar color and there may be other sugars which give it.

A 1 per cent solution of diphenylamine in 5:2 ethanol and concentrated sulfuric acid reacts with hydroxymethyl furfural,[68] using 3 ml. of reagent with 1 ml. of sample. Fructose gives the reaction but much more slowly.

Sample—*Distilled liquors.*[69] Distill 200 ml. with 35 ml. of water and a few grains of carborundum slowly until 200 ml. of distillate is collected. Dilute to volume and develop an aliquot with aniline acetate in alcoholic solution.

Xylene extraction of precursors. Reflux 5 ml. of aqueous solution of the sample with 3 ml. of concentrated hydrochloric acid and 25 ml. of xylene for 150 minutes in all-glass apparatus. Cool, separate the acid layer, and dry the xylene layer with anhydrous sodium sulfate. Determine by p-bromoaniline.

Procedure—*By aniline acetate in aqueous solution.* Neutralize a sample containing 0.025-0.25 mg. of furfural to phenolphthalein by dropwise addition of 10 per cent sodium hydroxide solution. Allowing

[65] P. Fleury and G. Poirot, *J. Pharm. Chim.* **26**, 87-96 (1922); *J. Chem. Soc.* **122**, 666 (1922); M. Pedinelli and V. Pessarelli, *Atti. X° congr. intern. chim.* **3**, 454-5 (1939); K. T. H. Farrar, *Australian Chem. Inst. J. and Proc.* **11**, 186-90 (1944).

[66] E. K. Nikitin, *J. Gen. Chem.* (USSR) **7**, 9-13 (1937).

[67] R. A. McCance, *Biochem. J.* **20**, 1111-3 (1926).

[68] A. D. Braun, *Byull. Eksptl. Biol. Med.* (USSR) **3**, 454-6 (1937).

[69] "Official and Tentative Methods of Analysis of the Association of Official Agricultural Chemists," Seventh Edition, p. 1304, Association of Official Agricultural Chemists, Washington, D. C. (1950).

for the sodium chloride produced by neutralization, add sufficient 20 per cent solution to give approximately 1 gram. To intensify color development and stabilize the color, add 5 ml. of a solution containing 2.5 per cent of oxalic acid and 5 per cent of disodium phosphate. Add water to approach 25 ml. Add 25 ml. of a 10 per cent solution of freshly distilled aniline in glacial acetic acid. Dilute to 50 ml. and keep in the dark at 20° ± 0.5° for 45-60 minutes. Read at 500-520 mμ against a reagent blank.

By aniline acetate in alcoholic solution. Dilute to 40 per cent of alcohol by volume and use a 20-ml. sample. If copper is present, add about 1 gram of slaked lime, shake, and let settle. All the copper compounds are precipitated. Filter and use the filtrate as sample. Add 5 ml. of 10 per cent solution of freshly distilled aniline in glacial acetic acid and mix. Store at 20° in the dark for 10 minutes and read at 500-520 mμ.

By p-bromoaniline. Formaldehyde absent. As reagent dissolve 2 grams of *p*-bromoaniline in 95 ml. of 95 per cent acetic acid saturated with urea. Mix 5 ml. of reagent with 1 ml. of the sample in xylene. After 30 minutes read at 520 mμ against a reagent blank. The color is constant for 20 minutes thereafter.

Formaldehyde present. For the preceding technic dilute so that formaldehyde is below 0.13 mg. per ml. in the sample.

With Schiff's reagent. Dilute a sample containing 0.1-0.3 mg. to about 40 ml. Adjust the pH with a glass electrode to 2.7 by addition of 1:10 hydrochloric acid. Adjust the temperature to 18° and add 5 ml. of Schiff's reagent (page 251). Dilute to 50 ml. and read at once at 560 mμ.

With orcinol. Mix a sample containing 0.1-0.3 mg. of furfural with 10 ml. of a 0.006 per cent solution of ferric chloride in concentrated hydrochloric acid, and 8 ml. of a 0.03 per cent solution of orcinol in glacial acetic acid. Heat in boiling water for 1 minute, let stand in the air for 10 minutes, cool to 20°, and dilute to 25 ml. Read against a reagent blank.

With acetophenone. Add to a tube 2 ml. of aqueous sample solution containing 0.1-0.5 mg. of furfural and a similar standard to another tube. To each add 2 ml. of 0.1 per cent solution of acetophenone in ethanol and 2 ml. of 60 per cent potassium hydroxide solution. After 10 minutes add 2 ml. of each to 20 ml. of 6:4 sulfuric acid and compare by balancing.

With m-phenylenediamine. Add 25 ml. of reagent to a sample containing 0.25-2.5 mg. of furfural and dilute to 50 ml. with absolute ethanol.

Heat at 65° for 30 minutes, cool in ice for 1 minute, and read at 440 mμ within 3 minutes after cooling.

HYDROXYMETHYLFURFURAL

At 35° hydroxymethylfurfural reacts with diphenylamine at a rate appropriate to its determination in the presence of fructose.

Procedure—As reagent dissolve 2 grams of diphenylamine in a mixture of 12.5 ml. of ethanol and 5 ml. of concentrated sulfuric acid. For estimation place in a bath at 35° for 5 minutes, cool, and read against a reagent blank which contains any amount of fructose present in the sample.

BENEZALDEHYDE

The concentration of benzaldehyde in aqueous solution is read directly at 283 mμ or at 255 mμ.[70] Color in the visible range is developed in the absence of other aldehydes by the general reaction of Schiff's reagent. For very small amounts a refinement of the method is essential.[71] The method is accurate to 5 per cent from 0.5 to 0.05 per cent of benzaldehyde and to ±7 per cent down to 0.02 per cent. In alkaline solution it reacts with benzenesulfohydroxamic acid which after neutralization given a color with ferric chloride.[72] The reaction with acetophenone is too insensitive.[73]

Sample—*Benzyl alcohol*. Dilute a 5-ml. sample to 100 ml. with 50 per cent methanol and read directly.

Almond extract. Dilute 10 grams of extract to 50 ml. with 50 per cent aldehyde-free ethanol. Dilute 2 ml. of this to 20 ml. with 50 per cent aldehyde-free ethanol and use a portion of this as sample.

Solutions in general. If sufficiently concentrated, use as is. Otherwise adjust the pH to about 7-8, distil 10 ml. in an atmosphere of nitrogen, and protect the sample by nitrogen until used.

Procedure—*Direct reading*. Read at 283 mμ against a blank of the same menstruum as the sample.

---

[70] Herbert L. Rees and Donald H. Anderson, *Anal. Chem.* **21**, 989-91 (1949).

[71] A. G. Woodman and E. F. Lyford, *J. Am. Chem. Soc.* **30**, 1607-11 (1908); Hubert N. Alyea and Hans L. J. Bäckström, *J. Am. Chem. Soc.* **51**, 90-109 (1929).

[72] H. Damköhler and W. Eggersglüss, *Phys. Chem.* **51B**, 157 (1942).

[73] E. K. Nikitin, *J. Gen. Chem.* (USSR) **7**, 9-13 (1937).

With Schiff's reagent. Mix 5 ml. of sample solution and 5 ml. of aldehyde-free ethanol. Cool at 0° for 1 minute. Add 2.5 ml. of Schiff's reagent (page 251) previously cooled to 0°. Mix well and keep at 0° for 30 minutes. Read at 560 mμ against a reagent blank.

o-NITROBENZALDHYDE

Acetone and *o*-nitrobenzaldehyde condense in alkaline solution to give indigotin.[74] The coloring agent tends to separate from aqeous solution but may be extracted with chloroform. *p*-Nitrobenzaldehyde interferes, but the *m*-isomer does not. The color conforms to Beer's law. Hydroxylamine reduces *o*-nitrobenzaldehyde in ammoniacal solution to give a red color.[75] The nature of the reaction is not known.

Procedure—Dilute a sample containing up to 5 mg. of *o*-nitrobenzaldehyde, free from ethanol, with 5 ml. of acetone and water to make about 20 ml. Add 2.5 ml. of 4 per cent sodium hydroxide solution, dilute to 25 ml., and let stand for an hour. Extract with successive 10-ml. portions of chloroform until the extracts are no longer blue. Read the combined chloroform solutions at 600 mμ.

p-ACETYLAMINOBENZALDEHYDE THIOSEMICARBAZONE, AMITHIOZONE

When ω-bromoacetophenone is added to the sulfur atom of Amithiozone, there is first hydrobromic acid, then water, split off.[76] A more conventional reaction is to diazotize and couple with an amine. Direct reading at 328 mμ [77] or 321 mμ is not interfered with appreciably by either of the fission products.[78]

Sample—*Tablets.* Macerate a tablet with four successive portions of anhydrous methanol, decanting through a filter each time. Dilute to under 0.5 mg. per ml. with methanol. Dilute an aliquot to 3 ± 1 microgram per ml. for reading in the ultraviolet.

[74] W. Davey and J. R. Gwilt, *J. Soc. Chem. Ind.* **69**, 330-7 (1950).

[75] J. Deshusses, *Pharm. Acta Helvit.* **21**, 183-6 (1946); J. H. Merz and W. A. Waters, *J. Chem. Soc.* **1949**, Suppl. Issue No. 1, 515-25.

[76] O. Wollenberg, *Deut. med. Wochschr.* **75**, 899-902 (1950).

[77] A. Spinks, *Brit. J. Pharmacol.* **4**, 254-9 (1949); Gabor B. Levy and David Fergus, *Anal. Chem.* **23**, 384-5 (1951).

[78] Alex E. Motchane and Wilbur M. Benson, *Proc. Soc. Exptl. Biol. Med.* **78**, 422-5 (1951).

Drug. Dissolve in methanol and continue as for tablets from "Dilute to under 0.5 mg. . . . ."

Procedure—*By ω-bromoacetophenone.* Mix 6 ml. of sample, such as urine, with 2 ml. of 8 per cent sodium hydroxide solution and 12 ml. of methanol. Shake and, after the precipitate settles, centrifuge. Decant and dilute to 20 ml. with methanol. Add 1 ml. of ω-bromoacetophenone in methanol and read at 430 mμ after exactly 2 minutes. Subtract a blank from which the reagent is omitted.

By diazotizing and coupling. Heat 5 ml. of sample with 2 ml. of 1 per cent *p*-toluenesulfonic acid in boiling water for 1 hour. Cool and dilute to 10 ml. with acetic acid. Cool and remove 2 ml. of the solution. Mix and add 1 ml. of 0.5 per cent sulfamic acid solution. Add 15 ml. of acetic acid and 2 ml. of 0.1 per cent phenyl-*α*-naphthylamine in 76 per cent acetic acid. Dilute to 25 ml. with acetic acid and after 1 hour read at 570 mμ against acetic acid.

In the ultraviolet. Read at 328 mμ and 20° against methanol.

Cinnamic Aldehyde

The Schiff base formed between *m*-phenylenediamine dihydrochloride and cinnamic aldehyde gives a highly sensitive coloration in 80 per cent ethanol, in the presence of oxalic acid.[79] The reaction also takes place in acetic acid with *p*-phenylenediamine.[80] Neither benzaldehyde nor acetaldehyde interferes. The following interfere in the cold: citral, acrolein, furanacrolein, thienyl acrolein, formaldehyde, cuminic aldehyde, vanillin, *p*-hydroxybenzaldehyde, *m*-methoxybenzaldehyde, mesityl oxide, isophorone, methyl vinyl ketone, and glyoxal. When heated there is slight interference by carvone and more by isobutylaldehyde, 2-ethyl hexaldehyde, cyclamol, and pyruvic aldehyde. It is thus specific for *α-β*-unsaturated aldehydes and ketones. There is no interference by limonene, *α*-pinene, cadinene, eugenol, menthol, salol, linalool, methyl salicylate, salicylic acid, carvone, and phenol. Reproducibilty is within ±1 per cent. The color remains constant for approximately 3 minutes after the addition of the reagent. Heating the reaction mixture accelerates fading. By reading at different wave lengths the same reaction is applicable to crotonaldehyde and furfuraldehyde with heat to accelerate formation of a stable color. All three colors conform to Beer's law.

79 Richard B. Wearn, William M. Murray, Jr., Mathilde P. Ramsey, and Nelladeane Chandler, *Anal. Chem.* **20**, 922-4 (1948).

80 H. Wachsmuth and R. Lenaers, *J. pharm. Belg.* (NS) **1**, 65-8 (1946).

Cinnamic aldehyde gives a bluish red color with isobutanol and concentrated sulfuric acid.[81] The sulfuric acid dehydrates isobutanol to isobutylene. This unsaturated hydrocarbon reacts in turn with cinnamic aldehyde to form a complex dye. The color changes in hue on dilution, so that the sample and standard must be of nearly the same concentration. Isobutanol must be present in large excess for cinnamic aldehyde to react quantitatively because only a fraction of the higher alcohol is changed to the unsaturated hydrocarbon.

Vanillin also gives the reaction. Benzaldehyde reacts with the reagent but the intensity of color produced is negligible as compared with that from cinnamic aldehyde.

Sample—*Cinnamon essence.* Prepare a 1 per cent solution in ethanol.

Cinnamon tincture. Extract 25 ml. of tincture with 50 ml. of ether, 75 ml. of water, and 5 ml. of 1:1 hydrochloric acid. Separate the ether layer and wash the aqueous layer with two 20-ml. portions of ether. Discard the aqueous layer and wash the combined ether extracts with 10 ml. of water, then 10-ml. with two 10-ml. portions of 0.4 per cent sodium hydroxide solution, finally with 10 ml. of water. Evaporate the ether, take up the residue in ethanol, and dilute to 50 ml. with that solvent for the use of aliquots.

Cinnamon powder. Extract 1 gram with 25 ml. of ethanol, then with 10 ml. Finally wash with ethanol to make a total volume of 50 ml. for the use of aliquots.

Distillation from cinnamon. Transfer 1 gram of finely pulverized cinnamon to a flask and add 40 ml. of ethanol. Connect to a condenser with a 100-ml. volumetric flask as receiver. Heat to boiling and keep just boiling for 10 minutes. Heat more strongly and distil over the remaining ethanol as far as possible without charring. From 5 to 10 ml. of ethanol will be left. Boil 150 ml. of water meanwhile, to free it of dissolved oxygen. Partially cool, then add 100 ml. of this to the flask. Distil rapidly until the total distillate amounts to nearly 100 ml. Dilute to volume. Use an aliquot of this diluted distillate as sample.

Procedure—*With m-phenylenediamine.* As reagent [82] digest 3-5 grams of *m*-phenylenediamine hydrochloride for about 5 minutes in 25

---

[81] T. von Fellenberg, *Mitt. Lebensm. Hyg.* **6**, 254-66 (1915).

[82] "Official and Tentative Methods of Analysis of the Association of Official Agricultural Chemists," 6th Edit. p. 372, Association of Official Agricultural Chemists, Washington, D. C. (1945).

ml. of ethanol. Decant and repeat three times. Dry the crystals on a steam bath. Then dissolve 1 gram in 45 ml. of 85 per cent ethanol and 1 gram of oxalic acid in 45 ml. of ethanol of the same strength. Mix the two solutions, add 2-3 grams of fuller's earth, dilute to 100 ml. with 85 per cent ethanol, mix, and filter through a double folded filter.

Add 5 ml. of reagent to a sample containing 0.125-1.25 mg. of cinnamic aldehyde and dilute to 50 ml. with absolute ethanol. Read at 370 mμ against a blank exactly 1.5 minutes after addition of the reagent.

With p-phenylenediamine. To 1 ml. of sample solution in ethanol and to a comparable standard, add 5 ml. of fresh 5 per cent solution of p-phenylenediamine in ethanol and 5 ml. of glacial acetic acid. Compare by balancing.

With isobutanol and sulfuric acid. To an aliquot of the sample, usually 5 ml., and a corresponding standard of the bisulfite compound of cinnamic aldehyde, add 2 ml. of a 5 per cent solution of isobutanol in ethanol. Add 3 ml. of 38 per cent ethanol, prepared by diluting 40 ml. of 95 per cent ethanol to 100 ml. with distilled water. Add 20 ml. of concentrated sulfuric acid, letting it flow down the side of the flask. Rotate and let stand 45 minutes. Dilute each to 100 ml. with water and compare. Either sample or standard can be further diluted with a mixture of 2 volumes of concentrated sulfuric acid to 1 of water.

VANILLIN

Vanillin is read at 231.3 mμ in the ultraviolet.[83] On standing, results become low which is attributed to formation of vanillic acid, 4-hydroxy-3-methoxybenzoic acid.[84] Vanillic acid and coumarin do not alter on standing. Increase in strength of solution and the presence of ethanol decrease the oxidation. Ethylvanillin oxidizes similarly. By paper chromatography, vanillin and ethyl vanillin are separated and read at 347.5 mμ and 346 mμ.[85] Vanillin and other mono-, di-, and tri-hydric phenolic compounds [86] develop with phosphotungstic-phosphomolybdic acid reagent. The presence of sucrose, caramel, or glycerol does not interfere.

---

[83] D. T. Englis and D. J. Hanrahan, *Ind. Eng. Chem., Anal. Ed.* **16**, 505-7 (1944).

[84] D. T. Englis and Merle Manchester, *Anal. Chem.* **21**, 591-3 (1949).

[85] R. M. Way and W. R. Gailey, *J. Assoc. Official Agr. Chem.* **34**, 726-3 (1951).

[86] Otto Folin and W. Denis, *J. Ind. Eng. Chem.* **4**, 670-2 (1912); John B. Wilson, *J. Assoc. Offic. Agr. Chemists* **25**, 155-9 (1942); "Official and Tentative Methods of Analysis of the Association of Official Agricultural Chemists," 7th Edition, p. 306, Association of Official Agricultural Chemists, Washington, D. C. (1950).

The reagent is subject to many interfering substances among which the principal groups are aromatic amines, hydroxyphenyl compounds, naphthol, oxyquinoline, hydroxy- and keto-acids, many sugars, and many alkaloids. Tannin and tannic acid, which are present in true vanilla extract, would interfere if not removed by basic lead acetate. The basic lead acetate also precipitates vanillin in fairly dilute solution, but not in the extreme dilutions employed here. Theoretical results are obtained with artificial extracts containing known amounts of vanillin. A slight variation in the amount of reagent added can make a great difference in the intensity of color developed. The method estimates 0.2 mg. with a high degree of accuracy.[87]

The o-iodoxy ammonium benzoate reagent [88] for free phenolic groups has been applied photometrically to vanillin.[89] The results conform to Beer's law over at least a range of 10-70 mg. per liter.

Vanillin reacts with acetone in alkaline solution to give a reddish brown condensation product.[90] The reaction is proportional to concentration so that the reagent is used in large excess. The initial information is of vanillalacetone and after 2 hours some vanillalbiacetone can be produced from the mono condensation product, particularly if acetone is in large excess.

Vanillin produces a bluish red with isobutanol and concentrated sulfuric acid.[91] Isobutanol is dehydrated by the sulfuric acid to isobutylene which reacts with the vanillin. As only a small fraction of the isobutanol reacts, a large excess must be used. The reaction is general for aromatic aldehydes. Other aldehydes present in the vanilla bean include piperonal and, in Tahiti vanilla, anisic aldehyde. Piperonal gives a bluish color with the reagent; the color is 80 per cent of that produced by vanillin. Although the total aromatic aldehyde content is determined by this method, the amount of aldehydes other than vanillin present in the vanilla bean is relatively small. The procedure has been given (page 280) as applied to cinnamic aldehyde.

Samples—*Vanilla beans.* To take an average sample of the bean, weigh the whole pod, then cut it into cross sections. Weigh about 1

[87] Sidi A. Castro, *Anales farm. bioquim.* (Buenos Aires) **13**, 53-77 (1942).

[88] Chauncey D. Leake, *Proc. Soc. Exptl. Biol. Med.* **28**, 148-50 (1930).

[89] T. C. Daniels, Byron Emery, and Dorothy Prather, *Ind. Eng. Chem. Anal. Ed.* **10**, 320-21 (1938).

[90] E. K. Nikitin and S. A. Vershinskiĭ, *J. Gen. Chem.* (USSR) **7**, 1306-14 (1937).

[91] T. von Fellenberg, *Mitt. Lebensm. Hyg.* **6**, 267-74 (1915).

gram, taking a section from the middle and other sections equally distant from the middle. Cut these into cross sections of 1-2 mm. in thickness, letting the sections hang together on one edge.

Extract 4 times with water under a reflux condenser, using a total volume of about 90 ml., boiling each time for 3-5 minutes. Grind the residue with a few ml. of water and add the liquid to the previous extracts. Dilute to 100 ml. shake with 0.5 gram of diatomaceous earth, and filter through a folded filter. Extract 50 ml. of this filtrate 5 times with a total of 150 ml. of anhydrous ether. Dry the ether extract with solid calcium chloride and filter through a dry filter. Wash the calcium chloride with 10 ml. of anhydrous ether. Distil off the ether, removing the last traces by warming the flask while passing a current of air through it. Add 30 ml. of water and heat to 50-60° to extract vanillin from the oily residue. Dilute to 100 ml. and filter from wax particles. Use 5 ml. of filtrate as sample for development with phosphotungstic-phosphomolybdic acid reagent.

Vanilla Extract. Mix a sample containing 8-12 mg. of vanillin with about 75 ml. of cold water and 4 ml. of a solution containing 0.5 per cent of basic and 0.5 per cent of neutral lead acetate. Mix and dilute to 100 ml. with water. Filter through a folded filter paper. Use 5 ml. of filtrate as sample for development by the phosphotungstic-phosphomolybdic acid reagent.

For determination by *o*-iodoxy ammonium benzoate mix 10 ml. of extract with 25 ml. of water and 5 ml. of 8 per cent lead acetate solution and dilute to 50 ml. with water. Filter through a dry filter and use 5 ml. of filtrate.

Concentrated extracts. [92] Dilute an amount to contain 8-12 mg. of vanillin to 100 ml. To 5 ml. and 5 ml. of a standard vanillin solution containing 1 mg. add 0.2 ml. of lead acetate solution containing 0.5 per cent of basic and 0.5 per cent of the neutral form. Develop with phosphotungstic-phosphomolybdic acid reagent.

Ether extract of vanillin. After the vanillin has been extracted from aqueous solution with ether, distil off the ether. To examine the extracted residue for purity, dissolve it in the smallest possible quantity of 25 per cent ethanol, dilute with water so that the final concentration will approximate 1 mg. of residue in 10 ml. of solution, and use 5 ml. of this solution as sample for development by the phosphotungstic-phosphomolybdic acid reagent.

---

[92] H. J. Lynch and Neulon Deahl, *J. Assoc. Official Agr. Chem.* 23, 429-31 (1940); Cf. A. L. Curl and E. K. Nelson, *Ibid.* 22, 684-8 (1939).

Imitation vanilla flavor.[93] Transfer a 2-ml. sample and dilute to about 80 ml. with water. Add 2 ml. of a solution containing 5 per cent each of neutral lead acetate and basic lead acetate. Dilute to 250 ml. and mix. Filter, discarding the filtrate until clear. Use an aliquot of the clear filtrate for development with phosphotungstic-phosphomolybdic acid reagent.

Carbohydrate-rich or protein-rich food.[94] Treat a 5-gram sample with 100 ml. of absolute ethanol, disperse the sample well, and let stand for 2 hours, with occasional shaking. Filter, wash the residue three times with 10-ml. portions of the solvent, and evaporate the combined filtrates. Take up the residue in water and dilute to 100 ml. for estimation with phosphotungstic-phosphomolybdic acid.

Fatty food. Disperse a 5-gram sample in 50 ml. of ether, shaking occasionally for 30 minutes. Decant through a filter and repeat the extraction. Filter and wash the filter twice with 10-ml. portions of ether. Evaporate the combined filtrates and take up the residue with 100 ml. of absolute ethanol. Filter, evaporate the filtrate to dryness, and take up the residue in water. Dilute to 100 ml. for estimation with phosphotungstic-phosphomolybdic acid.

Preserved fruits and compotes. Treat a 5-gram sample with 100 ml. of ether, shaking occasionally for an hour. Filter, wash the filter twice with 10-ml. portions of ether, and evaporate the filtrates to dryness. Take up the residue in water and dilute to 100 ml. for estimation with phosphotungstic-phosphomolybdic acid.

Procedure—*With phosphotungstic-phosphomolybdic acid reagent.* To 10 ml. of clear sample add 5 ml. of phosphotungstic-phosphomolybdic acid reagent (page 296) and exactly 5 minutes later add 10 ml. of 25 per cent sodium carbonate solution. Mix and after exactly 10 minutes dilute to 100 ml. with water. Mix, filter, discarding the first fraction of filtrate, and read at 610 mμ or 650 mμ against a reagent blank.

With o-iodoxy ammonium benzoate. To 5 ml. of clear solution add 25 ml. of accurately adjusted 0.167 N hydrochloric acid. Shake and add 3 ml. of 0.5 per cent solution of o-iodoxy ammonium benzoate. Dilute to 50 ml. and read at about 430 mμ after exactly 15 minutes. Correct for a reagent blank.

---

[93] Anon, *J. Assoc. Off. Agric. Chemists* **34**, 72-3 (1951); Luther G. Ensminger. *Ibid.* **34**, 330-40 (1951); *Ibid.* **35**, 264-71 (1952).

[94] V. A. Rozanova, *Obshchestvennoe Pitanie* **9**, No. 1. 19-25 (1941).

With acetone. To 5 ml. of sample solution and an appropriate standard having the same menstruum, add 2 ml. of acetone and mix. Add 5 ml. of 50 per cent potassium hydroxide solution and mix. Compare by balancing.

CHAPTER 12

KETONES [1]

THE KETONE family treated here is complex. Acetone and the next member of the family, methyl ethyl ketone, also called butanone, are the simplest forms. From them some more complex forms follow:

```
CH3      CH3      CH2OH     CH3      CH3       CH3       CH3       CH3
 |        |         |        |        |         |         |         |
C:O      C:O       C:O      C:O      C:O       C:O       C:O       C:O
 |        |         |        |        |         |         |         |
CH3      CH2       CH2OH    COOH     CH2       CH2       HCOH      C:O
          |                           |         |         |         |
Acetone  CH3     Dihydroxy  Pyruvic  COOH      C:O       CH3       CH3
                  acetone    acid              |                  
         methyl            Acetoacetic  CH3            Diacetyl
         ethyl               Acid                 Acetoin
         ketone                       Acetyl
                                      acetone
```

Of these it seems logical that acetoacetic acid be presented in this chapter as a ketone primarily because it is usually but not always decomposed to acetone and so determined. That immediately raises the question of pyruvic acid which is structurally even more closely related. The best answer to a doubtful situation has seemed to be to leave both with monobasic acids.

The most common reaction of the family is with aldehydes or hydrazines, often nitrated to add weight to the molecule and intensify the color.

KETONES IN GENERAL

The method for carbonyl groups with 2,4-dinitrophenylhydrazine determines ketones in general in the absence of aldehydes (page 253).

ACETONE

The concentration of acetone in mixtures with diisopropyl ether, isopropanol, and monoolefines is read directly at 280 mμ, with the sample diluted with 2,2,4-trimethyl pentane if necessary.[2]

---

[1] See Chapter 1 for details of organization, condensation, etc.

[2] G. L. Barthauer, F. V. Jones, and A. V. Metler, *Ind. Eng. Chem., Anal Ed.* **18**, 354-5 (1946).

The determination often includes other ketone bodies. These are based upon the conversion of acetoacetic acid to acetone by acid hydrolysis, or oxidation of β-hydroxybutyric acid to acetone with acid dichromate. The acetone is then separated either by distillation or by precipitation as a complex mercury salt.

The major method of color development is by reaction of acetone with salicylic aldehyde in alkaline solution to form dihydroxydibenzal acetone.[3] The method will estimate 0.01 mg. per ml. with accuracy to ±2 per cent by reading around 530 mμ.[4] The developed sample may be acidified before reading.[5] A modification for clinical use provides for addition of the bisulfite addition product of salicylic aldehyde in solid form mixed with enough hydroxide to decompose the bisulfite and liberate the salicylic aldehyde.[6] The color is also developed with furfural.[7]

The condensation of acetone with vanillin as the aldehyde in alkaline solution gives a reddish-brown color [8] of vanillalacetone. By suitable manipulation it is applicable to concentrations of 0.0025 mg. per ml. and is accurate to better than ±5 per cent except at the extreme limits of range. Methylethyl ketone, aromatic ketones, formaldehyde, and moderate amounts of acetaldehyde do not interfere.

Acetone reacts with 2,4-dinitrophenylhydrazine to form the corresponding hydrazone. This is extracted from aqueous solution with carbon tetrachloride and the yellow color read.[9] Some hydrazones, due to their differential solubilities, can be fractionated with alcohol and give intense colors in sodium hydroxide solution.[10] This has been applied to the deter-

[3] F. A. Csonka, *J. Biol. Chem.* **27**, 209-12 (1916); N. O. Engfeldt, *Berlin klin. Wochschr.* **52**, 458, 796 (1919); J. A. Behre and S. R. Benedict, *J. Biol. Chem.* **70**, 487-94 (1926); Jeannette A. Behre, *J. Lab. Clin. Med.* **13**, 1155-9 (1928); *J. Biol. Chem.* **136**, 25-39 (1940); Fritz Laurensen, *Biochem. Z.* **280**, 38-40 (1935); *Klin. Wochschr.* **15**, 339-41 (1936); A. Krautwald, *Ibid.* **22**, 17-18 (1943); Oscar Eichler and Helmut Hindemith, *Biochem. Z.* **314**, 73-81 (1943); Takashi Kodama, Saburo Kanno, Kobuo Muto, Taro Kawamura, and Shigetsugu Hoshino, *Igaka to Seibutsugaku* **19**, 1-3 (1951).

[4] Carl Urbach, *Biochem. Z.* **236**, 164-73 (1931); A. Ravin, *J. Biol. Chem.* **115**, 511-18 (1936); Per W. Krog and Jacob C. Lund, *Acta Physiol. Scand.* **12**, 141-6 (1946).

[5] E. K. Nikitin and S. A. Vershinskiĭ, *J. Applied Chem.* (USSR) **10**, 755-7 (1937).

[6] Jonas Kamlet, U. S. 2,283,262 (1942).

[7] E. K. Nikitin, *J. Applied Chem.* (*USSR*) **9**, 1704-9, 1711-15 (1936).

[8] E. K. Nikitin and S. A. Vershinskiĭ, *J. Gen. Chem.* (USSR) **7**, 1306-14 (1937).

[9] Leon A. Greenberg and David Lester, *J. Biol. Chem.* **154**, 177-90 (1944); David Lester and Leon A. Greenberg, *Ibid.* **174**, 903 (1948).

[10] H. D. Dakin and H. W. Dudley, *Ibid.* **15**, 127-43 (1913).

mination of keto acids, using carbon tetrachloride for the extraction, but the procedure is not very successful.[11] Acetone hydrazone in acid solution is readily extractable with carbon tetrachloride, so that determination of the yellow acetone hydrazone is accomplished without interference from keto acids. Results are not reproducible unless the carbon tetrachloride is shaken vigorously with the acid solution of hydrazone, so that there can be distribution of the reagent throughout the solution. The method is rapid and sensitive. In a determination of acetone in 0.2 ml. of blood, it detects 0.1 ± 0.05 mg. per 100 ml.

When acetone is condensed with o-nitrobenzaldehyde in alkaline solution, the blue dye which results is extractable with chloroform for estimation.[12]

Acetone and acetoacetic acid are precipitated as a complex with mercuric sulfate, which is dissolved and the mercury converted to mercuric sulfide for estimation.[13] The color is not affected by the acid concentration, is stable, and can be read immediately after development. The mercury is also estimated by its interference with formation of the red color of thiocyanate and ferric nitrate.[14] Accuracy to 5 per cent is attained.

An alkaline reagent containing mercuric cyanide gives a characteristic opalescence with 0.01 mg. of acetone in 50 cc. of solution.[15] The sample must contain no ammonia, aldehydes, or sulfides. Furfural and acetone condensed with alkali and then acidified offer another technic.[16]

The product formed according to conditions is furfurylidene acetone and difurfurylidene acetone in varying proportions.[17] Benzene diazonium salts give a pink to red with 0.001 mg. of acetone,[18] but acetaldehyde gives the same color. Others depend on colors with potassium triiodide [19] in crude methanol and hydroxylamine hydrochloride [20] in the presence of bromophenol blue.

Acetone and acetoacetic acid give a red color with sodium nitro-

[11] T. E. Friedemann and G. E. Haugen, *Ibid.* **147**, 415-41 (1943).

[12] Lorraine F. Noyes, *J. Lab. Clin. Med.* **26**, 1216-19 (1941).

[13] Georges Debrue, *Arch. intern. Med. Exptl.* **8**, 215-22 (1933).

[14] Latham A. Crandall, Jr., *J. Biol. Chem.* **133**, 539-50 (1940).

[15] W. M. Marriott, *Ibid.* **16**, 289-91 (1913-14); Otto Folin and W. Denis, *Ibid.* **18**, 263-71 (1914); Philip A. Kober, *J. Ind. Eng. Chem.* **10**, 556-63 (1918).

[16] E. K. Nikitin and I. I. Paul, *J. Applied Chem.* (USSR) **9**, 1711-15 (1936).

[17] V. I. Tikhonova, *Zhur. Obshcheĭ Khim.* **20**, 2213-18 (1950).

[18] R. Berg, *Mikrochemié ver. Mikrochim. Acta* **30**, 137 (1941) (all I page).

[19] Antoni Feill and Mieczyslau Mysona, *Przeglad Chem.* **5**, 54-6 (1947).

[20] A. I. Bulycheva, *Gigiena i Sanit.* **13**, No. 11, 30 (1948).

prusside.[21] The intensity due to the acetoacetic acid is 30 times that due to the acetone. The reagent gives a color with only sulfur, mercaptans, and reduced glutathione in addition to acetone and acetoacetic acid. It is sensitive to 1 part in 50,000. The amount of sodium nitroprusside added must be carefully controlled as too much will destroy the color. A reagent containing 1 per cent of sodium nitroprusside, 49.5 per cent of sodium carbonate, and 49.5 per cent of ammonium sulfate gives a range of colors with the addition of 1 drop of urine to 0.2 gram.[22]

The turbidity produced in Nessler's solution by volatilizing acetone into it from acidified urine gives an approximate measure of the acetone content. [23] Acetone is also determined as iodoform, the technic being described (page 263) under acetaldehyde.

Sample—*Tissue.*[24] *Total acetone bodies.* Grind a 1-gram sample with 0.5 gram of sand, 8 ml. of water, and 1 ml. of 1:50 sulfuric acid. Add 1 ml. of 10 per cent sodium tungstate solution, dilute to 25 ml., and filter. Treat 15 ml. of filtrate with 0.8 ml. of 10 per cent copper sulfate solution and mix. Add an excess of a 10 per cent slurry of hydrated lime, about 2 ml., and let stand for an hour. This removes polysaccharides. Add 0.4 ml. of concentrated sulfuric acid and 1.2 ml. of a 5 per cent solution of potassium dichromate in 1:17 sulfuric acid. Distil at the rate of 1 ml. per minute until about 4.5 ml. are collected and dilute to 5 ml. Use an aliquot for development by the micro method with salicylaldehyde.

Urine. Preformed acetone. Add 0.5-5 ml. of the sample urine to 1 ml. of 10 per cent sulfuric acid in a large test tube. This sample should contain about 0.5 mg. of acetone. Mix and attach connections for aspirating air through the sample and through a second tube. Place in the second tube 10 ml. of a 2 per cent solution of sodium bisulfite, with which the acetone will combine. The sodium bisulfite solution must not be more than a week old. Immerse the tube of sample in a beaker of water at 35-50°. Pass the current of air through the sample for 10 minutes. Dilute the solution containing the acetone in a volumetric flask to a suitable volume for taking aliquots for development with salicylic aldehyde by the macro method.

21 Legal, *Breslauer Arztliche Z.* **5**, 38-40 (1883) ; A. C. H. Rothera, *J. Physiol.* **37**, 491-4 (1908) ; Leo Lorber, *Biochem. Z.* **181**, 366-74 (1927) ; F. E. Raurich Sas, *Anales soc. espan. fis. quim.* **32**, 185-232 (1934).

22 Alexander Galat, *British Patent* 580,778 (1946) : Cf. Robert M. Dumm and Reginald A. Shipley, *J. Lab. Clin. Med.* **31**, 1162-6 (1946).

23 Julius C. Abels, *J.. Biol. Chem.* **119**, 663-7 (1937).

24 D. E. Kagan and Yu. A. Troitskii, *J. Physiol.* (USSR) **27**, 252-8 (1939).

For development with 2,4-dinitrophenylhydrazine add 0.2 ml. of sample to 1 ml. of water and follow with 3 ml. of 5 per cent trichloro-acetic acid solution. Filter or centrifuge and take a 3-ml. aliquot of clear fluid for analysis.

Acetone and acetoacetic acid. In fresh urine the acetoacetic acid content may be from 2 to 10 times as great as the acetone. The older the urine the greater the relative proportion of acetone due to spontaneous decomposition of the acetoacetic acid. In general urine which gives a strong ferric chloride reaction contains more than 0.5 mg. of acetoacetic acid per ml.

Transfer a suitable fraction of urine, usually not more than 1 ml., to a test tube with 1 ml. of 10 per cent sulfuric acid. Connect with another tube containing 10 ml. of 2 per cent sodium bisulfite solution. Immerse the sample tube in a beaker of boiling water. Pass an extremely slow current of air through the tube for 10 minutes, then increase the speed moderately. Continue for about 5 minutes and all the acetone, including that equivalent to the acetoacetic acid, will be in the bisulfite tube. Dilute the distillate to a suitable volume for taking aliquots for development with salicylic aldehyde by the macro method.

Alternatively,[25] decarboxylate by making urine strongly acid with hydrochloric acid at 100° for 5 minutes. Mix 2 ml. of this with 10 ml. of 1 per cent sodium hydroxide solution. Use for development with salicylic aldehyde.

Total acetone bodies. Blood. Add 0.2 ml. of sample to 2.3 ml. of water in a centrifuge tube and allow to lake. Add 1 ml. of 5 per cent barium hydroxide solution, mix, and follow with 1 ml. of 2.5 per cent zinc sulfate solution. Stopper and centrifuge 2-3 minutes. Transfer 3 ml. of the supernatant liquid to the clean, dry, refluxing tube shown in Figure 19, containing several beads and add 0.6 ml. of 0.46 per cent potassium dichromate in 1:1.3 sulfuric acid. Stopper lightly with the cold finger. Connect with a rubber tube to the cold finger and start the flow of cold water. Reflux gently for 10 minutes. Wait until boiling ceases before lifting the cold finger enough to allow the introduction of 0.5 ml. of 10 per cent dichromate solution. Allow this solution to run down the cold finger. Restopper the tube tightly and continue boiling for another 10 minutes. Discontinue the flow of water through the apparatus and cool the entire tube under a water tap. Invert the tube to wash down any material that may have condensed on the upper walls of the tube.

---

[25] Paul Fleury, M. Froissant, and Renée Eberhardt, *Ann. biol. clin.* (Paris) **8**, 156-61 (1950).

Take a 3-ml. aliquot for analysis. Add 0.4 ml. of 15 per cent anhydrous sodium sulfite solution to destroy the dichromate and treat as described (page 288) for preformed acetone in urine.

Blood. Acetone and acetoacetic acid. Macro. Mix 5 ml. of blood with 35 ml. of water. Add 5 ml. of a 10 per cent solution of tungstic acid and mix. Add 5 ml. of 1:54 sulfuric acid and mix. The presence of much oxalate or citrate will interfere with the coagulation. The color of the coagulum gradually changes from pink to dark brown. If this does not occur, too much citrate or oxalate is present. In that case add 1:17 sulfuric acid drop by drop, shaking and letting stand after each addition, until coagulation is satisfactory.

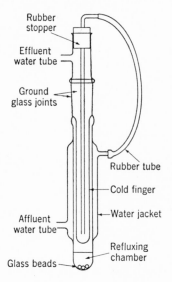

Rubber stopper

Effluent water tube

Ground glass joints

Rubber tube

Cold finger

Water jacket

Affluent water tube

Refluxing chamber

Glass beads

FIG. 19. Micro refluxing apparatus

Pour on a filter and cover with a watch glass. If necessary, return the first part of the filtrate to the paper. The filtrate should be just acid to Congo red paper. If this is to be kept more than a day, add a drop of toluene as preservative. Transfer a suitable portion of the filtrate, according to the acetone content, to a distilling flask and complete as for acetone and acetoacetic acid in urine.

Micro. Fill a 0.2-ml. pipet, coated on the inside with potassium oxalate, with blood. Discharge this slowly with mixing into 10 ml. of 0.0133 N sulfuric acid in a centrifuge tube. Rinse the pipet with the acid and mix. After 10 minutes slowly add 0.2 ml. of a neutral 10 per cent sodium tungstate solution to the brown sample solution and mix. Let stand for 10 minutes and centrifuge for 5 minutes. If properly deproteinized, the coagulum is on the bottom and the supernatant liquid is clear. Add 5 ml. of 1:1 sulfuric acid to the special flask shown in Figure 20, or equivalent. The side arm is jacketed as a water condenser and finally leads into a 5-ml. mixing cylinder containing 1 ml. of water. The exit is narrowed and is under this liquid. Transfer the supernatant sample solution to this flask. Because of the dilution the centrifuge tube and precipitate need not be washed. Slowly pass a stream of air through the tube. Warm the flask so that the acetone is distilled in 3-4 minutes. During distillation move the receiver down so that the tip of the outlet tube is always just under the surface. Dilute the contents of the cylinder to 5 ml. with water used to rinse out the condenser, and mix well. The resulting solution contains in a substantially pure state all of the preformed acetone and that from decomposition of acetoacetic acid. Develop with salicylic aldehyde by the micro technic.

Preformed acetone. Macro. Treat as for acetone and acetoacetic acid through ''The side arm is jacketed as a water condenser. . . .'' Do not run water through the condenser. Add 5 ml. of 1:1 sulfuric acid. Attach

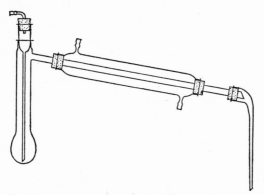

FIG. 20. Special flask for distillation of acetone and related substances

an adapter to the end of the condenser and have the end dip into 10 ml. of fresh 1 per cent sodium bisulfite solution. Warm the flask in a bath at 40-45° and pass a rather rapid stream of air through the solution for 1 hour. Add 5 ml. of 0.8 per cent sodium hydroxide solution to the acetone-bisulfite solution and transfer to a fresh distilling flask. Distil as for acetone and acetoacetic acid.

Acetoacetic acid. After removal of the acetone by aeration treat the residue in the flask for distillation as described for acetone and acetoacetic acid.

β-Hydroxybutyric acid.[26] After distillation of acetone and acetoacetic acid withdraw the flame. Add 5 ml. of water to the remaining liquid in the flask. Put a fresh receiving cylinder in place and heat the contents of the flask to boiling. Quickly add 1 ml. of 2 per cent potassium bichromate solution and distil as usual. Multiply the acetone found in the distillate by 1.25 to convert the results to β-hydroxybutyric acid.

Total acetone bodies. Follow the procedure for acetone and aceto-

---

[26] Oscar Cantoni, *Biochem. Z.* **274**, 45-50 (1934); *Ibid.* **277**, 488-50 (1935).

acetic acid with this modification. When brought to boiling, add 1 ml. of 2 per cent potassium bichromate solution and avoid loss of acetone by careful manipulation.

Spinal fluid. Use the sample without deproteinizing. Develop with salicylic aldehyde.

Milk. Mix 20 ml. of milk with 80 ml. of water and distil as described for urine. Develop the color with vanillin.

Air. Place 3 ml. of reagent as described under the procedure for development with 2,4-dinitrophenylhydrazine in a tube and evacuate with a water pump. Read the negative pressure from a mercury manometer. Expose the tube to air which is to be sampled, then close the tube and shake for 1-2 minutes. Calculate the volume of air taken by

$$V = \frac{(V_1 - S)(P_1 - P_2)\,273}{760\,(273 + t)}$$

where V_1 = total volume of the air-sampling tube
S = volume of hydrazine solution
P_1 and P_2 = prevailing barometric pressure and residual pressure in the tube after evacuation in mm. of mercury.

Take a 1-2 ml. aliquot for analysis and dilute to a volume of 5 ml. with 1 ml. of acid 2,4-dinitrophenylhydrazine reagent and water. Treat as in the procedure starting at "Follow with exactly 2 ml. of carbon tetrachloride."

Procedure—*With salicylic aldehyde. Macro.* Transfer 5 ml. of sample to a test tube. Add 4 ml. of 40 per cent sodium hydroxide solution and mix. Add 1 ml. of a 20 per cent solution of salicylic aldehyde in ethanol. Heat in a water bath at 50° for 20 minutes. Place in a cold water bath for one-half hour and read at 530 mμ.[27]

Micro. Transfer 2 ml. of the aqueous acetone distillate to a small test tube and add 0.5 ml. of a saturated aqueous solution of sodium hydroxide. Mix well and add a drop of salicylic aldehyde. Mix quickly, add another drop, and mix again. Delay in mixing results in a precipitate which is difficult to dissolve. Stopper lightly and heat for 5 minutes in a boiling water bath, shaking every 1-2 minutes. Let stand for 6-12 hours and read at 530 mμ against a reagent blank.

With vanillin. To 2 ml. of the sample add 2 ml. of 60 per cent potassium hydroxide solution. Mix and add 1 ml. of a 10 per cent solution of vanillin in absolute methanol. Mix and place in a heated water bath.

---

[27] Paul Seifert, *Klin. Wochschr.* **26**, 471-3 (1948).

After exactly 20 minutes remove from the bath, add 10 ml. of water, and mix. Read at 508 mμ at once. Accurate control of the temperature to which the sample is heated is essential to obtain reproducible results.

With 2,4-dinitrophenylhydrazine. Prepare a solution of 0.1 per cent 2,4-dinitrophenylhydrazine in 1:5 hydrochloric acid as a reagent. Add the appropriate aliquot of sample to 2 ml. of reagent, dilute to 5 ml. with water, and follow with 2 ml. of carbon tetrachloride. Stopper and shake mechanically for 10 minutes. Draw off the acid supernatant solution and add enough water to bring the volume to 10 ml. Shake and discard the water. Repeat this step once more and then add 3 ml. of 2 per cent sodium hydroxide solution. Shake for 3 minutes and then read the aqueous layer at 350 mμ against a tube of carbon tetrachloride. From this reading subtract the reading of a reagent blank.

METHYL ETHYL KETONE

Salicylic aldehyde and methyl ethyl ketone [28] condense in alkaline solution. Acetone must be absent. The greenish yellow color is applicable to the range of 0.0025-0.1 mg. per ml. with accuracy to ±5 per cent except at the extreme limit of concentration.

Procedure—Transfer 2 ml. of sample and 2 ml. of a suitable standard. To each add 2 ml. of 60 per cent potassium hydroxide solution. Mix and add 1 ml. of a 10 per cent solution of salicylic aldehyde in ethanol to each. Mix and place in a water bath at 40° for 20 minutes. On removal, at once add 15 ml. of 20 per cent ethanol, mix, and compare.

DIHYDROXYACETONE

The reducing action on a phosphomolybdic acid reagent is used for estimation of dihydroxyacetone.[29] It gives a slightly different blue color from that with glucose. The general reaction given by acetaldehyde, acrylic aldehyde, and pyruvic aldehyde with veratrol is also applied to dihydroxyacetone in the absence of interfering substances.[30]

Procedure—*With phosphomolybdic acid reagent.* Mix 2 ml. of sample with 2 ml. of the phosphomolybdic acid reagent (page 205).

---

[28] Hubert N. Alyea and Hans L. J. Bäckström, *J. Am. Chem. Soc.* **51**, 90-109 (1929).

[29] W. R. Campbell, *J. Biol. Chem.* **67**, 59-69 (1926).

[30] Erich Baer, *Arbeitsphysiol.* **1**, 130-5 (1928).

Heat in boiling water for 15 minutes. Cool and dilute to 25 ml. for reading. In the case of the tungstated blood filtrate, subtract 0.05 mg. from the results to allow for the direct effect of glucose and other reducing substances on the reagent.

With veratrol. Use the method for estimation of acrylic aldehyde (page 265).

ACETYLACETONE

β-Diketones condense in acid solution with *o*-phenylenediamine to give a purple color of 2,4-dimethyl(1,5)benzodiazapine.[31] It follows that this reagent can be used to estimate acetylacetone in the absence of other β-diketones. If present, triacetic acid, more specifically β, δ-diketohexanoic acid, and ethyl triacetate will be determined and reported as acetylacetone. During color development, triacetic acid appears to be decarboxylated to acetylacetone.[32] Ethyl triacetate appears to be partially hydrolyzed during color development. Color developed per mole of ester is less than with acetylacetone.

Triacetic lactone

$$CH_3—C=CH—CO—CH_2—CO$$

(with O bridging) lacks the diketone linkage and does not react with the reagent, but is converted to acetylacetone by hot acid hydrolysis.

In determination of acetylacetone there is no interference by 100 micromoles of diacetyl, acetoin, acetone, acetaldehyde, succinic acid, fumaric acid, acetoacetic acid, oxalacetic acid, levulinic acid, citric acid, ethyl acetoacetate, ethyl levulinate, or diethyl acetonedicarboxylate. Bisulfite, hydroxylamine, and semicarbazide inhibit color formation. Pyruvic acid in amounts of 100 micromoles inhibits the color reaction 10-15 per cent. Ascorbic acid present in a concentration of 50 micromoles causes a 10-15 per cent inhibition. A 10 per cent solution of glucose or 2.4 per cent urea does not cause interference in the determination of acetylacetone. Tungstic acid precipitates the pigment at pH 1.3-2. Oxidizing agents oxidize the *o*-phenylenediamine.

Crotonaldehyde in amounts of 10-50 micromoles reacts with *o*-phenylenediamine to give a yellow to orange color. This interference is elim-

[31] S. B. Vaisman, *Trans. Inst. Chem. Kharlov Univ.* **4**, No. 13, 157-74 (1938); *Ibid.* **5**, 57-92 (1940); *Khim. Referat. Zhur.*, **4**, No. 7-8, 46 (1941); Robert F. Witter, Jeanette Snyder and Elmer Stotz, *J. Biol. Chem.* **176**, 493-500 (1948).

[32] Robert F. Witter and Elmer Stotz, *Ibid.* **176**, 485-92 (1948).

inated by the addition of 2 ml. of 0.5 per cent sodium bisulfite to 10 ml. of solution after the color has been developed. It then requires 15-20 minutes for decolorization.

As applied to triacetic lactone interferences are similar, except that 1 per cent of glucose gives split products from hydrolysis and 2.4 per cent of urea causes low results. Glucosamine does not interfere.

Acetylacetone is also determinable by oxidation to acetone, distillation in that form, and determination as disalicylacetone.[33]

Procedure—Prepare a buffer for pH 7.4 by dissolving 43.5 grams of dipotassium phosphate and 20 ml. of 17 per cent phosphoric acid in 500 ml. of 1:14 sulfuric acid and diluting to 1 liter. Then dissolve 100 mg. of o-phenylenediamine in 25 ml. of the phosphate-sulfuric acid solution. Always prepare the reagent just prior to use.

Free diketone. Add 2 ml. of o-phenylenediamine reagent to 12 ml. of test solution containing 2.5-10 mg. of the diketone. Mix and allow to stand at room temperature for 30 minutes. Read against a reagent blank at 500 mμ. Subtract a blank on the sample if necessary. Interpret in terms of an acetylacetone standard.

Total diketone, triacetic lactone. This method is used for total diketone content when triacetic lactone is present with free diketones. The difference between "free diketone" and "total diketone" is a measure of triacetic lactone.

The apparatus required is shown in Fig. 18. Add 1 ml. of concentrated sulfuric acid to 13 ml. of test solution containing 2-8 micromoles of diketone. Add a quartz pebble or a few crystals of cholesterol to prevent foaming during subsequent boiling. Place the flask in a heated sand-bath and collect 10-11 ml. of distillate in about 15-20 minutes. Use a 25-ml. graduated cylinder in an ice bath as receiving vessel. Dilute the distillate to 12 ml. Add 2 ml. of o-phenylenediamine reagent. Mix, allow the color to develop for 30 minutes, and read at 500 mμ against a reagent blank. Interpret from a standard selected according to the β-diketone present in the sample.

ACETYLCARBINOL, ACETOL

Acetol is estimated by reaction with phosphomolybdic-phosphotungstic acid reagent to produce a blue color.[34] This is more sensitive than

---

[33] F. Lauersen, *Klin. Wochschr.* **16**, 1187-90 (1937).
[34] W. Morton Grant, *J. Biol. Chem.* **174**, 93-8 (1948).

the titrimetric method employing this same reagent. Methanol or its oxidation products, formaldehyde and formic acid, do not interfere. Blood substances which can cause interference are eliminated by low temperature vacuum distillation of the sample before analysis. Recovery exceeds 90 per cent.

Acetol also reacts with *o*-aminobenzaldehyde in alkaline solution to form 3-hydroxyquinaldine.[35] On irradiation with ultraviolet light this gives a strong blue fluorescence which conforms to Beer's law over the range 0.3-6 mg. per liter. Close pH control by buffering is necessary to duplicate results. Diacetyl and low concentrations of formaldehyde reduce the value obtained. High concentrations of formaldehyde and any amount of furfural cause high values. Considerable amounts of acetaldehyde or pyruvic acid lower the values. At 1000:1, methanol, ethanol, acetone, lactic acid, and levulinic acid do not interfere.

FIG. 21. Special distilling apparatus

Sample—*Blood*. Deprotenize heparinized blood by mixing 1 ml. of it with 2 ml. of 5 per cent sulfosalicylic acid solution. The addition of 1:90 sulfuric acid solution to the sulfosalicylic acid will permit the simultaneous distillation of formaldehyde and formic acid and their determinations in the same distillate. Centrifuge and vacuum-distil 1-2 ml. of the supernatant fluid in an apparatus as shown in Figure 21.[36] Distil to dryness, condensing at the temperature of dry ice. Develop with phosphomolybdic-phosphotungstic acid.

Procedure—*With phosphomolybdic-phosphotungstic acid.* As reagent dissolve 26 grams of phosphomolybdic acid and 2 grams of phosphotungstic acid in water at room temperature and dilute to 80 ml. Add 10 ml. of concentrated hydrochloric acid and 10 ml. of 85 per cent phosphoric acid, and centrifuge.

Heat 1 ml. of sample containing up to 0.02 mg. of acetylcarbinol and 1 ml. of reagent together on a boiling water bath for 15 minutes and im-

[35] Oskar Baudisch, *Biochem. Z.* **89**, 279-80 (1918); Oskar Baudisch and H. Deuel, *J. Am. Chem. Soc.* **44**, 1585-87 (1922); Arlington A. Forist and John C. Speck, Jr., *Anal. Chem.* **22**, 902-4 (1950).

[36] W. Morton Grant, *Ind. Eng. Chem., Anal. Ed.* **18**, 729 (1946).

mediately add 2 ml. of saturated sodium carbonate solution. Read the blue color against a reagent blank similarly treated.

With o-aminobenzaldehyde. As reagent dissolve 0.05 gram of *o*-aminobenzaldehyde in 25 ml. of concentrated hydrochloric acid. This reverses any polymerization of the solid which has occurred. Adjust to pH 7.0 with the glass electrode by addition of 10 per cent sodium hydroxide solution and dilute to 250 ml.

To 1 ml. of sample containing 0.0003-0.006 mg. of acetol add 1 ml. of the *o*-aminobenzaldehyde reagent and 5 ml. of 0.8 per cent sodium hydroxide solution. At the same time prepare a blank. Immerse in boiling water for 30 minutes and cool at once to room temperature. To each solution add 2 ml. of 1:25 hydrochloric acid and 5 ml. of a buffer for pH 6.6 (Vol. I, pp. 174, 176). Dilute to 25 ml. with water and read the fluorescence with Coleman B-1 and PC-1 filters or equivalent. Compare with a calibration curve. There is no decay of fluorescence for 2 hours and the precision is limited only by that of the instrument.

ACETYLMETHYLCARBINOL, ACETOIN

Acetylmethylcarbinol, better known as acetoin, is determined in blood and tissues by conversion to diacetyl with acid ferric chloride [37] and precipitated as nickel dimethylglyoxime by addition of hydroxylamine, nickel chloride, and sodium acetate. The nickel in the precipitate is determined by oxidation with bromine [38] and formation of a soluble colored complex with excess dimethylglyoxime.[39] Each 0.001 mg. of nickel is equivalent to 0.00307 mg. of acetoin or 0.00293 mg. of diacetyl. The method will detect 0.005 mg. of either acetoin or diacetyl.

There is no interference by glucose, lactic or pyruvic acids, acetaldehyde, ethanol, or 2,3-butylene glycol. An alternative is to convert the dimethylglyoxime to the nickelic complex in ammoniacal solution for reading.[40]

Acetoin is also determinable by the color developed with dinitrobenzoic acid, in the absence of diacetyl, butylene glycol, and creatinine.[41]

[37] Elmer Stotz and Jane Raborg, *J. Biol. Chem.* **150**, 25-31 (1943).

[38] A. P. Rollet, *Compt. rend. acad.* **183**, 212 (1926).

[39] F. Feigl, *Ber. chem. Ges.* **57**, 758 (1924).

[40] Michel Hooreman, *Compt. rend.* **222**, 1257-9 (1946).

[41] E. Komm and J. Flügel, *Z. Untersuch. Lebensm.* **79**, 246-50 (1940).

Sample—*Acetoin and diacetyl in blood.* Mix 3 ml. of blood with 6 ml. of water. Add 3 ml. of 10 per cent sodium tungstate and 3 ml. of 1:54 sulfuric acid. When well coagulated, centrifuge and use 7 ml. of the supernatant layer.

Tissue. Use the tungstic-acid filtrate of an extract.

Procedure—*Development as nickel dimethylglyoxime.* Add 1 ml. of 1:3.6 sulfuric acid and 2 ml. of 50 per cent ferric chloride solution to the aliquot of sample, stopper lightly, heat to 100° for 15 minutes, and cool.

Neutralize 10 per cent hydroxylamine hydrochloride with 24 per cent sodium hydroxide to a phenol red endpoint. Transfer 0.5 ml. of this neutral hydroxylamine, 0.5 ml. of 20 per cent sodium acetate solution, and 0.2 ml. of 0.5 per cent nickel chloride to the receiver of the distillation apparatus shown in Figure 18.

Transfer an aliquot of the sample solution to the flask. With the end of the condenser dipping into the nickel solution distil until the volume of the contents of the receiving flask is about 4.5 ml. This takes about 2 minutes. Disconnect the apparatus, stopper the tube, and mix by rotation. Heat for a half hour at 55° and refrigerate for at least 12 hours without shaking to allow the dioxime to form. There will be no crystals if less than 0.005 mg. of acetoin is present.

Prepare an aqueous solution saturated with nickel dimethylglyoxime and octyl alcohol. This is used as wash water. Add 5 ml. of this solution to the tube with the crystals and centrifuge for 5 minutes. Shake gently to pick up floating precipitate and recentrifuge. Withdraw supernatant fluid down to the 0.5-ml. mark. Allow 10 ml. of wash solution to run down the side of the tube without disturbing the precipitate. Centrifuge, remove the liquid, and repeat the washing.

Add 2 ml. of 1:500 hydrochloric acid to the washed precipitate, shake, and place in a boiling water bath. When the precipitate is dissolved, add 0.6 ml. of 0.1 per cent by volume bromine water. If there is no residual color, add more till a color persists for at least 0.5 minute while the tube is in the bath. Allow to cool and add 2-3 drops of concentrated ammonium hydroxide to decolorize the bromine. Dilute to about 5 ml. and add 1 ml. of 1 per cent alcoholic dimethylglyoxime solution with rapid mixing. The amount is not important, but the mixing is to avoid the formation of a precipitate. Dilute to 10 ml. with water and read at 460 mμ against water.

2,3-Butanedione, Diacetyl

Like formaldehyde, solutions of pure diacetyl give a purple color with chromotropic acid-sulfuric acid mixture.[42] The molar extinction of the dye is almost equal to that of formaldehyde.

All the substances that interfere in formaldehyde determination (page 256) by chromotropic acid, interfere in this determination. Methylethyl ketone diminishes the color. Hexoses and pentoses yield diacetyl as a result of acid degradation,[43] and give brown or purple colors with the reagent.[44] Acetyl propionyl, a homolog of diacetyl, does not give a purple color with chromotropic acid. The solution conforms to Beer's law over the range 0.01-0.1 mg. per ml.

After diacetyl is converted to its dioxime the compound is stable to oxidation and is further processed to give a red color.[45] It can also be converted by reaction with diaminobenzidine to yellow diphenylquinoxaline,[46] a reaction which will detect 0.05 mg.

Diacetyl gives a color with creatine and α-naphthol.[47] The reaction is also applicable to acetylmethylcarbinol after oxidation to diacetyl by ferric chloride and separation of the latter by distillation. Trichloroacetic gives color under the conditions only in the ultraviolet. α-Alanine interferes but β-alanine does not.

As another reaction, it may be precipitated as nickel diglyoxime and dissolved in chloroform for reading.[48] The nickel complex is also developed by a method described under acetoin (page 298). The reaction with dinitrobenzoic acid, originally used for creatinine, is adaptable to estimation of diacetyl in the absence of acetoin, butylene glycol, and creatinine.[49]

Sample—*Food.* Place a 50- or 100-gram sample in a flask closed by a 2-holed Neoprene stopper. Rubber absorbs diacetyl. Introduce carbon dioxide through a partially inserted tube to be later used for steam distillation. A reflex condenser used for fractionation occupies the second

[42] John C. Speck, Jr., *Anal. Chem.* **20**, 647-8 (1948).

[43] R. Nodzu and K. Matsui, *Bull. Chem. Soc. Japan* **10**, 467-71 (1935).

[44] Edwin Eegriwe, *Z. anal. Chem.* **110**, 22-5 (1937).

[45] E. A. Prill and B. W. Hammer, *Iowa State Coll., J. Sci.* **12**, 385-95 (1938).

[46] Jean Pien, Jacques Baisse, and Robert Martin, *Lait* **17**, 675-98 (1937) ; G. A. Cox and W. J. Wiley, *J. Council Sci. Ind. Research* **12**, 227-31 (1939).

[47] P. Eggleton, S. R. Elsden, and Nancy Gough, *Biochem. J.* **37**, 526-9 (1943).

[48] Elmer Stotz and Jane Raborg, *J. Biol. Chem.* **150**, 25-31 (1943).

[49] E. Komm and J. Flügel, *Z. Untersuch. Lebensm.* **79**, 246-50 (1940).

hole. Pass in steam and so control the reflux that about 5 ml. will pass it for condensation in 30 minutes. For estimation as the dioxime, place 1 ml. of sodium acetate-hydroxylamine reagent—see procedure—in a calibrated tube used as receiver. The sample is complete when the total volume reaches 6 ml. Otherwise condense 5 ml. or more, avoiding undue air exposure.

Procedure—*With chromotropic acid.* Add 0.5 ml. of 10 per cent chromotropic acid solution to 1 ml. of solution containing 0.03-0.1 mg. of diacetyl per ml. Gradually add 5 ml. of concentrated sulfuric acid. Mix and heat in a water bath at 100° for 1 hour. Cool and dilute with water. Read at 570 mμ against a reagent blank.

As the dioxime. As reagents prepare a 35 per cent solution of sodium acetate trihydrate and a 4.4 per cent solution of hydroxylamine. For use mix them in a 1:4 ratio just before use. Add one ml. of this reagent to a 5-ml. sample. Heat the reagent and sample at 85° for 1 hour to form the dioxime and remove from the bath. While still warm, add 1 ml. of a reagent containing 20 per cent of acetone and 14.5 per cent of dipotassium orthophosphate. After 5 minutes add 0.3 ml. of concentrated ammonium hydroxide and 2.2 ml. of a saturated sodium potassium tartrate solution. A deep red will appear on addition of 0.2 ml. of a 5 per cent solution of ferrous sulfate heptahydrate in 1:100 sulfuric acid. Read and compare with a curve which may, for convenience, be prepared from a solution of diacetyldioxime, better known as dimethylglyoxime.

With diaminobenzidine. To the diacetyl concentrated in 10 ml. of distillate add 0.5 ml. of a fresh 2.5 per cent aqueous solution of diaminobenzidine. Mix well and add 0.5 ml. of concentrated hydrochloric acid. Mix well and read after 2 minutes.

By creatine and α-naphthol. As reagent mix 2 ml. of saturated solution of creatine in water with 6 ml. of 1 per cent α-naphthol solution. Add 4 ml. of this to a solution containing less than 0.1 mg. of diacetyl and dilute to 15 ml. Mix and after 30 minutes read against a reagent blank.

ACETOPHENONE

In the absence of interfering substances, acetophenone is condensed with salicylic aldehyde for colorimetric estimation.[50] It also condenses with furfural in alkaline solution.[51] When both acetophenone and acetone

[50] Bernard Rolland, *J. pharm. Belg.* (N.S.) **2**, 54-61 (1947).

[51] V. I. Tikhonova. *Zhur. Obshchei Khim.* **20**, 2213-18 (1950); *Zhur. Priklad. Klaim.* **23**, 1113-15 (1950).

are present, the color with acetophenone is developed if not over 20 moles of acetone are present per mole of acetophenone. The general reaction of ketones with 2,4-dinitrophenylhydrazine is applicable to acetophenone.[52] An extract of the color in carbon tetrachloride is stable for several hours. The maximum is in the ultraviolet at 370 mμ but, with less sensitivity, can be read at 420-440 mμ.

Procedure—*With salicylic aldehyde.* Adjust the sample to contain 0.1-1 mg. of acetophenone per ml. in 70 per cent ethanol. To 0.5 ml. of such solution add 3 ml. of fresh 42 per cent potassium hydroxide solution and mix. Add 1 drop of 10 per cent solution of salicylic aldehyde in ethanol and mix. Read the color at 470 mμ against a reagent blank, every 2 minutes for 20 minutes and take the maximum reading for comparison with a calibration curve.

With 2,4-dinitrophenylhydrazine. Mix 5 ml. of aqueous sample containing 0.015-0.04 mg. of acetophenone with 5 ml. of 0.1 per cent 2,4-dinitrophenylhydrazine in 1:5 hydrochloric acid. After 2 hours, extract by shaking mechanically with 10 ml. of carbon tetrachloride for 10 minutes. Wash the nonaqueous layer with four 50-ml. portions of water to remove excess reagent. Dry with sodium sulfate and read at 370 mμ or 430 mμ against a reagent blank.

CAMPHOR

Camphor gives a rather general series of color reactions with aldehydes. That with furfural and sulfuric acid is red to violet.[53] Accuracy to about 10 per cent is obtainable. A color reaction is also developed with benzaldehyde.

Procedure—*With furfural.* Mix 1 ml. of an aqueous camphor solution with 3 ml. of ethanol. Add 2 drops of 1 per cent alcoholic furfural solution. Mix and carefully add 2 drops of concentrated sulfuric acid. Mix and heat in boiling water until the color is developed. Cool and add 5 ml. of ethanol to each. Mix and read.

With benzaldehyde. Mix 1 ml. of aqueous sample with 1 ml. of ethanol. Add 2 ml. of a fresh 1 per cent solution of benzaldehyde in ethanol. Mix and add 2 ml. of concentrated sulfuric acid drop by drop. Let stand for

---

[52] Kerstin Matérn and Göran Schill, *Svensk. Farm. Tids.* **54**, 445-50 (1950).
[53] Lad. Ekkert, *Pharm. Zentralh.* **68**, 563 (1927); Angelo Castiglioni, *Ann. chim. applicata* **26**, 53-5 (1936).

5 minutes at the temperature developed, for the color to intensify. Cool, add 5 ml. of ethanol, mix, and read.

CYCLOHEXANONE

Cyclic ketones react with *o*-nitrobenzaldehyde to give an intense blue color in alcoholic solution, suitable for reading photometrically.[54] As set up it is directed to analysis of solvent mixtures. Methyl cyclohexanone gives the same color but reaches the maximum in 16 minutes. The blue color of cyclohexanone oxime with chlorinated urea is suitable for its estimation.[55] It is given by ketoximes, cyclopentanone oxime, and cyclohexanone oxime.

Procedure—*With o-nitrobenzaldehyde.* Mix 0.5 ml. of sample solution with 5 ml. of a 1 per cent solution of *o*-nitrobenzaldehyde in 5 per cent potassium hydroxide solution. Dilute to 25 ml. with ethanol and read after 1 hour.

With chlorinated urea. Prepare chlorinated urea by absorption of about 30 grams of chlorine by 60 grams of urea and 15 ml. of water. Mix a sample containing 10-50 mg. of cyclohexanone with 3 ml. of 1.65 per cent solution of hydroxylamine in glacial acetic acid. After 20 minutes, add 20 ml. of glacial acetic acid and 0.5 ml. of chlorinated urea for reading.

---

[54] G. Zeidler and H. Kreis, *Angew. Chem.* **54**, 360 (1941).

[55] O. Wichterle and M. Hudlicky, *Collection Czechoslov. Chem. Communs.* **12**, 661-71 (1947).

CHAPTER 13

UNSUBSTITUTED MONOBASIC ALIPHATIC ACIDS AND THEIR ESTERS [1]

ESTERS are necessarily combined with the acids because the acid is usually determined rather than the alcohol. In general, the acids appear in approximate order of chain length.

The salts of the acids rarely show color until the chain length is substantial. Therefore, the short chain acids are commonly converted to more reactive compounds such as aldehydes and oxyacids.

FORMIC ACID

When formic acid is reduced to formaldehyde with magnesium in acid solution, the methods for formaldehyde are applicable [2] (page 255). Schiff's reagent applies over the range 0.04-1.0 mg.[3] In a micro form,[4] chromotropic acid [5] will determine 0.00025-0.015 mg. in 0.5 ml. with accuracy to 0.00013 mg. Formaldehyde need not interfere as it can be preliminarily removed with phenyl hydrazine. Both conform to Beer's law over the specified ranges. Few other substances are reduced to formaldehyde by magnesium.

By reaction of formic acid with mercuric chloride to give mercurous chloride and subsequent reduction of phosphotungstic-phosphomolybdic acid to molybdenum blue with the washed precipitate quantities of 0.005-0.03 mg. per ml. are estimated to ±0.001 mg. Formic acid itself does not reduce the reagent. Deviation from Beer's law is not significant over the specified range. Other reducing agents for mercuric chloride such as formaldehyde and ascorbic acid must be absent. The high sensitivity avoids the necessity for concentrating larger samples with attendant loss.

Samples—*Carbonate solutions.* Add 1:10 hydrochloric acid drop-

---

[1] See Chapter 1 for details of organization, condensation, etc.

[2] H. J. H. Fenton and H. A. Sisson, *Proc. Cambridge Phil. Soc.* **14**, 385 (1908); Hugo Droller, *Z. physiol. Chem.* **211**, 57-64 (1932).

[3] W. Morton Grant, *Ind. Eng. Chem., Anal. Ed.* **19**, 206-7 (1947).

[4] W. Morton Grant, *Anal. Chem.* **20**, 267-9 (1948).

[5] Edwin Eegriwe, *Z. anal. Chem.* **110**, 22-5 (1937); Douglas A. MacFadyen, *J. Biol. Chem.* **158**, 107-33 (1945).

wise until adjusted roughly to pH 2 so as to avoid reduction of carbon dioxide to formaldehyde.[6] Develop with chromotropic acid.

Blood. Mix 1 ml. of blood with 2 ml. of a 5 per cent solution of sulfosalicylic acid in 1:150 sulfuric acid and centrifuge. If formaldehyde is present, add 4 drops of 10 per cent phenylhydrazine hydrochloride solution and wait 5 minutes for reaction to be complete. Then distil, using the type of flask shown in Figure 21. Alternatively, add 1 ml. of saturated copper sulfate solution to 5 ml. of filtrate. Add about 1 gram of calcium hydroxide and shake frequently for an hour. Centrifuge and use a portion of the upper layer for reduction with magnesium ribbon and development with Schiff's reagent.

Skin. Cut 0.1-1.5 mg. into fine pieces and weigh to 0.01 mg. Cover with 5 ml. of fresh 10 per cent metaphosphoric acid solution. Shake mechanically for 6 hours, filter, and insure absence of protein in the filtrate by testing with sulfosalicylic acid. Proceed as for the alternative treatment for blood starting at "Add 1 ml. of saturated copper sulfate. . . ."

Fruit juice or syrup. If sulfur dioxide is present add 5 ml. of 1 per cent sodium hydroxide solution to a 20-ml. sample. Add 0.5 ml. of 30 per cent hydrogen peroxide solution and let stand for 4 hours at room temperature. Add an excess of mercuric oxide paste prepared by pouring saturated mercuric chloride into boiling 10 per cent sodium hydroxide solution, settling, and decanting the liquid to waste. This will decompose excess hydrogen peroxide in one-half hour. Filter, wash the filter with water, dilute the filtrate to a known volume, and use as below. In the absence of sulfur dioxide skip this paragraph and use the juice directly.

Add 0.3 gram of tartaric acid to 10 ml. of juice and distil as for blood.

Procedure—*With chromotropic acid.* Add a sample of 0.5 ml. containing not over 0.015 mg. of formic acid to a test tube containing an 80-mg. coil of clean magnesium ribbon. Immerse in an ice bath and add a drop of concentrated hydrochloric after each 1-3 minute interval until 10 drops are added, a total of 0.5 ml. One minute after the last addition remove from the bath and add 1.5 ml. of a reagent made by mixing 20 ml. of 3 per cent aqueous chromotropic acid and 180 ml. of concentrated sulfuric acid. Place in a boiling water bath protected from bright light for 30 minutes. Centrifuge to remove the white precipitate resulting from magnesium and chromotropic acid and read at 570 mμ against a reagent blank.

---

[6] Henry John Horstman Fenton, *J. Chem. Soc.* **91**, 682-93 (1907).

With Schiff's reagent. Proceed as for chromotropic acid development until reduction is complete at ". . . a total of 0.5 ml." Add 1 ml. of Schiff's reagent (page 251) and mix. Let the solution stand for 12 hours to clarify, or centrifuge after 1 hour, and read the color at 560 mμ.

Mercurous chloride with phosphomolybdic-phosphotungstic acid. To 1 ml. of sample solution containing not over 0.03 mg. of formic acid, add 0.5 ml. of a reagent containing 20 per cent of mercuric chloride, 30 per cent of hydrated sodium acetate, and 8 per cent of sodium chloride. Heat the lower part of the tube in a steam bath for 3 hours, with the upper two-thirds of the tube protected from the heat. Cool and add 2 ml. of a 20 per cent suspension of diatomaceous earth in water. Run in 10 ml. of ethanol that has been treated with activated carbon and filtered, which prevents particles floating. Centrifuge for 10 minutes and decant without loss of precipitate. Wash with two 10-ml. portions of water by the same technic.

As a reagent for reduction dissolve 10 grams of phosphotungstic acid and 130 grams of phosphomolybdic acid in water, dilute to 400 ml., and add 50 ml. of concentrated hydrochloric acid and 50 ml. of 85 per cent orthophosphoric acid. A small sediment forms and the yellow solution is stable for several weeks. A green tinge increases the blank.

Add 1 ml. of reagent, mix with the precipitate, and heat in the steam bath for 15 minutes. Without cooling add 4 ml. of saturated sodium carbonate solution and read the color without waiting for the developed solution to cool. Residual diatomaceous earth does not interfere and the color does not vary for at least 10 minutes.

ACETIC ACID AND ETHYL ACETATE

Ethyl acetate is determined by converting to the potassium salt of the corresponding hydroxamic acid with hydroxylamine hydrochloride and alkali. Addition of ferric chloride then yields a violet-colored complex.[7] The reaction is a very general one obtainable with alcohols, ethers, carboxylic acids, acid chlorides, acid anhydrides, aldehydes, phenols, oximes, lactones, sulfonic acids, nitro-compounds, amides, and cyanates. Therefore, as applied to ethyl acetate such interferences must be absent.

The color is not stable so that readings should be made within a few minutes of its development. The intensity does not vary with temperature in the range of 20-30°. As applied to ethyl acetate in methanol, the method is accurate to within 1-2 ppm.

---

[7] Zbyněk Brada, *Chem. Listy* **37**, 289-90 (1943). A. G. Keenan, *Can. Chem. Process Inds.* **29**, 857-8 (1945).

Lanthanum is a specific reagent for detection of acetate[8] which is applied quantitatively under appropriate conditions.[9] The mixture of acetate, iodine, lanthanum nitrate, and ammonium hydroxide yields a jelly-like substantially clear solution of basic lanthanum acetate. The iodine sorbs on the acetate giving a characteristic blue to green color which may or may not be distributed homogeneously. Inorganic, interfering ions must be removed. Acetate in the final solution is detected at 0.2 mg. per ml.[10] Smaller amounts of acetate are detected by heating the mixture.

Vapors of acetic acid, absorbed in alcohol, are determined without saponification by the color with p-dimethylaminobenzaldehyde and sulfuric acid.[11] The differential rate of oxidation by bichromate is also applicable.[12]

Procedure—*With ferric chloride.* As reagent, dissolve 10 grams of anhydrous ferric chloride in 40 ml. of concentrated hydrochloric acid and dilute to 100 ml. Store in a black bottle and filter before using.

Mix 2 ml. of sample, 1 ml. of 1 per cent hydroxylamine hydrochloride solution, and 1 ml. of 1.32 per cent potassium hydroxide solution, in that order. Shake, allow to stand for 10 minutes, and add 1 ml. of hydrochloric acid solution prepared by dilution of 17 ml. of concentrated acid to 100 ml. Add 2 drops of ferric chloride reagent, mix, and take the first steady reading within 1 minute, using a green filter. After the reagent has been added, the procedure should take less than 2 minutes.

With lanthanum. To 3 ml. of acetate solution add the following in the order indicated with suitable modification where necessary to provide for larger amounts of contaminants. To remove chloride, add 1 ml. of 0.5 per cent silver nitrate solution. To remove excess silver, add 1 ml. of 0.17 per cent potassium iodide solution and allow 2-3 minutes for coagulation of silver iodide. To remove sulfate, phosphate, calcium, and magnesium, add 1 ml. of a solution containing 1.4 per cent of barium hydroxide octahydrate and 1.2 per cent of barium nitrate. Centrifuge and use the filtrate. The final pH should be about 9.5.

To 1 ml. of acetate sample containing 0.08-0.25 mg. of acetic acid, add 2 ml. of a 1:1 solution of 2.5 per cent lanthanum nitrate and 1:200

[8] Deodata Kruger and Erich Tschirch, *Ber.* **62B**, 2776-83 (1929).

[9] John O. Hutchens and Beatrice M. Kass, *J. Biol. Chem.*, **177**, 571-5 (1949).

[10] F. Feigl, "Qualitative Analysis by Spot Tests," New York, 330 (1939).

[11] H. M. Custance and M. Higgins, *Analyst* **74**, 310-15 (1949).

[12] E. Ciaranfi and A. Fonnesu, *Biochem. J.* **50**, 698-701 (1952).

ammonium hydroxide. Follow this with 1 ml. of 0.25 per cent iodine solution. Stopper the tube, heat in a boiling water bath for 5 minutes, cool, and read at 625 mμ against a reagent blank. Poorly stoppered tubes result in a color that fades quickly.

BUTYRIC ACID

Copper butyrate dissolved in chloroform gives a blue color.[13] The color intensity varies with the concentration of butyrate, the acidity, and the amount of copper present, so that the latter two must be constant. The presence of propionic acid causes the results to be high, as cupric propionate is partially soluble in chloroform and produces a blue color. It is not normally produced by butyric acid cultures. Amounts of formic acid up to 25 per cent of the total do not influence the results; larger amounts give low results. The method is therefore applicable to pure culture work and not to mixed cultures. It will detect about 20 mg. of butyric acid. The intense color in high concentration is difficult to match. Accurate results are obtained against pure mixture of acetic and butyric acids.

Butyric acid is also oxidized to acetoacetic acid by hydrogen peroxide in the presence of a ferrous salt as catalyst.[14] The product gives an intense red color with sodium nitroprusside.

Sample—*Cultures.* Add 20 grams of monosodium phosphate monohydrate to 50 ml. of culture. If this yields less than 0.15 gram of volatile acid, increase the sample to a quantity that will give at least that amount. Add 15 ml. of 85 per cent phosphoric acid and distil off the volatile acids. Keep the volume of liquid in the distilling flask to within 10-15 ml. of 50 ml., by adding water through a dropping funnel at about the same rate as the liquid distils. Collect 200 ml. of distillate which will contain substantially all of the volatile acids. Add 2 per cent sodium hydroxide solution, dropwise, to a phenolphthalein end point. Evaporate to a volume such that the concentration will be slightly greater than equivalent to the salt from 2 per cent of sodium hydroxide. If any trace of a pink color appears, decolorize with 1:20 hydrochloric acid and dilute to exactly equivalent to 2 per cent for development as copper butyrate.

Procedure—*As copper butyrate.* Prepare a cupric chloride reagent by dissolving 85.26 grams of cupric chloride dihydrate in a liter of 1:10

---

[13] R. J. Allgeier, W. H. Peterson, and E. B. Fred, *J. Bact.* 17, 79-87 (1929).
[14] G. Deniges, *Ann. chim. anal.* 23, 27-31 (1918).

hydrochloric acid. Add 0.4 ml. of this reagent to 3 ml. of the neutralized volatile acid distillate in a separatory funnel. Mix, add 5 ml. of chloroform, and shake until the maximum color develops in the chloroform layer. This is usually 20-30 seconds. Draw off the chloroform layer and read against a chloroform blank.

By hydrogen peroxide oxidation. To 5 ml. of sample solution add 5 ml. of hydrogen peroxide of a strength approximately equal to that of the butyric acid solution. For butyric acid up to 0.05 per cent, use a 0.02 per cent hydrogen peroxide. Add 1 ml. of 5 per cent ferrous ammonium sulfate solution in 1:100 sulfuric acid. Heat on a water bath for 5 minutes at 68-70° and render slightly alkaline with 6 drops of 50 per cent sodium hydroxide solution. Mix well, cool, and filter out ferric hydroxide. To exactly 5 ml. of filtrate add 3 drops of 50 per cent sodium hydroxide solution and 3 drops of 5 per cent sodium nitroprusside solution, and mix well. Add glacial acetic acid until only slightly alkaline, which will require not over 0.5 ml. Mix well to get the rose-red color representative of the butyric acid content and read against a reagent blank.

ACRYLIC ACID ESTERS

A method developed for terminal olefinic groups and applied for estimation of undecylenic acid (page 309) is also applicable to acrylic acid esters soluble in ethanol.

ISOVALERIC ACID

Isovaleric acid on heating with ninhydrin, triketohydrindene hydrate, is converted to isobutyric aldehyde which is determinable by its reaction with salicylic aldehyde.[15]

Procedure—To a volume of sample solution which will contain 0.02-0.25 mg. of isovaleric acid, add 0.1 gram of monopotassium phosphate, 0.15 gram of sodium chloride, and 1.5 grams of ninhydrin. Heat at 120° for 5 minutes to dehydrate the acid to the aldehyde. Steam distil collecting exactly 6 ml. of distillate. To 3 ml. of distillate add 2 ml. of an exactly titrated 10.5 N sodium hydroxide solution. Then add 1 ml. of 1:4 salicylic aldehyde. Heat at 50° for 70 minutes and cool. At the end of 10 minutes read against a reagent blank at 500 mμ and compare with a calibration curve derived by similar treatment of isovaleric acid.

15 K. A. J. Wretline, *Acta Physiol. Scand.* **3**, 329-34 (1942).

10,11-UNDECYLENIC ACID

A terminal olefinic linkage will be converted to a glycol group by potassium permanganate. This is then split with periodic acid to yield formaldehyde and a higher aldehyde. Distillation of the formaldehyde and its estimation constitute a measure of the undecylenic acid present.[16] Other compounds forming formaldehyde under these conditions interfere. They include allyl alcohol, allyl chloride, allyl bromide, allyl isothiocyanate, allyl thiourea, styrene, isoprene, pinene, citral, citronellol, itaconic acid, and α-methylenebutyrolactone. There is substantially no reaction with oleic acid, cinnamic acid, indene, coumarin, and indole. Citraconic and aconitic acids show some interference without giving quantitative results. Substances such as methanol and 1,2-glycols which yield formaldehyde interfere. Some compounds distil and react with the reagent, examples being phenylethyl alcohol, benzaldehyde, and acetone. Reproducibility is to ±5 per cent. The reaction is not stoichiometric and therefore not applicable to determination of the percentage of end unsaturation.

Procedure—The sample must be in ethanol as solvent. Dilute an aliquot expected to yield 2 mg. of formaldehyde to 3 ml. with 5 per cent ethanol. Add 1 ml. of 20 per cent aqueous periodic acid. Add 1 per cent aqueous potassium permanganate in 0.2 ml. portions until the solution remains pink for 1 minute. Transfer to the distillation apparatus shown in Figure 18 and distil, collecting about 15 ml. Take the contents of the tube nearly to dryness. Mix 1 ml. of distillate with 50 mg. of chromotropic acid and add 5 ml. of concentrated sulfuric acid. Heat in boiling water for 30 minutes. Cool, dilute to 50 ml., and read at 570 mμ against a reagent blank.

ELEOSTEARIC ACIDS

The characteristic component of tung oil is α-eleostearic acid present to 70-80 per cent. Direct ultraviolet reading of the triene is feasible.[17]

---

[16] G. Hoepe and W. D. Treadwell, *Helv. Chim. Acta* **25**, 353-61 (1942); Marvin J. Johnson, *Ind. Eng. Chem.*, *Anal. Ed.* **16**, 626-7 (1944); R. C. Reinke and E. N. Luce, *Ibid.* **18**, 244-5 (1946); Benjamin Warshowsky and Philip J. Elving, *Ibid.* **18**, 253-4 (1946); Philip J. Elving, Benjamin Warshowsky, Edward Shoemaker, and Jack Margolit, *Anal. Chem.* **20**, 25-9 (1948); Clark E. Bricker and Karl H. Roberts, *Ibid.* **21**, 1331-4 (1949).

[17] Robert T. O'Connor, Dorothy C. Heinzelman, A. F. Freeman, and F. C. Pack, *Ind. Eng. Chem.*, *Anal. Ed.* **17**, 467-70 (1945).

No correction for overlapping diene or tetraene absorption is necessary. On aging some isomerization to β-eleostearic acid occurs, which has a slightly different maximum.[18] Then total eleostearic acid can be read or the α- and β-acids with some difficulty to ±1 per cent.

Procedure—α-*eleostearic acid.* Dissolve a weighed sample of tung oil compound in isooctane, or cyclohexane. Dilute to approximately 0.005 gram of α-eleostearic acid per liter. For the first solvent read at 270 mμ; for the second, at 271 mμ. The respective extinction coefficients are 169.8 and 168.6.

α-*and β-eleostearic acid.* For moderate accuracy a very narrow spectrum band, less than 1 mμ is essential, with accuracy of setting to ±0.2 mμ. Read at 276.5 mμ, 271.5 mμ and 269.0 mμ in cyclohexane.

$$\text{Total eleostearic acid} = 0.8163\,E_{276.5}$$
$$\alpha\text{-Eleostearic acid} = 100\,(0.027\,E_{271.5}- 0.02375\,E_{269.0})$$
$$\beta\text{-Eleostearic acid} = 100\,(0.02248\,E_{269.0}- 0.01994\,E_{271.5})$$

trans-OCTADECANOIC ACIDS, ESTERS, and ALCOHOLS

Infrared spectrophotometry at 10.36μ differentiates *trans*-octadecanoic acid with its esters and alcohols from corresponding *cis* and saturated compounds.[19] The absorption corresponds to Beer's law and permits determination of oleic acid, petroselinic acid, palmitic acid, stearic acid, elaidic acid, petroselaidic acid, methyl oleate, methyl stearate, methyl elaidate, methyl petroselaidate, triolein, trimyristin, palmitostearins, trielaidin, oleyl alcohol, stearyl alcohol, and eliadyl alcohol.

Procedure—Dilute a weighed sample to 10 ml. with carbon bisulfide. This should not contain over 150 mg. of a *trans* compound or over 30 mg. of a *cis* saturated or monounsaturated acid. It may contain up to 450 mg. of methyl esters of the *cis* compounds. Read at 10.36μ with an optical density of 0.2-0.6.

Calculations—*Mixtures containing cis- and trans-octadecanoic components only.*

---

[18] Robert T. O'Connor, Dorothy C. Heinzelman, R. C. McKinney, and F. C. Pack, *J. Am. Oil. Chem. Soc.* **24**, 212-16 (1947).

[19] O. D. Shreve, M. R. Heether, H. B. Knight, and Daniel Swern, *Anal. Chem.* **22**, 1261-3 (1950).

$$trans \text{ component, weight } \% = \frac{100 \ (k_{ob} - k_c)}{k_T - k_c} \tag{1}$$

where k_{ob} = "observed extinction coefficient" for the mixture =
$$\frac{\text{optical density at } 10.36\mu}{(\text{total concn., grams/liter}) (\text{cell thickness, cm.})}$$
k_c = extinction coefficient of pure cis compound
k_T = extinction coefficient of pure trans compound

Mixtures containing trans-octadecenoic and saturated components only.

$$trans \text{ component, weight } \% = \frac{100 \ (k_{ob} - k_s)}{k_T - k_s} \tag{2}$$

where k_s is the extinction coefficient of the pure saturated compound.

Mixtures containing cis- and trans-octadecanoic and saturated components.

$$trans \text{ component, weight } \% = \frac{100 \ (k_{ob} - k_c Y - k_s Z)}{k_T - k_c} \tag{3}$$

where the k values are as defined above; Y is the total weight fraction of octadecanoic components (*cis* plus *trans*), and Z is the weight fraction of saturated components. Y is calculated from the iodine value of the mixture and Z is obtained by difference.

In practical applications to unknown mixtures, the *cis*- and *trans*-octadecanoic fractions may each consist of one or more compounds in which the exact position of the double bond is unknown. Also the relative proportions of long-chain saturated compounds in the saturated fraction are often unknown. Therefore, it is fortunate that shifting the double bond from the Δ^9 to the Δ^6 position in either the *cis*- or *trans*-octadecanoic acids produces only a small change in extinction coefficient. The same holds for the *trans*-methyl esters, and therefore might be expected to hold for the *cis*-methyl esters, and the *cis*- and *trans*-glycerides and alcohols. Furthermore, it seems safe to assume that an equivalent shift in the opposite direction to Δ^{12} or to any intermediate position would likewise produce little change.

The extinction coefficients for the various *cis*-octadecanoic and saturated acids studied are all approximately the same. This relation also holds for the *cis* and saturated glycerides and alcohols and to a somewhat lesser degree for the *cis* and saturated methyl esters.

In unknown acid mixtures that contain no octadecanoic acids outside the Δ^6 to Δ^{12} range, the total percentage of *trans* acids present can be calculated with acceptable accuracy by using the average k value of the two *trans* acids for k_T, that of the two *cis* acids for k_c, and that of the two saturated acids for k_s in the appropriate formula. Results on unknown methyl ester, glyceride, or alcohol mixtures may be similarly calculated by using appropriate average or single values. In view of the above statement, determination of iodine number in a *trans-cis*-saturated mixture of the four types can be eliminated if desired, and results calculated from the following simplified formula:

$$trans \text{ component, weight } \% = \frac{100 \; (k_{ob} - k_{av.})}{k_T - k_{av.}} \qquad (4)$$

where k_T is the appropriate average or single k value for *trans* compounds and $k_{av.}$ is the average k value for both *cis* and saturated compounds.

For given selected values of k_c and k_s, Formulas 3 and 4 will yield identical results expressed as per cent *trans*, to the nearest 0.01 per cent when $Y = Z = 0.5$—that is, when total per cent octadecanoic components equal total per cent saturated components. As Y departs from 0.5 in either direction, the absolute error entailed by use of Formula 4 increases. In the most unfavorable cases likely to be encountered in analyzing acid mixtures ($Y = 0.03$ or $Y = 0.97$), this error is about 0.5 per cent when the average value for the two *trans* acids is used for k_T, that of the two *cis* acids for k_c, that of the two saturated acids for k_s, and that of the latter for $k_{av.}$. In most cases, the error will be much less.

Fatty Acids and Esters

Fatty acids and their esters are determined by conversion of the carboxylic acids to hydroxamic acids of the general formula $R \cdot CO(NHOH)$ which give a red or violet color with ferric chloride in acid solution.[20] Free fatty acids must first be esterified, conveniently by conversion to the acid chloride, and reaction with methanol. Anhydrous conditions are essential. Typical applications are determination of small amounts of palm oil, cottonseed oil, dibutyl sebacate, lanolin, etc. Time after development of color and temperature must be controlled as affecting the color intensity.

---

[20] Uno T. Hill, *Ind. Eng. Chem., Anal.. Ed.*, **18**, 317-9 (1946); *Ibid.* **19**, 932-3 (1947).

Excess hydroxylamine causing slow reduction of the iron complex is avoided by addition of nitric acid or hydrogen peroxide. The method is also applicable to fatty acids extracted from saponified serum.[21]

Fatty acid is esterified with rosaniline to give a green dye which is read photometrically.[22] Saturated acids such as palmitic or stearic are suitable for preparation of a standard. Fatty acids, free or combined, which are unsaturated give yellow to dark red with tetranitromethane.[23] Thus the intensity of color increases with the iodine value and is a quick method of checking within ±5 units of iodine value. Knowing the iodine value, results can be read in terms of the amount of fatty acid present.

Small amounts of fats are saponified and the fatty acids converted to lead soaps. The lead soaps are desirably separated into ether-soluble, chloroform-soluble, and insoluble soaps.[24] The ether-soluble lead soaps are those of the acids lower than oleic, the chloroform-soluble lead soap is primarily lead oleate, and the insoluble lead soap is lead stearate. The fractions are separately decomposed, the lead converted to lead nitrate, and finally the lead estimated as lead sulfide. Alternatively the lead is determined [25] as the chromate.

Free fatty acids form red soaps with neutral red in xylene.[26] In their absence the dye base is orange-yellow in solution. The results average 10 per cent lower than by titration. Small amounts of fatty acid in the absence of other reducing substances are used to reduce potassium dichromate in strong sulfuric acid (page 325). Details are given under lipids.[27]

Samples—*Oil on metal surfaces.* Wash a known area, such as 4 square inches in the form of discs, successively with three 15-ml. portions of ether at room temperature and treat an aliquot as a sample containing fatty acids.

Fatty acids. To an ethereal solution containing 0.05-1 mg. of fatty acid in 10 ml. of ether, add about 3 ml. of thionyl chloride and evaporate

---

[21] Frederick C. Bauer, Jr., and Edwin F. Hirsch, *Arch. Biochem.* **20**, 242-50 (1949).

[22] H. G. Krainick and F. Müller, *Mikrochemie ver. Mikrochim. Acta* **30**, 7-14 (1941).

[23] H. P. Kaufmann, Bao Wei King, and Lan-Sun Huang, *Ber.* **75B**, 1201-14 (1942).

[24] Ludwig Princussen and Sonja Kolodny, *Biochem. Z.* **223**, 347-51 (1930).

[25] A. D. Marenzi and C. E. Cardini, *Rev. soc. argentina biol.* **19**, 118-30 (1943).

[26] Vladimir N. Krukovsky and Georges Knaysi, *J. Dairy Sci.* **25**, 659-62 (1942).

[27] W. R. Bloor, *J. Biol. Chem.* **170**, 671-4 (1947).

almost to dryness. Add a few drops of methanol and heat briefly. Evaporate excess reagents by the use of a gentle current of air, add about 20 ml. of anhydrous ether, and complete by conversion to hydroxamic acids.

Esters. Dissolve in ether and convert to hydroxamic acids.

Blood or plasma. Mix 0.1 ml. with 0.5 ml. of 40 per cent sodium hydroxide and heat to saponify. When complete, cool and add 0.6 ml. of 1:2.6 sulfuric acid. Extract the liberated fatty acids with 10 ml. of benzene. Use all or an aliquot of the extract for development with rosaniline. Alternatively extract with ether, dry the extract with sodium sulfate, and determine by conversion to hydroxamic acids.

Tissue. Mix 5 grams of finely ground tissue, 3 ml. of water, 0.025 gram of zinc oxide, and 0.025 gram of zinc dust. Heat in an autoclave at 10-12 atmospheres pressure for 8 hours. This completely hydrolyzes the fat to fatty acid. Transfer the treated sample quantitatively to a separatory funnel. Extract with three 10-ml portions of ether. Extract the remaining solution with three 10-ml. portions of chloroform. Combine the ether and chloroform extracts in a large centrifuge cup and evaporate to dryness on a sand bath. The residue is a brownish-yellow mass of fatty acid. Add 250 mg. of lead acetate dissolved in 2 ml. of water and heat on a boiling water bath for 5 hours, stirring frequently. Stir the precipitate with sucessive wash waters until the washings give no test with hydrogen sulfide. Decant the water completely and add 15 ml. of ether. Mix well and centrifuge. Repeat the washing with 2 additional 15-ml. portions of ether and dilute the ether extracts to 50 ml. Similarly, wash the lead soaps with three 15-ml. portions of chloroform. Dilute this also to 50 ml. as the solution of chloroform-soluble soaps. Reserve the insoluble soaps as a third fraction.

Transfer 10 ml. of the ether extract to a centrifuge tube and evaporate to dryness. Add 1 ml. of concentrated nitric acid to the residue and let stand for a few minutes. Add 3 per cent hydrogen peroxide and heat at 160° on a sand bath until only a white residue remains. Further amounts of nitric acid and hydrogen peroxide may be added as necessary to complete the ashing. Cool the tube and dissolve the residue in water. Dilute the lead nitrate solution to 50 ml.

Carry through the same procedure with the chloroform-soluble lead soaps. Similarly ash the insoluble lead soaps and dilute to a suitable volume according to the amount of this fraction. Develop all three portions as lead sulfide or as chromate.

Procedure—*As hydroxamic acids.* As reagent dissolve 0.4 gram of iron or its equivalent in 20 ml. of 1:3 nitric acid. Add 15 ml. of 70 per cent perchloric acid solution and evaporate to copious fumes of perchloric acid. Take up in 40 ml. of water, add 10 ml. of concentrated nitric acid, and dilute to 100 ml. with 70 per cent perchloric acid. This stock keeps indefinitely. For use make a 1 per cent solution of the stock in methanol or ethanol. This keeps about a week.

To a solution containing 0.05-1 mg. of ester in absolute ether, add exactly 0.3 ml. of 2.5 per cent sodium hydroxide solution in ethanol and 0.3 ml. of 2.5 per cent hydroxylamine hydrochloride in ethanol. Evaporate to dryness at 60-70° on a water bath and then heat an extra 5 seconds. Add 10 ml. of the ferric chloride reagent at once and allow to stand until all salts are dissolved. Adjust the temperature to 27° and read at once at 520 mμ against a reagent blank.

By esterifying with rosaniline. As reagent reflux 2 grams of finely ground rosaniline with 75 ml. of benzene for an hour. Centrifuge to remove undissolved dye from the cooled solution after 24 hours, and read the yellow color at 470 mμ. The extinction coefficient should be 0.40-0.45. The solution should be used within 2 weeks. Evaporate an aliquot of fatty acid solution containing 0.05-0.5 mg. to dryness and take up in 1 ml. of isopropanol. Add 1 ml. of the reagent and heat at 75° for 0.5 hour. Cool and dilute to 10 ml. with benzene. Read at 530 mμ against a reagent blank.

As lead sulfide. Use this solution as sample by the procedure in Volume II, page 41. Multiply the lead from the ether solution by 2.5 to give the fatty acid in this fraction. Similarly multiply the lead from the chloroform-soluble fraction by 2.73 to give results in terms of oleic acid. The lead from the insoluble fraction multipled by 2.75 gives the result as stearic acid. The sum of the fatty acids in the 3 fractions gives the total of those present in the original sample.

As chromate. Use the lead solution as sample by the procedure in Volume II, page 42. Multiply by the factors cited for development as lead sulfide.

In milk fat by neutral red. Dissolve 1 ml. of milk fat in 3 ml. of a saturated solution of neutral red in xylene and compare with a series of standards of known oleic-acid content. As such standards, weigh 0.5647 gram of pure oleic acid into a 50-ml. flask and dilute to volume with xylene to give a 0.04 N solution. Dilute 1 ml. of this to 10 ml. to give a 0.004 N solution. From these, prepare standards to cover a range of 0.0005-0.002 N oleic acid.

FATS AND OILS

Fats and oils are analyzed in terms of saturated acids, oleic acid, linoleic acid, linolenic acid, and arachidonic acid by measurement of the ultraviolet absorption, both before and after conjugation of the poly-unsaturated constituents.[28] The conjugated constituents are read in purified iso-octane. The non-conjugated poly-unsaturated constituents are conjugated by heating in glycol containing potassium hydroxide. The sample is protected from oxidation during the isomerization period by blanketing with nitrogen. The poly-unsaturated constituents are calculated from the absorption, after isomerization, using constants obtained by isomerization of pure acids and their mixtures.

The absorption at 210 mμ is particularly valuable for reading the composition of oils in terms of unsaturation [29] but unfortunately lies below the range of most instruments. Small amounts of triglycerides are determinable by reduction of dichromate in the absence of other reducing substances. Details are given under lipids (page 325). Fat extracted by absolute ethanol includes the lecithin and may be estimated turbidimetrically. Substituting acetone for the ethanol gives the fat without the value for lecithin.[30]

Sample—For accurate results, particular attention must be paid to (1) the concentration of potassium hydroxide in the glycol isomerization mixture, (2) the isomerization time as the factors used in the calculation are based on an exact isomerization time of 25 minutes, (3) isomerization temperature, and (4) purity of reagents at the time of use.

Apparatus—Since this method is more dependent on the specific apparatus than usual, it is described in some detail with respect to Beckman catalogue numbers.

Spectrophotometer. Use the Beckman Model DU No. 2500 with accessories 2501 and cell compartment assembly 2510. Thus this provides

[28] Thomas Moore, *Biochem. J.* **31**, 138-41 (1937); E. S. Miller and G. O. Burr, *Chem. Rev.* **29**, 419-38 (1941); J. H. Mitchell, Jr., H. R. Kraybill, and F. P. Zscheile, *Ind. Eng. Chem., Anal. Ed.* **15**, 1-3 (1943); R. W. Beadle, B. F. Daubert, R. H. Ferguson, R. T. Milner, R. T. O'Connor, and R. C. Stillman, *J. Am. Oil Chemists' Soc.* **26**, 400-404 (1949). Cf. Leah C. Berk, Norman Kretchmer, Ralph T. Holman, and George O. Burr, *Anal. Chem.* **22**, 718-20 (1950); B. A. Brice, M. L. Swain, S. F. Herb, P. L. Nichols, Jr., and R. M. Reimenschneider, *J. Am. Oil Chemists' Soc.* **29**, 279-87 (1952).

[29] R. H. Barnes, I. I. Rusoff, E. S. Miller, and G. O. Burr, *Ind. Eng. Chem., Anal. Ed.* **16**, 385-6 (1949).

[30] Gyula Suranyi and Péter Véghelyi, *Magyar Orvosi Arch.* **36**, 169 (1935); *Biochem. Z.* **283**, 415-21 (1936).

an absorption cell compartment assembly for cells up to 10 cm. long. Adjust the focus of the hydrogen discharge lamp No. 2230 in housing 2240 so that, with the slit open to maximum width and with the sensitivity knob at the counter-clockwise limit, and with no absorption cell in the beam, the meter balances at the lowest possible wave length. This is usually 211 mμ or lower. Thereafter leave the sensitivity knob at about 3 counter-clockwise turns and use the slit with adjustment for balancing the instrument.

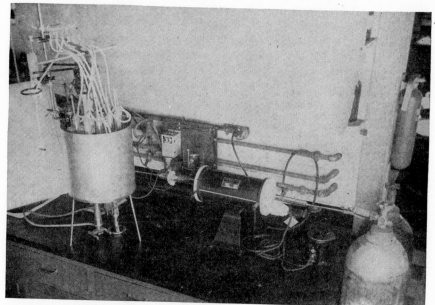

Procter & Gamble Co.

FIG. 22. Typical isomerization bath

Absorption cells. The demountable type with an outside diameter of 28 mm. is preferable. Each should consist of a Pyrex glass cell body of outside diameter of approximately 22 mm. with centered ground-glass stopper, threaded metal jackets or ends with threaded metal cans, polished crystalline quartz windows, and cork gaskets; bodies to be in matched pairs of lengths 1.000, 2.500, and 5.000 cm., ±0.005 cm. Non-demountable cells may be used if more expedient. Matched cells should show the same optical density to 0.01 unit when filled with a solvent such as water or iso-octane.

Constant temperature bath. Many types of isomerization baths may be used. For convenience one is described and illustrated in Figure 22 with sample tubes in place. Regardless of the type used, nitrogen blanketing must be provided.

A cylindrical bath 12 inches in diameter, 12 inches high, of stainless steel, is equipped with an Aminco mercury thermoregulator, No. 4—202, with No. 4—210 protective case; supersensitive mercury relay, Aminco No. 4—291 and Aminco motor stirrer. The bath is heated to just below

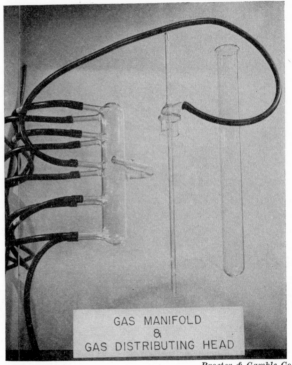

GAS MANIFOLD
&
GAS DISTRIBUTING HEAD

Procter & Gamble Co.

Fig. 23

180° with a Meker burner, with the burner so regulated, the additional and controlled heat is provided by a 250-watt bayonet heater. The bath is equipped with a sample rack with about 20 holes. Usually a maximum of 8 samples are handled at one time. The balance of the holes aid in securing good circulation.

Sample tubes and nitrogen supply. The tubes are 10 inch × 1 inch diameter Pyrex. They are provided with a special distributing head shown in Figure 23. The nitrogen is passed into a manifold which is also shown in the figure. From the manifold, gas may be passed to any number of isomerization tubes. The gas passes from one of the manifold outlets through a rubber tube connection to the top of the gas distributing head. The rubber tubing is constricted at the point where it leaves the gas manifold by a small piece of capillary tubing which serves to insure a uniform flow of gas to each of the distributing heads. In the distributing head, the nitrogen enters at the top of the test tube, flows downward through the space above the sample, and leaves the test tube through the 7-mm. tubing, which forms the center part of the gas distributing head. This 7-mm. tubing is open at the bottom and has two small holes approximately 1 inch and 1½ inches from the bottom. The lower end of the 7-mm. tube is open to allow any glycol which passes into the tube to condense and return back to the reaction mixture. A uniform flow of gas to each of the tubes is obtained by maintaining a constant pressure of nitrogen to the manifold.

Furnace and nitrogen purification. Nitrogen used for purification must be low in oxygen. Nitrogen in cylinders containing less than 0.01 per cent of oxygen is used directly without further purification. If purification is necessary, satisfactory apparatus consists of an electric multiple-unit furnace, 12 inches long, made by Hevi-Duty Electric Company, Milwaukee, Wis. Either 110- or 220-volt is suitable. The temperature is controlled by a Variac, Type 200 GM made by General Radio, Cambridge, Mass. Setting 88 has been found to give a satisfactory temperature of about 300° C. Any other furnace that will give controlled temperatures around 300° C. would be satisfactory.

The Pyrex combustion tube is of special design. It contains a copper gauze coil to remove any oxygen present in cylinder nitrogen which is used to blanket the samples while in the isomerization bath. After use, the coil is reduced to metallic copper by cylinder hydrogen. The excess gas is conducted from the muffle tube through a by-pass.

The purified nitrogen passes from the furnace through a train of two wash bottles, the first containing glass beads only and the second containing concentrated sulfuric acid and glass beads. From the wash bottles, the nitrogen passes to the distributing manifold. The rate of flow is controlled by a manometer, which contains water, methyl orange, and a trace of sulfuric acid.

Reagents—All reagents should be of the best quality originally and especially purified where necessary.

Absolute methanol. This can be purchased of acceptable quality. Check the transmittancy against distilled water through the range of wave lengths used on conjugated and non-conjugated analysis. The spectral density of a 1-cm. layer compared with distilled water should be less than 0.4 at 220 mμ. If not acceptable, place 2 liters in a 3-liter flask provided with standard-taper connections. Add one heaping teaspoonful of 85 per cent potassium hydroxide and one heaping teaspoonful of zinc dust. Place a glass stopper in one outlet of the flask and a reflux tube in the other. Reflux on the steam bath for 3 hours. Remove from the steam bath and distil from a hot water bath. Catch the distillate in a flask, store in stoppered glass bottles, and check the quality of the distillate.

Ethanol. This must conform to the same standards as absolute methanol.

Iso-octane. Place approximately 3½ inches of glass wool in a 32 × 1.75 inch glass filter tube above the stop cock. Add about 12 inches of silica gel. Support the filter tube upright on a ring stand with a flask as receiver. Pour iso-octane into the tube slowly, filling it approximately ¾ full. Loosely place an aluminum-covered cork stopper in top of the narrow-neck tube and wait for the iso-octane to filter.

A uniform rate of flow and column action is obtained without trouble by using a column nearly filled with silica, and supplying the iso-octane to the column by an inverted 1-liter flask supported in a ring stand. A constant head is thus maintained without attention, by immersing the mouth of the flask in the iso-octane in the column.

Check the transmittance of the filtered iso-octane against distilled water through the range of wave lengths used on conjugated and nonconjugated analyses. The resultant curve should be smooth and the transmittance above 85 per cent at all points.

Alkaline glycol reagent. This should be accurately 6.5-6.6 per cent potassium hydroxide in ethylene glycol.

Weigh approximately 750 grams of dry ethylene glycol into a 1-liter round-bottom glass-stoppered Pyrex flask. In place of the solid glass stopper, insert a glass stopper containing two glass openings, one of which reaches to the bottom of the flask and through which nitrogen can be passed. The other opening serves as an exit for the nitrogen. Connect to an oxygen-free nitrogen supply and bubble sufficient nitrogen through the glycol to exclude all air and to agitate the sample slightly.

Raise an oil bath at 100 to 150° C. around the flask, raise the bath temperature to 190°, and hold at 190° for 10 minutes. Remove the bath and allow the temperature to drop to 150°. Add, with care, 60 grams of 85 per cent grade potassium hydroxide, keeping the sample under nitrogen. Again raise the oil bath around the flask and reheat to 190°.

Hold at 190° for 10 minutes, remove the bath, and allow to cool. Keep under nitrogen throughout the preparation and during storage. Check the concentration of potassium hydroxide in the cooled mix by dissolving a weighed sample in alcohol and titrating to phenolphthalein with standard hydrochloric acid.

If the per cent of potassium hydroxide is above the range of 6.5 to 6.6 per cent, adjust to this concentration by addition of pure dried glycol prepared by the same technic.

For conjugation. Melt the sample carefully on the steam bath and stir thoroughly. Filter if not clear. Weigh out in Pyrex cups, one sample of approximately 200 mg. in size to the nearest mg., and two samples of approximately 100 mg., to the nearest 0.5 mg. The 200-mg. sample is for analysis of conjugated constituents and the 100-mg. samples are for analyses in duplicate on non-conjugated constituents. More than 200 mg. may be used if necessary to bring the optical density up to 0.2.

For turbidimetry. Extract a 0.05-ml. sample with 5 ml. of absolute ethanol at 100° and filter. This extract includes lecithin. Repeat by extraction of another similar sample with 5 ml. of acetone at 75°. This extract excludes lecithin.

Procedure—*Analysis for conjugated constituents.* Drop the 200-mg. sample into a beaker holding about 75 ml. of purified iso-octane, hexane, or cyclohexane. Dissolve by warming if necessary. Transfer quantitatively to a 100-ml. glass-stoppered volumetric flask and dilute to volume.

Measure the optical density at 233, 262, 268, 274, 310, 316, and 322 mμ against a solvent blank. Start with the solution in a 5-cm. cell, adjusting subsequent dilutions and cell lengths so that, whenever possible, observed densities lie between 0.2 and 0.8. Tabulate wave lengths, densities, dilutions, cell lengths, and weight of sample.

Analysis for non-conjugated constituents. Weigh 11-gram portions of the glycol-potassium hydroxide solution into 10 × 1 inch Pyrex test tubes. Suspend the tubes at a constant depth of 4½ inches in a constant temperature bath operated at 180° C. ± 0.5° C. Place the nitrogen protection covers (Figure 23) in place and start the nitrogen through the tubes. The flow of nitrogen should be controlled by a manometer. A minimum of 50 to 100 ml. of nitrogen should be passed through each tube per minute. If blanks do not check, increase the volume of nitrogen used.

After 20 minutes of heating, remove the nitrogen distributing head and drop the Pyrex cup containing the weighted sample into a reaction tube. Remove the tube from the bath and swirl it vigorously for a few seconds. Return it to the bath. Then replace the nitrogen head. At the end of one minute of heating in the bath, remove and inspect the tube. If the solution is clear, return the tube to the bath. If saponification or solution is not complete, again swirl the tube two or three times, and then return the tube to the bath. Keep the nitrogen head in place at all times.

At intervals of three minutes, introduce other samples in other tubes into the bath, repeating the same procedure. Drop an empty sample container into the tube containing the blank. Follow the swirling steps carefully to assure complete saponification of fat samples.

Exactly 25 minutes after dropping each sample into the tube, remove the tube from the bath, wipe clean, and place in a 3-liter beaker of cold water to cool. Continue to blow nitrogen over the sample during cooling. When cool, wash the cover into the tube with approximately 20 ml. of purified methanol or ethanol. With a long stirring rod having a curved end, work the sample cup up and down until the alkaline glycol and alcohol are completely mixed. Transfer the contents quantitatively to a 100-ml. glass-stoppered volumetric flask. Dilute to volume with the alcohol and mix thoroughly.

Read optical density at the same wave lengths and under the conditions specified for conjugated constituents. When further dilutions of sample are required for making density measurements, make similar dilutions of the blank solution. Tabulate wave lengths, densities, dilutions, cell lengths, and weights of samples.

Turbidimetric. To a 2-ml. aliquot of a solution in ethanol or acetone, add 5 ml. of 1:2 hydrochloric acid containing 1 per cent of butanol. Shake and read.

Calculations—For this the following factors are used.

Absorption coefficient is defined as $k = D/bc$ where D is the observed spectral density of a solution of thickness b in cm. as compared with a solvent layer of the same thickness and of concentration c in grams per liter. The concentration c is equal to W/v, where W is the weight of sample in grams, and v is the total volume of solution in liters. In the equations which follow, subscripts 2, 3, and 4 refer to the number of double bonds; subscripts 233, 268, etc., refer to wave lengths.

Conjugated Constituents

1. Specific extinction coefficient at 233 mμ corrected for COOR and C = C Groups; P_1 is the estimated proportion of oleic acid.

$$k_2 = k_{233} - 0.029 - 0.052\,P_1$$

2. Specific extinction coefficient at 268 mμ corrected for background absorption.

$$k_3 = 2.8\,[k_{268} - \tfrac{1}{2}\,(k_{262} + k_{274})]$$

3. Specific extinction coefficient at 316 mμ corrected for background absorption.

$$k_4 = 2.5\,[k_{316} - \tfrac{1}{2}\,(k_{310} + k_{322})]$$

4. % Conjugated diene = $C_2 = 0.87\,k_2$.
5. % Conjugated triene = $C_3 = 0.47\,k_3$.
6. % Conjugated tetrane = $C_4 = 0.49\,k_4$.

If the quantities within the brackets are zero or negative, no characteristic absorption maxima are present and the corresponding constituent is reported as absent.

Non-conjugated Constituents

7. Specific extinction coefficient at 233 mμ corrected for conjugated diene acids originally present. k_{233} and k'_{233} are observed specific extinction coefficients before and after isomerization (diene region).

$$k'_2 = k'_{233} - k_{233}$$

8. Specific extinction coefficient at 268 mμ corrected for background absorption (triene region).

$$k'_3 = 4.1\,[k'_{260} - \tfrac{1}{2}\,(k'_{262} + k'_{274})]$$

9. Specific extinction coefficient at 268 mμ corrected for undestroyed conjugated triene (the value k_3 is taken from the conjugated analyses data, equation 2).

$$k''_3 = k'_3 - k_3$$

10. Specific extinction coefficient at 316 mμ corrected for background absorption (tetraene region).

$$k''_4 = 2.5 \left[k'_{316} - \tfrac{1}{2} (k'_{310} + k'_{322}) \right]$$

11. Specific extinction coefficient at 316 mμ corrected for undestroyed conjugated tetraene (the value k_4 is taken from equation 3).

$$k''_4 = k'_4 - k_4$$

12. % Linoleic acid $= X = 1.16\, k'_2 - 1.33\, k''_3 + 0.09\, k''_4$

♦	Non Conjugated	W.L.	D	b	c	W.L.	D	b	c				
	8/100→10/100→10/100	233	.452	1.000	0.0100	260	.757	2.500	1.000	$k'_2 = 45.0180$	$k'_{233} = 45.2000$	$k'_{268} = .1300$	$k'_{316} = .0236$
	S/100	262	.495	2.500	1.0000	264	.382	"	"	$k'_3 = .0000$	.1820	$k'_{262} = .1980$	$k'_{310} = .0284$
	"	268	.325	"	"	266	.342	"	"	$k''_3 = .0000$	45.0180	$k'_{274} = .1028$	$k'_{322} = .0186$
	"	274	.257	"	"	270	.303	"	"	$k'_4 = .0003$		2 | .3008	2 | .0470
	"	310	.142	5.000	"	272	.275	"	"	$k''_4 = .0003$		.1504	.0235
	"	316	.118	"	"	276	.254	"	"			.1300	.0236
	"	322	.093	"	"	278	.257	"	"			.1504	.0235
	Sample Wt.					280	.249	"	"			xxx	.0001
						282	.223	"	"				

2.7476	% Linoleic acid = 1.16 (45.0180) − 1.33 (.0000) + 0.09 (.0003) = 52.2
2.6476	% Linolenic acid = 1.88 (.0000) − 4.43 (.0003) = 0.00
.1000	% Arachidonic acid = 4.43 (.0003) = 0.00

	% Saturated Acid = 29.5	I.V. = 107.2
Treatment:	% Oleic Acid = 13.8	T.V. = 62.8
Glycol − KOH	% Linoleic Acid = 52.2	% Composition from I.V. & T.V.
Isomerized	% Linolenic Acid = 0.00	% Linoleic Acid = 52.3
25 min. at 180° C.	% Arachidonic Acid = 0.00	% Oleic Acid = 14.9
Methyl Alcohol Solvent	Polymerization Index =	% Saturated Acids = 28.4
	Assuming 95.6% T.F.A.	95.6% T.F.A. Basis

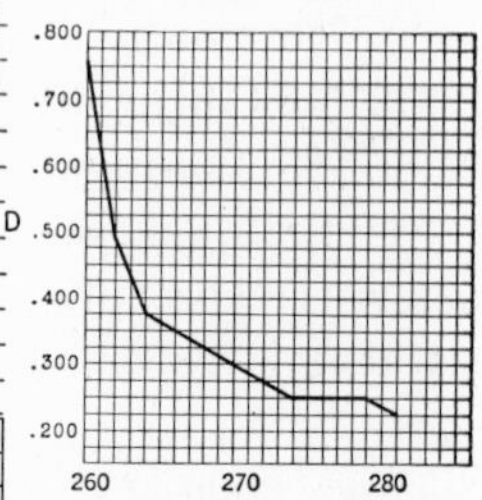

	Conjugated	W.L.	D	b	c	Bl.6 Va.8				$k_2 = .1452$
	S/100	233	.364	1.000	2.0000	W.L.	%T			$k_3 = .0025$
	"	262	.244	5.000	"	233	97.			$k_4 = .0000$
	"	268	.244	"	"	262	97.			
	"	274	.226	"	"	268	97.			$k_{233} = .1820$
	"	310	.067	"	"	274	98.			.0290
	"	316	.048	"	"	310	99.			.1530
	"	322	.043	"	"	316	99.			.0078
	Sample Wt.					322	99.			.1452
	.2000 gm.									

$k_{268} = .0244$	$k_{316} = .0048$
$k_{262} = .0244$	$k_{310} = .0067$
$k_{274} = .0226$	$k_{322} = .0043$
2 | .0470	2 | .0110
.0235	.0055
.0244	.0048
.0235	.0055
.0009	xxx

In purified neohexane	% Conjugated-diene = 0.13
	" -triene = 0.00
	" -tetraene = 0.00

$$k_2 = k_{233} \quad -0.029 - 0.052\, F_1$$

$$k_2 = \frac{364}{1 \times 2} -0.029 - 0.052\,(15) - .1452$$

FIG. 24. Typical spectrophotometric analysis of fat or oil

13. % Linolenic acid $= Y = 1.88\, k''_3 - 4.43\, k''_4$
14. % Arachidonic acid $= Z = 4.43\, k''_4$

Total Composition

15. % Conjugated and non-conjugated poly-unsaturated acids are calculated as the above.
16. % Oleic acid =

$$\frac{\text{I.V. of sample} - \left[1.811\,(C_2 + X) + 2.737\,(C_3 + Y) + 3.337\,(C_4 + Z) \right]}{0.899}$$

17. % Saturated acids = % total fatty acid (Note 1) − (% oleic + % conjugated + % unconjugated polyunsaturated acids)
18. To calculate to a fatty acid basis, multiply all values above by 100, divided by total fatty acid. (Note 2.)

Note 1—This value is 95.6 for most naturally occurring oils.
Note 2—This value is 1.046 for most naturally occurring oils.

Figure 24 reproduces a typical report form for this analysis.

LIPIDES

The lipides in plasma consist of triglycerides of relatively unsaturated fatty acids, free and combined sterols, lecithins, sphingomyelin, and cephalin. From oxidation with bichromate in acid solution the total lipides are determined [31] by reading the reduced chrome ion. If desired, by calculation from separate estimation of the phospholipides, the triglycerides are calculated.[32] Necessarily an extract of lipines must be prepared which is free of extraneous reducing substances. Urea cannot be avoided in the extracts, but fortunately does not reduce dichromate under the test conditions. The reaction is about 95 per cent complete. Catalysts such as mercury, palladium, and silver are undesirable.

As a general method, lipides are estimated nephelometrically in salt solution.[33] Alternatively saponify the lipides and determine cholesterol by acetic anhydride and sulfuric acid [34] (Vol. IV).

Sample—*Blood, plasma, or serum.* To about 75 ml. of 3:1 redistilled ethanol-ether add slowly 3 ml. of blood, plasma, or serum. Shake during the addition to prevent clumping. Heat in boiling water with constant shaking, cool, and filter. Wash the filter with the same mixture. Evaporate the filtrate to dryness and take up the residue in hexane. Filter, wash the filter, and dilute to about 1 mg. of oxidizable material per ml. for development with bichromate.

Procedure—*By bichromate.* Prepare a solution of 0.2 gram of powdered potassium bichromate per 100 ml. of concentrated sulfuric acid at

---

[31] W. R. Bloor, *J. Biol. Chem.* **170**, 671-4 (1947).

[32] Joseph H. Bragdon, *Ibid.* **190**, 513-7 (1951).

[33] Henry G. Kunkel and Edward H. Ahrens, Jr., *Conf. on Liver Injury, Trans. 7th Conf.* **1948**, 93-4 (discussion 94-5).

[34] Margaret Oleson Hunter, R. A. Knouff, and J. B. Brown, *Ohio J. Sci.* **45**, 47-54 (1945).

about 100°. The solution will darken a little with age, but this does not affect its use other than to increase the blank.

Evaporate an aliquot containing the lipids from 0.1-0.7 ml. of plasma in a 25-ml. flask in a stream of nitrogen at under 60°. Add 10 ml. of reagent promptly. Stopper quickly, seal with a drop of reagent, and place in boiling water for 30 minutes. Cool in water and add about 12 ml. of water. In doing this, point the orifice of the flask away from the face and mix by gentle rotation. Restopper, recool, and dilute to volume at 25°. Read at 580 mμ against a reagent blank. The color is stable for 15-90 minutes. Interpret in terms of mg. of dichromate reduced to potassium chromic sulfate.

The following table shows the dichromate reduced by typical ingredients.

TABLE 1. THEORETICAL DICHROMATE-REDUCING POWER AND RATIO OF MOLECULAR WEIGHT TO PHOSPHORUS OF SEVERAL PLASMA LIPIDES

Lipide	$K_2Cr_2O_7$ mg. per mg. lipide	$\dfrac{Mol.\ wt.}{phosphorus}$
Palmitic acid	17.60	
Stearic acid	17.92	
Oleic acid	17.71	
Linoleic acid	17.49	
Dioleyl palmitin	17.69	
Cholesterol	19.28	
Cholesterol stearate	19.22	
Cholesterol linoleate	19.06	
1-Palmityl, 2-oleyl lecithin	14.87	25.10
1-Stearyl, 2-oleyl lecithin	15.09	26.00
1-Stearyl, 2-oleyl cephalin	15.12	24.06
Sphingomyelin	15.89	26.88

A plausible distribution of phospholipides in plasma is 78 per cent lecithins, 17 per cent sphingomyelin, and 5 per cent cephalins.[35] Hence normal plasma phospholipides will reduce about 15.2 mg. of dichromate per mg. Each mg. of mixed glycerides will reduce about 17.7 mg. of dichromate. Calculation of triglycerides is best illustrated by an example in mg. per 100 ml. Total cholesterol 158, free cholesterol 44, phospholipide 175, dichromate reduced 11,833 mg. Esterified cholesterol $(158 - 44) \times 1.68 = 1.92$ mg. of cholesterol ester. $192 + 44 = 236$ mg. free cholesterol and cholesterol ester.

---

[35] M. H. Hack, *J. Biol. Chem.* **169**, 137-43 (1947).

$238 \times 19.1 = 4508$ mg. of dichromate

$175 \times 15.2 = 2660$ mg. of dichromate

$11,883 - 7168 = 4715$ mg. of dichromate reduced by triglycerides

$4715/17.7 = 266$ mg. of triglycerides

Nephelometrically. Dilute 1 volume of serum with 17 volumes of a reagent containing 1 per cent of phenol and 12 per cent of sodium chloride. Read the turbidity at 650 mμ after 30 minutes.

CHOLESTERYL LINOLEATE

Cholesteryl linoleate is insoluble in alkaline ethylene glycol and requires a modified technic [36] from that described for linoleic and linolenic acids.

Sample—Treat a sample containing about 0.1 gram of cholesteryl linoleate with 1 ml. of a solution of 55 grams of potassium hydroxide per 100 ml. of 99 per cent ethanol. Heat at 60° for 90 minutes and add 10 ml. of the potassium hydroxide in ethylene glycol described (page 320) for isomerization of fats. Heat at 180° in an atmosphere of nitrogen for 30 minutes and cool. Dilute an aliquot for reading as described for linolenic acid (page 321).

LANOLIN

In the absence of interferences, the familiar Lieberman-Burchard reaction is applicable to lanolin.[37]

Sample—*Wool.* Extract a 0.5 gram sample by boiling with 10 ml. of chloroform. Wash the residue with chloroform and dilute the filtrate to 100 ml.

Procedure—Treat 1 ml. of prepared sample solution with 1 ml. of acetic anhydride and 10 drops of concentrated sulfuric acid. After 3 minutes compare with standards similarly prepared.

---

[36] Jacqueline S. Front and B. F. Daubert, *J. Am. Chem. Soc.* **67**, 1509-10 (1945).

[37] E. K. Zil'berkveit and L. A. Vasil'ev, *J. Applied Chem.* (USSR) **10**, 570-7 (1937).

CHAPTER 14

SUBSTITUTED MONOBASIC ALIPHATIC ACIDS [1]

THE SUBSTITUTED monobasic aliphatic acids include a group of industrial materials with a somewhat greater number of biological substances. The ketonic acids react primarily as ketones after decomposition but are included here largely because of their names. One of the vitamins, ascorbic acid, is also included. The substitution of an aromatic group on an essentiially aliphatic acid leaves it in this chapter. Amino acids as a rather concrete and definable group are excluded for separate treatment. Methods are sufficiently diverse to prevent suggestion of a general class method.

GLYCOLIC ACID

Glycolic acid is determined by its reaction with 2,7-dihydroxynaphthalene in concentrated sulfuric acid to give tetrahydroxydinaphthylmethane. It is colorless but is oxidized to a deep red dyestuff.[2] There is no intereference by formic, acetic, succinic, tartaric, citric, benzoic, or salicylic acid, nor does unreduced oxalic acid give the color. Results conform to Beer's law for samples containing up to 0.02 mg. per ml. Another technic is by the violet color of glycolic acid with chromotropic acid, 1,8-dihydroxynaphthalene-3,6-disulfonic acid.[3]

Procedure—*By 2,7-dihydroxynaphthalene.* Adjust the sample to 1:18 with sulfuric acid. If neutral mix with an equal volume of 1:9 sulfuric acid. Chill 0.2 ml. of sample solution, containing not over 0.02 mg. of glycolic acid in cold water. Add 2 ml. of a 0.01 per cent solution of 2,7-dihydroxynaphthalene in concentrated sulfuric acid. Mix, heat in boiling water for 20 minutes, and cool in water. Add 4 ml. of 1:18 sulfuric acid and agitate until there is no further heat of reaction. Read against a reagent blank at 530 mμ.

By chromotropic acid. Mix 0.5 ml. of sample solution, 0.5 ml. of 5 per cent solution of chromotropic acid, and 5 ml. of concentrated sulfuric acid. Read against a reagent blank when cool.

---

[1] See Chapter 1 for details of organization, condensation, etc..

[2] Vincent P. Calkins, *Ind. Eng. Chem., Anal. Ed.* 15, 762-3 (1943).

[3] Paul Fleury, Jean Courtois, and Roland Perlès, *Mikrochemie ver. Mikrochem. Acta* 36/37, 863-5 (1951).

N-Carbamylglycine, Hydantoic Acid

Hydantoic acid gives the reactions of citrulline with diacetyl oximes.[4] Details are given under citrulline. Sorb the citrulline on zeolite or resin. Treat the residual solution with uricase (page 435) to destroy uric acid. Determine thereafter as described for citrulline with diacetylmonoxime (page 360).

Guanidinoacetic Acid, Glycocyamine

Guanadinoacetic acid is estimated by its color with α-naphthol followed by addition of sodium hypobromite.

Diphenlglycollic Acid, Benzilic Acid

Benzilic acid in concentrated sulfuric acid gives an intense purple color [5] with which benzil and benzophenone do not interfere. Benzohydrol gives a brick red color under the same conditions, but this is much less intense and can be extracted from an alkaline solution of the sample.

Procedure—Dissolve the sample in 0.5 ml. of water and dilute to 25 ml. with concentrated sulfuric acid. Compare with standards prepared from 0.5 to 5 mg. of benzilic acid in the same way.

p-Aminophenylglycollic Acid, p-Aminomandelic Acid

Determine as described for m-aminohippuric acid (page 331).

o-Hydroxybenzoylaminoacetic Acid, o-Hydroxyhippuric Acid

o-Hydroxyhippuric acid reacts with 2,6-dichloroquinone chloroimide in buffered solution for development of color.[6] Many other hippuric acid derivatives give the same reaction and in the absence of each other are determined by the same reaction. These include other hydroxy- and aminohippuric acids.

Sample—*Plasma*. To 1 volume of plasma add 10 volumes of water. Add 3 volumes of a solution containing 34.667 grams of cadmium sulfate,

[4] A. F. Lazarev, *Biokhimiya* **15**, 401-7 (1950).

[5] H. Klinger, *Ber.* **19**, 1862-70 (1886); Arthur Lashman, *J. Am. Chem. Soc.* **44**, 330-40 (1922).

[6] Homer W. Smith, Norma Finkelstein, Lucy Aliminosa, Betty Crawford, and Martha Graber, *J. Clin. Investigations* **24**, 388-404 (1945).

$3CdSO_4 \cdot 8H_2O$ plus 169 ml. of 1:35 sulfuric acid per liter. Mix and add 1 volume of 4.4 per cent sodium hydroxide solution, and shake. Let stand for 10 minutes, centrifuge, and filter.

Cells. Centrifuge and remove the plasma carefully with a capillary pipet. Stir the cells with 1 volume of water and dilute to about 2.5 times the volume of cells taken. Stir until hemolysis is complete. Treat as for plasma starting at "Add 3 volumes of a solution. . . ."

Urine. Dilute appropriately and treat as for plasma.

Procedure—To 10 ml. of sample add 2 ml. of a 2 per cent veronal solution adjusted to pH 9.1 with sodium hydroxide solution. Add 2 ml. of a freshly prepared solution of 25 mg. of 2,6-dichloroquinone chloroimide in 100 ml. of absolute ethanol. Centrifuge the reagent solution if not clear. Read at 600 mμ against a reagent blank. The slope of the curve is 0.82, indicating an inhibitor of color development in biological filtrates.

m-HYDROXYBENZOYLAMINOACETIC ACID, m-HYDROXYHIPPURIC ACID

Determine exactly as described for o-hydroxyhippuric acid.

p-HYDROXYBENZOYLAMINOACETIC ACID, p-HYDROXYHIPPURIC ACID

p-Hydroxyhippuric acid is determined by diazotization and heating.[6] A trichloroacetic acid filtrate can also be used and results in less dilution of the sample[7]

Sample—Prepare as for o-hydroxyhippuric acid (page 329).

Procedure—To 5 ml. of sample add 7 ml. of a fresh mixture of 3 parts of 20 per cent mercuric sulfate in 1:6 sulfuric acid, and 4 parts of 0.2 per cent sodium nitrite solution. Immerse in boiling water for 4.5 minutes. Cool, mix, and read at 490 mμ against a reagent blank.

m-AMINOBENZOYLAMINOACETIC ACID, m-AMINOHIPPURIC ACID

m-Aminohippuric acid, when diazotized, couples with N-(1-naphthyl) ethylenediamine dihydrochloride to give an appropriate color. The same reaction is given by other acids with intensities shown in the tabulation.

---

[7] Jean Hamburger, Ryckwaert, Duizand, and Mlle. Argant, *Ann. biol. clin.* (Paris) **6**, 358-62 (1948).

	Per cent color intensity	Time in minutes
p-Aminohippuric acid	100	10
m-aminohippuric acid	96	30
p-aminobenzoic acid	97	20
p-aminomandelic acid	90	60
p-aminophenylsuccinic acid	75	90
p-aminophenaceturic acid	83	300

Sample—Prepare as described for *o*-hydroxyhippuric acid (page 329).

Procedure—To 10 ml. of sample add 2 ml. of 1:8 hydrochloric acid, and 1 ml. of 0.1 per cent sodium nitrite solution. Mix and let stand 3-5 minutes. Add 1 ml. of 0.5 per cent ammonium sulfamate solution, and mix. Let stand 3-5 minutes and add 1 ml. of 0.1 per cent aqueous solution of N-(1-naphthyl)ethylenediamine dihydrochloride, and mix. Let stand for 10 minutes and read against a reagent blank at 540 mμ.

p-AMINOBENZOYLAMINOACETIC ACID, *p*-AMINOHIPPURIC ACID

Determine the unconjugated acid by coupling with N-(1-naphthyl) ethylenediamine dihydrochloride exactly as described under *m*-aminohippuric acid.[8] A special technic is applied to the sample when conjugated.

Sample—Deproteinize as described for *o*-hydroxyhippuric acid (page 329).

Conjugated acid. To a suitable aliquot of sample add 2 ml. of concentrated hydrochloric acid, dilute to 50 ml., and mix. Cover with about 1 ml. of toluene and place in an oven at about 96° for 3.5 hours. Cool and use 10 ml. for determination as described for *m*-aminohippuric acid.

p-ACETAMINOBENZOYLAMINOACETIC ACID, *p*-ACETAMINOHIPPURIC ACID

After saponification the acetamino acid is estimated in the same way as the amino acid.

Sample—Prepare the sample as described for *o*-hydroxyhippuric acid (page 329). Then continue with a 10-ml. aliquot. Add 2 ml. of 1:8 hydrochloric acid and mix. Heat in boiling water for 1 hour. Cool, dilute to 12.5 ml., and continue as for *m*-aminohippuric acid above.

[8] C. S. McArthur, *J. Lab. Clin. Med.* **35**, 836-41 (1950).

p-Amino-N-q-toluylglycollic Acid, p-Aminophenaceturic Acid

Determine as described for m-aminohippuric acid (page 331).

Thioglycolic and Dithioglycolic Acids

The phosphotungstic acid reagent for uric acid will also determine thioglycolic acid.[9] Use the method for cysteine (page 482) but use the thioglycolic acid standard. For estimation of dithioglycolic acid use the corresponding method for cystine (page 487) but use a dithioglycolic acid standard. On addition of solid sodium nitrite to a thioglycolic acid solution and acidification with acetic acid a red nitroso compound is formed.[10] It has limited stability.

Monofluoroacetic Acid

Monofluoracetic acid is estimated by the use of 1 ml. of sample containing 0.1-0.4 mg. of test substance applying the method with lanthanum given for acetates (page 306).[11]

An alternative is to determine as inorganic fluorides.[12] This as developed for sodium monofluoroacetate known as 1080, a rodenticide of extreme toxicity for warm-blooded animals, consists of essentially four steps. Protein is removed from the sample by aqueous extraction or enzymatic digestion. Ether extraction for removal of acids follows. Separation of fluoroacetate and inorganic fluorine compounds by means of partition chromatography is concluded by conversion of fluorine to inorganic fluoride and determination as such. The chromatographic separation of monofluoroacetic acid from inorganic acids is the critical point in the procedure to establish specificity. The percolate from the chromatographic column contains only fluorine-containing organic acids. Foods and biological tissues do not contain such acids. Commercial 1080 contains very small amounts of difluoroacetic and trifluoroacetic acids which are included. The method will determine 0.01-0.04 mg. of monofluoroacetic acid and is not affected by 1000-fold excess of mineral fluorides.

Samples—*Sugar.* Dissolve 100 grams in water and dilute to about 350 ml.

---

[9] Kamenosuke Shinohara, *J. Biol. Chem.* **109**, 665-79 (1935); *Ibid.* **110**, 263-77 (1935).

[10] Fritjoff Hirsch, *Seifen-Ole-Fette-Wachse* **77**, 457-8 (1951).

[11] John O. Hutchens and Beatrice M. Kass, *J. Biol. Chem.* **177**, 571-5 (1949).

[12] L. L. Ramsey and P. A. Clifford, *J. Assoc. Official Agr. Chem.* **32**, 788-97 (1949).

Flour. Comminute 100 grams of flour with 400 ml. of water and 5 grams of pancreatin for about 2 minutes. Adjust to pH 7-8 to test paper with saturated trisodium phosphate solution. Transfer to a 1-liter conical flask and wash in with three 25-ml. portions of water. Incubate at 35-40° for 3 hours or longer. Add 5 ml. of 1:1 sulfuric acid and mix. Add 20 ml. of 20 per cent phosphotungstic acid solution and mix. Dilute to about 750 ml., stopper, and shake vigorously for about 2 minutes. Filter on a Büchner funnel and use 375 ml. of filtrate. Neutralize to just alkaline to phenolphthalein with 50 per cent sodium hydroxide solution. Evaporate to about 100 ml. for use as the sample.

Wheat. Grind finely in a suitable mill and proceed as for flour.

Corn, chili peppers, cacao beans, etc. Grind and treat as corn meal.

Corn meal. Comminute 100 grams with 400 ml. of water for about 2 minutes. Complete as for flour starting at "Add 5 ml. of 1:1 sulfuric acid and mix."

Peanuts. Grind finely. Treat as corn meal but substitute 100 ml. of 20 per cent phosphotungstic acid solution for 20 ml.

Cheese. Treat as corn meal, but substitute 40 ml. of 20 per cent phosphotungstic acid solution for 20 ml.

Biological tissues. Grind tough or fibrous tissues through a food chopper; soft tissues need not be ground. Boil 100 grams of sample with about 300 ml. of water, for about 0.5 hour. Blend and rinse twice with 25-ml. portions of water to a tared liter flask. Add 5 ml. of 1:1 sulfuric acid, and mix. Add 50-75 ml. of 20 per cent phosphotungstic acid solution until all proteins have precipitated and water to make the weight 600 grams. Shake vigorously for about 2 minutes. Filter through a fluted filter or with suction through a Büchner funnel. If the material does not filter rapidly, add another 10 ml. of the phosphotungstic acid solution, shake, and refilter. Use an aliquot of the filtrate as sample.

General—Transfer a protein-free sample containing 0.01-0.04 mg. of test substance to a large continuous extractor of the type shown in Figure 25.[13] The inner tube is preferably flared at the top to about 25 mm. in diameter. To aid in getting smaller droplets of extracting solvents, use an extra-coarse fritted filter tip on the bottom end of the inner tube. For every 50 grams of solution, add 1 ml. of 1:1 sulfuric acid solution. Extract with ether for 3-4 hours, checking that all of the

13 "Official and Tentative Methods of Analysis of the Association of Official Agricultural Chemists," 6th Ed., p. 304. Association of Official Agricultural Chemists, Washington, D. C. (1945).

monofluoroacetic acid has been extracted. Transfer the extract to a separatory funnel.

Wash the extraction flask with 20 ml. of water, two drops of 1 per cent phenolphthalein solution, and enough 0.4 per cent sodium hydroxide solution to give a strong alkaline color upon swirling. Pour this into the separatory funnel and add alkali until the alkaline color of the indicator persists in the aqueous phase even after shaking. Note the volume of alkali used. Draw off the aqueous layer and wash the extraction flask and ether with two 10-ml. portions of water. Make the extract and washings just alkaline to phenolphthalein with 1:360 sulfuric acid. Evaporate the extract just to dryness on the steam bath and if the alkaline color disappears during the evaporation, add just enough 0.4 per cent sodium hydroxide solution to make it reappear. Excess heating will give low results.

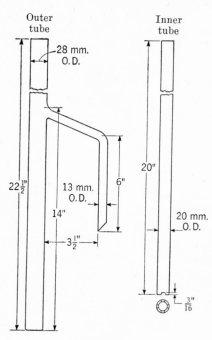

FIG. 25. Liquid extractor for monofluoroacetic acid

Place 5 grams of silicic acid in a mortar and add 2.5-4 ml. of 1:75 sulfuric acid until it nearly becomes sticky. Mix well with a pestle and add about 35 ml. of 1:9 tertiary amyl alcohol or n-butanol with chloroform. Work into a smooth slurry; if there are agglomerations, too much sulfuric acid was used. Place a cotton plug in the bottom of an 18 × 250 mm. Pyrex chromatographic tube and pour in the slurry while the tube is tilted. Apply 2-10 pounds of pressure with a gas pressure regulator to pack down the silicic acid. When excess solvent has drained through, the column will resist pouring when tipped, and is ready to use.

To the dry residue in the 100-ml. beaker, add enough of 1:1 sulfuric acid to give an excess of 0.25 ml. of sulfuric acid solution over the amount calculated to convert all the salts to the free acids, based on the amount of sodium hydroxide solution required to neutralize the acid extracted by the ether. Wet the salts thoroughly with the acid and use a glass rod to mix up the slurry. Add 5-10 grams of anhydrous granular sodium sulfate to take up excess liquid, and stir well with the rod, breaking up any lumps that may form. Add 10 ml. of the higher alcohol in chloroform. Stir and decant the solvent and residue carefully onto the column.

Place a graduated cylinder under the column and apply pressure until the solvent has passed halfway through the sodium sulfate. Add 5 ml. of higher alcohol in chloroform to the beaker and stir. Decant the solvent onto the column and apply pressure until the solvent has passed halfway through the sodium sulfate. Rinse the beaker with 5 ml. more of solvent and transfer to the column. Collect percolate under pressure at 3-4 ml. per minute until the fluoroacetic acid has passed through, usually 50 ml. Add 20 ml. of water and 4 per cent sodium hydroxide solution to give an alkaline reaction with phenolphthalein, after vigorous shaking. Draw off the aqueous layer. Wash the solvent layer with two 10-ml. portions of water and add to the washings. Aerate the solution to remove traces of chloroform.

As lime suspension, slake about 56 grams of low fluorine calcium oxide with about 250 ml. of water and slowly add 250 ml. of 60 per cent perchloric acid solution. Boil to copious fumes of acid, cool, add 200 ml. of water, and boil again. Repeat dilution and boiling once more and cool. Dilute considerably and filter through a fritted-glass filter if any precipitation occurs. Pour the clear solution into a liter of 10 per cent sodium hydroxide solution with stirring. Allow the precipitate to settle and siphon off the supernatant liquid. Remove sodium salts by washing the precipitate 5 times. Shake the precipitate into suspension and dilute to 2 liters.

Transfer the aqueous extract to a platinum dish, using a little water, and mix with about 20 ml. of the lime suspension. Evaporate to dryness and ash for 15-20 minutes at 600°. Control excessive swelling of high sugar samples by playing a flame over the surface of the sample occasionally and charring slowly. When a clean ash is obtained, cool and add 10 ml. of water. Cover with a watch glass and cautiously introduce enough perchloric acid under the cover to dissolve the ash.

Transfer to a distillation unit. The flask is preferably about 100 ml. Claisen-type with the auxiliary neck sealed off immediately above the side-arm to prevent pocketing and refluxing of distillate. With an ordinary distilling flask there is more danger of spraying over of distilling acid. Equip the still with a dropping funnel and with a 0-150°

thermometer extending to within 5 mm. of the bottom of the flask. Rubber stoppers must previously be boiled in 10 per cent sodium hydroxide solution. Shield the flask to prevent over-heating of the upper walls. Use a straight-tube condenser of minimum length. Rinse in with small amounts of water and add a few glass beads and enough 50 per cent silver perchlorate solution to precipitate all chlorides.

Begin the distillation, maintaining the temperature at $137° \pm 2°$. Add 1-2 drops of *p*-nitrophenol indicator to the first few ml. of distillate and keep the distillate alkaline to this indicator by adding 0.25 per cent potassium hydroxide solution dropwise from a buret. Regulate the addition so that the distillate is neutralized as it approaches 200 ml. Record the volume of alkali used. Dilute to 200 ml. and mix thoroughly.

Procedure—Determine fluoride colorimetrically according to Chapter 54 of Volume II.

TRICHLOROACETIC ACID

Trichloroacetic acid in strongly alkaline solution reacts with pyridine to give a reaction like that developed for estimation of chloroform.[14]

Procedure—*Urine*. To 25 ml. of sample add 10 ml. of 50 per cent sodium hydroxide solution and 10 ml. of acetone. Agitate vigorously for exactly 5 minutes. Add 4 ml. of a reagent containing 40 ml. of water and 0.5 ml. of 15 per cent sodium hydroxide solution per 100 ml. of pyridine. Heat at 70° for 7 minutes and cool. Add 1 ml. of boiled water and read at 540 mμ against a reagent blank. Apply a correction for a sample blank.

2,4-DIHYDROXYPHENYLACETIC ACID, HOMOGENTISIC ACID

Homogentisic acid, 2,5-dihydroxyphenylacetic acid, and phosphomolybdic acid gave a dark green color in acid solution and an intense blue in alkaline solution.[15] Hydroquinone gives the identical reaction in which 1 mg. of hydroquinone is equivalent to 0.79 mg. of homogentisic acid. Phenol, cresol, resorcinol, and uric acid in amounts equivalent to the homogentisic acid cause errors of about 1 per cent. Pyrocatechol similarly gives an error of about 3 per cent. Sulfides give an intense blue-green and must be removed by addition of a slight excess of silver

---

[14] R. Frant and J. Westendorp, *Analyst* **75**, 462-6 (1950) .

[15] A. P. Briggs, *J. Biol. Chem.* **51**, 453-4 (1922).

sulfate solution to the sample. Albumin must be removed with trichloroacetic acid. Salicylates and p-hydroxyphenylpyruvic acid must be
absent. An alternative reaction is reduction of silver ion at pH 4.4 to
give a golden-brown coloration.[16]

Sample—To 5 ml. of urine add 5 ml. of 10 per cent trichloroacetic
acid and 5 ml. of 0.5 per cent silver sulfate solution. Mix well and add
about 0.5 gram of solid sodium chloride. Mix well, centrifuge, and use
the clear supernatant liquid for development with phosphomolybdic
acid.

Procedure—*With phosphomolybdic acid.* Dilute a sample to about
15 ml. Add 2 ml. of a 5 per cent solution of ammonium molybdate in 1:6
sulfuric acid and mix well. Add 2 ml. of a 1 per cent solution of monopotassium phosphate. Dilute to volume and read against a reagent blank.
The standard curve may be one in which 1 mg. of hydroquinone has been
used as equivalent to 0.79 mg. of homogentisic acid.

With silver ion. Mix 1 ml. of 1:80 acetic acid, 0.5 ml. of 1.65 per
cent sodium acetate solution, 2 ml. of clear 5 per cent gum arabic solution, 1 ml. of 1 per cent silver nitrate solution, and 0.5 ml. of dilute
colloidal silver sol. Add 1 ml. of sample containing no more than 0.2 mg.
of homogentisic acid. Dilute to 10 ml., mix well, and let stand for 2
hours. Read against a reagent blank.

4-CHLORO-2-METHYLPHENOXYACETIC ACID

This is read at 287 mμ without serious interference by the 6-chloro
and dichloro isomers,[17] or in the infra red at 12.38μ[18]

2,4-DICHLOROPHENOXYACETIC ACID, 2,4-D

The red color of 2,4-D with concentrated sulfuric acid and 1,8-dihy-
roxynaphthalene-3,6-disulfonic acid is appropriate for reading.[19] The
color is also given by other halogen derivatives of phenoxyacetic acid
but not by benzoic or phenoxyacetic acid. It will detect 0.2 ppm. In a
more complex reaction the chlorine is replaced by an amino group and
then reacted with 1,2-naphthoquinone-4-sulfonate.[20]

---

[16] A. Neuberger, C. Rimington, and J. M. G. Wilson, *Biochem. J.* 14, 431-8 (1947).

[17] Elsa Grabe, *Acta Chem. Scand.* 4, 806-9 (1950).

[18] Bertil Sjoberg, *Ibid.* 4, 798-805 (1950).

[19] Roland P. Marquardt and E. N. Luce, *Anal. Chem.* 23, 1484-6 (1951).

[20] V. H. Freed, *Science* 107, 98-9 (1948); Cf. R. S. Bandurski, *Botan. Gaz.* 108,
446-9 (1947).

The compound 2,4-D is read to ±5 per cent in ether or in aqueous solution at 284 mμ, in the range of 6-250 mg. per liter.[21] Other materials may be present and read at the same level. A complex distribution between tributyl phosphate and a phosphate buffer for pH 7 has been applied with a 24-plate countercurrent distribution technic,[22] reading the ultraviolet absorption of several of the fractions. Separation by partition chromatography permits reading of 2,4-D and 2,4,5-trichlorophenoxyacetic acid[23] as described in detail for liquid insecticides. Amounts recovered are accurate within 5 per cent.

Procedure—*Milk*. Mix 1 pint of milk with 200 ml. of ethylene glycol and 2 ml. of 50 per cent sodium hydroxide solution. Extract successively with two 100-ml. portions of ether and discard the extracts. Heat the extracted milk at 65° with stirring to drive off the dissolved ether. Add 25 ml. of concentrated hydrochloric acid to precipitate casein. Cool to 30°, filter on a Büchner funnel, and discard the precipitate. Add 25 ml. of 20 per cent aqueous tungstic acid slowly with stirring to precipitate protein. Filter on a fluted filter and discard the precipitate.

Extract 2,4-D from the filtrate with two successive 100-ml. portions of ether. Make up an extraction solution for pH 7.9 containing 2.5 per cent of disodium phosphate dodecahydrate and 1 per cent of monosodium phosphate monohydrate. Extract the combined ether extracts with 25 ml. and 25 ml. of this solution. Combine the buffered extracts and filter. Add 1 ml. of concentrated hydrochloric acid and extract with 10 ml. and 10 ml. of carbon tetrachloride. Filter these combined extracts as the sample.

Evaporate the carbon tetrachloride extract containing 2,4-D on a boiling water bath to about 0.1 ml. Add 5 ml. of fresh 0.15 per cent solution of chromotropic acid in methanol. Evaporate just to dryness. Add 5 ml. of concentrated sulfuric acid, mix until homogeneous, and incubate at 130-135° for exactly 20 minutes. Cool to room temperature and pour the wine-colored solution dropwise into 30 ml. of water. Cool, dilute to 50 ml. with water, filter, and read at 565 mμ against water and correct for a small blank attributed to milk solids.

Liquid insecticide. To a 1-gram sample add 10 ml. of fresh 25 per cent aqueous sodium hydroxide solution and a glass bead. If not already

---

[21] Robert S. Bandurski, *Botan. Gaz.* **108**, 446-9 (1947).

[22] Byron Williamson and Lyman C. Craig, *J. Biol. Chem.* **168**, 687-97 (1947); Benjamin Warshowsky and Edward J. Schantz, *Anal. Chem.* **20**, 951-4 (1948); *Ibid.* **22**, 460-3 (1950).

[23] Nathan Gordon, *Anal. Chem.* **24**, 1968-71 (1952).

present, add a little wetting agent. Reflux, with glass joints for 1 hour. Rinse down the condenser with 10-15 ml. of water. Cool the flask, transfer to a separatory funnel, and wash in with about 25 ml. of water. Shake for 1 minute with 75 ml. of ether and separate. Repeat with 75 ml. more of ether. Save the aqueous alkaline solution. Shake the second extract with 10 ml. of 15 per cent sodium hydroxide for 2 minutes and separate. Discard the ether and shake the first extract with the same alkaline solution. Separate the ether and discard it. Combine the alkaline solution and alkaline washings. Add a drop of phenolphthalein indicator solution, carefully neutralize with 1:1 sulfuric acid, and add 1 ml. excess. Cool while neutralizing and shake for 3 minutes with 25 ml. of distilled carbon tetrachloride. Separate and repeat with another 25 ml. of the solvent. Filter the combined carbon tetrachloride extracts through a cotton pledget. Wash the funnel with carbon tetrachloride, add a couple of beads, and distil the carbon tetrachloride in an all-glass assembly to about 5-10 ml. Evaporate the balance *in vacuo* while warming at 35-40°.

Mix 2 ml. of 1:5 90 per cent formic acid-glacial acetic acid mixture with 18 ml. of 90 per cent methanol as immobile solvent. Add 10.5 ml. of 15 grams of silicic acid which has been dried at 105°. Grind vigorously in a mortar for 1 minute and add mobile solvent, which is n-hexane saturated with immobile solvent, to form a thick slurry. Grind until smooth and add

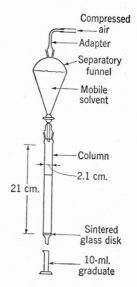

FIG. 26. Chromatographic column for isolation of DDT

mobile solvent to form a free flowing slurry. This requires 35-40 ml. of mobile solvent.

The chromatographic column is shown in Figure 26. Transfer the slurry to it, not necessarily quantitatively, and wash down the sides with mobile solvent until there is about 1.5 inches on top of the silicic acid column. Attach the adapter and apply 6-7 lbs. air pressure per square inch to force the solvent through at about 2 ml. per minute. Tap the sides of the column to release air bubbles and give an even surface. Remove the adapter when the solution is just above the approximately 12-cm. column of silicic acid.

Take up the sample in 3 ml. of mobile solvent and transfer with a dropping pipet, touching the side of the column to flow gently onto the surface of the silicic acid. Reapply pressure until the solvent approaches but does not reach the column, receiving the effluent at 2 ml. per minute in a graduate. Rinse the flask with 1 ml. of mobile solvent and wash down the sides of the column. Force this into the gel and repeat the washing process.

Fill the column to a height within 1 inch of the joint, fill the reservoir separatory funnel with mobile solvent, and put in place. Open the stopcock, lubricated with mobile solvent, and apply pressure to the top of the funnel with the adapter. Collect the effluent in 10-ml. increments and read at 284 and 289 mμ. The 2,4,5-T is generally delivered at 120-180 ml., and 2,4-D at 190-290 ml. The 2,4,5-T is characterized by a sharp rise in the absorption at 289 mμ compared with 284 mμ; the 2,4-D by the opposite. Combine the fractions containing each and dilute to 100 ml. If the readings just before and after the fractions are significantly higher than the solvent, apply a blank correction.

$$\text{Mg } 2,4,5\text{-T} = \text{ml.} \times 289 \text{ m}\mu \text{ reading}/9.82$$
$$\text{Mg } 2,4\text{-D} = \text{ml.} \times 284 \text{ m}\mu \text{ reading}/8.96$$

2,4,5-Trichlorophenoxyacetic Acid

The method of determination is by chromatographic separation followed by reading in the ultraviolet as described under 2,4-dichlorophenoxyacetic acid.

Imidazole Acetic Acid

Follow the procedure under histamine for development with p-phenyldiazonium chloride (Vol. IV).

Guanidylacetic Acid, Guanyl glycine, Glycocyamine

Glycocyamine gives a red color when treated with α-naphthol solution and then sodium hypobromite solution.[24] It is closely related to a method for methyl guanidine. Methylglycocyamine is creatine. Urea, ammonia, creatinine, and amino acids must be removed.

---

[24] C. J. Weber, *J. Biol. Chem.* **86**, 217-22 (1930); *Ibid.* **88**, 353-9 (1930); Mario Zappacosta, *Diagnostica tec. lab.* (Napoli) *Riv. mensile* **6**, 441-60 (1935); Meyer Bodansky, Virginia B. Duff, and Cornelius L. Herrman, *J. Biol. Chem.* **115**, 641-52 (1936); Horace W. Davenport and Reginald B. Fisher, *Biochem.. J.* **32**, 602-6 (1938); Jacob W. Dubnoff and Henry Borsook, *J. Biol. Chem.* **138**, 381-8 (1941).

Sample—*Urine*. Dilute 5-fold. If arginine may be present, remove with a 0.9 gram column of pretested Permutit in a tube 100 mm. long and 5 mm. inside diameter. For this pass 5 ml. of solution through in about 15 minutes and follow with 5 ml. of 0.3 per cent sodium chloride solution. Dilute to 10 ml. for use. The arginine is left in the Permutit which can be regenerated by treatment with 25 per cent sodium chloride solution and washing until chloride-free.

Blood. Adjust the pH to 6, heat to boiling, and filter. Alternatively, treat 3 ml. of 1:2 dilution with 1 ml. of 10 per cent sodium tungstate and 1 ml. of 1:54 sulfuric acid, and filter. Complete as for urine from "If argenine may be present . . . ."

Tissue extracts. Dilute so that 10 ml. represents 0.25 gram of tissue and adjust the pH to 6. Heat in boiling water, cool, and filter. Complete as for urine from "If argenine may be present . . . ."

Procedure—Chill 2 ml. of sample and the reagents in an ice bath. Add 0.4 ml. of a 1:20 dilution of 0.2 per cent α-naphthol in absolute ethanol with water. Mix and after 5 minutes add 0.2 ml. of a solution of 0.66 ml. of liquid bromine in 100 ml. of 5 per cent sodium hydroxide solution. Mix and read at 525 mμ after 20 minutes and before 60 minutes, first warming to room temperature.

β-Indolylacetic Acid

When β-indolylacetic acid, also known as *β-indoleacetic acid,* is oxidized by ferric chloride in acid solution, the unstable red color is extracted with amyl alcohol for photometric estimation.[25] Strong oxidizing or reducing substances interfere, but the method tolerates small amounts of trichloroacetic acid, acetic acid, urea, sugars, etc. In fact, the complex may be different but satisfactory in the presence of trichloroacetic acid.[26]

The reaction or reactions result with tryptophan, indole, indoleethylamine, and indolecarbonic acid. Moderate concentrations of indolepropionic acid, indolepyruvic acid, and indolealdehyde do not interfere. In any case the colors they develop are different. Reduction of the ferric chloride to a low value accentuates the color of indolylacetic acid as compared with that from tryptophane.[27]

[25] Zyunki Tanaka, *J. Pharm. Soc. Japan* **60**, 76-83 (1940).

[26] Andreas O. M. Stoppani, *Anales asoc. quim. argentina* **33**, 63-70 (1945).

[27] Albert Berthelot, Germaine Amoureux and Suzanne Deberque, *Compt. rend. soc. biol.* **131**, 981-3 (1939).

The reaction of indolylacetic acid with potassium nitrite and nitric acid is suitable for determination in aqueous solutions over a range of 0.01-0.15 mg. per ml.[28] The resulting stable red color is accurate to ±3 per cent.

Another method [29] is to treat with ferric chloride and perchloric acid. Indoleacetic acid reacts in a mixture of equal parts of methanol and fuming hydrochloric acid to give a yellow color read at 445 mμ.[30] Colors by indole and derivatives such as indolepropionic acid may interfere. Tryptophan does not react.

Sample—*Urine*. Adjust an 80-ml sample to pH 3 with glacial acetic acid. Extract with 20 ml. of ether by shaking mechanically for 30 minutes. Repeat the extraction twice and steam-distil the ether from the combined extracts. Add 30 per cent sodium hydroxide dropwise until alkaline to phenolphthalein and steam-distil about 10 ml. in 10 minutes. Dilute to 12 ml. for the development of a 3-ml. aliquot with nitrite and acid.

Procedure—*With ferric chloride*. Add 1 ml. of a 2 per cent solution of ferric chloride hexahydrate in concentrated hydrochloric acid to a 5-ml. sample containing 0.4-1.5 mg. of indolylacetic acid. Incubate at 37° for 4 hours and cool. Extract with 5 ml. of amyl alcohol. Read at 500 mμ against a blank of amyl alcohol.

With potassium nitrite and nitric acid. Combine a 3-ml. sample containing not over 0.1 mg. of indolylacetic acid with 6 ml. of concentrated hydrochloric acid and 2 ml. of half-saturated urea solution. Add a drop of 2 per cent sodium nitrite solution and mix quickly. Read at 510-570 mμ against a blank containing everything except the sodium nitrite.

With ferric chloride and perchloric acid. Mix 1 ml. of sample containing 0.0002-0.045 mg. of test substance with 2 ml. of a mixture of 1 ml. of 8 per cent ferric chloride solution and 50 ml. of 35 per cent perchloric acid solution. Read at 530 mμ against a reagent blank between 30 and 300 minutes after development.

β-Indolylcarbonic Acid

For determination by ferric chloride follow the technic for indolylacetic acid.

---

28 John W. Mitchell and B. C. Brunstetter, *Botan. Gaz.* **100**, 802-16 (1939); P. F. Holt and H. J. Callow, *Analyst* **68**, 351-5 (1943).

29 Solon A. Gordon and Robert P. Weber, *Plant Physiol.* **26**, 192-5 (1951).

30 S. Grisolia, *Trabajos inst. nacl. méd.* (Madrid) **3**, 367-72 (1943-4).

Lactic Acid

Just as formic acid is usually determined by reduction to formaldehyde, the general procedures for lactic acid call for its dehydration to the more reactive acetaldehyde which is then determined. The methods applied to estimation of acetaldehyde are varied. Ordinarily sulfuric acid is used for the dehydration, and the final color is a function of the concentration used.[31] Interfering substances in the dehydration include sugars, α-hydroxy acids, paraldehyde, formaldehyde, and acetaldehyde. Carbohydrates except 1-rhamnose and most of the pyruvic acid[32] are removed with cupric ion and calcium hydroxide. Fatty acids, ketones, alcohols, and dicarboxylic acids do not interfere.

In estimation by the rose color developed by acetaldehyde with veratole[33] increase of the reagent[34] or of ethanol beyond an optimum amount decreases the color developed. The maximum color developable varies inversely as the temperature being twice as strong at 0° as at 25°. At 0° color develops for 60 minutes and is constant for at least 1.5 hour thereafter.

The purple color developed with p-hydroxydiphenyl[35] is read at 570 mμ[36] with a standard deviation of 3.3 ± 2.7. The reaction is markedly affected by iron, copper, and cerium ions. The presence of ferric or ferrous ion alone causes no serious disturbance, but a suitable mixture of the two results in a color which is 3-5 times more intense than the color given by variation of the procedure, and the specificity of the reaction is increased. The ratio between ferrous and ferric ion must be carefully maintained, as an excess of ferric ion produces a green color with the reagent. Interfering cations are conveniently removed by ion-exchange resins.[37] The addition of cupric ion to the reaction

[31] Georges Denigès, *Bull. soc. chim.* **5**, 647 (1909); *Ann. chim. phys.* **18**, 149-91 (1910); Marcell Vas and Alexander Láng, *Biochem. Z.* **172**, 428-31 (1926); R. Milton, *Analyst* **61**, 91-6 (1936).

[32] Birger Carlström, Karl Myrbäck, Niles Holmin, and Alvar Larsson, *Acta Med. Scand.* **120**, 175-213 (1939); *Biedermanns Zentr. B. Tierernähr.*, **11**, 322-56 (1939).

[33] Bruno Mendel and Ingeborg Goldscheider, *Biochem. Z.* **164**, 163-74 (1925); F. Rappaport and I. Reifer, *Mikrochem. Acta* **2**, 62-4 (1937); Hans Mauer, *Biochem. Z.* **319**, 553-60 (1949).

[34] Raynvald Nordbö, *Biochem. Z.* **271**, 213-4 (1934).

[35] Edwin Eegriwe, *Z. anal. Chem.* **95**, 323-7 (1933); Richard H. Koenemann, *J. Biol. Chem.* **135**, 105-9 (1940); S. B. Barker and William H. Summerson, *Ibid.* **138**, 535-54 (1941); Jane A. Russell, *Ibid.* **156**, 463-5 (1944).

[36] F. Villano and G. Langella, *Boll. soc. ital. biol. sper.* **18**, 173-4 (1943).

[37] Richard L. Markus, *Arch. Biochem.* **29**, 159-65 (1950).

enhances color development. Cerium behaves like copper but offers no advantages. Lead, mercury, nickel, and cobalt are without effect. A complex micromethod [38] is applicable with this reagent to such small samples as 2 ml. of urine. The details of the equipment require consulting the original.

Several methods are of lesser importance. The red color with Schiff's reagent is subject to the usual interferences with that reagent. The orange-brown with hydroquinone [39] is similar to that with veratrol. The color is also produced by aldol, aldehydes, methylglyoxal, diacetone, and glucose, but not by acetone, acetoacetic acid, amino acids, urea, uric acid, creatine, creatinine, casein, and casein hydrolyzate. It is constant for 24 hours. A yellow color is developed with codeine [40] in the presence of 1-3 per cent of albumin. The red given by guaiacol [41] and the color with thiophene [42] have received relatively little attention in recent years.

As an alternative to dehydration to aldehyde, lactic acid is oxidized to pyruvic acid by means of the yeast enzyme, lactic dehydrogenase, in the presence of potassium ferricyanide, which acts as a hydrogen acceptor.[43] The resulting potassium ferrocyanide is then determined colorimetrically as Prussian blue.[44] Of 32 substances structurally related to lactic acid, there is interference from glycolic, α-hydroxybutyric and glyceric acids, α-glycerophosphate, hexosediphosphate, and hexosemonophosphate. The first two compounds do not occur in interfering quantities in bological fluids; the last four are removed by treatment with copper sulfate and calcium hydroxide.[45] Ascorbic acid reacts directly with potassium ferricyanide and is removed by this same procedure. Lactic acid is also oxidized to pyruvic acid with saturated bromine water in acid solution[46] and thereafter determined by methods for pyruvic acid.

[38] Makepeace U. Tsao, M. L. Baumann, and Shirley Wark, *Anal. Chem.* 24, 722-5 (1952).

[39] Zacharias Dische and Daniel Laszlo, *Biochem. Z.* 187, 344-62 (1927).

[40] L. Chelle, *Bull. trav. soc. pharm. Bordeaux* 53, 289-93 (1914); Michael Polonovski, *Compt. rend. soc. biol.* 83, 475-6 (1920); *J. pharm. chim.* 21, 449-50 (1920); L. Servantie, *Compt. rend. soc. biol.* 92, 700-2 (1925).

[41] G. A. Harrop, Jr., *Proc. Soc. Exptl. Biol. Med.* 17, 162-3 (1919); R. Markus, *Helv. Chim. Acta* 31, 831-49 (1948).

[42] W. R. Fearon, *Biochem. J.* 12, 179-83 (1918); C. N. H. Long, *J. Physiol.* 58, 455-60 (1924).

[43] Jörgen Lehmann, *Skand. Arch. Physiol.* 80, 237-64 (1938).

[44] Margaret E. Greig, *Science* 105, 665-6 (1947).

[45] Theodore E. Friedemann and Arthur I. Kendall, *J. Biol. Chem.*, 82, 23-43 (1929).

[46] H. Caron and D. Raquet, *J. pharm. chim.* (9) 2, 333-5 (1942).

The red to blue color of lactic acid with azobenzene-phenylhydrazine-sulfonic acid is also developed.[47] Acetaldehyde, benzaldehyde, and iso-butyric acid interfere. No reaction was observed with formaldehyde, acetic acid, β-hydroxybutyric acid, malonic acid, citric acid, succinic acid, tartaric acid, benzoic acid, p-aminobenzoic acid, glycine, pyruvic acid, or ascorbic acid.

Lactic acid gives a violet-green to yellow with phenol and ferric chloride [48]; an orange to purple with potassium thiocyanate.[49] The yellow with ferric ion [50] is dependent for its intensity on pH. That makes an important limitation on its applicability, although it is used on milk, reconstituted dried milk,[51] and eggs.[52]

One of the very important limitations of these methods is deproteinizing. Recovery is dependent on the conditions of deproteinizing,[53] and trichloroacetic acid is the preferable method as it gives 97.4 per cent recovery from blood at pH 1.5 with 2.4 standard deviation.[54] Dilution is a factor using metaphosphoric acid,[55] tungstic acid,[56] and zinc hydroxide.[57] With tungstic acid the pH range is 2.9-5 [58] with optimum recovery near the upper limit where the volume of precipitate also reaches a maximum.

Samples—*Blood*. Mix 1 ml. containing 2 mg. of ammonium fluoride

[47] R. A. McAllister, *Analyst* **76**, 238-9 (1951).

[48] F. Klein and J. Mĕlka, *Wiener med. Wochschr.* **79**, 1053 (1929).

[49] Frederick G. Germuth, *Ind. Eng. Chem.* **19**, 852-3 (1927).

[50] E. Ernst and J. Truka, *Biochem. Z.* **272**, 51-5 (1934).

[51] Fred Hillig, *J. Assoc. Official Agr. Chem.* **20**, 130-40, 303-7, 605-10, (1937); *Ibid.* **23**, 467 (1940); *Ibid.* **25**, 253-64, 602 (1942); *Ibid.* **26**, 199 (1943); I. A. Gould and F. E. Potter, *Southern Dairy Products J.* **44**, No. 1, 34-5, 46 (1948); Official and Tentative Methods of the Association of Official Agricultural Chemists, 7th Ed., pp. 228-31, 284, 334, Association of Official Agricultural Chemists, Washington, D. C. (1950); J. N. Venekamy and C. J. Kruisher, *Netherlands Milk Dairy J.* **4**, 165-74 (1950).

[52] Henry A. Lepper, M. T. Bartram, and Fred Hillig, *J. Assoc. Official Agr. Chem.* **27**, 204-23 (1944).

[53] Julius Mondschein and O. von Fuerth, *Biochem. Z.* **42**, 105-23 (1912); S. L. Ørskov, *Ibid.* **219**, 409-21 (1930).

[54] Samuel Elgart and J. S. Harris, *Ind. Eng. Chem., Anal. Ed.* **12**, 758-62 (1940).

[55] Bruno Mendel and Ingeborg Goldscheider, *Biochem. Z.* **164**, 163-74 (1925); Benjamin F. Miller and John A. Muntz, *J. Biol. Chem.* **126**, 413-21 (1938).

[56] Ethyl Ronzoni and Zonja Wallen-Lawrence, *Ibid.* **74**, 363-77 (1927); H. T. Edwards, *Ibid.* **125**, 571-83 (1938).

[57] Michael Somogyi, *Ibid.* **86**, 655-63 (1930).

[58] Otto Folin and Hsien Wu, *Ibid.* **38**, 81-110 (1919); A. T. Merrill, *Ibid.* **60**, 257-60 (1924).

with 7 ml. of water in a 15-ml. tube and let stand to hemolyze. Slowly add 7 ml. of 10 per cent trichloroacetic acid solution with vigorous agitation, stopper, and let stand for 20 minutes. Centrifuge and transfer 4 ml. of the supernatant liquid to another tube. Add 1 ml. of 15 per cent copper sulfate solution and mix. Add 1 gram of hydrated lime, stopper with rubber, and shake vigorously at intervals for 30 minutes. Centrifuge for 10 minutes but do not filter. Use an aliquot of the supernatant liquid for dehydration and development by veratrole.

Alternatively,[59] mix 0.2 ml. of blood and 0.9 ml. of 0.4 per cent sodium hydroxide solution. After 30 seconds add 0.9 ml. of thorium sulfate solution and mix. Heat at 80° for 2 minutes, conveniently in boiling water and centrifuge. Use an aliquot of the supernatant liquid for dehydration and development with veratrole. This removes both proteins and carbohydrates in one operation.

Muscle. Measure exactly 1 ml. of 5 per cent metaphosphoric acid solution freshly prepared from the glacial acid. Cut up 0.3-0.5 gram of muscle very fine, using an ice-cold glass plate. Add it at once to the metaphosphoric acid. The acid should cover the sample. Add 6 ml. of water and stir. Cover and let stand for 40 minutes. Values will be low if the sample stands too short a time; high if it stands too long.

Shake and filter through a small dry filter. Transfer 4 ml. of protein-free filtrate, or if the lactic acid content is high, 2 ml. of filtrate and 2 ml. of water. Add 1 ml. of saturated copper sulfate solution and 1 gram of pulverized calcium hydroxide. Shake, let stand for 30 minutes, and centrifuge. The solution should be clear. If particles float on the surface, filter through clean, dry, glass wool. Use this filtrate as sample for dehydration with veratrole.

Whole and skim milks. To 50 ml. add 6 ml. of 1:35 sulfuric acid and mix. Add 5 ml. of 20 per cent phosphotungstic acid solution. Dilute to 100 ml. and filter through fluted paper. This filtrate is next to be extracted in the equipment shown in Figure 25. The outer tube is at the left, the inner tube at the right.

Transfer 50 ml. of the prepared filtrate and 0.5 ml. of 1:1 sulfuric acid to concentric tubes shown. Connect with an efficient condenser with the lower outlet at least 12 mm. in diameter to prevent backing up of the ether. Connect the side arm of the outer tube to an extraction flask containing 200 ml. of ether. Heat the flask, protecting the extractor by an asbestos shield. With rapid boiling of the ether and a steady stream

---

[59] F. Rappaport and I. Reifer, *Mikrochim. Acta* 2, 62-4 (1937).

of ether from the condenser to the inner tube, three hours' operation will usually extract all of the lactic acid. At any rate the passage of 7500 ml. of ether through the sample is usually required. This extract is to be developed by ferric chloride.

Alternatively,[60] mix 1 ml. of sample with 3 ml. of water and treat as in the first method for blood starting at "Add 1 ml. of 15 per cent copper sulfate solution . . . ."

Dried, whole, and skim milks. Make 5 grams into a paste with water and dilute to about 50 ml. Then treat as whole milk.

Cream and ice cream. Dilute 20 grams to about 70 ml. with water. Add 6 ml. of 1:35 sulfuric acid and mix. Add 1 ml. of 20 per cent phosphotungstic acid solution for cream or 2 ml. for ice cream. Dilute to 100 ml. and filter through fluted paper. Extract this filtrate as though from whole milk, starting at "Transfer 50 ml. of the prepared filtrate . . .".

Sweetened condensed milk and evaporated milk. Dilute a 25-gram sample to about 75 ml. and complete as for whole milk.

Butter. Warm a 20-gram sample with 25 ml. of water. Neutralize to phenolphthalein with 4 per cent sodium hydroxide solution. Cool and mix well with 50 ml. of ether, avoiding violent agitation. Add 50 ml. of petroleum ether, mix well, and centrifuge. Recover the solvent layer and re-extract the aqueous part with 50 ml. of 1:1 ether-petroleum ether. Discard the non-aqueous extracts and warm the bottle to drive off residual ethers. Add 3 ml. of 1:35 sulfuric acid and mix. Cool and add 20 per cent phosphotungstic acid dropwise until precipitation ceases. Dilute to 100 ml. and filter through fluted paper. Complete as for whole milk, starting at "Transfer 50 ml. of the prepared filtrate . . .".

Liquid or frozen eggs.[61] Thoroughly mix a 40-gram sample with about 75 ml. of water and add 15 ml. of 1:35 sulfuric acid and 25 ml. of 20 per cent phosphotungstic acid solution. Dilute to 200 ml., shake for a minute, and filter through a folded filter. Evaporate 100 grams of filtrate to about 50 ml. and complete as for whole milk, starting at "Transfer 50 ml. of the prepared filtrate . . . ."

Dried eggs. Make a smooth paste of 10 grams with about 100 ml. of water. Add 10 ml. of 1:35 sulfuric acid, mixing well. Add 15 ml. of 20 per cent phosphotungstic acid solution. Dilute to 200 ml., shake

[60] Biordet Heinemann, *J. Dairy Sci.* **23**, 969-72 (1940).

[61] Official and Tentative Methods of the Association of Official Agricultural Chemists, 7th Ed., p. 284 (1950); Association of Official Agricultural Chemists, Washington, D. C.; *J. Assoc. Official Agr. Chem.* **27**, 204 (1944); *Ibid.* **31**, 134 (1948).

well, and filter through a fluted filter. Evaporate 100 grams of filtrate to about 50 ml. and complete as for whole milk, starting at "Transfer 50 ml. of the prepared filtrate . . . ."

Ensilage extracts.[62] Mix 1 ml. with 3 ml. of water and treat as in the first method for blood, starting at "Add 1 ml. of 15 per cent copper sulfate solution. . . ." Develop with guaiacol or *p*-hydroxybiphenyl.

Procedure—*Dehydration to acetaldehyde.* Transfer 1.2 ml. of sample solution containing 0.0005-0.03 mg. of lactic acid to a 22 × 175 mm. tube. Place in an ice bath for 10 minutes. Then add 6 ml. of cold concentrated sulfuric acid down the side of the tube with shaking. If a precipitate of calcium sulfate forms, it will dissolve later. The first half must not be added faster than 2 drops per second. Stopper loosely with rubber and immerse to two-thirds the length of the tube in a boiling water bath. Remove at the end of 5 minutes and replace in an ice bath for 2 minutes. The period of heating is not critical over the range 4-10 minutes.

The conversion can be somewhat improved by varying the amount of sample over the range 0.9-1.8 ml. for 6 ml. of sulfuric acid and then using the ratio giving the maximum conversion. That specified above is a usual optimum.

By veratrol. Add 0.1 ml. of 0.125 per cent solution of veratrol in absolute ethanol. Mix, restopper, and replace in the ice bath. Remix at 30 minutes and 60 minutes. At 75 minutes read at 527 mμ against a reagent blank and read from a curve prepared with the same bottle of sulfuric acid. An appropriate standard solution for treatment to develop the curve contains 0.1063 per cent of lithium lactate, equivalent to 1 mg. of lactic acid per ml.

With Schiff's reagent. See the procedure for acetaldehyde (page 261).

With hydroquinone. To the dehydrated sample add 0.1 ml. of a 10 per cent solution of copper sulfate and 0.1 ml. of a 20 per cent solution of hydroquinone in ethanol. Mix and compare with a standard by dilution with a blank.

With codeine. To the dehydrated solution add 5 drops of a 1 per cent solution of codeine in alcohol and compare with a series of standards.

With p-hydroxydiphenyl. An appropriate sample has been deproteinized by trichloroacetic acid, tungstic acid, zinc hydroxide, or cadmium hydroxide. Remove the precipitated protein by centrifugation

---

[62] R. Markus, *Helv. Chim. Acta* **31**, 831-49 (1948).

rather than filtration to avoid contamination from the filter paper. Neutralize excessively acid or alkaline solutions.

Add 1-5 ml. of protein-free filtrate containing 0.02-0.1 mg. of lactic acid to 1 ml. of 20 per cent copper sulfate solution and dilute with water to a total volume of 10 ml. Add about 1 gram of powdered calcium hydroxide and shake vigorously immediately. If a blue color does not form, add more calcium hydroxide. Allow to stand at least a half-hour with occasional shaking and then centrifuge. Pipet out a 1-ml. aliquot from beneath the surface film and use this for color development.

To the aliquot containing 0.002-0.01 mg. of lactic acid, add 0.05 ml. of 4 per cent copper sulfate pentahydrate solution. From a buret, run in 6 ml. of concentrated sulfuric acid, mixing constantly while the acid is being added. The temperature of the solution will rise to about 70-80°. Place the tube in boiling water for 5 minutes and then cool to below 20° in cold water. From a pipet add exactly 0.1 ml. of 1.5 per cent solution of p-hydroxydiphenyl in 0.5 per cent sodium hydroxide solution. Disperse the precipitated reagent as quickly as possible through the solution and place in a water bath at 30° for 30 minutes or more. Place in boiling water for 90 seconds to dissolve excess reagent, then cool in cold water to room temperature. Read at 560 mμ against a reagent blank.

With ferric chloride. Add 20 ml. of water to the ether solution of the sample and evaporate the ether on a water bath. Neutralize the solution to phenolphthalein with saturated barium hydroxide solution and dilute to about 90 ml. with water. Heat almost to boiling on a steam bath, cool, and dilute to 110 ml. Filter and evaporate exactly 100 ml. of filtrate to about 10 ml. Add 50 ml. of water and again evaporate to about 10 ml. Add 6.6 ml. of 1:120 hydrochloric acid and dilute to about 40 ml.

To prepare acid-washed carbon, mix 10 grams of Nuchar W or equivalent with 250 ml. of 1:100 hydrochloric acid and agitate occasionally with air on a steam bath for 20 minutes. Filter on a Büchner funnel. Disperse in 200 ml. of water and refilter three times. Dry and store.

Add 0.2 gram of this acid-washed activated carbon and stir on a steam bath at intervals for 10 minutes. Cool and dilute to 50 ml. Filter clear. To 40 ml. of filtrate containing not over 12 mg. of lactic acid add 1.2 ml. of 1:120 hydrochloric acid and 5 ml. of 1 per cent ferric chloride hexahydrate in 1:500 hydrochloric acid. Protect from light during this development and read at 460 mμ also protected from exposure. Dilution after color development is not permissible.

By azobenzene-phenylhydrazine-sulfonic acid. Dilute a sample containing 2-3 mg. of lactic acid to 1 ml. with water and add 2 ml. of concentrated sulfuric acid. Heat in boiling water for exactly 2 minutes with gentle agitation. Chill in ice and add 3.5 ml. of an 0.018 per cent solution of azobenzene-phenylhydrazine-sulfonic acid slowly, with shaking. Prepare this by shaking 0.018 gram of the compound in 80 ml. of water and letting stand overnight. Dilute to 100 ml.

Add to sample plus reagent, 1.5 ml. of aldehyde-free ethanol, 5 ml. of chloroform, and 2.5 ml. of concentrated hydrochloric acid. Shake until all the color has been extracted by the chloroform. Read against a blank.

Conversion to pyruvic acid for development. As reagent prepare the yeast by drying at room temperature and pulverizing. Wash several times with 10 times the weight of distilled water, dry, and powder again. This yeast yields the enzyme, lactic dehydrogenase, and keeps indefinitely in the refrigerator. Before using, wash the yeast with 100 times its weight of phosphate buffer for pH 7.4 (Vol. I, pages 174, 176), centrifuge, and resuspend in the same volume of the buffer. Test the activity of the enzyme by incubating 1 ml. of the yeast suspension alone, and with 0.180 mg. of lactate in the presence of 1 ml. of a 1:50,000 solution of o-chlorophenol-indo-2:6-dichlorophenol, in an open test tube. In the presence of lactic acid, the indicator, should be decolorized in 3 minutes or less. The control should take at least 10 minutes.

As another reagent soak 20 grams of gum ghatti in a cheesecloth bag for 24 hours in a liter of water. Remove the bag and add 5 grams of anhydrous ferric sulfate, and 75 ml. of 85 per cent phosphoric acid in 100 ml. of water. Mix and add 15 ml. of 1 per cent potassium permanganate to destroy reducing materials. Use after standing a few days.

Neutralize the clarified sample, deproteinized with an equal volume of 10 per cent trichloroacetic acid, and dilute so that 1 ml. contains no more than 0.2 mg. of lactic acid. If any of the substances known to cause interference are present, treat the sample with copper sulfate-calcium hydroxide as for blood (page 346), starting at "Add 1 ml. of 15 per cent copper sulfate . . ." and ending at ". . . but do not filter." Remove the precipitate and neutralize.

Incubate 1 ml. with 1 ml. of 1 per cent yeast suspension in phosphate buffer for pH 7.4 and 1 ml. of 0.16 per cent potassium ferricyanide solution for 0.5 hour at 30°. Centrifuge after incubation. Add 1 ml. of ferric sulfate reagent to 2 ml. of the supernatant fluid, dilute to 10 ml., and read at 620 mμ against a reagent blank.

If the sample contains less than 0.075 mg. per ml. of lactic acid, get a deeper color by use of 2 ml. of the enzyme mixture, 1 ml. of ferric sulfate reagent, and 2 ml. of water.

ACETOACETIC ACID

In general acetoacetic acid, often known as diacetic acid, is converted to acetone by many methods of determination. Because of this factor and because the methods normally determine the two together, several methods have been given in the chapter on ketones (pages 288 to 292).

A specific method for acetoacetic acid is to couple with diazotized 4-nitroaniline to give a green color.[63] The product is not the rose-colored hydrazone [64] which is of low tinctorial power. Ethyl acetoacetate and acetylacetone give more color than acetoacetic acid, oxalacetic and θ,γ-diketovaleric acid about the same as acetoacetic acid, tyrosine 20 per cent as much, pyruvic acid about 10 per cent as much, and guanine or thymine about 1.5 per cent as much. In general, α-alkyl monosubstitution products of acetoacetic acid react. The reaction is used for histamine (Vol. IV), but the color does not overlap that from acetoacetic acid. Interfering colors must be removed from tissue extracts or urine by sorption, as on a resin column.

There is no significant color from acetone, acetonylacetone, oxalosuccinic acid, α-ketoglutaric acid, levulinic acid, α-ketoisocaproic acid, dehydroacetic acid, β-hydroxybutyric acid, malonic, maleic, and malic acids.

A correction for a sample blank after destruction of acetoacetic acid is essential, primarily due to pyruvic acid. Other material which would give background color is largely removed by the deproteinizing agent. The pyruvic acid decreases at room temperature with an alkaline buffer. Since the pyruvic acid content of whole blood decreases on standing, the decrease before the plasma is separated is unknown.

Acetoacetic acid and its esters condense with phenol in the presence of a dehydrating agent to give β-methylcoumarin which has an intense fluorescence. Similarly acetoacetic ester and resorcinol condense in the presence of sulfuric acid to give β-methylumbelliferone which has a blue fluorescence.[65] The maximum color is at pH 9. The solution is sensitive

---

[63] Sanford M. Rosenthal, *J. Biol. Chem.* **179**, 1235-44 (1949).

[64] Theodore E. Friedemann and Gladys E. Haugen, *Ibid.* **147**, 415-42 (1943).

[65] H. von Pechmann and C. Duisberg, *Ber.* **16**, 2119-28 (1883); Victor Arreghine and Edward D. Garcia, *Ann. soc. quim. argentina* **7**, 224 (1919); *Ann. chim. anal. chim. appl.* **2**, 36-41 (1920); R. Coquoin and R. Lupu, *Compt. rend. soc. biol.* **109**, 801-3 (1932).

to light, but alcoholic standards are stable. Condensation in the presence of hydrochloric acid is specific for β-ketonic acids and their esters. While some alkaloids and aromatic acids would interfere, there are no such substances present in normal or pathological body fluids. Neither acetone nor hydroxybutric acid reacts.

While ferric chloride gives a brown color with acetoacetic acid, there are sufficient interfering substances in biological samples to make this of limited value. Its application depends [66] on decomposing the aceto-acetic acid in one portion of the sample so that this can be used as a base for development of the color of the test substance by duplication.

Sample—*Blood*. To 5 ml. of blood or plasma, add 10 ml. of water and the amount of 12.6 per cent barium hydroxide solution found by titration equivalent to 5 ml. of 10 per cent zinc sulfate decahydrate solution. Mix and add the 5 ml. of zinc sulfate solution. Shake vigorously, centrifuge, and filter the supernatant liquid. Use for development with 4-nitrobenzene diazonium salt.

Procedure—*With 4-nitroaniline*. As a sample blank treat 5 ml. of sample containing 0.00125-0.02 mg. of acetoacetic acid with 0.5 ml. of 1:6 sulfuric acid, heat in boiling water for 5 minutes, cool in ice water, and neutralize with 0.5 ml. of 20 per cent sodium hydroxide.

As a buffer mix one volume of 9 per cent oxalic acid solution, one volume of 21.2 per cent tripotassium phosphate solution, and 2 volumes of 50 per cent potassium carbonate solution. Cool in ice and use the day it is mixed.

Chill the sample blank and 5 ml. of sample in ice. Add 4 ml. of the buffer to each and mix. As diazo reagent mix 10 ml. of ice-cold 0.1 per cent 4-nitroaniline in 1:360 sulfuric acid and 1 ml. of 4 per cent sodium nitrite solution. Add 2 ml. of this reagent to each tube and keep in the ice bath for exactly 10 minutes. Add 1 ml. of 20 per cent sodium hydroxide solution to stop the reaction and replace in the ice bath for 2 minutes. Add 5 ml. of 1:1 butanol-benzene to these tubes and to a reagent blank. Stopper, shake well, and centrifuge. This extraction is incomplete but standardized. Add 3 ml. of each to 0.5 ml. of 0.2 per cent sodium hydroxide solution in absolute ethanol. Read at 650 mμ against the reagent blank. Subtract the value obtained with the sample blank in which acetoacetic acid has been destroyed.

With resorcinol. Transfer 1 ml. of deproteinized sample to a tube. Add 0.1 gram of resorcinol and 2 ml. of concentrated hydrochloric acid.

---

[66] J. Melka and F. Klein, *Bratislav. Lekarske Listy* **8**, 188-92 (1928).

Stopper and let stand in the dark for 12 hours. Neutralize with 0.4 per cent sodium hydroxide solution until the solution is pink and fluorescent. Dilute to 100 ml. with a buffer solution containing 7.32 grams of boric acid and 100 ml. of 0.4 per cent sodium hydroxide solution per liter. Compare the fluorescence under ultraviolet light with that of a series of standards, preferably prepared from a 0.1725 per cent solution of β-methylumbelliferone in 90 per cent ethanol of which each ml. is equivalent to 1 mg. of acetoacetic acid.

TRIACETIC ACID, β,δ-DIKETOHEXANOIC ACID, AND ITS ETHYL ESTER

A method for acetylacetone (page 294) includes triacetic acid and its esters and is applicable in the absence of the former. The name "triacetic acid," which is β,δ-diketohexanoic acid, has been loosely applied to triacetic lactone [67] which is 6-methylpyranone.[68]

TRIACETIC LACTONE, 6-METHYLPYRANONE

A modification of the method for acetyl acetone (page 295) gives triacetic lactone.

α-KETOPROPIONIC ACID, PYRUVIC ACID

The most sensitive method for pyruvic acid is by precipitation with nitrophenylhydrazines. The precipitation is highly specific for keto acids but not for pyruvic acid. After precipitation, the 4-nitrophenylhydrazones of pyruvic, glyoxylic, and phenylglyoxylic acids can be separated from that of propionic acid by differential solubility in sodium carbonate or ethanol.[69] The acid hydrazones give an intense red color; those of the aldehydes blue or purple which fades to red. While 4-nitrophenylhydrazine may be used, 2,4-dinitrophenylhydrazine is preferable because its solution is stable and its reacts more rapidly.

Pyruvic acid in a trichloroacetic acid blood filtrate is converted to its 2,4-dinitrophenylhydrazone and so extracted with ethyl acetate [70] to separate from excess reagent. Then when extracted from the ethyl

---

[67] F. L. Breusch, *Enzymologia* **11**, 169 (1944); F. L. Breusch and E. Ulusoy, *Arch. Biochem.* **14**, 183 (1947).

[68] Robert F. Witter and Elmer Stotz, *J. Biol Chem.* **176**, 485-92 (1948).

[69] H. D. Dakin and H. W. Dudley, *J. Biol. Chem.* **15**, 127-43 (1913).

[70] G. D. Lu, *Biochem. J.* **33**, 249-54 (1939); E. Bueding and H. Wortis, *J. Biol. Chem.* **133**, 585-91 (1940); P. Fornaroli and A. Pardi, *Bull. soc. ital. biol. sper.* **15**, 511-13 (1940); K. Kato and P. K. Li, *Am. J. Dis. Child.* **61**, 1222 (1941); Theodore E. Friedemann and Gladys E. Haugen, *J. Biol. Chem.* **147**, 415-42 (1943); Taiji Shimizu, *J. Japan Biochem. Soc.* **22**, 108-14 (1950); Igakuto Seibutsugaku, *Med. and Biol.* **17**, 102-5 (1950); Tsutomu Tsubosaka, *Vitamins* (Japan) **4**, 49-52 (1951).

acetate into 10 per cent sodium carbonate solution, addition of sodium hydroxide stabilizes the red color for reading. For 0.002 mg. in 10 ml. the error is only ±1.5 per cent.

Even without extraction, there is but little interference by hexoses, glucuronic acid, ascorbic acid, or kojic acid. Up to 10 per cent error may be introduced by acetylpyruvic acid, acetoacetic acid, or levulinic acid, and even larger error by formaldehyde, urotropin, acetaldehyde, glyoxal, methylglyoxal, glyceraldehyde, acetone, glyoxylic acid, oxalacetic acid, or α-ketoglutaric acid. Trichloroacetic acid is suitable for protein precipitation, but in time produces interfering substances. Solutions deproteinized with metaphosphoric acid are more stable. Interference by acetoacetic acid is avoided by destroying that substance.[71] To avoid interference by oxalacetic and ketoglutaric acids, treat with hydrazine which modifies them to heterocycles.[72]

Methyl red, methyl orange, alizarin, litmus, fuchsin, eosin, safranine, gentian violet, and methylene blue interfere because they are extracted by the solvent and reextracted by the carbonate solution. They are quantitatively removed by not over a gram of Lloyd's reagent in 1:360 sulfuric acid solution for each 10 ml. of solution without loss of pyruvic acid.

The reaction is a general one for keto acids modified to avoid interferences.[73] So modified it is applicable to total hydrazones and reactive neutral keto compounds. Rather than carry out successive extractions, equilibrium distribution between solvent and aqueous layer is relied on.

The color developed by pyruvic acid with salicyclic aldehyde in alkaline solution is suitable for photometric estimation.[74] The presence of alkali prevents interference by oxalacetic acid. The method is accurate to 10 per cent on biological specimens. Both acetone and acetoacetic acid also give the reaction [75] but are volatilized in an air current at 20°. The acetoacetic acid is decarboxylated to acetone for removal. The rose color of pyruvic acid with a fresh alcoholic solution of α-methylindole can be applied [76] but not to trichloroacetic acid filtrates of blood.[77]

[71] Daniel Klein, *J. Biol. Chem.* **137**, 311-16 (1941); Samuel Elgart and Norton Nelson, *Ibid.* **138**, 443-4 (1941).

[72] K. Slavik and C. Michalec, *Chem. Listy* **43**, 102-4 (1949).

[73] Theodore E. Friedemann and Gladys E. Haugen, *J. Biol. Chem.* **147**, 415-42 (1943).

[74] F. B. Straub, *Z. physiol. Chem.* **244**, 117-27 (1936); G. Delrue, *Compt. rend. soc. biol.* **133**, 708 (1940); Raymond Derris, *Ibid.* **140**, 673 (1946).

[75] F. Villano and L. Rota, *Boll. soc. ital. biol. sper.* **22**, 554-6 (1946).

[76] Zacharias Dische and Seymour S. Robbins, *Biochem. Z.* **271**, 304-8 (1934).

[77] S. E. de Jough and J. Pickard, *Arch. Néerland. physiol.* **22**, 117-22 (1937).

The background at 650 mμ of a blood plasma deproteinized by precipitation of zinc sulfate with barium hydroxide after destruction of acetoacetic acid by heating to boiling and development with diazotized nitroaniline is a measure of the pyruvic acid present [78] (page 352).

Pyruvic acid gives a blue color in a saturated solution of ammonium sulfate on addition of sodium nitroferricyanide and ammonium hydroxide.[79] Acetone dicarboxylic acid gives the same color, hence it must be absent. The color develops in an hour and is stable thereafter for a half-hour. An appropriate concentration for color development is 0.05 per cent of pyruvic acid.

Sample—*Muscle.* Disperse a 1-gram sample in 3 ml. of water and add 0.5 ml. of 10 per cent sodium tungstate solution. Add 0.5 ml. of 1:9 sulfuric acid and let stand for protein coagulation. Filter for the development of aliquots with salicylic aldehyde.

Blood. Acetoacetic acid absent. Withdraw the blood from the vein by a dry 2-ml. syringe fitted with a 21-gauge needle. There should be a minimum of stasis before collection. The syringe should not be above room temperature. Eject the sample as a fine stream into 5 volumes of fresh 10 per cent metaphosphoric acid. Shake and centrifuge. It may be stored in a refrigerator at this point for 2 days. Develop with 2,4-dinitrophenylhydrazine.

Acetoacetic acid present. Precipitate 0.1-0.5 ml. of blood with 4.5 ml. of 1:500 sulfuric acid and 1 ml. of 5 per cent sodium tungstate solution. Centrifuge, remove the supernatant fluid, and wash the precipitate with 2 ml. of a solution consisting of 4.5 ml. of 1:500 sulfuric acid, 1 ml. of 5 per cent sodium tungstate solution, and 0.5 ml. of water. To the combined supernatant liquids, add 0.5 ml. of concentrated hydrochloric acid and boil for an hour in a water bath. Add enough 40 per cent sodium hydroxide solution to neutralize the hydrochloric acid. Allow the solution to cool and use an aliquot for development by 2,4-dinitrophenylhydrazine.

Urine. Collect a specimen with 0.5 ml. of 1:1 sulfuric acid for every 100 ml. The sample can be stored under refrigeration for 24 hours. Add 2 ml. of sample to 10 ml. of 10 per cent trichloroacetic acid solution. If at this point the sample shows unprecipitated color, discard and start with a new sample. Add 0.75 gram of Lloyd's reagent for every 10 ml. of acidified urine, shake, and filter at once. Then deproteinize by adding

[78] Sanford M. Rosenthal, *J. Biol. Chem.* **179**, 1235-44 (1949).

[79] H. Caron and D. Raquet, *J. pharm. chim.* (9) **2**, 333-5 (1942).

2 ml. of filtrate to 10 ml. of 10 per cent trichloroacetic acid solution. In either case develop with 2,4-dinitrophenylhydrazine.

Procedure—*With 2,4-dinitrophenylhydrazine. Pyruvic acid.* As reagent grind 100 mg. of 2,4-dinitrophenylhydrazine with 100 ml. of 1:5 hydrochloric acid and filter. Place a 3-ml. aliquot of sample solution in a water bath for 10 minutes at 25°. Add 1 ml. of reagent and mix. After 5 minutes add 8 ml. of ethyl acetate and pass a stream of nitrogen or air through the mixture for exactly 2 minutes. Remove the lower aqueous layer.

Add exactly 6 ml. of a 4 per cent solution of sodium carbonate to the solvent and aerate rapidly again for 2 minutes. After the two phases have separated, withdraw 5 ml. of the lower layer. Add exactly 5 ml. of 6 per cent sodium hydroxide solution and mix. Read with 420 mμ and 520 mμ filters, 5-10 minutes after addition of the alkali.

Extractable indicators, dyes, and other colored compounds will seriously affect the results. If treatment with Lloyd's reagent has not removed such interfering colors, set up A, a reagent blank with 1 ml. of reagent; B, a sample with 1 ml. of reagent; C, a reagent blank with 1 ml. of 1:5 hydrochloric acid; and D, a sample with 1 ml. of 1:5 hydrochloric acid. Determine the reading by D after the apparatus is set to maximum transmission by means of C. Then, $B - D$ is the corrected pyruvic acid content of the sample, provided other keto acids are absent.

Chloroform is an alternative extractant. Color in the original sample at the wave length read is corrected with an undeveloped sample as blank. If the ratio $L_{420}:L_{520}$ exceeds 1:3, a-ketoglutaric acid is probably present and other procedures must be applied. Otherwise calculate from the calibration curve prepared with pyruvic acid.

Pyruvic acid in the presence of other diketocarboxylic acids. Set up two tubes containing 3 ml. of sample at 25° for 10 minutes. Add 1 ml. of reagent to each. For pyruvic acid add 3 ml. of xylene or toluene after 5 minutes. Complete as before starting at "... and pass a stream of nitrogen or air. ..." Read this at 520 mμ.

For total keto acids wait 25 minutes after addition of the reagent and complete as before starting at "... add 8 ml. of ethyl acetate and ..." Read at 540 mμ, 420 mμ, and 400 mμ.

Express each reading as pyruvic acid and calculate as follows.

$$\text{Pyruvic acid} = 1.1\,V_{520} - 0.1\,V_{540}$$
$$\text{or} \quad 3.2\,V_{400} - 2.2\,V_{420}$$
$$\text{or} \quad 2.1\,V_{540} - 1.1\,V_{400}$$

$$\alpha\text{-ketoglutaric acid} = 1.9 \ (V_{400} - V_{540})$$
$$\text{or} \quad 3.85 \ (V_{420} - V_{400})$$
$$\text{or} \quad 1.95 \ (V_{540} - V_{520})$$

Total hydrazones. Follow the procedure for pyruvic acid through "... reacting for exactly 5 minutes. ..." Add 5 ml. of 10 per cent sodium hydroxide and read after 10 minutes against a reagent blank at 520 mμ. Calculate as pyruvic acid as a form of expression of the result.

With salicylic aldehyde. To 1 ml. of solution containing not over 0.5 mg. of pyruvic acid add 1 ml. of 60 per cent potassium hydroxide solution and shake mechanically for 10 minutes at 37°. Add 0.5 ml. of 2 per cent salicylic aldehyde in ethanol and mix. Cool, centrifuge, and read against a reagent blank.

PHENYLPYRUVIC ACID

When ferric chloride is added to an aqueous solution of phenylpyruvic acid, a green color is obtained which will determine 0.04 mg. per ml.[80]

Procedure—To 20 ml. of trichloroacetic-acid blood, or spinal-fluid filtrate add 2 ml. of 1 per cent aqueous ferric chloride. Read the green color at once at 620 mμ, taking the maximum coloration for comparison.

p-HYDROXYPHENYLPYRUVIC ACID

The reaction of pyruvic acid with 2,4-dinitrophenylhydrazine is also applicable to estimation of *p*-hydroxyphenylpyruvic acid.[81] Pyruvic acid must be absent. The hydrazone formed is sorbed from anhydrous solvent on a column of aluminum oxide, then eluted with 95 per cent acetone. The color developed with Millon's reagent is also applicable.[82]

Procedure—*Urine.* Treat 1 ml. of freshly collected urine with 4 ml. of a saturated solution of 2,4-dinitrophenylhydrazine in 1:5 hydrochloric acid, in order to form the yellow hydrazone. Let stand for an hour. Extract with several 5-ml. portions of anhydrous alcohol-free ether until the ether extract is colorless. Discard the aqueous solution.

Prepare aluminum oxide by working with a 5 per cent sodium hydroxide solution. Pour off the supernatant liquid, dry the alumina at 105°, and keep in a desiccator over silica gel. As the sorption column introduce this into a glass tube 20 cm. long and 7 mm. in diameter, drawn

---

[80] E. Erlenmeyer, Jr., *Ann. Chem.* **271**, 137 (1892); George A. Jervis, Richard J. Block, Diana Bolling, and Edna Kanze, *J. Biol. Chem.* **134**, 105-13 (1940).

[81] Hans Diedrich Cremer and Heinz Berger, *Klin. Wochschr.* **24/25**, 222-4 (1947); Ernst Kirberger, *Ibid.* **27**, 48-50 (1949).

[82] W. Stubenrauch and L. Huber, *Deut. med. Wochschr.* **74**, 404-6 (1949).

to a fine capillary at the lower end, and closed with a small mass of filter paper. Make a paste of the alumina in anhydrous ether and transfer sufficient to the tube to give a height of 1 cm. Introduce the yellow ether extract into the sorption column without disturbing the alumina.

Wash the ether extract of urine on the alumina column with anhydrous ether, then with alcohol-free anhydrous acetone. Prepare this by distilling the acetone from potassium permanganate, then letting it stand for several days over potassium carbonate, and drying over anhydrous copper sulfate. Next wash with acetone containing 1 per cent of water. The change of solvent occurs when the filtrate becomes colorless.

Elute the dinitrophenylhydrazone from the alumina column with acetone containing 5 per cent of water. Dilute the eluate to 50 ml. and read at 434 mμ against a sample blank.

Alternatively, mix 5 ml. of fresh urine and 5 ml. of saturated solution of 2,4-dinitrophenylhydrazine in 1:12 hydrochloric acid. After 0.5 hour, shake, and mix 2 ml. of the reaction mixture with 4 ml. of 4 per cent sodium hydroxide solution. After a few minutes dilute to 30 ml. with water. Centrifuge for 3 minutes and read the clarified solution at 500 mμ within 1 hour.

2-Phenyl-β-Hydroxypropionic Acid, Tropic Acid

Tropic acid is determined by reaction with p-dimethylaminobenzaldehyde in strong sulfuric acid solution.[83] Atropine, hyocyamine, and scopalamine interfere.

Procedure—Add a drop of 10 per cent borax solution and evaporate a sample containing about 0.2 mg. of tropic acid. Cool to room temperature and add 7 drops of a 10 per cent solution of p-dimethylaminobenzaldehyde in 9:1 sulfuric acid. After 2 minutes heat in boiling water for 3 minutes. Chill, add 5 ml. of acetic anhydride, and read at 515 mμ against a reagent blank.

Imidazolepropionic Acid

For imidazole propionic acid, develop with p-phenyldiazonium chloride as described for histamine (Vol. IV).

Indolylpropionic Acid

Indoylpropionic acid, also known as *indolepropionic acid,* in solution reacts with two volumes of fuming hydrochloric acid to give a brown

---

[83] K. R. Gottlieb, *Dansk. Tids. Farm.* **24**, 40-8 (1950).

color read at 540 mμ.[84] The reagent also gives color with indole and indole acetic acid. It does not give color with tryptophan.

METHYL-α-CHLOROACRYLATE

This ester is determined in air by reduction of the color of permanganate.[85] Other reducing agents interfere.

Procedure—Draw a known volume of air through 0.003 per cent potassium permanganate to give an observable reduction in color. Read at 525 mμ.

β-HYDROXYBUTYRIC ACID

The usual form of estimation of β-hydroxybutyric acid is as acetone. For this determination acetoacetic acid must have been decomposed and the acetone so formed distilled along with the preformed acetone. Then for determination the β-hydroxybutric acid is oxidized to acetone with potassium dichromate and sulfuric acid. This is distilled and condensed with salicylic aldehyde to form dihydroxybenzylidene acetone.[86] Sugar and other interfering substances must first be removed. The acetone from β-hydroxybutyric acid can also be precipitated as a mercuric sulfate complex, dissolved, and converted to mercuric sulfide.[87]

Sample—*Urine.* Mix a suitable sample of urine, not to exceed 25 ml., with 20 ml. of water and 25 ml. of 40 per cent copper sulfate solution. Add 25 ml. of a 20 per cent slurry of hydrated lime in water. Shake and test with litmus. If not alkaline, add more of the lime slurry. Dilute to 100 ml. and let stand for one-half hour. Filter through a dry folded filter. This removes up to 8 per cent of glucose, together with other interfering substances. Boiling a portion of the filtrate will give a yellow precipitate if the glucose has not been completely removed.

Place a portion of filtrate equivalent to 2 to 50 ml. of urine in a distilling flask. Add 4 drops of 1:1 sulfuric acid and distil as described for acetone (page 289). After distillation of the acetone, replace the receiver. Heat the contents of the distilling flask to boiling and gradually add through a separatory funnel inserted in the stopper, 30 ml. of 1:1 sul-

---

[84] S. Grisolia, *Trabajos inst. cienc. méd.* (Madrid) **3**, 367-72 (1943-4).

[85] J. Haslam, S. M. A. Whettem, and W. W. Soppet, *Analyst* **76**, 628-34 (1951).

[86] J. A. Behre and S. R. Benedict, *J. Biol. Chem.* **70**, 487-94 (1926); Fritz Lauersen, *Klin. Wochschr.* **15**, 339-41 (1936); H. G. Krainick, *Ibid.* **17**, 450-1 (1938); Oscar Eichler and Helmut Hindemith, *Biochem. Z.* **314**, 73-81 (1943).

[87] Georges Debrue, *Arch. intern. med. exptl.* **8**, 215-22 (1933).

furic acid and 20 ml. of 0.2 per cent potassium bichromate solution. Let stand for 10 minutes and add 50 ml. more of 0.2 per cent potassium bichromate solution. Repeat after another 10 minutes. Distil so that the 100 ml. of distillate will be collected in 30 minutes and develop by salicylic aldehyde.

Blood. Treat a deproteinized blood filtrate by oxidation, as for urine starting at "Add 4 drops of 1:1 sulfuric acid. . . ." If the volume used contains 0.1 mg. or more of β-hydroxybutyric acid as acetone, collect 100 ml. of distillate and use as sample. If less, redistil the first distillate, which need not be of an exact volume, collecting 25 ml. of sample distillate which will contain all of the acetone.

Alternatively see details under acetone (page 291).

Procedure—*By salicylic aldehyde.* Follow that for acetone but read against a curve developed with β-hydroxybutyric acid.

3-Indolylbutyric Acid

The reaction of 3-indolylbutyric acid with mercuric sulfate and sulfuric acid is appropriate for reading.[88] The corresponding propionic acid gives the same color intensity, indolylacetic acid much less which fades on standing, and indole gives negligible color. Colors from the butyric and propionic acid derivatives are extractable with amyl alcohol.

Procedure—To a 5-ml. sample containing not over 0.2 ml. of test substance, add 1 ml. of 1 per cent mercuric sulfate solution in 1:8 sulfuric acid. Add 10 ml. of 21:15 sulfuric acid, mix, and after 10 minutes cool to room temperature. Read at 550 mμ against a reagent blank.

α-Amino-δ-semicarbamidovaleric Acid, Citrulline

The reaction product of tryptophan with citrulline in molar proportions, catalyzed by strong acid, gives a purple with diacetylmonoxime.[89] The same reaction is given by ureides. The color conforms to Beer's law.

Procedure—Place 10 mg. of tryptophan- and ureide-free sample in each of 4 flasks. Add successively 0.15, 0.1, 0.05, and 0 ml. of water. Add 1.1 ml. of 85 per cent phosphoric acid to each and mix. Add 0.1

[88] C. W. Ballard and S. Spice, *Analyst* **76**, 664-5 (1951).

[89] V. N. Orekhovich and A. A. Tustanovskiĭ, *Doklady Akad. Nauk.* (USSR) **67**, 333-6 (1949).

ml. of 5 per cent diacetylmonoxime solution to each. Successively add 0.03, 0.035, 0.4, and 0.45 ml. of 0.005 per cent tryptophan solution. Heat in boiling water for 10 minutes, cool, and add 3.35 ml. of a 1:99 mixture of 0.18 per cent sodium nitrite solution and 85 per cent phosphoric acid. After a minute add a drop of 0.18 per cent aqueous sodium nitrite. The most intense purple color signifies the flask in which the proportions were approximately molar. Read and interpret in terms of the test substance being in 1:1 relation in that flask to the molecular weight of tryptophan, 204.22.

Ascorbic Acid, Vitamin C

If an excess of 2,6-dichlorophenolindophenol is introduced into a solution containing ascorbic acid, the unreduced dye remaining after reaction measures the ascorbic acid by difference.[90] Thus the method is in effect a relatively simple modification of a titrametric method. As applied to colorless solutions, this leaves only doubt as to reduction by substances other than Vitamin C, often avoidable by rapid manipulation. Thus cysteine gives the same reaction but sufficiently more slowly to permit differentiating. fading of the dye at too high acidity is avoided by buffering.

The unreduced dye can be extracted with nitrobenzene,[91] and xylene,[92] amyl acetate,[93] chloroform,[94] or amyl alcohol.[95] The final stage in simplification is that reached by merely shaking the sample solution with the dye in xylene, to extract as much as will react.[96]

The presence of 4 mg. of reduced glutathione, cysteine hydrochloride,

[90] C. Glen King, *Physiol. Rev.* **16**, 238-62 (1936); *Ind. Eng. Chem., Anal. Ed.* **13**, 225-7 (1941); Rowland L. Mindlin and Allan M. Butler, *J. Biol. Chem.* **122**, 673-85 (1937-8); K. A. Evelyn, H. T. Malloy, and C. Rosen, *Ibid.* **126**, 645-54 (1938); Otto A. Bessey, *Ibid.* **126**, 771-84 (1939); H. J. Loeffler, *Ind. Eng. Chem.* **33**, 1308-4 (1941); S. A. Morell, *Ind. Eng. Chem., Anal. Ed.* **13**, 793-4 (1941); Leonard P. Pepkowitz, *J. Biol. Chem.* **151**, 405-12 (1943); V. B. Fish, R. B. Dustman, and R. S. Marsh, *Proc. Am. Soc. Hort. Sci.* **44**, 196-200 (1944); W. L. Nelson and G. F. Somers, *Ind. Eng. Chem., Anal. Ed.* **17**, 754-6 (1945); Cf. Robert A. Herzner and Carl Graf Kuefstein, *Biochem. Z.* **317**, 37-42 (1944); P. Brandt Rehbert, *Acta Physiol. Scand.* **5**, 277-88 (1943).

[91] Franz Bukatsch, *Z. physiol. Chem.* **262**, 20-8 (1939).

[92] Franz Folkmann, *Österr. Chem.-Ztg.* **41**, 193-4 (1938); Elmer Stotz, *J. Lab. Clin. Med.* **26**, 1542-5 (1941).

[93] Akizi Huzita and Isamu Numata, *Biochem. Z.* **308**, 321-33 (1941).

[94] H. F. W. Kirkpatrick, *J. Soc. Chem. Ind.* **62**, 39-41 (1943).

[95] E. Gero, *Bull soc. chim. biol.* **31**, 817-38 (1949).

[96] Doris M. Highet and Edward S. West, *J. Biol. Chem.* **146**, 655-62 (1942).

tannic acid, pyrogallol, or dilute strong acids does not affect the color in the 15 seconds contact provided in the procedure.[97] The presence of 2 per cent metaphosphoric acid used for deproteinizing does not affect the dye but can cause emulsification; the presence of 3 per cent prevents loss of ascorbic acid during preparation of the sample.[98] There is no destruction of ascorbic acid by 1:400 hydrochloric acid in an hour. Sulfur dioxide interferes,[99] addition of 10 per cent of acetone prevents this.[100] Addition of mercuric chloride retards reduction of the dye by such other substances as glutathione.[101] There is no significant interference by the iron and copper commonly present in multivitamin pharmaceuticals, nor by the other usual ingredients such as cod-liver oil, liver extract, etc.[102]

Vitamin C, ascorbic acid, causes methylene blue to bleach mole for mole, on exposure to sunlight or the artificial equivalent.[103] The leuco base of methylene blue so produced does not oxidize spontaneously on exposure to the air in the presence of sodium thiosulfate and carbon dioxide from sodium bicarbonate, but rapid operation is preferable. Glutathione, cysteine, and other reducing substances do not affect the method. Accuracy to ±4 per cent is obtained. Trichloroacetic acid filtrates of plasma are suitable,[104] but neither trichloroacetic acid nor sulfosalicylic acid should be used with whole blood.[105] Solubility of the methylene blue reagent is promoted with very dilute alkali.[106]

Ascorbic acid reduces diazotized sulfanilamide irreversibly in acid solution, probably to give phenylhydrazine-*p*-sulfonamide and azoben-

[97] Cf. F. Lanersen and W. Orth, *Vitamine u. Hormone* **4**, 62-89 (1943).

[98] Carl M. Lyman, M. O. Schultze, and C. Glen King, *J. Biol. Chem.* **118**, 757-64 (1937); S. A. Morell, *Ind. Eng. Chem., Anal. Ed.* **13**, 793-4 (1941).

[99] Cf. H. F. W. Kirkpatrick, *J. Soc. Chem. Ind.* **60**, 226-9 (1941).

[100] L. W. Mapson, *Chemistry and Industry* **60**, 802 (1941); H. J. Loeffler and J. D. Ponting, *Ind. Eng. Chem., Anal. Ed.* **14**, 846-9 (1942).

[101] Christopher Carruthers, *Ibid.* **14**, 826-8 (1942).

[102] D. G. Chapman, Odette Rochon, and J. A. Campbell, *Anal. Chem.* **23**, 1113-15 (1951).

[103] C. Emilio Martini and Arturo Bonsignore, *Boll. soc. ital. biol. sper.* **9**, 388-9 (1934); Helge Lund and Herbert Lieck, *Nature* **137**, 784 (1936); *Skand. Arch. Physiol.* **74**, 269-71 (1936); K. Wahren, *Klin. Wochschr.* **16**, 1496-8 (1937); Wilhelm Zimmermann, *Ibid.* **17**, 1728-31 (1938); W. K. Kapuscinski, *Acta Polon. Pharm.* **3**, 109-16 (1939); K. Z. Tul'chinskaya, *Trudy Vsesoyuz. Konferentsii Vitaminam* **1940**, 282-3; Francesco Silvio Trucco, *Ann. chim. applicata* **34**, 127-35 (1949).

[104] Martin Odin, *Acta Paediat.* **26**, 339-50 (1939).

[105] Eugenio E. Vonesch and Carlos A. Zimman, *Anales. farm. bioquím.* (Buenos Aires) **12**, 1-12 (1941).

[106] Akiji Fujita and Tsutomu Elihara, *Biochem. Z.* **290**, 172-81 (1937).

zene-p,p'-disulfonamide.[107] Over the range used the color conforms to Beer's law within ±4 per cent. Hydroquinone and gluco-reductones interfere somewhat but cysteine, tyrosine, histidine, creatinine, ammonia, phenol, and uric acid do not. Results on fruit juices agree with those with 2,6-dichlorophenolindophenol.

Ferribipyridine sulfate gives a stable deep pink to red color of ferrobipyridine on reduction by ascorbic acid.[108] Accuracy is to ±0.5-2 per cent. There is no interference by arsenious acid, formaldehyde, acetaldehyde, formic acid, and methanol.

Ascorbic acid reduces phospho-18-tungstic acid, Folin's uric acid reagent, in acid solution, to give a blue color. In the absence of interfering substances the color is suitable for estimation of vitamin C.[109] Cystine, cysteine, and glutathione give the same reaction and epinephrine interferes. Corrections are applicable. The method is accurate to ±1 per cent if yellow color is filtered out and cloudiness removed centrifugally.[110]

Reduction of silicomolybdic acid gives molybdenum blue [111] suitable for reading around 700 mμ. Ferrous and stannous ions, cysteine, sulfites, and thiosulfates interfere. Silicotungstic acid [112] and phosphomolybdic acid [113] react similarly but are preferably read at 650 mμ. The same blue is obtained with arsenotungstate and arsenotungstomolybdate reagents.[114]

The corresponding blue from reduction of 5 per cent ammonium molybdate and 0.3 per cent antimony trichloride is also used. Phenylhydrazine and sodium hydrosulfite give the reaction. The development of

---

[107] John V. Scudi and Herman D. Ratish, *Ind. Eng. Chem., Anal. Ed.* **10**, 420-3 (1938).

[108] Ruth Adele Koenig, T. L. Schiefelbusch, and C. R. Johnson, *Ind. Eng. Chem., Anal. Ed.* **15**, 181-2 (1943); Cf. E. Schulek and I. Floderer,*Angew. Chem.* **52**, 615-16 (1939).

[109] Grace Medes, *Biochem. J.* **29**, 2251-5 (1935); A. Langon and A. D. Marenzi, *Anales farm. bioquim.* (Buenos Aires) **6**, 70-8 (1935); Kamenosuke Shinohara, *J. Biol. Chem.* **112**, 671-721 (1936); Akiji Fujita and Tsutomu Elihara, *Biochem. Z.* **290**, 182-91 (1937); Akizi Huzita and Isamu Numata, *J. Agr. Chem. Soc. Japan* **16**, 265-70 (1940); Silvio Camozzo, *Ann. chim.* (Rome) **41**, 188-93 (1951).

[110] Grace Medes, *Biochem. Z.* **30**, 1753-5 (1936).

[111] M. L. Isaac, *Ind. Eng. Chem., Anal. Ed.* **14**, 948-9 (1942).

[112] Joachim Augusto de Almeido Baltazar, *J. farm.* (Lisbon) **7**, 72-6 (1948).

[113] B. Naganna and P. Ramachandra Roe, *Current Sci.* (India) **18**, 250 (1949); G. Manelli, *Mikrochemie ver. Mikrochim. Acta* **35**, 29-33 (1950).

[114] Eugenio E. Vonesch and Alfredo L. Remezzano, *Anales farm. bioquim.* (Buenos Aires) **11**, 70-81 (1940); Eugenio E. Vonesch, *Ibid.* **14**, 48-53 (1943).

a blue color between ascorbic acid and sodium tungstate on neutralization is used for estimation of 0.003 mg. of the vitamin against an artificial standard.

The violet color produced by monomolybdophosphotungstic acid with vitamin C is specific for the dienol group, $-(HO)C:C(OH)-$.[115] Sulfhydryl groups such as in cysteine do not react. Urea interferes as well as some reducing agents not apt to be present in biological material such as hydroquinone and quinhydrone.

Ascorbic acid reacts with peri-naphthindranetrione hydrate to give a reddish color of dihydroxy-peri-naphthindone.[116] The color is suitable for reading at 475 mμ. Excess reagent does not interfere at that wave length. There is no color developed with glucose, fructose, alanine, leucine, isoleucine, phenylalanine, lactic acid, acetoacetic acid, pyruvic acid, urea, uric acid, acetone, or dehydroascorbic acid.

Reaction of uranyl nitrate gives an immediate pink to red color.[117] Slight acidity or moderate alkalinity does not affect the intensity. Dehydroascorbic acid and reducing agents do not react. After oxidation with iodine, ascorbic acid is developed with p-sulfophenylhydrazine.[118] The precision is ±2 per cent and applicable down to 0.1 mg. per liter. Dehydroascorbic acid and diketogulonic acid also react.

Boiling an acid extract of plant or animal tissue treated with sorbant carbon converts the oxidized ascorbic acid to furfural.[119] As a selection from the available methods for furfural, that with diphenylamine is convenient. Also, after oxidation of ascorbic acid to dehydroascorbic acid by activated carbon, the osazone of diketo-l-gulonic acid can be precipitated with 2,4-dinitrophenylhydrazine and separated.[120] After reduction with stannous chloride, the dehydroascorbic acid is liberated without interfering substances and readily oxidized to furfural. As an alterna-

115 Nikolai Bezssonoff, *Biochem. J.* 17, 420-1 (1921); Nikolai Bezssonoff, *Klin. Wochschr.* 14, 1364-5 (1935); Nikolai Bezssonoff and E. Stoerr, *Z. Vitaminforsch.* 5, 193-221 (1936); Nikolai Bezssonoff and W. Woloszyn, *Compt. rend. soc .biol.* 124, 353-5 (1937); F. Cislaghi, *Boll. ist. serioterap. Milano* 1935, 800; A. Verda, *Pharm. Acta Helv.* 10, 185-94 (1935).

116 Radwan Moubasher, *J. Biol. Chem.* 176, 529-34 (1948); M. S. El Ridi, Radwan Moubasher, and Z. Hassam, *Science* 112, 751-2 (1950).

117 M. Z. Barakat, N. Badran, and S. K. Shehab, *J. Pharm. Pharmacol.* 4, 46-51 (1951).

118 J. Baraud, *Bull. soc. chim. France* 1951, 837-43.

119 Joseph H. Roe, *Science* 80, 561 (1934); *J. Biol. Chem.* 116, 609-19 (1936).

120 Joseph H. Roe and James M. Hall, *Ibid.* 128, 329-37 (1939).

tive, treatment of this osazone with 85 per cent sulfuric acid[121] or acetic acid [122] gives a reddish product suitable for reading at 500-550 mμ. There is no difference between the reactions of d-glucoascorbic, d-arabo-ascorbic, and 2,3-diketo-l-gluconic acids and the usual l-ascorbic acid.[123] Development with 2,4-dinitrophenylhydrazine appears under diketo-l-gulonic acid (page 370).

Carbon dioxide inactivation of hemoglobin in blood before deproteinization prevents oxidation of ascorbic acid to dehydroascorbic acid [124] by oxyhemoglobin. The dehydroascorbic acid is reduced to ascorbic acid by hydrogen sulfide above pH 6.[125] If dehydroascorbic acid is to be differentiated from ascorbic acid manipulation must be under nitrogen.[126]

Ascorbic acid is used as reducing agent to convert potassium ferricyanide to the ferrocyanide which is then estimated as Prussian blue.[127] Absorption in the ultraviolet at 265 mμ is also used for estimation in the absence of interference.[128]

Samples—*Blood.* Place a drop of 5 per cent potassium cyanide and a drop of 20 per cent potassium oxalate in a test tube and add 4-5 ml. of venous blood. Shake immediately and centrifuge. Pipet off 2 ml. of plasma into a test tube. Add 2 ml. of water and 4 ml. of 5 per cent metaphosphoric acid solution. Shake gently and filter. Use an aliquot of the clear filtrate for development by 2,6-dichlorophenolindophenol.

Urine. The determination of ascorbic acid in urine with 2,6-dichlorophenolindophenol is difficult because of the yellow color and the rapid fading of the dye. Add 10 ml. of 4 per cent metaphosphoric acid solution to 20 ml. of urine and centrifuge or filter if not clear. This buffers to pH 2.5-2.7. Dilute an aliquot of the buffered urine with metaphos-

---

[121] Joseph H. Roe and Carl A. Kuether, *Science* **95**, 77 (1942); *J. Biol. Chem.* **147**, 399-407 (1943); Akiji Fujita and Junga Teruuchi, *Vitamins* (Japan) **4**, 53-5 (1951).

[122] René A. Bolomey and A. R. Kemmerer, *J. Biol. Chem.* **165**, 377-8 (1946).

[123] J. R. Penney and S. S. Zilva, *Biochem. J.* **39**, 392-7 (1945).

[124] Carl A. Kuether and Joseph H. Roe, *Proc. Soc. Exptl. Biol. Med.* **47**, 487-9 (1941).

[125] Akizi Kuzita and Tutoma Elihara, *Biochem. Z.* **300**, 136-42 (1939).

[126] Melvin Hochberg, Daniel Melnick, and Bernard L. Oser, *Ind. Eng. Chem., Anal. Ed.* **15**, 182-8 (1943).

[127] Donato Greco and Roberto Argenziano, *Boll. soc. ital. biol. sper* **19**, 173-5 (1944).

[128] André Chevallier and Yvonne Choron, *Compt. rend. soc. biol.* **124**, 453-5, 743-4 (1937).

phoric acid solution to the proper concentration instead of the 1:400 hydrochloric acid called for in the procedure. If urine is to be collected for 24 hours before this determination, add to each container as preservative 75 ml. of 1:6 sulfuric acid and 5 ml. of 1.45 per cent 8-hydroxyquinoline solution in ethanol. Interfering substances are removed with barium acetate when sulfuric acid has not been added.[129]

Liver, kidney, and brain tissue.[130] Do not wash the samples after removal from the body because this removes the ascorbic acid. Weigh each slice of tissue immediately after cutting and consider the dry weight as 20 per cent of the wet weight. In the case of kidney, cut away the outer cortex containing about 20 per cent less vitamin before taking slices. Grind the tissue with twice its weight of isotonic phosphate solution and centrifuge. Determine the ascorbic acid content in an aliquot of the clear liquid by development with 2,6-dichlorophenolindophenol.

Citrus and other fruit juices. Use directly or with appropriate dilution for development with 2,6-dichlorophenolindophenol.

Tomato juice. Use a filtered sample for development with 2,6-dichlorophenolindophenol.

Fresh, frozen, or dehydrated berries and vegetables. For leafy vegetables, raspberries, strawberries, asparagus, and others high in ascorbic acid use a 25-gram sample. For material with a lower ascorbic acid content such as stored potatoes, yams, peaches, plums, apricots, etc., use a 50-gram sample. For dehydrated fruits or vegetables, use 5 or 10 grams of sample and soak 0.5 hour before disintegrating. Blend frozen foods without preliminary thawing.

Disintegrate the sample with 350 ml. of 1 per cent metaphosphoric acid solution in a blender for 5 minutes at high speed. Filter through a coarse, fluted paper. If the extract is starchy, use a Büchner funnel or centrifuge. Develop the color with 2,6-dichlorophenolindophenol.

Procedure—*With 2,6-dichlorophenolindophenol. Protein absent.* As reagent dissolve 40 mg. of 2,6-dichlorophenolindophenol in hot water, filter, and cool. Dilute to 100 ml. and store at 3-5°. For use dilute to such an extent that 5 ml. mixed with 2 ml. of the buffer described below and 5 ml. of the same acid used in extracting the samples will give a transmittance approximating 30 per cent when extracted with xylene free from oxidizing substances.

[129] Myron A. Elliott, Alfred L. Sklar, and S. F. Acree, *J. Research Natl. Bur. Standards* **26**, 117-28 (1941).

[130] C. V. Smythe and C. G. King, *J. Biol. Chem.* **142**, 529-41 (1942).

To a 1-10 ml. sample add 2 ml. of a buffer containing 250 grams of sodium acetate trihydrate and 500 ml. of glacial acetic acid per liter and mix. Immediately add 5 ml. of the prepared dye solution. Mix briefly and after 15 seconds add 15 ml. of xylene and shake for 15 seconds. To clarify let stand, centrifuge, or filter through cotton. Read at 520 mμ. For Beer's law to hold the transmittance must be between 35 and 90 per cent.

Protein present. Dilute a sample containing 0.02-0.06 mg. of ascorbic acid to 15 ml. with 1:400 hydrochloric acid. Add 1 ml. of a clear saturated solution of rosin in kerosene. A correction based on predetermination must be later applied for the dilution of the xylene with kerosene. Continue as for protein absent, starting at ". . . add 2 ml. of a buffer containing. . . ."

By methylene blue. To sample solution containing 0.002-0.02 mg. of ascorbic acid, add 0.2 ml. of 0.01 per cent methylene blue solution. Add a buffer for pH 4.2 (Vol. I, page 178), and dilute to 10 ml. Read at 600 mμ. Then expose to a strong light for 20 seconds, or until no more fading appears. Read again at once, as the reaction is reversible, and compare the reduction with a calibration curve.

By diazotized sulfanilamide. As reagent combine 5 ml. of 0.005 per cent sulfanilamide solution, 1 ml. of 0.05 per cent sodium nitrite solution, and 1 ml. of 20 per cent sulfosalicylic acid solution. After 3 minutes add 1 ml. of 1 per cent urea solution.

Adjust the sample extract to contain 10 per cent of acetic acid. To 10 ml. containing 0.1-0.4 mg. of ascorbic acid add the reagent. After 5 minutes add 7.4 ml. of 0.2 per cent solution of 1-dimethylnaphthylamine in ethanol. Mix and read after about 30 minutes against a reagent blank.

By ferrodipyridyl solution. As reagent dissolve 1.76 grams of ferrous ammonium sulfate hexahydrate in water and add 10 ml. of 1 per cent sulfur dioxide solution. Dilute to about 800 ml., add 2.5 grams of 2,2'-bipyridine, and stir to dissolve. To complete the reaction, let stand overnight and dilute to a liter. The reagent at this stage is a clear red. Heat 200 ml. to 80° and titrate to a yellow color with a filtered solution containing 28 ml. of concentrated sulfuric acid and 40 grams of commercial ceric sulfate per liter. Usually about 11 ml. are required. Back titrate with 1 per cent sulfur dioxide to a faint pink. Adjust the pH to 3.6 with 7-9 per cent ammonia solution prepared by absorption of the gas—commercial aqua ammonia contains undesirable reducing agents. Excess at any time may precipitate ferric hydroxide. Dilute to 400 ml. and let any precipitate settle. Maintain a faint pink by addition of sulfur dioxide as necessary.

Adjust the pH of a sample solution containing about 0.1 mg. of ascorbic acid with 1:1 ammonium hydroxide to match the color of Congo red in a buffer for pH 3.6. Add 25 ml. of a buffer containing 6 ml. of glacial acetic acid and 1 gram of sodium acetate trihydrate per 100 ml., adjusted to pH 3.6. Add 5 ml. of reagent and heat to 70-80° for 25 minutes. Cool and dilute to 25 ml. Alternatively let stand for 48 hours before dilution. Read at 510 mμ against a blank of reagent and buffer.

With phospho-18-tungstic acid. Mix 1-5 ml. of sample containing 0.5-2.5 mg. of ascorbic acid and 1 ml. of 3 per cent formaldehyde solution. Add 6.5 ml. of sodium acetate-acetic acid buffer for pH 5.0 prepared by mixing 100 ml. of 27 per cent sodium acetate trihydrate solution with 30 ml. of 12 per cent acetic acid.

Transfer 2 ml. of fresh standard solution containing 17.6 mg. of ascorbic acid per ml. to one 25-ml. flask. To two others add prepared samples. Add 20 per cent sodium carbonate solution to the third flask until distinctly alkaline. Let this stand for one hour to destroy the ascorbic acid in the third flask. To each add 0.2 ml. of 20 per cent sodium sulfite solution. Mix, let stand for 2 minutes, and add 0.2 ml. of 20 per cent lithium sulfate solution. Add 2 ml. of the phospho-18-tungstate reagent (page 437) to each and mix. Let stand for 4 minutes and dilute each to 25 ml. with 2 per cent sodium sulfite solution. Read each at 620 mμ. The first flask of standard compared with the second gives the color due to background color and interferences plus ascorbic acid. The first flask compared with the third gives the value for the background color and interference alone. The value for ascorbic acid is obtained by difference.

With silicomolybdic acid. As reagent dissolve 2 grams of ammonium molybdate in about 50 ml. of water around 55°, add 10 ml. of fresh 1 per cent solution of sodium metasilicate nonahydrate, then 5 ml. of glacial acetic acid, and dilute to 100 ml. Let stand overnight before use. To a volume of extract containing up to 1 mg. of ascorbic acid diluted to about 25 ml. add 5 ml. of reagent and dilute to 50 ml. Read after 15 minutes at 700 mμ against a reagent blank.

With peri-naphthindanetrione hydrate. To a sample containing 0.2-2 mg. of ascorbic acid in ethanol add 1 ml. of 0.2 per cent solution of peri-naphthindanetrione hydrate in ethanol. The color develops to its full intensity in 10 minutes at room temperature and is stable for 24 hours. Read at 475 mμ against a reagent blank.

By uranyl nitrate. Mix 5 ml. of sample containing 0.5-10 mg. of ascorbic acid with 3 ml. of 30 per cent uranyl nitrate. After 3 minutes read at 530 mμ against a reagent blank.

By iodine and p-sulfophenylhydrazine. Titrate a sample containing up to 10 mg. of ascorbic acid with iodine. Add 50 ml. of 0.8 per cent boric acid solution. Adjust the pH to 7.4 and dilute to 200 ml. with water. Let stand for 2 hours to destroy dioxytartaric acid. To 10 ml. of the solution add 2 ml. of 0.5 per cent *p*-sulfophenylhydrazine. Adjust this to pH 7.4 with 1:120 hydrochloric acid. To another 10 ml. add the reagent and the determined amount of hydrochloric acid. Heat in boiling water for 75 minutes and cool. Dilute to 20 ml. with water and read at 436 mμ.

DEHYDRO-*l*-ASCORBIC ACID

Methods of conversion to furfural and determination as such are discussed under ascorbic acid (page 364). Also it is determinable as diketo-*l*-gulonic acid by 2,4-dinitrophenylhydrazine (page 370).

DIKETO-*l*-GULONIC ACID

On treatment of a solution of diketo-*l*-gulonic acid with 2,4-dinitrophenylhydrazine, the corresponding hydrazone is precipitated. On treatment with 85 per cent sulfuric acid, a reddish color is produced which has its maximum absorption at 500-550 mμ and 350-380 mμ [131] and conforms to Beer's law. A corresponding reaction is given with *l*-ascorbic acid and dehydro-*l*-ascorbic acid, but the results are separable by suitable manipulation.

From data on melting points, nitrogen content, and chromatographic sorption, the 2,4-dinitrophenylhydrazine derivatives obtained from *l*-ascorbic acid, dehydro-*l*-ascorbic acid and diketo-*l*-gulonic acid appear to be the same compound. So it is believed that 2,4-dinitrophenylhydrazine couples only with diketo-*l*-gulonic acid and that *l*-ascorbic acid and dehydro-*l*-ascorbic acid react with the 2,4-dinitrophenylhydrazine only after they have been converted to diketo-*l*-gulonic acid.[132]

---

[131] Joseph H. Roe and Carl A. Kuether, *J. Biol. Chem.* **147**, 399-407 (1943); J. R. Penney and S. S. Zilva, *Biochem. J.* **37**, 39 (1943); M. B. Mills, C. M. Damron, and J. H. Roe, *Anal. Chem.* **21**, 707-9 (1949).

[132] J. R. Penney and S. S. Zilva, *Biochem. J.* **37**, 39 (1943); Joseph H. Roe, Mary B. Mills, M. Jane Oesterling, and Charlotte M. Damron, *J. Biol. Chem.* **174**, 201-8 (1948).

Sample—*Tissue.* Grind a sample of tissue under 1 volume of 10 per cent stannous chloride solution in 5 per cent metaphosphoric acid solution and add 19 volumes of the stannous chloride-metaphosphoric acid solution. Mix the slurry thoroughly but do not use any mechanical device which might increase the amount of oxygen in the slurry. Filter and dilute so that there is 1 part of tissue in 100 parts of extract and so that the sample contains 0.001-0.10 mg. per ml. of total ascorbic acid, dehydro-*l*-ascorbic acid and diketo-*l*-gulonic acid. Work rapidly to prevent changes in partition of the three compounds.

Procedure—*Diketo-l-gulonic acid.* Pass hydrogen sulfide through 100 ml. of stannous chloride-metaphosphoric acid extract for 15 minutes using a gas filter tube with a sintered glass filter. Shake 0.4 gram of powdered thiourea with 40 ml. of the saturated extract and filter. Bubble in carbon dioxide for 5 minutes. Remove three 4-ml. aliquots for analysis, one aliquot to act as a blank. To the other two tubes, add 1 ml. of 2 per cent solution of 2,4-dinitrophenylhydrazine in 1:3 sulfuric acid. Place in a water bath at 37° for 6 hours and cool in ice. Then add 5 ml. of 85 per cent sulfuric acid solution dropwise from a buret, taking about 1 minute for the addition. Finally add 1 ml. of 2,4-dinitrophenylhydrazine reagent to the blank, and after 30 minutes read the samples at 540 mμ against the reagent blank.

Dehydro-l-ascorbic acid. This technic gives a value which is the sum of dehydro-*l*-ascorbic acid and diketo-*l*-gulonic acid. Omit the preliminary treatment and using the original extract, follow the same procedure as for diketo-*l*-gulonic acid starting at "Remove three 4-ml. aliquots for analysis, one aliquot to act as a blank." Subtract the diketo-*l*-gulonic acid value from the value obtained here to get the dehydro-*l*-ascorbic acid content.

Ascorbic acid. The sum of the three acids is obtained on the hydrogen-sulfide treated portion. Follow the technic for diketo-*l*-gulonic acid through ". . . with a sintered glass filter." Through this solution, pass a current of air which has been previously drawn through a water trap. This will remove the hydrogen sulfide present in the solution. Add sufficient bromine to color the solution and remove excess bromine by bubbling air through. Add enough powdered thiourea to make a 1 per cent solution. Continue as for diketo-*l*-gulonic acid starting at "Remove three 4-ml. aliquots . . .". Finally subtract the values for the other two acids to give ascorbic acid by difference.

3,12-DIHYDROXYCHOLANIC ACID, DESOXYCHOLIC ACID

When desoxycholic acid is treated with benzaldehyde and 75 per cent sulfuric acid, a dark red color is obtained. If acetic acid is added, the color changes to green.[133] Conjugated desoxycholic acid gives a blue color with benzaldehyde. Anthropodesoxycholic and hyodesoxycholic acids give a violet color by this reaction, but it develops slower than the reaction with desoxycholic acid.[134] Accuracy in the determination is promoted by reading in a narrow wave band.

Desoxycholic acid, while it reacts with benzaldehyde,[135] vanillin [136] and furfural,[137] is better determined with salicylic aldehyde.[138]

Sample—*Bile.* Reflux 0.5-1 gram of bile sample with 50 ml. of 15 per cent sodium hydroxide solution. After 6 hours let cool and make acid to Congo red paper with concentrated hydrochloric acid. Cool and extract with 50 ml. of ether for 5 minutes. Extract the separated aqueous layers with 5 successive 50-ml. portions of ether. This separates the bile acids by extraction. Combine the ether extracts and wash with 50 ml. of water. Concentrate the ether extracts to 20 ml., take up in ethanol, and dilute to 200 ml. with ethanol. Dilute 20 ml. of this to 100 ml. with ethanol and mix.

Procedure—Evaporate 4-ml. aliquots of the sample dissolved in ethanol in tubes in boiling water and dry at 110° for 15 minutes. Cool to room temperature. Add 3 ml. of a fresh solution of 1 ml. of salicylic aldehyde in 35 ml. of 2:1 sulfuric acid and swirl. The reagent is not necessarily clear. Place in a 40° bath for 15 minutes and let cool for 5 minutes. Add 20 ml. of glacial acetic acid and shake for 10 minutes. The solution should be clear and of uniform color. Read at 680 mμ 5 minutes after adding the glacial acetic acid against a blank.

---

[133] Tosio Simada, *J. Biochem.* (Japan) **29**, 41-50 (1939).

[134] Tosio Simada, *Ibid.* **28**, 169-74 (1938).

[135] K. Kajiro and T. Simada, *Z. physiol. Chem.* **254**, 57-60 (1938); I. Scherrer, *Helv. Chim. Acta* **22**, 1329-40 (1939); T. Shimada, *J. Biochem.* (Japan) **28**, 149-60 (1938).

[136] Yoshimi Abe, *J. Biochem.* (Japan) **25**, 181-9 (1937); S. Kawaguti, *Ibid.* **28**, 445-9 (1938).

[137] R. Gregory and T. A. Pascoe, *J. Biol. Chem.* **83**, 35-42 (1929); J. G. Reinhold and D. W. Wilson, *Ibid.* **96**, 637-46 (1932); T. Shimada, *J. Biochem.* (Japan) **28**, 149-60 (1938).

[138] C. R. Szalkowski and M. J. Mader, *Anal. Chem.* **24**, 1602-4 (1952).

3,7,12-Trihydroxycholanic Acid, Cholic Acid

Cholic acid as determined includes conjugated cholates such as glycocholate and taurocholate. The reaction with furfural and sulfuric acid under hydrous conditions gives a red color,[139] but with sufficient reduction in moisture content the color is blue, more accurately determinable, and subject to fewer interferences.[140] The concentration of sulfuric acid used must be very carefully controlled. Acetic acid stabilizes the developed color over a period of at least one hour. No color is developed with glycine, taurine, cholesterol, lanolin, lecithin, or cephalin; or with oleic, desoxycholic, lithocholic, dehydrocholic, chenodesoxycholic, α- or β-hyodesoxycholic, or 3-hydroxy-6-ketoallocholanic acids. Tryptophan and indoles give the reaction.

To avoid loss of cholic acid by precipitation or by sorption on precipitated proteins, alcoholic precipitation and removal of pigments by barium hydroxide is desirable. That permits recovery at 92 ± 5 per cent, at 15-20 mg. per 100 ml., and 85 ± 6 per cent at 5-10 mg. per 100 ml. From bile, recovery is 96 ± 2.1 per cent.

Somewhat equivalent reactions to that with furfural are given by other aldehydes. Thus levulose and concentrated hydrochloric acid give a carmine color which is quite specific for cholic acid.[141] There is no interference by cholesterol, cephalin, glycine, lanolin, phospholipines, lecithin, taurin, and cholesteryl oleate. Proteins give the reaction. It is accurate to ±5 per cent.

Cholic acid develops a red color with vanillin as the aldehyde. In this case also the strong acid must be carefully controlled as to concentration.[142] At another controlled concentration, both cholic and desoxy-

---

[139] M. Pettenkofer, *Ann. Chem. Pharm.* **52**, 90-100 (1844); F. Mylius, *Z. physiol. Chem.* **11**, 492-6 (1887).

[140] Raymond Gregory and T. A. Pascoe, *J. Biol. Chem.* **83**, 35-42 (1929); John G. Reinhold and D. Wright Wilson, *Ibid.* **96**, 637-46 (1932); Bertil Josephson, *Biochem. J.* **29**, 1519-24 (1935); H. Doubilet, *J. Biol. Chem.* **114**, 289-308 (1936); L. H. Schmidt, *Am. J. Physiol.* **120**, 75-82 (1937); Toshio Simada, *J. Biochem.* (Japan) **28**, 149-60 (1938); Bertil Josephson and H. Larsson, *Acta med. Scand.* **99**, 140-6 (1939); J. Logan Irvin, Charles G. Johnston, and Joseph Kopala, *J. Biol Chem.* **153**, 439-57 (1944).

[141] L. D. Scott, *J. Lab. Clin. Med.* **19**, 523-39 (1934); Yoshitaka Ohyama, *J. Biochem.* (Japan) **27**, 351-62 (1938).

[142] M. A. Etcheverry, *Arch. argent, enfern. ap. digest, nutr.* **7**, No. 3 (1932); *Rev. sud-americana endocrinol. immunol. quimioterap.* **15**, 713-15 (1932); Etienne Chabrol, R. Charonnat, Jean Cottet, and P. Blonde, *Compt. rend. soc. biol.* **115**, 834-8 (1934); Yoshimi Abe, *J. Biochem.* (Japan) **25**, 181-91 (1937); *Ibid.* **26**, 323-6 (1937):

cholic acid react, giving a method for determining the latter by difference. This difference of both being developed occurs at 88 per cent phosphoric acid, whereas only cholic acid develops at 78 per cent phosphoric acid. Accuracy approaches ±1 per cent. The reaction is somewhat more sensitive than that with furfural. Indoxyl and proteins give the reaction. In 85 per cent phosphoric acid the maximum for desoxycholic acid is at 545 mμ; that for cholic acid and apocholic acid at 465 mμ.[143] If sulfuric acid is substituted for phosphoric acid, then lithocholic acid and cholic acid give maxima at the same wave length as desoxycholic acid.

Sucrose can also be used as the aldehyde.[144] Phosphoric acid and furfural give the reaction, with a difference in the color developed.[145] Other reactions applied to cholic acid determination include oxidation with benzoyl peroxide to give a green;[146] treatment in acetic anhydride with sulfuric acid to develop a brown;[147] and development of the iron of iron glycocholate with thiosalicylic[148] or thioglycolic acid.[149]

Samples—*Whole blood and plasma.*[150] For this separation it is necessary to maintain conditions as anhydrous as possible.

Prepare a saturated aqueous solution of barium hydroxide containing 1 per cent of barium acetate. Add 5 ml. of this solution to 50 ml. of absolute ethanol. While agitating, slowly add 10 ml. of heparinized whole blood or plasma. Oxalate or citrate are undesirable because they will precipitate the barium. Immerse in boiling water for 5 minutes.

L. Dubois, G. Barac, and A. Lambrechts, *Bull. soc. chim. biol.* 20, 1282-4 (1938); Synsaburo Kawaguti, *J. Biochem.* (Japan) 28, 445-9 (1938); R. Charonnat and P. Blonde, *Ann. pharm. franc.* 3, 115-19 (1945); R. Charonnat and G. Gauthier, *Compt. rend.* 223, 1009-11 (1946); Eiichiro Murakami, *J. Biochem.* (Japan) 39, 17-29 (1952).

[143] E. L. Pratt and H. B. Corbitt, *Anal. Chem.* 24, 1665-7 (1952).

[144] E. Navarini, *Acta. trab. V. congr. nac. med.* 7, 415 (1934); *Anales. asoc. quim. argentina* 24, 18B.

[145] E. E. Herzfeld and A. Haemmerli, *Schweiz. Med. Wochschr.* 54, 141-5 (1924); M. Chiray and L. Cuny, *J. pharm. chim.* 7, 97-106 (1928); M. Jenke, *Klin. Wochschr.* 18, 317-18 (1939).

[146] P. Szilard, *Biochem. Z.* 159, 325-6 (1925).

[147] W. A. Perlzweig and E. G. Barron, *Proc. Soc. Exptl. Biol. Med.* 24, 233-4 (1926-7).

[148] Paul Szilard, *Biochem. Z.* 173, 440-8 (1926).

[149] Stuart A. Peoples, *Proc. Soc. Exptl. Biol. Med.* 30, 1117-20 (1927).

[150] For a more detailed research method of treatment of blood extracts for greater specificity, see J. Logan Irvin, Charles G. Johnston, and Joseph Kopala, *J. Biol. Chem.* 153, 439-57 (1944).

Add absolute ethanol to make the volume of the solution to almost 250 ml. and allow to stand for 12 hours at room temperature to precipitate. Adjust the volume to 250 ml. and filter. Collect about 210 ml. of filtrate and do not wash the precipitate.

Add a drop of concentrated sulfuric acid to precipitate excess barium. Make the solution alkaline to litmus by the addition of 2 or 3 drops of 50 per cent sodium hydroxide solution. The dilution error so introduced is negligible. Allow to stand for several hours to permit complete precipitation of barium sulfate and sodium sulfate, and filter. If the filtrate becomes turbid due to precipitation of sodium sulfate, another filtration is not necessary. If the solution is colored at this stage, discard it and repeat the analysis.

Evaporate exactly 200 ml. of filtrate *in vacuo* at not over 35°. When reduced to about 10 ml., filter to remove any precipitate formed during evaporation. Wash the flask, funnel, and residue several times with small portions of absolute ethanol to make the transfer quantitative. The total volume of the solution should not exceed 20 ml. Evaporate to dryness *in vacuo* below 35°.

Dissolve the residue in 3 ml. of 0.4 per cent sodium hydroxide solution and add approximately 10 ml. of peroxide-free ethyl ether. Close the tube with a ground-glass stopper and shake for several minutes to extract fats and sterols. Separate the ether layer and extract with 3 more portions of ether. Extract the combined ether extracts with 1 ml. of water made alkaline with sodium hydroxide solution. Discard the ether and remove residual ether from the combined alkaline solutions by immersing the tube in hot water for a few minutes. Cool, neutralize to litmus, and adjust the volume to 5 ml. Use 1 ml. of this solution for color development by furfural or vanillin.

Bile. Precipitate the protein from 1 ml. of gall-bladder bile by addition of 3 ml. of ethanol. Filter and extract the residue with hot ethanol. Evaporate the combined filtrate to dryness *in vacuo*. Dissolve the residue in water and dilute to a concentration where 1 ml. can be expected to contain 0.02-0.3 mg. of cholic acid per ml. The bile pigments present at that concentration do not ordinarily interfere. If they do apply the alternative method. Develop by furfural or vanillin.

Alternatively, measure 1 ml. of bladder bile, 3 ml. of dog fistula bile, 10 ml. of human fistula bile, or 20 ml. of duodenal drainage fluid. Add 3 ml. of 11.2 per cent potassium hydroxide solution and mix. Add, dropwise, 3 ml. of a 40 per cent solution of crystallized zinc sulfate. Mix well, centrifuge, and decant. Wash the residue 3 times with hot water, mixing each time and centrifuging. Combine the decanted liquid and washings. Wash the precipitate with 20 ml. of cold ethanol and twice with 20-ml. portions of hot ethanol. Evaporate the alcoholic washings to dryness on a water bath. Dissolve the residue in 5 ml. of 15 per cent potassium carbonate solution, add to the aqueous washings, and dilute the colorless solution to 100 ml. Develop an aliquot by furfural or vanillin.

For development by levulose, either dilute 1 ml. of the sample to 100 ml. and treat as for urine or add 0.25 ml. of the sample to 30 ml. of absolute ethanol and treat as for gastric juice by direct extraction.

Urine. To 25 ml. of urine add 0.05 ml. of fresh blood or serum. This furnishes a necessary trace of protein to prevent adherence of the precipitate to the sides of the tube. Mix and add 2 ml. of concentrated hydrochloric acid. Mix and add 25 grams of solid ammonium sulfate. Shake to saturate the solution. Let stand for 10 minutes, shaking occasionally to precipitate bile acids and urinary pigments. Filter and use portions of the filtrate for transfer. Wash the tube and the precipitate on the filter with 50 ml. of a saturated aqueous solution of ammonium sulfate. Dry the paper in the funnel at 100° for one hour or at 37° for 12 hours. Extract the paper and residue by boiling with successive 10-ml. portions of absolute ethanol and decant.

Add 2 ml. of saturated barium hydroxide solution to precipitate the urinary pigments and boil gently in a water bath for three minutes. Cool and dilute to 50 ml. with absolute ethanol. Filter to remove turbidity. Transfer 45 ml. of the filtrate and evaporate to dryness on a boiling water bath. This is a prepared sample for development with levulose.

Gastric juice. Add 2 ml. of sample to 30 ml. of absolute ethanol and heat in boiling water for three minutes. Cool and dilute to 50 ml. with absolute ethanol. Filter and treat 45 ml. of filtrate with 3 ml. of saturated barium hydroxide solution. Boil gently in a water bath for 3 minutes, and cool. Dilute to 45 ml. and filter. Evaporate 40 ml. of filtrate to dryness in a water bath for development with levulose.

Duodenal fluid. Dilute 2 ml. to 25 ml. and treat as for urine for development with levulose. For development with vanillin, mix 2 ml. of sample with 0.5 ml. of 25 per cent neutral lead acetate solution. Dilute to 10 ml. with ethanol and filter.

Feces. Weigh 2-3 grams of wet feces into 30 ml. of absolute ethanol. Mix well and heat in boiling water for 3 minutes. Cool and dilute to 50 ml. with absolute ethanol. Let the sediment settle and decant the supernatant liquid through a filter. To 40 ml. of filtrate add 2 ml. of saturated barium hydroxide solution and heat in boiling water for 3 minutes. Cool and dilute to 40 ml. Filter and evaporate 35 ml. of the filtrate to dryness in boiling water. Fats and pigments still present will be precipitated by the hydrochloric acid used in development of color with levulose.

Liver. Grind a 5-gram sample of small slices with sand in a mortar and extract 4 times with 25-ml. portions of boiling absolute ethanol. Combine the extracts, filter, cool, and dilute to 100 ml. for development with furfural or vanillin.

Procedure—*With furfural.* Evaporate an aliquot of sample containing 0.02-0.3 mg. of cholic acid to dryness on the steam bath. Take up the residue in 1 ml. of water. Add 6 ml. of sulfuric acid, adjusted to 16 N with analytical accuracy, and 1 ml. of 1 per cent aqueous solution of freshly distilled furfural. Heat with a reagent blank for 13 minutes at 65° ± 0.1°. Chill in a cold bath and add 5 ml. of glacial acetic acid. Read at 620 mμ and 660 mμ. Unless results at the two wave lengths show an approximate check, there is reason to believe that extraneous substances are interfering. The values at 620 mμ are slightly more accurate. Correct when necessary by carrying through another sample to which furfural is not added.

With levulose. The sample containing 0.6-1 mg. of cholic acid for this technic has been evaporated to dryness. Add 1 ml. of 1 per cent levulose solution in saturated aqueous benzoic acid. Shake and add 9 ml. of concentrated hydrochloric acid. Mix, stopper, and place in a water bath at 40° for 20 minutes. Shake occasionally. This develops the maximum carmine color with a greenish-blue fluorescence. Cool and, if cloudy, filter through a dry paper. Read against a reagent blank within 1.5 hours. The use of 9 ml. of 85 per cent phosphoric acid in place of the hydrochloric acid gives a more stable color on heating for 1 hour but it is not as sensitive. The color with phosphoric acid reaches 3 to 4 times the intensity in 24 hours.

With vanillin. Cholic acid. Evaporate an aliquot of sample containing 0.02-0.2 mg. of bile acids to dryness. Add 0.2 ml. of a 2 per cent solution of vanillin in ethanol and again evaporate to dryness. Add 5 ml. of 79 per cent phosphoric acid (sp. gr. 1.625) and heat for 10 minutes at 50°. Read the color developed against a reagent blank.

Desoxycholic and cholic acid. Repeat the foregoing technic but use 89 per cent phosphoric acid (sp. gr. 1.750). The result includes both acids. Subtract the value for cholic acid to give that for desoxycholic acid.

Alternative. Dissolve the solid sample in acetone and dilute to 1 mg. per ml. Heat 1-ml. portions of sample and a comparable standard containing 1 mg. of desoxycholic acid per ml. in tubes at 70-80° until the acetone is all evaporated. Heat for 10 minutes at 100° to dry thoroughly. Stopper and cool in an ice bath. After 5 minutes add 10 ml. of filtered reagent containing 1 mg. per ml. of 85 per cent phosphoric acid, filtered through a coarse Selas crucible. This reagent keeps for a few days in the dark. Stopper immediately after each addition. Place the sample and standard with a blank, in a bath at 70° ± 1°. Mix at the end of 5 minutes and 15 minutes. After 20 minutes remove to room temperature for 30 minutes. Read the standard and sample at 545 and 465 mμ against the blank.

$$\text{Desoxycholic acid in mg.} = U_{545} - 0.314\, U_{465}/S_{545} - 0.314\, S_{465}$$

$$\text{Cholic acid in mg.} = U_{465} \cdot S_{545} - U_{545} \cdot S_{465}/S_{545} - 0.314\, S_{465}$$

$$U = \text{absorption by unknown}$$

$$S = \text{absorption by sample}$$

3,7,12-TRIKETOCHOLANIC ACID, DEHYDROCHOLIC ACID

Dehydrocholic acid gives a readable color with 3,5-dinitrobenzoic acid in aqueous trimethylbenzyl ammonium hydroxide. Androsterone, progesterone, and testosterone give the same reaction. It is given in detail under androsterone (Vol. IV).

GLYCOCHOLIC ACID

Reactions of cholic acid also determine glycocholic acid at the same time, (page 372) that is, both conjugated and unconjugated forms of 3,7,12-trihydroxycholanic acid.

TAUROCHOLIC ACID

Reactions of cholic acid also determine taurocholic acid at the same time (page 372), that is, both conjugated and unconjugated forms of 3,7,12-trihydroxycholanic acid.

CHAPTER 15

POLYBASIC ALIPHATIC ACIDS [1]

THIS chapter includes the polybasic aliphatic acids where the acid function predominates. That implies correctly that the molecular weight will usually be relatively small and that a complex molecule carrying two or more carboxyls somewhere in the structure will appear elsewhere. Some carry other substituents such as hydroxyls, the amino group, etc. There is no class reaction. An exception is aminosuccinic acid included with other α-amino acids. In a number of cases insoluble salts with metals, such as copper and cerium, are separated and determined indirectly as the combined metallic ion.

OXALIC ACID

Magnesium [2] or zinc [3] in acid solution reduces oxalic acid to glycolic acid. Many inorganic ions do not interfere. Each can be determined in the presence of the other by difference, the oxalate being precipitated from an aliquot. The reaction of glycolic acid with 2,7-dihydroxy-naphthalene is then used to give a red color.[4]

The low solubility of cerium oxalate is also a basis for a method of estimation of oxalic acid. The cerium oxalate is separated, well washed, and oxidized with hydrogen peroxide to a brown color.[5] The impossibility of separating cerium oxalate and cerium phosphate prevents the application of this method to biological samples. Accuracy to 5-10 per cent is obtained.

The reaction of oxalic acid with sodium metavanadate is used for colorimetric estimation in the absence of interfering substances.[6] The stability of the color is increased by also adding hydrogen peroxide. Mineral acids must be absent as they produce a pervanadic acid of

---

[1] See Chapter 1 for details of organization, condensation, etc.

[2] Edwin Eegriwe, *Z. anal. chem.* **89**, 121-5 (1932).

[3] Marcel Paget and Raoul Berger, *Compt. rend.* **207**, 800-2 (1938); Carlos M. Vega, *Rev. farm.* **93**, 22-5 (1951).

[4] Vincent P. Calkins, *Ind. Eng. Chem., Anal. Ed.* **15**, 762-3 (1943); Rubens Salomé Pereira, *Mikrochemie ver. Mikrochim. Acta* **36/37**, 398-406 (1951).

[5] Shoichi Izumi, *Japan J. Med. Sci., II Biochem.* **2**, 195-204 (1933).

[6] C. Ainsworth Mitchell, *Analyst* **58**, 279 (1933).

similar color. The reaction with oxalic acid is about 4 times as intense as with tartaric acid. The method is applicable in the presence of moderate amounts of formic, acetic, citric malic, or succinic acids. The limit of sensitivity is about 0.03 per cent.

The use of oxalate to decrease the color formed by the complex of ferric ion and 7-iodo-8-hydroxyquinoline-5-sulfonic acid, the reagent known as ferron, is accurate within 5 per cent.[7]

Procedure—*As glycolic acid.* Prepare the sample by adjustment to 2 N with sulfuric acid. If neutral mix with an equal volume of 1:9 sulfuric acid. To 0.2 ml. of sample containing not over 0.04 mg. of oxalic acid, in a tube chilled in cold water, add 5 mg. of magnesium. Let stand for an hour. Then determine as glycolic acid (page 328), starting at "Add 2 ml. of a 0.01 per cent solution of 2,7-dihydroxy-naphthalene . . ." Read the color against a calibration curve prepared with oxalic acid.

Alternatively shake 1.2 ml. of sample and 1 ml. of 1:11 hydrochloric acid with pure zinc foil. To 2 ml. of this solution add 2 drops of 1 per cent aqueous phenylhydrazine hydrochloride. Heat in boiling water for 2 minutes and cool with ice. Add 1.8 ml. of concentrated hydrochloric acid and 2 drops of 30 per cent hydrogen peroxide. Read against a reagent blank after 10 minutes in the dark. If necessary for greater sensitivity, extract the color body with a lesser volume of chloroform before reading.

As ceric ion. To 10 ml. of clear sample solution add sufficient 4 per cent sodium hydroxide solution or 1:10 hydrochloric acid to give a violet color with Congo red paper. Add a few drops of 0.25 per cent cerium chloride solution and mix. Let stand for 30-60 minutes and centrifuge for 10 minutes. Carefully remove the supernatant liquid. Wash the precipitate with water and centrifuge again. Repeat the washing twice more and finally let the tube drain on a clean filter paper.

Dissolve the precipitate in 1 ml. of 1:35 sulfuric acid. Add 1 ml. of 30 per cent potassium carbonate solution containing 1 per cent of gum arabic. Mix well and add 2 drops of 30 per cent hydrogen peroxide to develop the brown color. Mix and read against a reagent blank.

With sodium metavanadate. Mix 5 ml. of sample with 5 ml. of a 1 per cent solution of sodium metavanadate, add 3 ml. of 3 per cent hydrogen peroxide, and read against a reagent blank.

---

[7] S. Burrows, *Analyst* **75**, 80-4 (1950).

Oxalacetic Acid

By rapid manipulation of an acid-deproteinized filtrate to avoid decarboxylation, an alkaline solution of oxalacetic acid reacted with hydrazine gives a yellowish red with sodium nitrite.[8] Some loss occurs in deproteinizing. The reaction is first to form a hydrazone which rapidly forms pyrazalone-3-carboxylic acid. Nitrite in alkaline solution converts that to 4-nitrosopyrazolone-3-carboxylate.[9] As an alternative convert to pyruvic acid and determine with salicylic aldehyde.[10]

Sample—*Blood and serum.* To 0.5 ml. of 1:9 sulfuric acid add sufficient sample to give 0.5-8 mg. of oxalacetic acid and dilute nearly to volume. Place in an 80° water bath for 2 hours and cool. Make up to volume and add 1 ml. of 10 per cent sodium tungstate solution. When coagulation is complete, filter, and determine as pyruvic acid with salicylic acid (page 357).

Procedure—*As 4-nitrosopyrazoline-3-carboxylate.* Prepare a reagent containing 3.5 gram of hydrazine dihydrochloride, 30 ml. of water, and 100 ml. of ethanol. Add 1.4 ml. of this reagent to 1 ml. of deproteinized filtrate containing not over 2 mg. of oxalacetic acid. Hold at 37° for 15 minutes, cool in ice water, add 0.1 ml. of saturated sodium nitrite solution, and shake. After 5 minutes, mix with 1 ml. of 60 per cent potassium hydroxide solution and centrifuge. Read the upper layer at 430 mμ against a reagent blank.

α-Ketoglutaric Acid

α-Ketoglutaric acid is determined by 2,4-dinitrophenylhydrazine, in the presence of pyruvic acid, by a method previously described (page 000).

Fumaric Acid

The familiar sensitive copper diethyldithiocarbamate reaction is used for estimation of fumaric acid. The copper fumarate is precipitated by cupric ion and pyridine, well washed, and the color developed.[11] Anisic,

[8] F. B. Straub, Z. physiol. Chem. **244**, 117-27 (1936).

[9] V. B. Bruckner, Ibid. **244**, 127-30 (1936).

[10] Sven Darling, Acta Physiol. Scand. **7**, 306-12 (1944).

[11] Lawrence M. Marshall, James M. Orten, and Arthur H. Smith, Arch. Biochem. **24**, 110-13 (1949).

anthranilic, benzoic, salicylic, and acetylsalicylic acids interfere unless removed by chromatographing.[12] Glycine, and maleic, succinic, malic, acetic, uric, *l*-aspartic, and *l*-glutamic acids do not form insoluble copper salts under the test conditions.

Procedure—*As copper diethyldithiocarbamate.* Prepare a reagent of 8 ml. of pyridine in 20 ml. of 20 per cent copper sulfate solution. Mix 1 ml. of protein-free filtrate with a drop of the reagent, shake, and when turbidity begins to appear after 1-2 minutes add 0.5 ml. of the reagent. Refrigerate for an hour and centrifuge for 15 minutes. Discard the liquid and drain on filter paper for about 4 minutes. Wash the precipitate with 2 ml. of 0.5 per cent aqueous pyridine solution at 5°, centrifuge, and drain. Dissolve the precipitate in 1 ml. of 20 per cent citric acid solution and use 9 ml. more to transfer to a 50-ml. flask. Rinse in further with 10 ml. of water and add 10 ml. of ammonium hydroxide solution made by dilution of 44 ml. of the concentrated solution to 100 ml. Dilute to volume and use a 5-ml. aliquot.

Add 1 ml. of a 2 per cent gum ghatti solution, strained through cloth after it is 24 hours old. Add 5 ml. of 0.2 per cent diethyldithiocarbamate solution, mix, and read after 4 minutes at 460 mμ against a reagent blank.

SUCCINIC ACID

Succinic acid is determined fluorimetrically after heating with resorcinol and sulfuric acid.[13] Malic acid may be present since this does not interfere appreciably in acid solution. For solutions containing 0.001-0.015 mg. of succinic acid per 100 ml. in the presence of 0.005-0.015 mg. of malic acid per 100 ml., the accuracy is about ±12 per cent. When applied to extracts of apple tissue, the method is accurate to about ±5 per cent.

Sample—*Plant tissue.* Acidify fresh plant tissue or the pressed juice to pH 1 with concentrated sulfuric acid and extract continuously with ether for 24 hours or more. If the organic acids present are difficultly soluble in ether,[14] this may be extended to 56 hours. After extraction is completed, mix the ether extract with 25 ml. of water and distil off the ether. Use the aqueous extract or an aliquot as sample.

[12] Lawrence M. Marshall, James M. Orten, and Arthur H. Smith, *J. Biol. Chem.* **179**, 1127-39 (1949).
[13] C. Guinn Barr, *Plant Physiology* **23**, 443-54 (1948).
[14] T. L. Isaacs and T. C. Broyer, *Plant Physiology* **17**, 296-301 (1942).

Procedure—Evaporate to dryness a sample solution containing about 0.2 mg. of succinic acid. Cool and moisten the residue with 0.04 ml. of concentrated sulfuric acid. Stir and add 10 mg. of freshly sublimed resorcinol with stirring. Heat at 126°-130° for 1 hour. Cool, dissolve in about 2 ml. of water, dilute to 200 ml., and mix. To a 10-ml. aliquot add 2-4 drops of 1:1 sulfuric acid to bring the pH to 1.5-2, and dilute to 100 ml. Read against a reagent blank in a fluorometer adjusted so that the galvanometer reads 100 per cent for the fluorescence of a slightly acid solution containing 0.05 mg. of fluorescein per 100 ml., using Corning filters No. 3389 and 5551 for transmission of the exciting light, and No. 3486 and 3397 as the secondary filter combination. The wave length of the activating light is 420-520 mμ.

Methylene Succinic Acid, Itaconic Acid

A method has been developed for terminal olefinic groups and applied to determination of undecylenic acid (page 309). Preliminary results indicate that it is applicable to itaconic acid by use of a calibration curve over a limited range. Samples below 3 mg. give abnormally high values so that this is not linear. Internal rearrangement in the molecule occurs.

p-Aminophenylsuccinic Acid

Determine as described for m-aminohippuric acid (page 330).

Tartaric Acid

When a colorless solution of sodium meta-vanadate is acidified with acetic acid, a clear yellow to orange color develops. Tartrate modifies this to red, in a depth proportional to the amount of tartrate present.[15] The color reaches a maximum in 10 minutes and then fading occurs. During this a greenish color appears which is not proportional to the tartarate content. Since the sample and standard, alter at the same rate, if of nearly the same concentration, comparisons may be carried out for some time after the color is developed.

None of the other fruit acids give the reaction, nor do the other substances present in body fluids or excretions, in the concentrations encountered. The reaction occurs with racemic and d-tartaric acid. Meso-tartaric acid does not react. Lactates in high concentration give a red color which fades rapidly, but are not present in sufficient concentrations

---

[15] Frank P. Underhill, F. I. Peterman, and A. G. Krause, *J. Pharmacol.* **43**, 351-8 (1931).

to interfere in practice. Oxalates alone give a rose color with meta-vanadates, but the color from a mixture of oxalate and tartarate corresponds to the tartarate only.

In the range of 1-2 mg. of tartaric acid in the sample, differences of 0.1 mg. are readily distinguished. The volume of sample is varied to make the usual determination fall within this range with an accuracy of around 5 per cent.

Tartaric acid, ferrous sulfate, and hydrogen peroxide give a lavender color in alkaline solution. With the other factors standardized, it is suitable for estimation of the tartaric acid content of a solution.[16] Citric, succinic, malic, and oxalic acids do not give the reaction. Aluminum does not interfere, but calcium and phosphates do. The color developed from *d*-tartaric acid, *l*-tartaric acid, *l*-ammonium tartrate, and meso-tartaric acid is equivalent. The color developed with racemic acid is, surprisingly, only half that of the above, or half that of a mixture of *d*- and *l*-acids. Accuracy in adjusting the pH of the sample and in measuring the amounts of reagents added is essential.

Samples—*Human and dog urine.* Boil a 100-ml sample vigorously with 4 grams of activated carbon for 4 minutes. Filter and wash the residue with hot water until the filtrate is nearly 200 ml. Add 0.4 per cent sodium hydroxide solution or 1:100 hydrochloric acid to neutrality, and dilute to 200 ml. Use 10 ml. or 20 ml. as sample. Decolorization is essential to avoid a large positive error. Dilute concentrated urines before decolorizing. Acidity or alkalinity does not affect the ease of decolorizing. Toluene present as preservative does not interfere. Develop by sodium meta-vanadate.

Rabbit urine. Measure out a suitable aliquot of the sample and dilute to 100 ml. Treat as described for human and dog urine but use 5 grams of carbon and boil for 2 minutes only. If too low in tartaric acid evaporate 100 ml. of sample to 25 ml. and filter. Evaporation of the decolorized sample causes some loss by oxidation.

Guinea pig and rat urine. Dilute the 24-hour sample to 100 ml. Add 2 grams of activated carbon, boil for 2 minutes, and filter. Wash the filter and evaporate the filtrate and washings to 25 ml. Use this as sample but in the procedure use 2 ml. of glacial acetic acid and 7 ml. of sodium meta-vanadate solution as reagents with sample and standard.

[16] H. J. H. Fenton, *Chem. News* **33**, 190 (1876); *Ibid.* **43**, 110-11 (1881); Arthur K. Anderson, Alvin H. Rouse, and Theodore V. Letonoff, *Ind. Eng. Chem., Anal. Ed.* **5**, 19-20 (1933).

Feces. Weigh 2 grams of fresh feces into a wide-mouthed bottle calibrated at 100 ml. Add 75 ml. of boiling 2 per cent trichloroacetic acid and mix vigorously. Dilute to 100 ml. with 2 per cent trichloroacetic acid and stir until cool. Add about 5 grams of activated carbon and stir for 30 minutes. Filter through a dry paper into a dry flask, refiltering if necessary. Neutralize aliquots of this solution with 10 per cent sodium hydroxide solution and develop with sodium meta-vanadate.

Blood. Pipet 5 ml. of oxalated blood into a 50-ml. volumetric flask. Add 25 ml. of 5 per cent trichloroacetic acid solution and shake. Dilute to volume with water and mix. Let stand for 15 minutes and filter. The filtrate should be clear and colorless. Neutralize aliquots of the filtrate with 10 per cent sodium hydroxide solution.

Grape juice. Mix 5 ml. of grape juice, 25 ml. of water, and 2 grams of activated carbon. Boil for 4 minutes and filter. Wash the residue on the paper with hot water. Carefully neutralize the filtrate and washings with 4 per cent sodium hydroxide solution and dilute to 100 ml. Use 2.5 ml. or 5 ml. for development of color with sodium meta-vanadate.

Baking powder. Disperse 1 gram of sample in water and dilute to 250 ml. Filter a portion of the solution and use 1 or 2 ml. for development with sodium meta-vanadate.

For development with ferrous sulfate and hydrogen peroxide, add water drop by drop to a 2-gram sample until no more carbon dioxide is evolved. Add 45 ml. of water and stir until the tartarates are all in solution. Filter, wash the residue on the paper with three 15-ml. portions of water and dilute nearly to 100 ml. The pH of this solution should be 5.7-6.7. If outside of that range, adjust the pH value and dilute to volume.

Procedure—*With sodium meta-vanadate.* To suitable volumes of clear colorless sample solution and standards, add 1 ml. of glacial acetic acid and 4 ml. of colorless 5 per cent sodium meta-vanadate solution. Dilute to 50 ml. and mix. Compare after 10 minutes. If foam is produced in mixing, add a drop of ether to break it.

With ferrous sulfate and hydrogen peroxide. To 10 ml. of sample solution and 10 ml. of a suitable standard add exactly 0.2 ml. of a 1 per cent solution of ferrous sulfate heptahydrate and 0.2 ml. of a 3 per cent hydrogen peroxide solution. Mix the resulting yellow solutions thoroughly. Let stand until they have become brownish and place in an ice bath. The brown color will disappear, leaving the solutions lavender. At once add 5 ml. of 4 per cent sodium hydroxide solution to each, stopper, and invert twice to mix. Place in the ice bath again for 10 minutes. Remove and invert twice to mix. Compare the sample with the standard by balancing.

MALIC ACID

The reaction product of malic acid and β-naphthol fluoresces and is suitable for estimation of either in the presence of excess of the other.[17] The reaction is carried out in sulfuric acid between 90 and 95 per cent and is quite significant as to the color intensity developed. Longer heating does not affect the color developed. Greater excess of β-naphthol than that used produces excessive fluorescence. The color is stable for at least 2 weeks in a refrigerator. The fluorescence conforms to Beer's law. Both l-malic acid and d,l-malic acid react. Citric and succinic acid do not interfere. Tartaric acid up to a ratio of 1:1 to the malic acid causes an error of less than 5 per cent. Precipitation as lead malate provides separation from sugars. The error can be expected to be well under 3 per cent.

Orcinol, in the presence of concentrated sulfuric acid, reacts with malic acid to give the highly fluorescent homoumbelliferone, 7-hydroxy-5-methyl-coumarin.[18] Interference by carbohydrates, which give an amber color, is avoided by addition of a small amount of 2,4-dinitrophenyl-hydrazine. There is no interference by 0.1 mg. of glucose, fructose, pyruvate, lactate, oxalacetate, isocitrate, aconitate, citrate, a-ketoglutarate, succinate, fumarate, β-hydroxybutyrate, acetoacetate, butyrate, tartarate, malonate, urate, glycerophosphate, aspartate, glutamate, alanine, and creatine in the sample. Maleic acid gives variable intensities of fluorescence. Fructose-1,6-diphosphate and glucose-6-phosphate are quantitatively precipitated by ethanol and interfere by forming a yellow color and blue fluorescence with the reagent. They are removed by preliminary hydrolysis for 10 minutes at 100° with 0.8 per cent sodium hydroxide solution. Glycogen also interferes and is removed by acid hydrolysis. The malic acid is precipitated as the calcium salt by ethanol. The fluorescence developed is substantially linear in the range specified. The intensity is about 9 times that of quinine sulfate in 1:360 sulfuric acid. Less than 6 per cent or more than 12 per cent of water in the sulfuric acid markedly reduces the fluorescence.

[17] Elmer Leininger and Sidney Katz, *Anal. Chem.* **21**, 1375-7 (1949).

[18] J. P. Hummel, *J. Biol. Chem.* **180**, 1225-8 (1949); Lawrence M. Marshall, Felix Friedberg, and William A. DaCosta, *J. Biol. Chem.* **188**, 97-100 (1951).

Another fluorimetric method uses the reaction product of malic acid and resorcinol,[19] in aqueous solution at about pH 10.5. In the presence of 0.002-0.015 mg. of succinic acid per 100 ml., the average error was about ±7 per cent for 0.005-0.015 mg. of malic acid per 100 ml. In plant extracts succinic acid will have practically no effect on malic acid determinations. Citric acid gives the same reaction. When present, the total amount of both malic and citric acids is determined, and the malic-acid content calculated by difference after citric acid has been determined by another method. Results for malic acid agreed with those by the oxidation method to ±6 per cent.

When malic acid is treated with potassium permanganate in the presence of bromide, it is converted to a bromine derivative volatile with steam. When subsequently that compound is heated with dinitrophenylhydrazine in acid solution, an extremely insoluble condensation product results in a definite ratio to the amount of malic acid. Dissolved in pyridine and made alkaline, this gives a blue suitable for colorimetric estimation.[20]

A precipitate is obtained with 0.2 mg. of malic acid under conditions where 25 mg. of acetic, lactic, fumaric, succinic, pyruvic, tartaric, maleic, glycolic, or glyoxylic acids give no precipitate. The oxidation converts citric acid into pentabromoacetone, which gives a precipitate under the test conditions. Its interference is prevented by extraction with petroleum ether from the oxidation mixture. When carbohydrates or some amino acids are oxidized by potassium permanganate, the resulting products form precipitates with dinitrophenylhydrazine. Malic and citric acids do not so react unless potassium bromide is present. Therefore, the interfering substances can be corrected for by two oxidations, one with bromide present, one without it. A control oxidation without bromide is necessary with blood, urine, and muscle extracts. The method is accurate to ±3 per cent.

Samples—*Apple juice.* Adjust a sample containing 20-75 mg. of malic acid to 15 ml. by evaporation or addition of water. Dilute to 100-ml. with ethanol. Mix and filter on a fluted filter with protection from evaporation. To 75 ml. of filtrate add 10 mg. of citric acid and 1 ml. of a lead acetate solution containing 30 grams of normal lead acetate and 0.2 ml. of glacial acetic acid per 100 ml. Mix and centrifuge.

---

[19] C. G. Barr, *Plant Physiol.* **23**, 443-54 (1948).

[20] George W. Pucher, Hubert B. Vickery, and Alfred J. Wakeman, *Ind. Eng. Chem., Anal. Ed.* **6**, 140-3, 288-91 (1934).

If the addition of a drop of the lead acetate reagent produces more precipitate, add another ml. and centrifuge again. Discard the solution and wash the precipitate with 75 ml. of 80 per cent ethanol in several portions. Suspend the precipitate in 50 ml. of water and saturate with hydrogen sulfide. Dilute volumetrically to 100 ml. and filter. Use aliquots of this filtrate for development with β-naphthol.

Plant tissue. For this purpose prepare a special extraction ether within 24 hours before use. Wash ether three times with water to remove alcohol. Shake each liter with 200 ml. of 10 per cent sodium hydroxide solution and 5 to 10 grams of powdered potassium permanganate. Redistil.

Dry the sample and grind to a fine powder. Mix 2 grams of sample with 1:9 sulfuric acid to give a mixture having a pH of 1. The amount of acid required must be determined by a preliminary experiment. Add 3.5 grams of asbestos and transfer the mixture to an extraction thimble. Extract in a rubber extractor with 150 ml. of the special ether at about 40 cycles an hour for 17 to 20 hours. When completed add 25 ml. of carbon dioxide-free water and 2 ml. of 20 per cent sodium hydroxide solution. Shake to extract the acids into the aqueous phase and warm to distil dissolved ether. Dilute to 100-ml with carbon dioxide-free water. The extract as prepared at this point is also suitable for estimation of citric acid as pentabromoacetone.

Dilute 5 ml. of the aqueous extract to about 20 ml. and add 3 ml. of 1:1 sulfuric acid. Cool and add 1 ml. of saturated bromine-water. Let stand for 5 minutes and filter with gentle suction. Wash the precipitate with small amounts of water until the filtrate totals 35 ml. Add 2 ml. of 1.2 per cent potassium bromide solution. Cool to about 20° and add 5 ml. of 15 per cent potassium permanganate solution. Let this mixture stand for 10 minutes, stirring occasionally.

As peroxide, dissolve 4 grams of sodium peroxide in 50 ml. of water, cool, and add 1:2 sulfuric acid until faintly acid to Congo red indicator. Normally this requires 7 to 8 ml. The solution keeps about 1 week. Chill to 5-10° and add the hydrogen peroxide reagent drop by drop until the solution is decolorized.

If citric acid is suspected in the sample, transfer the solution to a clean separatory funnel. Rinse it in with several portions of petroleum ether boiling at 35-50°, totaling 25 ml., added to the separatory funnel. Shake and draw off the aqueous layer. Again extract the aqueous layer with 20 ml. of the petroleum ether and separate the aqueous layer. The petroleum ether contains the pentabromoacetone from the citric acid. Wash it with 3 ml. of water and dilute the aqueous layer and aqueous extract to 100 ml. for development with dinitrophenylhydrazine. Another technic is given under succinic acid (page 381).

Tissue. Mince 0.5-5 grams of sample in acetone containing 3 ml. of 1:2.6 sulfuric acid per liter. Dilute to 100 ml. and let stand for 2 hours. Filter and take aliquots equivalent to 0.5-2 grams of tissue. Dry in air and add 1 ml. of 1:70 sulfuric acid.

Dilute siliceous sodium silicate to 20 ± 2 per cent solids. Titrate rapidly with concentrated hydrochloric acid until methyl orange turns pink. Add about 5 per cent by volume excess and let stand for 3 hours. Filter on a Büchner funnel and resuspend in about 2 volumes of concentrated hydrochloric acid. After standing overnight, filter by suction and wash successively with 5 parts of 1:1 hydrochloric acid, 10 parts of distilled water, 10 parts of absolute ethanol, and 5 parts of dry ether. Dry in warm air and resuspend in 4 parts of concentrated hydrochloric acid. After standing overnight, filter by suction, wash with 5 parts of 1:1 hydrochloric acid, 50 parts of water, and then 10 parts of absolute ethanol containing 1 per cent of 1:2 sulfuric acid. Wash with 5 parts of dry ether, air dry, and finally dry over phosphorous pentoxide for 24 hours before use. Brush through a 90-mesh sieve before use.

Add 1 gram of silica gel and mix. Add 15 ml. of 1:1 butanol-chloroform. Filter through a cotton plug in a 10-ml. tube with a constricted bottom and wash with 35 ml. of the solvent mixture. Evaporate the solvent and dissolve in 0.75 ml. of 3:7 tertiary amyl alcohol-chloroform and dilute to exactly 1 ml. Prepare a silica gel column of 1 gram in a 6 mm. tube with chloroform. This gives about a 20-cm. column. Dilute half the sample to 50 ml. with the 3:7 tertiary amyl alcohol-chloroform mixture. Pour on the column, discard the first 15 ml., and collect the next 30 ml. Evaporate 10 ml. aliquots for development with orcinol and sulfuric acid.

Procedure—*With β-naphthol.* Evaporate a sample containing 0.001-0.03 mg. of malic acid to dryness at 105°. Add 1 ml. of a reagent containing 12 mg. of β-naphthol per 100 ml. of 91.5-92.5 per cent sulfuric acid. The latter is prepared from 100 ml. of concentrated acid and 7 ml. of water. Completely wet the dried sample and heat at 90-95° for 30 minutes. Cool and dissolve in water. Dilute to 100 ml. at $25° \pm 1.5°$ and read the fluorescence from 365 mμ light. Use secondary yellow and blue filters and read against a reagent blank.

With orcinol. Samples deproteinized with trichloroacetic acid at about 1:6 are suitable. Dilute an aliquot containing 0.0001-0.001 mg. of malic acid to 1 ml. with 1:10 hydrochloric acid. Add, with shaking, 0.1 ml. of 0.1 per cent dinitrophenylhydrazine in 1:5 hydrochloric acid and 0.5 ml. of 10 per cent calcium chloride solution. After 30 minutes add 0.3 ml. of 1:2 ammonium hydroxide and 6 ml. of absolute ethanol. After 12 hours at room temperature, centrifuge and discard the supernatant liquid. Dry for 15 minutes at 105°.

Prepare the reagent by dissolving 80 mg. of orcinol in 100 ml. of 1:7 sulfuric acid. Dilute 8 ml. to 100 ml. with concentrated sulfuric acid. Add 3 ml. of this to the dried sample. Mix, heat for 10 minutes at 100°, and cool under the tap. Dilute to 10 ml. with concentrated sulfuric acid and read the blue fluorescence in a photofluorometer against a reagent blank.

With dinitrophenylhydrazine. Grind 5 grams of the solid reagent in a mortar with several successive portions of 1:4 hydrochloric acid. Boil for 1 to 2 minutes with vigorous stirring. Cool, dilute to 1 liter with the same acid, and filter. Filter again just before use.

Transfer a 25-ml. aliquot of the sample solution to a 300-ml. Kjeldahl flask. Add 25 ml. of water and a few quartz pebbles. Add 0.5 ml. of 15 per cent potassium permanganate solution to destroy any hydrogen peroxide present. Decolorize this with 2 ml. of 20 per cent sodium sulfite solution. Connect to a receiver by a tube bent as an air condenser. Use a 250-ml. wide-mouthed Erlenmeyer flask containing 10 ml. of freshly filtered dinitrophenylhydrazine reagent and 20 ml. of water as receiver. The end of the distillation tube must dip into this. Heat the Kjeldahl flask with a micro burner and distil until the volume remaining in the flask is about 10 ml. This should require 12 to 15 minutes. Remove the condenser and rinse with water. Let the distillate cool.

Transfer the precipitate as completely as possible with water to a small Gooch crucible. Dry at 100-110°. Take up the last trace of precipitate in the receiver with 3 to 4 ml. of hot pyridine and transfer these washings to a 25-ml. volumetric flask. Fit the crucible to a funnel in a side-arm test tube calibrated at 20 ml. Add boiling pyridine in small portions to the crucible, stir, and apply suction. Repeat this 3 or 4 times, but not using more than 20 ml. of solvent. Transfer the pyridine solution quantitatively to the 25-ml. flask. Let cool and dilute to volume with pyridine. Mix and filter if necessary to remove asbestos.

Transfer a 2-ml. or 5-ml. aliquot of the pyridine solution to a 100-ml. volumetric flask. Add 50 ml. of water and 5 ml. of 20 per cent sodium hydroxide solution. Dilute to volume, mix, and compare with a standard similarly treated at the same time. The blue color develops immediately and is stable for at least two hours.

With resorcinol. Proceed as for succinic acid (page 382) to ". . . dilute to 200 ml. and mix." To a 10-ml. aliquot add 1 ml. of 0.4 per cent sodium hydroxide solution and dilute to 100 ml. Read at once in a fluorometer adjusted to read 100 per cent for the fluorescence of a solution containing 0.3 mg. of quinine sulfate per 100 ml., using Corning filter No. 5970 as the primary filter, and Nos. 4308 and 3389 as the secondary filters. The wave length of the activating light is 320-420 mμ.

CITRIC ACID

Oxidation of citric acid with potassium permanganate in the presence of bromine gives quantitative conversion to pentabromoacetone. In sodium sulfide solution this gives a yellow color.[21] Instead of quantitative extraction in the technic, a single extraction with equilbrium of the partition coefficient is an alternative.[22] The final solution contains a stabilizing agent which may be the pyridine used in early work, glycerol,[23] or dioxane.

There is no interference by 100-200 mg. of acetone, glycogen, acid hematin, creatine, creatinine, cholesterol, amytal, urea, taurine, toluene, acid-digested casein, allantoin, uric acid, hippuric acid, lactic acid, malic acid, oxalic acid, ascorbic acid, tartaric acid, succinic acid, pyruvic acid, gluconic acid, isocitric acid, *cis*aconitic acid, *trans*aconitic acid, oxalacetic acid, maleic acid, fumaric acid, malonic acid, glutaric acid, α-ketoglutaric acid, or sucrose. The presence of 100 mg. of β-hydroxybutyric acid or ethyl acetone dicarboxylate gives colors equivalent to 0.1-0.5 and 0.9 mg. of citric acid respectively. Some interference occurs with α- and γ-fatty acids, triacetic acid, itaconic acid, oxalcitramalic acid and glyoxylcitra-

[21] George W. Pucher, H. B. Vickery, and C. S. Leavenworth, *Ind. Eng. Chem., Anal. Ed.* 6, 190-3 (1934); George W. Pucher, Caroline C. Sherman, and Hubert B. Vickery, *J. Biol. Chem.* 113, 235-45 (1936); L. B. Mendel and H. B. Vickery, *Carnegie Inst. Washington Yearbook* 34, 298-306 (1935); G. W. Pucher, A. J. Wakeman, and H. B. Vickery, *Ind. Eng. Chem., Anal. Ed.* 13, 244-6 (1941); H. J. Puinton and C. Schuck, *J. Biol. Chem.* 148, 237-43 (1943); George W. Pucher, *Ibid.* 153, 133-7 (1944); Samuel Natelson, Julius K. Lugovoy, and Joseph B. Pincus, *Ibid.* 170, 597-606 (1947); Cf. H. Weil-Malherbe and A. D. Bone, *Biochem. J.* 45, 377-81 (1949).

[22] David Perlman, Henry A. Lardy, and Marvin J. Johnson, *Ind. Eng. Chem., Anal. Ed.* 16, 515-16 (1944).

[23] Bertil Josephson and Ulla Forssberg, *J. Lab. Clin. Med.* 27, 267-8 (1941).

malic acids.[24] The color conforms to Beer's law. Accuracy is of the order of ±5 per cent.

The color developed from pentabromoacetone and various other sulfur compounds in alkaline solution is of greater intensity. Examples are thiourea, acetylthiourea, ethylthiourea, allylthiourea, *sym*-diethylthiourea, or *sym*-dimethylthiourea. Thiourea is used.[25] The colors fade slowly at room temperature.

In another version the pentabromoacetone is extracted with heptane and treated with alcoholic sodium iodide, acetic acid being added to facilitate substitution of bromine by iodine. This substitution liberates a yellow iodine complex which is read.[26] During oxidation, manganese sulfate is added to hasten the formation of manganese dioxide. For the determination of citric acid in the presence of glucose, substitution of permanganate by manganese dioxide suspension is feasible.[27] An alternative is to produce the pentabromoacetone and use it to give a violet color from molybdate and phosphate.[28]

The tedium of converting citric acid to pentabromoacetone is avoided by treating a deproteinized sample with warm acetic anhydride and pyridine under anhydrous conditions. Citric acid gives a carmine-red color, aconitic acid yields violet-red, and tartaric acid gives emerald-green.[29] Because dried residues of deprotenized serum give erratic color development, the necessity of an anhydrous sample is avoided by dehydrating with an excess of acetic anhydride instead of evaporating to dryness. Then both citric and aconitic acids give yellow upon addition of pyridine. In that form it is applicable to direct determination of citric acid or aconitic acid.

The intensity and stability of the color developed vary with temperature. At 60° rapid development and excellent stability are attained. There is no important interference by glutathione, glucose, purified plasma, protein, and urea, or by succinic, ascorbic, oxalic, and malonic acids. Less than 1 per cent as much color is given by fumaric, pyruvic,

---

[24] F. L. Breusch and Rasim Tulus, *Biochem. et Biophys. Acta* 1, 77-82 (1947).

[25] Samuel Natelson, Joseph B. Pincus, and Julius K. Lugovoy, *J. Biol. Chem.* 175, 745-50 (1948).

[26] Hertha H. Taussky and Ephraim Shorr, *Ibid.* 169, 103-18 (1947).

[27] Aaron S. Goldberg and Alice R. Bernheim, *Ibid.* 156, 33-46 (1944).

[28] Aaron S. Goldberg and Alice R. Bernheim, *Ibid.* 156, 33-46 (1944); Gladys H. Wolcott and Paul D. Boyer, *Ibid.* 172, 729-36 (1948).

[29] Otto Fürth and Heinz Herrmann, *Biochem. Z.* 280, 448-57 (1935); H. Grönvall, *Acta Ophth.* suppl. 14, 276 pp. (1937); Murray Saffran and Orville F. Denstedt, *J. Biol. Chem.* 175, 849-55 (1948).

and l-malic acids as by citric acid. The color from tartaric, itaconic, and isocitric acids is substantial. Recoveries from blood plasma or serum are consistently only 75-80 per cent, but from others accuracy to ±5 per cent is usual. Treatment of a protein-free sample with acetic anhydride and pyridine gives an applicable color reaction.[30]

If citric acid is refluxed with sodium carbonate and thionyl chloride under anhydrous conditions, aconityl chloride is formed. Anhydrous ammonia converts aconityl chloride to aconitamide at room temperature. On treating aconitamide with 76 per cent sulfuric acid at 165°, citrazinic acid is formed. Addition of ammonium hydroxide yields ammonium citrazinate which exhibits an intense blue fluorescence in ultraviolet light.[31] Increase in temperature of the solution at the time of reading causes a decrease in fluorescence. Hygroscopic compounds and compounds which decompose interfere by supplying water of hydration after the drying period. Tartaric and malic acids interfere by decomposing and discoloring the solution but less than 0.1 mg. is unimportant. Amounts of the order of 0.5 mg. of these acids decrease fluorescence. Sulfate ion in very small amounts interferes. Sodium carbonate in the original mixture obviates tar formation and increases the ultimate fluorescence ten-fold. The final fluorescence varies 10 per cent per 5°. Accuracy to about ±2 per cent is to be expected.

Samples—*Fermentation media.* Remove the mycelium and dilute to a degree depending on the citric acid content. Develop as pentabromoacetone.

Plant tissue. Prepare as described for malic acid (page 387).

Blood. Add 1.5 ml. of plasma or serum to 11 ml. of 10 per cent trichloroacetic acid solution. Stir and allow to stand at room temperature for about 10 minutes. Centrifuge for 10 minutes and use a portion of the clear layer for development with acetic anhydride and pyridine.

Plasma with acetone normal. Heparin will interfere. Stir 1.5 ml. with 11 ml. of 10 per cent trichloroacetic acid and centrifuge after 10 minutes. Filter the clear layer to use 10 ml. as sample.

Plasma with acetone abnormal. Prepare double the amount of filtrate for normal acetone content. Evaporate 20 ml. to 6 ml. on a hot plate. Filter, dilute to 20 ml., and use 10 ml. as sample. This does not destroy β-hydroxybutyric acid.

---

[30] Otto Fürth and Heinz Herrmann, *Biochem. Z.* **280**, 448-57 (1935); Murray Saffran and Orville F. Denstedt, *J. Biol. Chem.* **175**, 849-55 (1948).

[31] Elmer Leininger and Sidney Katz, *Anal. Chem.* **21**, 810-13 (1949).

Serum. To precipitate proteins, rapidly blow 1 ml. of 10 per cent trichloroacetic acid into 0.2 ml. of serum. Shake and allow to stand for 10 minutes. Centrifuge and pour off the supernatant layer as completely as possible. To a 1-ml. aliquot add 0.04 ml. of 1:1 sulfuric acid and evaporate to 0.4 ml. in an oil bath at 100-120°. Develop as pentabromoacetone with thiourea.

Urine. Normal. Glucose, albumin, and acetone are assumed to be absent. Mix 9.5 ml. of 9.3 per cent trichloroacetic acid with 0.5 ml. of urine and centrifuge after 10 minutes. Use the entire upper layer as sample.

Urine containing glucose. Mix 1 ml. with 90 ml. of 10 per cent tricholoroacetic acid solution and dilute to 100 ml. Use a 10-ml. aliquot as sample.

Urine containing albumin. Dilute 1 ml. to 20 ml. with 10 per cent trichloroacetic acid solution, filter, and use 10 ml. as sample.

Urine containing acetone bodies. Add 1 ml. of 3:1 sulfuric acid to 25 ml. of urine. Evaporate to about 10 ml., cool, and dilute to 25 ml. Dilute 0.5 ml. to 10 ml. with 9.3 per cent trichloroacetic acid solution and use the clear portion as sample.

Feces. Grind the sample with an adequate amount of water acidified to Congo red with sulfuric acid. Dilute to a known volume and mix an aliquot with an equal volume of 10 per cent trichloroacetic acid solution. Filter and use an aliquot of this.

Animal tissue. Grind 10 grams or more with sand in a mortar adding 10 per cent trichloroacetic acid solution as necessary. Filter and wash the residue on the filter with 10 per cent trichloroacetic acid solution. Use the entire filtrate as sample.

Citrus juices. Adjust the volume of a sample containing 40-75 mg. of citric acid, to 15 ml. Add 1.5 ml. of 1:10 hydrochloric acid and heat to 50°. Cool and dilute to 100 ml. with ethanol. Mix well and filter through a fluted filter paper covered with a watch glass. To 50 ml. add excess of 30 per cent lead acetate solution in 0.2 per cent acetic acid and mix thoroughly. Centrifuge. Test the supernatant liquid with lead acetate to assure complete precipitation of the citrate. Decant and discard the supernatant liquid. Wash the precipitate with small portions of 80 per cent ethanol, using 50 ml. in all. Suspend the precipitate in 50 ml. of water. Saturate the solution with hydrogen sulfide and dilute to 100 ml. with water. Mix well and filter through fluted paper. Dilute the filtrate 1:4 for estimation fluorimetrically as citrazinic acid.

Procedure—*As pentabromoacetone with sodium sulfide.* To an aliquot containing reducing substance and less than 25 mg. of citric acid, add 2 ml. of 1:1 sulfuric acid. Dilute to 20 ml. and boil for about 10 minutes. Cool and add about 5 ml. of saturated bromine water. Centrifuge off any precipitate after 10 minutes. Decant the supernatant liquid and adjust to a known volume to take an aliquot. In the absence of reducing substances omit this paragraph.

To an aliquot of sample free from reducing substances but containing 0.2-1.8 mg. of citric acid and a control standard, and a blank, add 0.3 ml. of 1:1 sulfuric acid, 0.2 ml. of 1.2 per cent potassium bromide solution, and 1 ml. of 4.75 per cent potassium permanganate solution. Dilute to 5 ml. and, after 5 minutes at room temperature, chill in an ice bath. Add 3 per cent hydrogen peroxide until the permanganate is decolorized, maintaining the temperature below 5°. It is easiest to overrun slightly with the peroxide and back titrate exactly with 0.3 per cent potassium permanganate. Excess peroxide will give low results. Saturated ferrous sulfate or hydrazine sulfate may replace hydrogen peroxide.[32] Adjust to exactly 10 ml. and add 13 ml. of acid-washed petroleum ether. Stopper and shake vigorously. If necessary centrifuge to break any emulsion formed.

Prepare a tube containing 5 ml. of a 1:1 mixture of dioxane and water, or pyridine and water. Add 5 ml. of a 4 per cent solution of sodium sulfide nonahydrate. Add 10 ml. of the petroleum ether solution of pentabromoacetone within 15 minutes after extraction. Stopper, shake vigorously, and centrifuge to break any emulsion. The yellow color is fully developed in 5 minutes and lasts for hours. Read at 450 mμ against a reagent blank. Correct too dark a color by development of a smaller aliquot of the petroleum ether solution.

As pentabromoacetone with thiourea. To the prepared sample, add 0.04 ml. of saturated bromine water to which 11.9 per cent of potassium bromide has been added and allow to stand for 10 minutes. Add 0.1 ml. of 5 per cent potassium permanganate solution, shake and allow to stand for 10 minutes. Cool to approximately 10° and decolorize excess permanganate with 0.03-0.06 ml. of cold 6 per cent hydrogen peroxide. Add 1.3 ml. of purified petroleum ether and stopper using a minimum of silicone grease. Extract the pentabromoacetone by shaking mechanically for 10 minutes. Centrifuge and take a 1-ml. aliquot for color development.

---

[32] Hertha H. Taussky, *J. Biol. Chem.* **181**, 195-8 (1949).

Dissolve 2 grams of borax in 100 ml. of 4 per cent thiourea solution and add 3.5 ml. of this to the test solution. Stopper, shake mechanically for 5 minutes, and then centrifuge. Aspirate off the petroleum ether layer and read at 445 mμ against a reagent blank.

As pentabromoacetone converted to the iodide. Prepare an aqueous bromide-bromate solution containing 42.88 grams of sodium bromide and 12.58 grams of sodium bromate in 250 ml.

To a 10-ml. aliquot of protein-free sample add 5 ml. of 3:1 sulfuric acid and 1 ml. of the bromide-bromate solution under a hood. Allow to stand for about 30 minutes until it reaches room temperature. Add 0.2 ml. of a solution containing 33 grams of hydrazine sulfate and 10 grams of sodium hydroxide per 100 ml. Shake until the free bromine is reduced. Add 6 ml. of heptane, stopper, and shake mechanically for about 3 minutes. Allow the layers to separate. Cool a 15-ml. aliquot of the aqueous phase in a water bath at 18°. The citric acid is now ready for oxidation to pentabromoacetone.

Add 1 ml. of 40 per cent manganese sulfate solution, 1 ml. of the bromide-bromate mixture, and 2 ml. of 5 per cent potassium permanganate solution to the sample. Shake well and let stand in a water bath at 18° for 30 minutes. Add the hydrazine solution dropwise until the brown color disappears, indicating that excess bromine and manganese dioxide have been reduced.

Add 11 ml. of heptane, stopper tightly, and shake mechanically for 6 minutes. Discard the aqueous phase. Then add about 10 ml. of water, shake for 20 seconds, and discard the wash water. Repeat until the color of the wash water matches that of water containing a few drops of indicator. Allow to stand for 30 minutes to insure complete drainage of wash water. This extract is stable for at least 2 weeks in the ice box.

To 10 ml. of the heptane extract or an appropriate aliquot diluted to 10 ml., add 3 ml. of 10 per cent alcoholic sodium iodide solution. Shake and keep stoppered in the dark for about 70 minutes. Read at 420 mμ.

As pentabromoacetone with molybdate-phosphate. Prepare a bromide-bromate solution by mixing 90 ml. of 12 per cent potassium bromide solution and 10 ml. of 15 per cent sodium bromate solution. Add 1 ml. of this solution to a sample containing 0.005-0.05 mg. of citric acid. Follow this with 2 ml. of 8 per cent potassium permanganate solution, added at a very slow rate with vigorous and continuous agitation. Allow to stand for 10 minutes, then add slowly 6.5 per cent hydrazine solution until the reaction mixture is decolorized. Wash the sides of the funnel with 1-2 ml. of distilled water. Add 15 ml. of petroleum ether and shake mechanically for 5 minutes. Release the pressure, allow the layers to separate, and discard the aqueous phase. Wash the petroleum ether solution and the funnel 4 times with water which has been redistilled in an all-glass still. Transfer the extract to a separatory funnel and rinse the first funnel with three small portions of petroleum ether. Then wash the extract twice with water. Allow sufficient time for complete separation after the last wash and remove the aqueous layer completely.

To the separatory funnel add exactly 15 ml. of a solution composed of 100 ml. of 6.3 per cent sodium sulfite solution and 200 ml. of 27.2 per cent sodium dihydrogen phosphate monohydrate solution. Shake vigorously for 5 minutes. Allow the layers to separate and take a 10-ml. aliquot of the solution. Heat in boiling water for 5 minutes and add 2 ml. of a solution containing 35 grams of chlorine and 44 grams of sodium hydroxide per liter. Mix well and continue heating for 4 minutes from the time that the hypochlorite was added. Add 1 ml. of 40 per cent sodium formate solution, remove from the bath, and shake carefully. Cool to room temperature. Add a drop of 10 per cent ammonium molybdate solution and follow with 5 ml. of 1:4 phosphoric acid. Mix and add 1 ml. of 5 per cent potassium iodide solution. Dilute to 25 ml., mix, and read at 400 mμ after 10 minutes.

By acetic anhydride and pyridine. Mix 1 ml. of deproteinized sample containing 0.015-0.4 mg. of citric acid and 5 per cent of trichloroacetic acid with 8 ml. of acetic anhydride. Stopper with rubber and place in a water bath at 60° ± 1° for 10 minutes. Add 1 ml. of pyridine, restopper, and place in the bath for 40 minutes, then transfer to an ice bath for 5 minutes. Read at 400 mμ or 420 mμ against a reagent blank.

Fluorometrically as citrazinic acid. The apparatus required is shown in Figure 27. Heat 1 ml. of sample solution containing 0.01-0.08 mg. of citric acid in flask A, of 25 ml. capacity, for 2 hours in a vacuum oven at 70° in order to obtain an anhydrous residue. Add approximately 15 mg. of anhydrous sodium carbonate and 2 ml. of thionyl chloride to the residue. Connect to tube B, 15 × 260 mm., and heat in an oil bath for 20 minutes at 95-100°. A plug of glass wool 160 mm. from the ground glass joint at A-B retains 130 mm. of dehydrite and a glass-wool plug. Remove both flask and tube from the oil bath and remove excess thionyl chloride through the tube and stopcock C-2. Swirl the tube to prevent spattering during this operation. Continue to evaporate the residue for 4 minutes after it appears dry and then allow air to flow into the flask by means of capillary C-3. Repeat this evacuation and flooding with dry air three times, using 1 minute periods of evacuation.

Place the flask and condenser tube in the ammonia chamber D and place the whole under a hood. Allow a current of ammonia to pass into the chamber slowly. Disengage the tube from the flask by placing block E over the tube, raising the whole assembly a few mm. and gently tap-

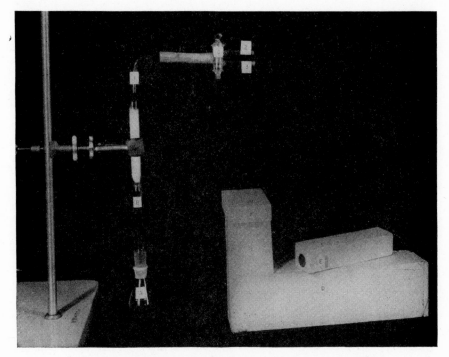

Fig. 27. Apparatus for conversion of citric acid to citrazinic acid
(*Courtesy E. Leinger and S. Katz*)

ping the block against the lip of the flask. Place the cover over the opening in the ammonia chamber and after 10 minutes remove the flask. Add about 2 ml. of carefully mixed 73:35 sulfuric acid to the flask and rotate it to permit thorough contact between the acid and the residue. Heat the flask for 6 ± 0.5 minutes in an oil bath at 162-8°. The solution should be colorless to straw-colored. Remove from the oil bath and dilute with 5 ml. of water. Transfer the solution quantitatively to a 100-ml. glass-stoppered flask with 25 ml. of water. Make the solution alkaline to litmus with 1:3 ammonium hydroxide, dilute to to 100 ml., and mix thoroughly. Adjust the temperature to $24° \pm 0.5°$ and determine the fluorescence. Use 365 mμ and, if obtained by filters, use a yellow filter for vitamin B$_1$ determination and Corning lantern blue 5543. This gives a range of 430-450 mμ for the determination. Adjust the fluorometer to 100 with 0.2 per cent sodium salicylate preserved with toluene, and to 0 with distilled water.

1,2,3-Propenetricarboxylic Acid, Aconitic Acid, Citridic Acid

At 0°, aconitic acid forms a yellow color with acetic anhydride and pyridine. Since citric acid does not react at 0°, the method is specific for aconitic acid.[33]

Oxidation of the ethylenic group of cis-aconitic acid with potassium permanganate in dilute metaphosphoric acid is determined by photometric reading of the decrease in permanganate color.[34] Citric acid is not oxidized. There is interference from allyl alcohol, itaconic acid, crotonic acid, maleic acid, ascorbic acid, oxalacetic acid, or fumaric acid. The presence of metaphosphoric acid prevents precipitation of manganese dioxide. There is no interference by α-ketoglutaric acid, malic acid, tartaric acid, pyruvic acid, isocitric acid, malonic acid, oxalic acid, fructose, and glucose.

Procedure—*By acetic acid and pyridine.* Prepare the samples in the same way as for citric acid (pages 392 and 393). Heat 1 ml. of sample containing 5 per cent of trichloroacetic acid for 10 minutes in a stoppered tube with 8 ml. of acetic anhydride at 60°, and cool in an ice bath for 5 minutes. Add 1 ml. of cold pyridine, mix by shaking gently, restopper, and place in the ice bath for 60 minutes. Read at 400 mμ or 420 mμ against a reagent blank.

By permanganate. To a cuvet add an aliquot of sample containing 0.1-0.4 mg. of aconitic acid, 0.1 ml. of 10 per cent metaphosphoric acid solution, no more than a few days old, or enough to reduce below pH 3. Dilute to 0.5 ml. with water. Add 1 ml. of 1:25 dilution of 0.316 per cent solution of potassium permanganate. Mix and, after 20-50 minutes, read at 530 mμ for comparison with a standard curve obtained by aging for the same period at the same temperature.

---

[33] Murray Saffran and Orville F. Denstedt, *J. Biol. Chem.* **175**, 849-55 (1948).
[34] Sherman R. Dickman, *Anal. Chem.* **24**, 1064-6 (1952).

ETHYLENEDIAMINE TETRAACETIC ACID

For determination of low concentrations of this chelating agent, nickel is used to displace other metals in the salt. Excess nickel is removed with dimethylglyoxime. Then by dissociating the nickel chelate in acid solution the bluish-red of nickel with potassium dithiooxalate is used as the measure of concentration of the test substance.[35] Calcium and iron do not interfere. Phosphates or copper do but are removed by appropriate modifications of the procedure.

Samples—*Phosphates and copper absent.* Dilute a sample solution containing 1-8 mg. of test substance to 100 ml. with water. Add 15 ml. of 1.33 per cent solution of nickel sulfate hexahydrate. Mix and after 10 minutes add 6 ml. of concentrated ammonium hydroxide. For precipitation of excess nickel add 15.5 ml. of 1.5 per cent dimethylglyoxime in absolute ethanol and mix. Filter after about 5 minutes.

Phosphates present. Adjust the sample solution containing 1-8 mg. of test substance to 98.5 ml. and pH 6.5. Add 15 ml. of 1.33 per cent solution of nickel sulfate hexahydrate. After 10 minutes add 1.5 ml. of 4.4 per cent aqueous calcium acetate, then add 5 ml. of concentrated ammonium hydroxide. Filter after 5 minutes. To 60 ml. of filtrate add 7.5 ml. of 1.5 per cent dimethylglyoxime in absolute ethanol. Filter after about 5 minutes.

Citrate present. Adjust the pH to 6.5 before dilution to 100 ml. Then proceed as for phosphates and copper absent.

Copper present. Dilute the sample solution containing 1-8 mg. of test substance to 88.3 ml., being sure it is neutral or faintly acid. Add 11.2 ml. of 0.5 per cent 5,7-dibromo-8-hydroxyquinoline in 2:3 hydrochloric acid. If precipitation of copper does not start within 5 minutes add 0.2 gram of sodium acetate to lower the acidity. Filter after 15 minutes. To 80 ml. of filtrate add 3.5 ml. of concentrated ammonium hydroxide to adjust the acidity to about pH 6.5. Add 12 ml. of 1.33 per cent solution of nickel sulfate hexahydrate. Mix and after 10 minutes, add 2.5 ml. of concentrated ammonium hydroxide. The pH should now be about 11. Add 12 ml. of 1.5 per cent dimethylglyoxime in absolute ethanol and stir. Filter after about 5 minutes.

Soap solutions. To 99.5 ml. of sample add 0.5 ml. of 4.4 per cent calcium acetate solution. Mix and filter after 5 minutes. To 50 ml. of

---

[35] Albert Darbey, *Anal. Chem.* **24**, 373-8 (1952).

filtrate add 7.5 ml. of 1.33 per cent solution of nickel sulfate hexahydrate and after 10 minutes 2.5 ml. of concentrated ammonium hydroxide. Add 7.5 ml. of 1.5 per cent dimethylglyoxime in absolute ethanol. Filter after 5 minutes.

Urine. To 100 ml. of urine add 15 ml. of 1.33 per cent solution of nickel sulfate hexahydrate. After 10 minutes add 5 ml. of concentrated ammonium hydroxide and 15.5 ml. of 1.5 per cent dimethylglyoxime in absolute ethanol. After 2 minutes stir in 3 grams of Nuchar. Filter after 5 minutes and if necessary further decolorize with 4 grams more of Nuchar.

Procedure—To 50 ml. of filtrate add 2.5 ml. of concentrated hydrochloric acid. The pH is now about 1. After 5 minutes add 10 ml. of fresh 0.25 per cent solution of potassium dithiooxalate. After 3 minutes add about 1.3 grams of solid sodium acetate to raise the pH to 3.5-4 and stir to dissolve. This delays development of turbidity. Read at 508 mμ at once against a reagent blank.

CHAPTER 16

CYCLIC ACIDS AND THEIR ESTERS [1]

CYCLIC acids as well as various more complex acids and their esters appear in almost all phases of life. Many occur naturally in the human and lower animal body; others occur in plants; and still others are taken into the body as medications or flavorings. Methods for the acids apply to their salts or the esters after saponification. Their concentrations are usually determined by extracting with organic solvents and developing a color with various reagents.

The actual methods of determination are usually those of an associated group rather than of the carboxyl. Thus amino groups are diazotized and coupled, or phenolic groups are often developed as ferric salts. Some of the simpler cycles are nitrated, and the color is developed by reduction, diazotization, and coupling. It follows from this that there is no class reaction for carbocyclic acids. Many acids in which a cycle appears as a side chain and in which the carboxyl is not on the cycle appear elsewhere.

BENZOIC ACID

When benzoic acid is nitrated by potassium nitrate and sulfuric acid, dinitrobenzoic acid is obtained. Ammonium sulfide or hydroxylamine reduces this to diaminobenzoic acid. The reddish brown ammonium salt of this is estimated colorimetrically.[2] The color from p-chlorobenzoic acid or the methyl ester of p-hydroxybenzoic acid is yellow, greenish yellow, or yellow-brown. If benzene has been used in extraction of the benzoic acid, it must be completely removed as it gives a red, but somewhat more of a wine color than that from benzoic acid. Cinnamic acid gives a similar color. Acetic and butyric acids do not interfere. Large amounts of sulfurous acid or of salts interfere. The color produced

---

[1] See Chapter 1 for details of organization, condensation, etc.

[2] E. Mohler, *Bull. soc. chim.* [3] **3**, 414-16 (1890); L. Grünhut, *Z. anal. Chem.* **36**, 200-12 (1897); C. Heide and F. Jakob, *Z. Untersuch. Lebensm.* **19**, 137-53 (1910); A. J. Jones, *Pharm. J.* **115**, 144-5 (1925); J. Grossfeld, *Z. Untersuch. Lebensm.* **30**, 271-3 (1915); *Ibid.* **53**, 467-83 (1927); H. Riffart and H. Keller, *Ibid.* **68**, 113-38 (1934); Heinrich Waelsch and Gertrud Klepetar, *Z. physiol. Chem.* **236**, 92-102 (1935); W. Davey and J. R. Gwilt, *J. Soc. Chem. Ind.* **69**, 330-7 (1950).

agrees qualitatively with that of ferric salts and thiocyanate solutions. The method will detect less than 0.1 mg. of benzoic acid and usually gives accuracy to 2 to 3 per cent.

The nitrobenzoic acid is also reduced with titanous chloride, diazotized, and coupled with N-(1-naphthyl)ethylenediamine hydrochloride for reading.[3] The same method is used for hippuric acid.

Benzoic acid is partially oxidized to salicylic acid by hydrogen peroxide and determined by the violet color with ferric chloride or the red with cupric ion. The oxidation is only about 10 per cent complete and requires rigorous control of the concentrations of reagent in order to be duplicable.[4] Chlorides and sulfates reduce the proportion of salicylic acid formed. Nitrates have no appreciable influence unless present in large amounts. Oxidizable substances can usually be removed with an alkaline solution of potassium permanganate, which does not oxidize benzoic acid. It does oxidize cinnamic acid to benzoic acid. Phenolphthalein is oxidized by hydrogen peroxide and must not be used as an indicator. Salicylic acid originally present must be removed. Saccharin interferes but is separated by extracting the benzoic acid with carbon tetrachloride, in which saccharin is nearly insoluble.

The copper-pyridine-benzoic acid complex in chloroform gives a red color which is suitable for estimation.[5] The usual sample is 2.5-20 mg. Since salicylic acid and acetylsalicylic acid gives the same color, they must be absent. Benzoic acid is also read in the ultraviolet in ethanol containing phosphoric acid.[6]

Samples—*Food products.* Neutralize any large excess of acidity from preliminary treatment. The final product should be slightly acid. Extract with three 50-ml. portions of chloroform, ether, or a mixture of equal parts of ether and petroleum ether. Wash the solvent solution of benzoic acid once with 50 ml. of water to remove water-soluble acids. Re-extract the washings once with 25 ml. of fresh organic solvent to avoid loss of benzoic acid. Extract the benzoic acid from the organic solvent with successive portions of 10, 10, and 5 ml. of 0.02 per cent sodium hydroxide solution. Combine these alkaline extracts and boil to remove dissolved solvent. To this aqueous solution at 50° add 0.1 per cent aqueous potassium permanganate solution until a pink color

[3] F. Dickens and Joan Pearson, *Biochem. J.* **48**, 216-21 (1951).

[4] J. R. Nicholls, *Analyst* **53**, 19-29 (1928).

[5] Ch. Lapière, *J. pharm. Belg.* [NS] **3**, 17-25, 123-8 (1948).

[6] Hector R. Hernandez and Albert M. Mattocks, *Bull. Natl. Formulary Comm* **19**, 1-3 (1951).

persists. Add 1:3 nitric acid until the solution is faintly acid. Add 0.1 per cent oxalic acid solution until the solution is just clarified. Do not clarify with sulfurous acid or sulfites. Determine by developing the color with ferric ion or cupric ion.

Liquids. Dilute an aliquot of a neutral or slightly alkaline solution of sample corresponding to not more than 4 mg. of benzoic acid, to 15 ml. Complete as for food products starting at "To this aqueous solution at 50° add. . . ."

Butter and oleomargarine. Weigh a 50-gram sample and add about 25 ml. of water and a drop of phenolphthalein indicator solution. Add 1 per cent sodium hydroxide solution until a permanent red color is obtained after shaking. Dilute to 100 ml. and let cool until the fat layer solidifies. Pipet out 50 ml. of the aqueous layer, add 5 ml. of 15 per cent potassium ferrocyanide solution, mix, and add 5 ml. of an aqueous 3 per cent solution of zinc sulfate. Shake, dilute to 200 ml. and filter. Use an aliquot of this for development by dinitration and reduction to diaminobenzoic acid.

Chopped meat or egg yolk. Mix 20 grams of meat with 1 gram of calcium carbonate and about 175 ml. of water. Add 1 per cent sodium hydroxide solution until alkaline, dilute to 200 ml., and heat for 15 minutes in a boiling water bath. Cool and filter. Transfer 50 ml. of the filtrate, add 1 ml. of 15 per cent potassium ferrocyanide solution, and mix. Add 1 ml. of a 3 per cent solution of zinc sulfate, dilute to 100 ml., and mix. Filter and use an aliquot for development by dinitration and reduction to diaminobenzoic acid.

Milk. Make 50 ml. of milk alkaline to phenolphthalein with 1 per cent sodium hydroxide solution, add 5 ml. of 15 per cent potassium ferrocyanide solution, and mix. Add 5 ml. of 3 per cent zinc sulfate solution, dilute to 100 ml., and mix. Filter and use an aliquot for development by dinitration and reduction to diaminobenzoic acid.

Berry juice. Make 50 ml. alkaline to phenolphthalein with 1 per cent sodium hydroxide solution and use an aliquot for development by dinitration and reduction to diaminobenzoic acid.

Beer. Make a 50-ml. sample alkaline to phenolphthalein with 1 per cent sodium hydroxide solution and use an aliquot for development by dinitration and reduction to diaminobenzoic acid.

Procedure—*With ferric ion.* To the oxidized sample, add 1 ml. of a solution of ferric salt made by diluting 50 ml. of 2.7 per cent ferric chloride hexahydrate solution and 13 ml. of 1:35 sulfuric acid to 100 ml.

Add 1 ml. of a 0.1 per cent solution of hydrogen peroxide, prepared by dilution of 1 ml. of 30 per cent hydrogen peroxide to 300 ml. Heat the sample just to boiling and add 0.5 ml. of 4 per cent sodium hydroxide solution. Mix well and filter while hot. Wash the precipitate with hot water. Cool, dilute to 50 ml., and add 1 drop of the prepared ferric solution. Read at 530 mμ against a blank and compare with a curve prepared from benzoic acid under the same rigidly controlled conditions.

With cupric ion. To oxidized sample add 1 ml. of a 2 per cent sodium nitrite solution and 1 ml. of 0.3 per cent copper sulfate solution in 10 per cent acetic acid. Heat in boiling water for 15 minutes, cool, and dilute to 50 ml. Read against a reagent blank and compare with a curve prepared from benzoic acid under the same rigidly controlled conditions.

Dinitration and reduction to diaminobenzoic acid. Measure a portion of the sample solution equivalent to about 1 mg. of benzoic acid. If the volume is over 20 ml., make just alkaline with sodium hydroxide solution and evaporate to 5 ml. Acidify with 0.5 ml. of 1:3 sulfuric acid. Extract twice with about 3 volumes of ether for one-half minute each. Combine the ether extracts and wash with 2-3 one-ml. portions of water. Add 1 ml. of 0.4 per cent sodium hydroxide solution and shake. If the solution is not alkaline to phenolphthalein, add more of the sodium hydroxide solution. Withdraw the aqueous extract and wash the ether with several 1-ml. portions of water. Evaporate the combined alkaline extracts and washings to dryness in an evaporating dish on a water bath.

To the residue add 1 ml. of concentrated sulfuric acid containing 10 grams of potassium nitrate per 100 ml. Heat in boiling water for 30 minutes. Cool and add 2 ml. of water. Add 2 ml. of a 2 per cent solution of hydroxylamine hydrochloride. Add 10 ml. of 1:1 ammonium hydroxide. Mix well, heat in a water bath at 60° for 5 minutes, cool, and read against a reagent blank.

Dinitration and coupling. Prepare a sample containing not over 10 mg. of benzoic acid as described in the preceding method through "Heat in boiling water for 30 minutes." Add 3.5 ml. of water and cool. Add 2.5 ml. of 40 per cent sodium hydroxide solution to reduce the acidity. Use 3 ml. of water to transfer to a separatory funnel. Extract with 10 ml. and 10 ml. of isoamyl alcohol. Wash the combined extracts with 5, 5, and 5 ml. of water. Discard the aqueous layers and extract the nitration products with 5 ml. and 5 ml. of 0.4 per cent sodium hydroxide solution. To the alkaline extracts add 15 ml. of concentrated hydrochloric acid, 12 grams of tartaric acid, and 1 ml. of 13-15 per cent titanous chloride solution. Heat in boiling water for exactly 15 minutes and cool below 5° in an ice bath. Gradually add 1 ml. of fresh 10 per cent sodium nitrite solution and keep in the ice bath for 30 minutes. Cautiously add 7 grams of urea to destroy excess nitrite. Add as coupling agent 5 ml. of 0.5 per cent N-(1-naphthyl)ethylenediamine hydrochloride in 1:10 hydrochloric acid. After 30 minutes at room temperature dilute to 100 ml. with 1:10 hydrochloric acid. After an hour read at 500-545 mμ against a reagent blank.

In the ultraviolet. Dilute an appropriate solution of the sample, not over 5 ml., to 100 ml. with 1 per cent phosphoric acid in ethanol. Read at 228 and 272 mμ and calculate from 52.7 $A_{228m\mu}$-30.4 $A_{272m\mu}$.

o-HYDROXYBENZOIC ACID, SALICYLIC ACID

The violet color given by salicylic acid with ferric ion is the most important method of estimation. The color is usually produced with ferric chloride,[7] and less frequently with ferric nitrate. The latter is advantageous in biological work because it may be applied directly to serum or urine without deproteinizing.[8] Maltol, isomaltol, 2-hydroxy-isophthalic acid, methyl-ethyl acetoacetate, orcin, arbutin, resorcin, phlorizin, tannins, sulfates, salts of alkaline earths, and free bases interfere, so that the salicylic acid must be isolated as completely as possible before the determination is made. This is usually by extraction with ether from acid solution, followed by extraction from the ether solution by a weak aqueous alkali. Tannins are removed as lead tannate, which is insoluble in a basic medium, where lead salicylate is readily soluble. Acetylsalicylic acid gives the same reaction. The color is suitable for reading photometrically[9] and susceptible of micromanipulation with 0.05 ml. in a capillary for estimation of 0.005 mg.[10] It is also applied as a quantitative spot test.[11]

The red color developed by salicylic acid when heated with copper

---

[7] H. Riffart and H. Keller, *Z. Untersuch. Lebensm.* **68**, 113-38 (1934); P. Fønss Bech, *Dansk. Tids. Farm.* **9**, 289-302 (1935); J. E. Helsterman, *Chem. Melkblad.* **32**, 463 (1935); P. Karsten, *ibid.* **32**, 526 (1935); A. L. Tarnoky and V. Anne L. Brews, *J. Clin. Path.* **3**, 289-91 (1950).

[8] William J. Keller, *Am. J. Clin. Path.* **17**, 415-17 (1947); John T. Peters, *Acta Med. Scand.* **129**, 299-310 (1947).

[9] U. Pellegrini and T. Rabaglia, *Boll. soc. ital. biol. sper.* **24**, 586 (1948).

[10] J. Browaeys, *Ann. inst. Pasteur* **72**, 149-53 (1946).

[11] Joseph H. Miller and Richard W. Whitehead, *Rocky Mt. Med. J.* **46**, 544-5 (1949).

sulfate, potassium nitrite, and acetic acid is also suitable for estimation.[12] Phenol, saligenin, and 2-hydroxyisophthalic acid interfere. Benzoic, cinnamic and tartaric acids, orcin, arbutin, resorcin, and phlorizin do not. The reaction is more sensitive than that with ferric chloride, and the color produced is stable for several hours. Biological samples need not be deproteinized. The red color of the copper-pyridine-salicylic acid complex in chloroform is also suitable for estimation.[13] Since benzoic and acetylsalicylic acid give the same color, they must be absent. A usual sample contains 2.5-20 mg.

Due to the phenolic group salicylic acid is estimated in the absence of interfering substances by diazotized p-nitroaniline.[14] The method gives rather poor recoveries from clinical samples. At pH 5.1, sodium salicylate is read directly at 295 mμ.[15] In trichloroacetic acid filtrates at pH 1.2 the peak is at 303 mμ. Acetylsalicylic acid does not interfere, having no peak between 220 mμ and 350 mμ. The peak for salicyluric acid is at 298 mμ and does not shift in the pH 1-6 range. Other peaks are gentisic acid in alkaline solution at 320 mμ and 2,6-dihydroxybenzoic acid at 302.5 mμ.

The direct absorption shows a maximum absorption at 296 mμ, gentisic acid at 320 mμ, and of the mixture at 306.5 mμ.[16]

The xanthoproteic reaction with nitric acid is applicable [17] to filtrates deproteinized with trichloroacetic acid. The reaction with phosphomolybdic-phosphotungstic acid is also applied.[18]

Samples—*Liquids free from tannins.* Extract a sample containing about 2 mg. of salicylic acid with 3 successive 50-ml. portions of ether. Combine the ether extracts and wash once with 50 ml. of distilled water. Extract the salicylic acid from the ether with two 50-ml. portions of

---

[12] H. C. Sherman and A. Gross, *J. Ind. Eng. Chem.* **3**, 492-3 (1911); F. Schott, *Z. Nahr. Genussm.* **22**, 77-8 (1911); S. M. K. Mallick and Ahsanulhaqq Rehmann, *Ann. Biochem. Expt. Med.* **5**, 97-100 (1945).

[13] Ch. Lapière, *J. pharm. Belg.* [N. S.] **3**, 123-8 (1948).

[14] Ruth C. Theis and Stanley R. Benedict, *J. Biol. Chem.* **61**, 67-71 (1924); Augustin D. Marenzi, *Compt. rend. soc. biol.* **109**, 321-2 (1932); Luis E. Ontaneda and Angel V. J. Ferloni, *Rev. soc. argentina biol.* **11**, 474-81 (1935); *Compt. rend. soc. biol.* **120**, 820-2 (1935).

[15] G. Ungar, E. Damgaard, and W. K. Wong, *Proc. Soc. Exptl. Biol. Med.* **80**, 45-7 (1952).

[16] Lewis J. Kleckner and Arthur Osol, *J. Am. Pharm. Assoc.* **41**, 103-5 (1952).

[17] Mario Volterra and Mildred D. Jacobs, *J. Lab. Clin. Med.* **32**, 1282-3 (1947).

[18] T. E. Weichselbaum and Irving Shapiro, *Am. J. Clin. Path., Tech Sect.* **9**, 42-4 (1945); M. J. H. Smith and J. M. Talbot, *Brit. J. Exptl. Path.* **31**, 65-9 (1950).

approximately 0.04 per cent sodium hydroxide solution. Repeat if both extracts are not distinctly alkaline, until 2 extractions yield extracts alkaline to phenolphthalein as shown by separate spot-plate tests. Neutralize by careful addition of 1:3 hydrochloric acid drop by drop. Warm to drive off organic solvent, cool, and dilute to 100 ml. for development of aliquots with ferric chloride.

Preserved fruits, fruit pulps, and jams. Mix 50 grams of crushed sample with 25 ml. of water and 20 ml. of saturated solution of basic lead acetate. Make distinctly alkaline with 4 per cent sodium hydroxide. Tannins are precipitated but lead and albuminoids are in solution. Filter and neutralize the filtrate with 1:10 hydrochloric acid. This throws down lead and albuminoids. Dilute to 300 ml., mix well, chill, and filter. Proceed with 200 ml. of filtrate, extracting as a liquid free from tannins.

Beer. Use a 100-ml. sample. Make this distinctly alkaline with 5 ml. of 4 per cent sodium hydroxide solution and heat just below boiling until the alcohol has been driven off. Cool and add 5 ml. of 1:10 hydrochloric acid. Mix well with 20 ml. of saturated basic lead acetate solution and make alkaline with 20 ml. of 4 per cent sodium hydroxide solution. Dilute to 200 ml. and filter. Acidify 100 ml. of filtrate with 1:1 hydrochloric acid and chill. Filter if lead chloride precipitates. Extract the acid solution as a liquid free from tannins.

Wine. Dilute 50 ml. to 100 ml. with water. Proceed as for beer starting at "Make this distinctly alkaline. . . ."

Whole blood.[19] To 5 ml. of acetone and 0.1 ml. of saturated calcium chloride solution add 1 ml. of whole blood, dropwise. Stopper and shake vigorously for a minute. After standing a half-hour centrifuge for 5 minutes to separate the protein. Decant the supernatant liquid, add 2.2 ml. of water, and shake thoroughly with 1 ml. of chloroform. Centrifuge for 5 minutes. Remove 4 ml. of the supernatant solution as sample for development by ferric chloride.

Blood serum. Free salicylic acid.[20] Deproteinize by mixing 2 ml. of serum with 2 ml. of 1:54 sulfuric acid, 4 ml. of water, and 2 ml. of 10 per cent sodium tungstate. Mix well and filter. Use 6 ml. of filtrate for estimation with ferric chloride.

Alternatively,[21] mix 1 ml. of serum with 10 ml. of ethanol, centrifuge, and evaporate the decanted supernatant liquid. Take up the residue in

---

[19] Pedro B. Companovo, *Rev. soc. argentina biol.* **21**, 309-15 (1945); *Rev. asoc. bioquím. argentina* **13**, 67-72 (1946).

[20] F. Velez Orozco and F. Guerra, *Arch. inst. cardiol. Mex.* **16**, No. 2 (1946).

[21] J. E. Galimard, *Ann. biol. chin.* (Paris) **5**, 231-8 (1947).

6 ml. of water for development with ferric chloride. The salicylic acid is also extracted from acidified plasma with ethylene dichloride,[22] then retransferred to the aqueous phase containing ferric nitrate.

Total salicylic acid.[23] When sodium salicylate has been administered, 15-30 per cent of the salicylic acid is in bound form, only liberated by double hydrolysis. Mix 17 ml. of water, 2 ml. of concentrated hydrochloric acid, and 5 ml. of serum or plasma. Reflux the mixture for an hour. Add 4 ml. of saturated aqueous sodium hydroxide solution and reflux the mixture for 15 minutes. Neutralize by dropwise addition of concentrated hydrochloric acid and add 2 ml. in excess. Boil for 5 minutes and cool. Extract with three successive 5-ml. portions of ether, combine the extracts, and filter. Evaporate *in vacuo,* take up with 6 ml. of water, and develop with ferric chloride.

Binding value of blood for salicylic acid.[24] Mix 1 ml. of blood, defibrinated with oxalate or citrate, with 9 ml. of 0.1 per cent solution of salicylic acid in ether. Mix and let stand for the blood to separate. Evaporate 1 ml. of the clear ether layer *in vacuo,* take up the residue in 6 ml. of hot water, cool, and develop with ferric chloride.

Urine. Free salicylic acid. Mix a 10-ml. sample with 5 drops of 1:5 acetic acid and 10 drops of 1:19 sulfuric acid. Extract with 3 successive 10-ml. portions of benzene. Filter the combined extracts, evaporate the solvent, and take up the residue in 25 ml. of 0.04 per cent sodium hydroxide solution for development with ferric chloride.

Total salicylic acid. When sodium salicylate has been administered 15-30 per cent of the salicylic acid is bound and only available after hydrolysis. Reflux a 10-ml. sample with 1 ml. of concentrated hydrochloric acid for 2 hours. Extract with 3 successive 5-ml. portions of ether, combine the extracts, and filter. Evaporate *in vacuo,* take up with 6 ml. of water, and develop with ferric chloride.

Pharmaceutical tablets. Disintegrate a 1-gram sample with 10 ml. of water and add a drop of 1:1 hydrochloric acid. If effervescence indicates the presence of carbonates, cautiously acidify and boil to drive off the carbon dioxide. Extract the acidified carbonate-free solution with 10 ml. of 1:1 mixture of ether and petroleum ether. Filter the extract and evaporate 5 ml. of extract to dryness *in vacuo.* Take up the residue in

22 Bernard B. Brodie, Sidney Udenfriend, and Alvin F. Coburn, *J. Pharmacol.* **80,** 114-17 (1944).

23 J. E. Galimard, *Bull. soc. chim. biol.* **26,** 386-92 (1944).

24 M. Obtutowicz, *Arch. Dermatol. Syphylol.* **174,** 633-4 (1936).

4 ml. of ethanol and dilute to 50 ml. for development of aliquots with ferric chloride.

Procedure—*With ferric chloride.* Dilute a sample containing 0.1-0.3 mg. of salicylic acid to about 9 ml. Add 0.2 ml. of 0.9 per cent solution of ferric chloride hexahydrate. Add 0.2 ml. of 1:10 acetic acid and dilute to 10 ml. Read at 530 mμ against a reagent blank.

With ferric nitrate. Prepare 0.07 N nitric acid by dilution of 4.69 ml. of concentrated acid to a liter. Prepare a 1 per cent solution of ferric nitrate nonahydrate in this and as reagent dilute 5 ml. with 4 ml. of water. Mix the 9 ml. of reagent with 1 ml. of serum or 0.5 ml. of urine and 0.5 ml. of water. As blank use 5 ml. of 0.07 N nitric acid, 4 ml. of water, and 1 ml. of serum or 0.5 ml. of urine and 0.5 ml. of water. Read at 530 mμ. The color is stable for several hours.

With copper ion. Samples suitable for development are neutral or faintly acid. Nearly neutralized milk is used as a sample against standards prepared by known additions to milk free from salicylic acid. Serum or blood filtrate is used directly.

To a 5-ml. sample containing 0.02-0.2 mg. of salicylic acid, add 4 drops of a 1 per cent solution of sodium nitrite, 4 drops of 1:1 acetic acid, and 2 drops of 1 per cent copper sulfate pentahydrate solution. Place in boiling water for 10 minutes. Cool and dilute to 10 ml. Compare with a series of standards similarly treated at the same time.

With diazotized p-nitroaniline. As sample use deproteinized serum or blood, or urine. To a 5-ml. sample and to a standard based on the same menstruum containing 0.025 mg. of sodium salicylate in 5 ml., add 1 ml. of 1 per cent gum arabic solution and mix. Add 1 ml. of 50 per cent sodium acetate solution and mix. Add 1 ml. of diazotized *p*-nitroaniline (page 421), mix, and let stand for 1 minute. Dilute to 10 ml. with 20 per cent sodium carbonate solution and mix. Compare after 15 minutes.

With nitric acid. Mix 2.5 ml. of deproteinized sample containing 0.1-2 mg. of salicylate with 1 ml. of concentrated nitric acid. Dilute to 5 ml. with water and heat in boiling water for 5 minutes. Cool and add 3 ml. of 60 per cent sodium hydroxide solution. Cool, dilute to 10 ml., and read against a reagent blank.

By phosphotungstic-phosphomolybdic acid. For the reaction mix 50 ml. of the usual reagent (page 116) with 21 ml. of ethanol and 129 ml. of water. As a check, titration by 8.5 per cent sodium carbonate solution should require 1.95 ± 0.05 ml. to titrate 10 ml. of reagent to methyl orange.

Mix 0.5 ml. of sample with 10 ml. of the reagent at 37°. Centrifuge and remove 5 ml. of the upper layer. Add 5 ml. of 8.5 per cent sodium carbonate solution and mix thoroughly. Place in a 37° water bath for about 20 minutes, allow to stand at room temperature for another 20 minutes, and read at 660 mμ against a reagent blank.

3,4-DIHYDROXYBENZOIC ACID, PROTOCATECHUIC ACID

The technic for determination with ferrous tartrate is described under catechol (page 127). The optimum pH for this phenol is 6.3-10.4.

3,4,5-TRIHYDROXYBENZOIC ACID, GALLIC ACID

Gallic acid, gallotannins, pyrogallol, or catechol in dilute solution gives a reddish violet color with osmium tetroxide.[25] As little as 0.5 mg. per liter can be detected. Phenol, salicylic acid, phloroglucinol, and resorcinol do not produce a color with the reagent. The solution should not be acid. A slight excess of alkali does not affect the result. The same weight of the different phenols does not give the same color intensity.

The general technic for development with ferrous tartrate is described under catechol (page 127). The optimum pH for this phenol is 5.9-10.3. A specific method for application to fats and oils is shown here.[26] Either that reagent or reading in acid solution in the ultraviolet is applicable.

Sample—*Tea, sawdust, coffee, hops.* Boil 1 gram of sample with successive portions of water for 1.5 hours. Dilute the combined extracts to 100 ml. for estimation with osmium tetroxide.

Nutgall extract. Extract 5 grams of crushed nutgalls with 3 successive 150-ml. portions of water, boiling 1 hour each time. Filter and dilute to 500 ml. Dilute 10 ml. of this solution to 100 ml. and use an aliquot for development with ferrous tartrate.

Gallic acid. Dissolve 2 grams of sample in water and dilute to 1 liter. To 10 ml. of this solution add 4.5 ml. of a 1 per cent quinine hydrochloride solution and 0.5 ml. of a 16 per cent sodium chloride solution. This will coagulate and precipitate gallotannins but leave gallic acid in solution. Centrifuge to throw down the precipitate or allow to sediment, and use the clear supernatant liquid for development with ferrous tartrate.

---

[25] C. A. Mitchell, *Analyst* **49**, 162-9 (1924).

[26] K. F. Mattil and L. J. Filer, Jr., *Ind. Eng. Chem., Anal. Ed.* **16**, 427-9 (1944).

Fats and oils. Heat a 10-gram sample to boiling with 65 ml. of water, set aside to cool, and filter through a wet paper. Wash the paper and residue with four 5-ml. portions of water. Dilute to 100 ml. to determine in the ultraviolet. Alternatively develop the solution with ferrous tartrate.

Procedure—*By osmium tetroxide. Gallic acid and gallotannic acid.* To 1 ml. of sample solution add about 90 ml. of water. Dilute a 1 per cent solution of osmium tetroxide with 10 parts of water. Treat the sample with 1 ml. of the diluted osmium tetroxide solution and 1 ml. of 0.4 per cent sodium carbonate solution, and dilute to 100 ml. Read against a sample blank.

Gallic acid. When gallotannic acid and gallic acid are present, add 2 ml. of sample solution to about 20 ml. of water. Add 25 ml. of 0.1 per cent quinine hydrochloride solution and dilute to 50 ml. The gallotannins are precipitated. Filter and dilute 25 ml. of filtrate to 90 ml. with water. Continue as if both were present from "Dilute a 1 per cent solution . . . ." The result is gallic acid. Subtract from the sum of the two to give gallotannic acid.

By ferrous tartrate. The sample is an aqueous filtrate. Add 2 ml. of fresh reagent containing 0.5 per cent of sodium potassium tartrate and 0.1 per cent of ferrous sulfate. Adjust the pH of the solution to 7 by adding 10 ml. of 10 per cent ammonium acetate solution and dilute to 100 ml. Read at 540 mμ against a reagent blank.

In the ultraviolet. Read at 270 mμ.

Methyl Salicylate

Oil of wintergreen, or methyl salicylate, is converted to salicylic acid and the latter distilled with steam and determined by the violet color with ferric chloride.[27]

Sample—*Dubbing.* Dubbing consists of any or all of the following: cod oil, mutton tallow, mineral oil, and oil of wintergreen. If the sample is not homogeneous, put the container in a water bath just warm enough to melt the dubbing, stir well, and cool. To 3 grams of sample add 25 ml. of 4 per cent sodium hydroxide solution and reflux for 30 minutes. Acidify with 1:4 sulfuric acid. Distil with steam until the volume of acidified solution is very small. Dilute the distillate to 500-ml. for the use of aliquots.

---

[27] A. E. Leighton, "Standard Methods of Analysis of Dubbing," Australia Dept. of Defence, Munitions Supply Board, May (1926).

Procedure—To 50 ml. of sample solution add 4 drops of a 1 per cent solution of ferric chloride. Compare by balancing, with a standard solution of salicylic acid containing 5 mg. per 50 ml. to which the same amount of ferric chloride has been added. The amount of methyl salicylate equals the amount of salicylic acid multiplied by 1.102.

2-THENYL SALICYLATE

The alkaline decomposition of 2-thenyl salicylate followed by estimation of the violet color of ferric salicylate is an appropriate procedure.[28]

Sample—*Cloth.* Transfer about 2 grams of 1-cm. squares to a Soxhlet. At least 5 mg. of the miticide should be present. Extract with ether for 1.5 hours and evaporate the ether from the extract. Add 25 ml. of 1 per cent potassium hydroxide and reflux until saponified. Carefully neutralize to a phenolphthalein end point with 1:10 hydrochloric acid and dilute to a known volume with water.

Procedure—As reagent dissolve 4.8 grams of ferric ammonium sulfate dodecahydrate in 50 ml. of water and add 0.1 ml. of 30 per cent hydrogen peroxide. Boil until the peroxide is destroyed and add 5 ml. of 1:1 sulfuric acid. When the solution is clear, cool, dilute to 100 ml. with water, and add 10 per cent potassium hydroxide to pH 1.4.

Dilute an aliquot equivalent to 0.04-0.8 mg. of saponified 2-threnyl salicylate to 10 ml. with water. Add 0.2 ml. of the color reagent, mix, and read at 540 mμ after 1 minute.

ACETYL-o-HYDROXYBENZOIC ACID, ACETYL SALICYLIC ACID, ASPIRIN

The preparations containing aspirin often contain other medicinals, particularly phenacetin and caffeine. Direct reading with avoidance of interference is feasible. Thus acetylsalicylic acid is read directly at 5.67μ[29] or at 277 mμ.[30] Alternatively develop the phenolic properties to give an orange-red or brown color with copper sulfate and hydrogen peroxide.[31]

Sample—Weigh a sample equivalent to about 220 mg. of aspirin. Phenacetin and caffeine may be present. Take up in about 80 ml. of

[28] Jerome Goldenson and Samuel Sass, *Anal. Chem.* **23,** 1170-2 (1951).

[29] T. V. Parke, A. M. Ribley, E. E. Kennedy, and W. W. Hiltz, *Anal. Chem.* **23,** 953-7 (1951).

[30] Marie Jones and R. L. Thatcher, *Ibid.* **23,** 957-60 (1951).

[31] K. von Fodor, *Kiserlet. Kozlemenyek* **33,** 155-78 (1930); *Z. Untersuch. Lebensm.* **61,** 94-100 (1931).

chloroform and extract with two successive 40-ml. portions of cold 4 per cent sodium bicarbonate solution, to each of which has been added 2 drops of 1:5 hydrochloric acid. Further extract with 20 ml. of water. Wash the combined extracts with 25 ml. of chloroform and add it to the previous layer. Reserve the chloroform layer for estimation of caffeine and phenacetin.

Acidify the sodium bicarbonate extracts at once with 25 ml. of 1:9 sulfuric acid, thus avoiding possible alkaline hydrolysis of aspirin. Make the additions in 5-ml. portions, mixing gently. The final pH should be 1-2. Extract the aspirin from this acidified solution with eight 50-ml. portions of chloroform, filter, and dilute to 500 ml. Dilute 20 ml. to 100 ml. with chloroform.

Antihistamines. The separation of aspirin is described under the antihistamines (Vol. IV).

Procedure—*In the ultraviolet.* Read at 277 mμ against chloroform.

With copper sulfate and hydrogen peroxide. Mix an aliquot of the sample solution containing about 5 mg. of aspirin with 3-4 drops of concentrated ammonium hydroxide and dilute to 5 ml. Mix well and add 2 drops of a 1 per cent solution of copper sulfate pentahydrate. Mix and add 4 drops of 3 per cent hydrogen peroxide solution. The orange-red color develops at once. Read against a reagent blank.

p-Hydroxybenzoic Acid

The acid present as such or that from the esters on saponification is determinable by various mercury reagents of which the best known is Millon's reagent.[32] The color developed is a function of both time and temperature up to 5 minutes at 100°. When benzene diazonium chloride is coupled with *p*-hydroxybenzoic acid in ether, treatment with sodium hydroxide solution gives an intense red.[33] The complexity of the proportion of mono-, bis-, and trisazo- derivatives interferes with its quantitative estimation.

After reaction with yellow mercury-silver oxide in concentrated sulfuric acid at 100°, methyl *p*-hydroxybenzoic acid, nipagin, couples to give a yellow dye with benzene diazonium sulfonate while propyl

---

[32] F. W. Edwards, H. R. Nanji and M. K. Hassan, *Analyst*, **62**, 178-85 (1937); Th. Sabalitscke, *Mikrochim. Acta* **2**, 111-19 (1937); W. Diemar, H. Riffart and E. Schmek, *Mikrochemie* **25**, 247-55 (1938); H. W. Johnson, *Analyst* **71**, 77-8 (1945).

[33] S. G. Stevenson, *Analyst* **63**, 152-5 (1938).

p-hydroxybenzoic acid couples to an orange dye under the same condi-tions. They are suitable for photometric estimation.

Sample—*Fat-free liquids*. Transfer a sample containing 0.2-5 mg. to a separatory funnel with 15 ml. of water. Add 2 ml. of 1:3 sulfuric acid and extract with two 25-ml. portions of ether. Dehydrate the com-bined ether extracts with anhydrous sodium sulfate, filter, and evaporate to dryness. Take up with water, dilute to a known volume, and develop an aliquot with Millon's reagent.

Foods. Stir a 10-gram sample with 0.5 gram of calcium carbonate and a little water. Add a few drops of phenolphthalein solution. Heat in a water bath for 15 minutes, cool, and dilute to 100 ml. Filter and transfer 50 ml. of filtrate. Add 5 ml. of 15 per cent potassium ferro-cyanide solution, mix well, and slowly add 5 ml. of 30 per cent zinc sulfate solution. The precipitation clarifies the solution. Dilute to 100 ml. and filter.

Neutralize 50 ml. of filtrate with 1:10 sulfuric acid added dropwise. Add 2 ml. of 5 per cent sodium bicarbonate solution and extract with a 30-ml. portion of ether. Repeat the extraction and combine the extracts. Benzoic or salicylic acid remains behind in the aqueous solution. Dry with anhydrous sodium sulfate, evaporate the ether, and take up in a suitable volume of water for the development of aliquots with Millon's reagent.

Millon's Reagent—Add 20 ml. of concentrated nitric acid to 2 ml. of mercury in a 100-ml. flask. Place under a hood at room temperature until the mercury is dissolved. Dilute with 35 ml. of water. If there is any precipitation, add concentrated nitric acid dropwise until the pre-cipitate is redissolved. Add 10 per cent sodium hydroxide solution until there is a slight permanent turbidity. Add 5 ml. of 1:4 nitric acid and mix well. This reagent is good for 1 day only.

Procedure—Pipet an aliquot of sample containing 0.5-2 mg. of p-hydroxybenzoic acid into a tube and dilute to about 20 ml. Heat in a boiling water bath and add 2 ml. of Millon's reagent. Immerse the tube in the boiling water bath for 5 minutes. Immediately dilute with 25 ml. of distilled water on removal. Cool, dilute to 50 ml., mix well, and within 5 minutes read the red color against a reagent blank. If over 1.5 mg. of test substance is present a slight opalescence may develop.

p-NITROBENZOIC ACID

Determination of *p*-nitrobenzoic acid is by reduction to the corresponding amine.[34] Large amounts of phosphates interfere.

Sample—*Blood or broth.* Prepare as described for *p*-aminobenzoic acid (page 417).

Procedure—As acidifying solution dissolve 36 grams of tartaric acid in 100 ml. of water and add 42 ml. of concentrated hydrochloric acid. To 10 ml. of sample solution add 1 ml. of this acidifying solution, and 2 drops of 20 per cent titanous chloride solution. The acid mixture prevents the formation of insoluble titanic acid on heating. Mix by rotating and place in boiling water for 10-15 minutes. Cool rapidly to room temperature and dilute with water to 12 ml. Add 1 ml. of 0.2 per cent sodium nitrite solution, mix, and allow to stand for 20 minutes with occasional swirling. Add 1 ml. of 2 per cent ammonium sulfamate, mix, and allow to stand for 2-3 minutes. Add 5 ml. of 0.4 per cent dimethyl-*α*-naphthylamine in ethanol and read after 4-5 hours against a reagent blank. Interpret the result from a standard curve prepared with *p*-aminobenzoic acid. Subtract the total amount of *p*-aminobenzoic acid present, as separately determined and multiply the result by 1.21 to convert to *p*-nitrobenzoic acid.

o-AMINOBENZOIC ACID

A complex reaction with oxidized hemoglobin is obtained with *o*-aminobenzoic acid.[35] There is no interference by *p*-aminobenzoic acid, sulfanilamide, or naphthylamines. The reaction is given at equal intensity by *m*-aminobenzoic acid.

Procedure—Mix 1 ml. of *o*-aminobenzoic acid solution, 1 ml. of fresh 0.002 per cent aqueous *p*-phenylaminediamine, 1 ml. of 2 per cent hydrogen peroxide, and 1 ml. of blood, laked and diluted 1:1000 the same day. Read between 10 and 13 minutes after development.

p-AMINOBENZOIC ACID

The conventional diazotizing and coupling determines *p*-aminobenzoic acid.[36] Coupling may conveniently be with dimethyl-*α*-naphthylamine,

---

[34] R. R. Nichols and H. W. Eckert, *N. Y. State Dept. Health, Ann. Rept. Div. Lab. and Research* **1941**, 26-7; H. William Eckert, *J. Biol. Chem.* **148**, 197-204 (1943).

[35] J. Garcia-Blanco and J. Viña, *Trabajos inst. nacl. cienc. méd.* (Madrid) **6**, 283-6 (1945-6); F. Roys Minué and J. Viña, *Ibid.* **6**, 333-8 (1945-6).

[36] H. William Eckert, *J. Biol. Chem.* **148**, 197-204 (1943).

thiamine,[37] N-(1-naphthyl)-ethylenediamine dihydrochloride,[38] or its diethyl derivatives [39] to give a red color. The solution conforms to Beer's law over the range 0.0025-0.05 mg. per 100 ml. There are many interferences such as phenol, cresol, and all primary arylamines including sulfa drugs.

The relative intensity of color developed by N-(1-naphthyl)-ethylenediamine dihydrochloride at a somewhat different wave length and technic is shown under m-aminohippuric acid (page 331) for a number of closely related acids. When the reaction is used in determination of esters such as benzocaine, procaine, butacaine, and butesin (Vol. IV) there is no interference by local anesthetics such as cocaine, metycaine, alypine, stovaine, diothane, nupercaine, and phenacaine. Epinephrine and ephedrine, often used with local anesthetics, do not interfere. The reaction is applicable to larocaine, tutocaine, monocaine, and panthaine.

The color develops to its full intensity in 2 minutes and is stable in diffuse light for at least 4 hours, except that from butacaine sulfate which starts to fade after an hour. Strong light causes fading. In the range of 0.01-0.05 mg. of developed sample, it is accurate to ±2 per cent.

To differentiate from sulfa drugs,[40] couple with β-naphthol, extract with chloroform in alkaline solution to remove color due to sulfa drugs, and read. If the color is not sufficiently intense after extraction of sulfa compounds, acidify and extract the coupled p-aminobenzoic acid with amyl alcohol. When the p-aminobenzoic acid is already conjugated in part, hydrolyze with hydrochloric acid and determine as usual.[41]

The pink from 0.01 mg. of p-aminobenzoic acid in 1 ml. of sample, 1 ml. of 3 per cent hydrogen peroxide, and 1 ml. of 1:1000 blood develops a maximum in 15 minutes and is suitable for reading.[42] Another reaction is that of acid-diazotized p-aminobenzoic acid with alkaline thymol solu-

[37] Ernest R. Kirch and Olaf Bergein, *Ibid.* **148**, 445-50 (1943).

[38] E. Strauss, F. C. Laven, and M. Finland, *J. Clin. Invest.* **20**, 189 (1941); Bruno Kisch and Eduard Strauss, *Exptl. Med. and Surg.* **1**, 66-70 (1943); F. J. Bandelin and C. R. Kemp, *Ind. Eng. Chem., Anal. Ed.* **18**, 470-1 (1946); Kuang S. Ting, Julius M. Coon, and Alvin C. Conway, *J. Lab. Clin. Med.* **34**, 822-9 (1949); Shuntaro Ogawa and Hideko Tsukamoto, *Vitamins* (Japan) **3**, 26-7 (1950).

[39] Harutada Negoro, *J. Pharm. Soc. Japan* **71**, 209-10 (1951).

[40] Walter Eissner, *Arch. Pharm.* **268**, 322-3 (1930); E. Havinga, *Rec. trav. chim.* **63**, 243-7 (1944).

[41] R. R. Nichols and H. W. Eckert, *N. Y. State Dept. Health, Ann. Rept., Div. Lab. and Research* **1941**, 26-7.

[42] J. Garcia-Blanco and J. Viña, *Trabajos inst. nacl. cienc. med.* (Madrid) **6**, 287-90 (1945-6).

tion. The yellow-orange color develops in 10 minutes and is stable for 3 hours.[43] Sulfonamides interfere. The base formed with *p*-dimethyl-aminobenzaldehyde in acetic acid is yellow and stable.

Sample—*Blood.* Add 30 ml. of water to 2 ml. of oxalated or citrated blood and mix thoroughly. Allow laking to take place for 5 minutes and then add 8 ml. of 15 per cent trichloroacetic acid slowly with rotation. Shake vigorously, allow to stand for 5 minutes, and filter. Develop with dimethyl-*a*-naphthylamine or N-(1-naphthyl) ethylenediamine dihydrochloride.

Blood containing procaine. Mix 1 ml. of blood with 3 ml. of water and add 1 ml. of 50 per cent trichloroacetic acid. Centrifuge for 3 minutes, and filter if necessary. If the filtrate is cloudy with fatty substances, extract with about 2 ml. of ether and discard the extract. Add a drop of phenolphthalein indicator to all or an aliquot and neutralize by dropwise addition of 30 per cent sodium hydroxide solution, avoiding excess. Add 0.5 ml. of 10 per cent sodium carbonate solution and 10 ml. of ether. Shake mechanically for 2 minutes and separate the aqueous layer. Extract this again with 10 ml. of ether. Neutralize the aqueous layer with 1:10 hydrochloric acid and add a drop in excess. This contains the *p*-aminobenzoic acid for development of all or an aliquot with N-(1-naphthyl) ethylenediamine dihydrochloride.

To the combined ether extracts containing the procaine add 3 ml. of 1:10 hydrochloric acid and 2 ml. of water. Shake mechanically for 2 minutes and separate the acid layer containing the procaine. Develop all or an aliquot with N-(1-naphthyl) ethylenediamine dihydrochloride.

Barbital solutions. Procaine, if present, must first be extracted. Follow the technic for blood containing procaine from "add a drop of phenolphthalein . . ." to ". . .again with 10 ml. of ether." Neutralize the remaining aqueous layer with 1:5 hydrochloric acid. Add 5 ml. of buffer for pH 3.4 (Vol. I, page 173). Extract with four successive 20-ml. portions of ether. Filter, evaporate to dryness, and take up the residue in 25 ml. of acetone for development of all or an aliquot.

Urine. Dilute 1-5 ml. of urine to about 20 ml. with water and add 0.3 ml. of a 35 per cent solution of acetic acid. Add 1.27 per cent iodine solution until a brown color forms, then add a few drops of 1 per cent sodium bisulfite solution. Use as the sample for development with diazotized thiamine.

Combined p-aminobenzoic acid. Dilute 1-5 ml. of urine to 9 ml. and

---

[43] José Antonio Salvá Miquel, *Ibid.* **11**, 205-12 (1948).

add 1 ml. of 1:2 hydrochloric acid. Heat in boiling water for an hour, cool, and dilute to 20 ml. Shake with two 5-ml. portions of isoamyl alcohol to extract colored products and discard the extract. Add 6 ml. of 4 per cent sodium hydroxide solution in place of the usual 4 ml. called for in the procedure in development with diazotized thiamine.

Broth cultures. Pass the culture through a porcelain filter. Mix 2 ml. of the filtrate with 8 ml. of distilled water and 2 ml. of 15 per cent trichloroacetic acid. Shake vigorously, let stand for 5 minutes, and filter. Centrifuge the filtrate after development of color by any of the usual methods before making the reading.

Procedure—*With dimethyl-a-naphthylamine. Free p-aminobenzoic acid.* To 10 ml. of acidified sample add 2 ml. of water and 1 ml. of 0.1 per cent sodium nitrite solution. After 15-20 minutes, add 1 ml. of 2 per cent ammonium sulfamate and allow to stand 2-3 minutes. Add 5 ml. of 0.4 per cent dimethyl-a-naphthylamine in ethanol and read after 30-60 minutes at 560 mμ against a reagent blank.

With N-(1-naphthyl)ethylenediamine. Free p-aminobenzoic acid. Mix 10 ml. of acidified sample solution, 2 ml. of water, and 1 ml. of 0.1 per cent sodium nitrite solution. After 20 minutes add 1 ml. of 2 per cent solution of ammonium sufamate. After 3 minutes add 5 ml. of 0.1 per cent aqueous solution of the reagent and dilute to 50 ml. After 30-60 minutes read at 430 mμ against a reagent blank.

Total p-aminobenzoic acid. This includes the acetylated form. To 10 ml. of sample solution add 0.5 ml. of 1:2 hydrochloric acid and heat in boiling water for an hour. Cool and make up to 12 ml. Continue as for the free acid by mixing with " . . . 1 ml. of 0.1 per cent sodium nitrite. . . ."

With β-naphthol. Follow the instructions for development of procaine with this reagent (Vol. IV).

With diazotized thiamine. Free p-aminobenzoic acid. If not already present, as in preparation of a urine sample, add 0.3 ml. of 35 per cent acetic acid, dilute to 20 ml. with water, and mix. The pH should be about 2.9. Add 5 ml. of a diazo solution made up of 2.5 ml. of 0.2 per cent aqueous thiamine chloride solution and 2.5 ml. of 2 per cent aqueous sodium nitrite solution. Next, add 4 ml. of 4 per cent sodium hydroxide solution and 5 ml. of isoamyl alcohol. Add about 0.5 ml. of 35 per cent acetic acid to cause the solubility of the colored compound to increase in the amyl alcohol and shake well. Remove the alcohol layer and dry over anhydrous sodium sulfate. Read at 500 mμ. If sulfa drugs are present substitute isopropyl ether for the isoamyl alcohol.

Conjugated p-aminobenzoic acid. To 10 ml. of sample solution add 0.5 ml. of 1:2 hydrochloric acid and place in boiling water for 1 hour. Cool to room temperature, and dilute to 10 ml. with water. Continue as for free *p*-aminobenzoic acid from "Add 5 ml. of a diazo solution...."

p-(Benzylsulfonamido)benzoic Acid
4'-Carboxyphenylmethanesulfonanilide, Caronamide

Carbonamide in alkaline solution in the presence of Raney nickel takes up hydrogen under pressure to give *p*-aminobenzoic acid.[44]

Sample—*Serum.* Mix 0.5 ml. of serum with 5 ml. of 5 per cent sodium hydroxide. Add 2 drops of octyl alcohol and 0.12-0.25 gram of Raney nickel. After 2 hours at room temperature under pressure of hydrogen, dilute to 50 ml. and filter.

Procedure—Develop an aliquot as a sample for *p*-aminobenzoic acid (preceding method).

p-Aminosalicylic Acid

Several general reactions are applicable to *p*-aminosalicylic acid, such as that with dimethylaminobenzaldehyde.[45] There is no interference by primary amines. Another appropriate reaction is that with diazotized *p*-nitroaniline in the presence of pyridine. The reaction gives either a red or blue from the same reagents [46] applied in different order. Interfering substances give the same colors regardless of the order of application.

Normal interfering substances in urine are equivalent to 0.1-0.2 mg. of test substance per ml.; those in blood, to 0.5 mg. per ml. Pyridine when already present destroys excess nitrous acid and serves as a buffer in the final mixtures. Excess reagents are provided to allow for interfering substances.

Uric acid interferes only at dilutions less than 1:10 for blood and 1:1000 for urine to give low results. Removal of uric acid with silver

---

[44] Carl Ziegler and James M. Sprague, *J. Lab. Clin. Med.* **33**, 96-100 (1948); Harvey Shields Collins and Maxwell Finland, *Ibid.* **34**, 509-15 (1949).

[45] Jörgen Lehmann, *Lancet* **250**, 14-15 (1946); W. Klyne and J. P. Newhouse, *Ibid.* **255**, 611 (1948); V. Barilli, *Boll. soc. ital. biol, sper.* **25**, 4-5 (1949).

[46] David M. Tennant and M. L. Leland, *J. Biol. Chem.* **177**, 873-81 (1949).

lactate may give low results. There is no significant interference by 1 mg. of allantoin, creatinine, hippuric acid, urea, sodium salicylate, acetylsalicylic acid, or streptomycin. Bilirubin produces a green color in the coupling reaction which results in a positive, but insignificant error. Sulfonamides may cause low results. m-Aminophenol gives the same colors at about the same intensity. Resorcinol and phloroglucinol produce considerable amounts of color, phenol does not. In a modified form the color with diazotized p-nitroaniline is developed in dilute ethanol with acid.[47] Streptomycin and p-aminobenzoic acid do not interfere.

By heating with about 1:6 sulfuric acid, p-aminosalicylic acid or its N-acetates are decarboxylated to m-aminophenol which is then conveniently determined with N-(1-naphthyl)ethylenediamine dihydrochloride [48] or diazotized and coupled with 2,4-dihydroxybenzoic acid.[49] The latter is formed after hydrolysis by diazotization and deamination.

The familiar indophenol method is also applicable.[50] Details can be picked up from other applications such as that to sulfonamides (Vol. IV). Another reaction used is that with ferric nitrate,[51] or ferric chloride.[52] The latter is read at 490 mμ. Each of these last three reagents is difficult of interpretation due to many interfering substances. Thus with iron salicylic acid gives a violet color. m-Aminosalicylic acid does not react. A simplified form of diazotizing and coupling is to read the color of the diazonium chloride after making it strongly alkaline.[53]

Sample—*Blood or cerebrospinal fluid.* Dilute 0.5 ml. of oxalated whole blood or cerebrospinal fluid to 7 ml. with water and after 3 minutes add 3 ml. of 20 per cent p-toluenesulfonic acid in 1:50 hydrochloric acid. Filter after 5 minutes and use as a sample for development with p-dimethylaminobenzaldehyde.

Alternatively, add 1 ml. of blood to 4 ml. of water. Dilute to 10 ml. with ethanol and mix. Let stand for 10 minutes and centrifuge. Use

---

47 Juan A. Sanchez, *Rev. asoc. bioquím. argentina* 16, 399-406 (1951).

48 A. L. Tarnoky and V. Anne L. Brews, *Biochem. J.* 45, 508-11 (1949).

49 Maurice Pesez, *Bull. soc. chim. biol.* 31, 1369-72 (1949) ; *Bull. soc. chim. France* 1949, 918-19; Cf. Ph. Jacobs, *Pharm. Weekblad* 87, 385-96 (1952).

50 E. Leong Way, Paul K. Smith, Donald L. Howie, Rowena Weiss, and Rollan Swanson, *J. Pharmacol. Exptl. Therap.* 93, 368-82 (1948).

51 A. Venkataraman, P. R. Venkataraman, and H. B. Lewis, *J. Biol. Chem.* 173, 641-51 (1948).

52 Gerardo Matta and M. Luiza Nunes, *Anias Azevados* (Lisbon) 2, 28-36 (1950).

53 G. Curci and V. De-Franciscis, *Arch. tisiol.* (Naples) 4, 59-64 (1949).

1 ml. of the supernatant liquid for each aliquot in the development with diazotized *p*-nitroaniline.

For development in the form of *m*-aminophenol, mix 0.2 ml. with 3.2 ml. of water and lake for 30 minutes. Add 0.6 ml. of 20 per cent trichloroacetic acid solution, mix, and centrifuge. Heat 2 ml. of the clear layer with 0.5 ml. of 6:4 sulfuric acid for 1 hour at 100°. Cool, partially neutralize the resulting *m*-aminophenol solution with 1 ml. of 32 per cent sodium hydroxide solution, and dilute to 4 ml. as sample.

Urine. Dilute to 0.00025-0.005 mg. of *p*-aminosalicylic acid per ml. and develop by *p*-dimethylaminobenzaldehyde or diazotized *p*-nitroaniline.

Procedure—*With p-dimethylaminobenzaldehyde.* Add to the sample solution or an aliquot 1 ml. of buffer consisting of 15.76 per cent citric acid in 1.4 per cent sodium hydroxide solution. Mix and add 2 ml. of 2 per cent solution of *p*-dimethylaminobenzaldehyde in ethanol. Read against a reagent blank.

With diazotized p-nitroaniline. Place duplicate aliquots containing 0.001-0.02 mg. of *p*-aminosalicylic acid in a water bath at 20° and dilute to 4 ml. As parallel standards with each take 4 ml. of a solution containing 0.0025 mg. of *p*-aminosalicylic acid per ml. Such a standard solution is stable under refrigeration for 30 days.

Prepare a fresh coupling reagent by mixing 1 volume of 2 per cent sodium nitrite solution, 8 volumes of 0.02 per cent *p*-nitroaniline solution, and 1 volume of concentrated hydrochloric acid. Pyridine for reagent use must have been refluxed for hours with solid potassium permanganate, fractionally distilled, and the fractions used have given a negative blank with the reagent.

To the first tube and standard of each set add 1 ml. of pyridine, and to the second tube and standard add 1 ml. of the coupling reagent. Mix each well. Then add 1 ml. of coupling reagent to the first tubes and 1 ml. of pyridine to the second tubes. Mix each again. After 5 minutes add 0.5 ml. of 20 per cent sodium hydroxide solution to each tube and mix again. This coupling time gives the maximum color. The color is stable for several hours.

After 20 minutes read the red solution at 620 mμ. Then read the blue solution at the same wave length. Subtract the second value from the first to give that due to the test substance. Correct for any reagent blank necessary.

As an alternative mix 3 ml. of sample solution, 0.5 ml. of ethanol, and 1 ml. of a 1:9 mixture of 10 per cent sodium nitrite and saturated aqueous *p*-nitroaniline. Add a drop of 30 per cent sodium hydroxide solution and, after 1 minute, 3 drops of 1:2 sulfuric acid. Read against a reagent blank.

With N-(1-naphthyl)ethylenediamine. Diazotize a 4-ml. sample with 0.2 ml. of 1 per cent sodium nitrite solution. After 5 minutes add 5 ml. of 5 per cent ammonium sulfamate solution and after 20 seconds add 1 ml. of 0.1 per cent aqueous N-(1-naphthyl)ethylenediamine dihydrochloride. After 2.5 hours read against a reagent blank.

With 2,4-dihydroxybenzoic acid. Hydrolyze a 4-ml. sample by refluxing for 30 minutes. This converts *p*-aminosalicylic acid to *p*-aminophenol by decarboxylation. Cool in ice and add 0.2 ml. of 1 per cent sodium nitrite solution and 1 ml. of 0.1 per cent solution of *p*-aminosalicylic acid. The latter is deaminated to 2,4-dihydroxybenzoic acid. After 3 minutes from the addition of sodium nitrite, make distinctly alkaline with 10 per cent sodium carbonate solution, and let it warm up to room temperature. The two combine to a yellow color. Read against a reagent blank.

PROPYL-*p*-AMINOSALICYLATE

Propyl-*p*-aminosalicylate is diazotized and coupled with thymol for estimation.[54] Accuracy is to ±2 per cent.

Procedure—Chill 2 ml. of 1:10 hydrochloric acid and add 2 ml. of sample containing 0.1-0.2 mg. of test substance. Add 0.5 ml. of fresh 0.5 per cent sodium nitrite solution and shake. Chill for exactly 30 seconds and add 0.5 ml. of 5 per cent thymol in 8 per cent sodium hydroxide solution and 1 ml. of 40 per cent sodium hydroxide solution. Dilute to 15 ml. and read against a reagent blank.

4-AMINO-5-IODOSALICYLIC ACID

The red dye formed by coupling 4-amino-5-iodosalicylic acid with diazotized sulfanilamide will determine 0.001 mg. per ml. of sample.[55] It is linear up to 300 times that concentration.

Procedure—As reagent chill 100 ml. of 2 per cent solution of sulfanilamide in 1:5 hydrochloric acid and add 8.2 ml. of chilled 10 per cent sodium nitrite solution. Add 1.5 ml. of this to 4.5 ml. of deproteinized sample. Read at 520 mμ.

---

[54] István Gyenes, *Magyar Kém. Folyoirat* **56**, 190-5 (1950).
[55] Mario Covello and Antonio Capone, *Ann. chim.* (Rome) **41**, 367-73 (1951).

Sulfosalicylic Acid

The violet color of sulfosalicylic acid in determination of iron is reversed for determination of the acid (Vol. II, pp. 322-4). At pH 2.4 they react in molar proportions.[56]

2,5-Dihydroxybenzoic Acid, Gentisic Acid

The color of gentisic acid with ferric chloride [57] or ferric-ferrous chlorides [58] is appropriate for its estimation. Ferrous chloride in the reagent inhibits oxidation. Proteins must be absent. Control of pH is essential, as is usual with phenol-ferric complexes. Alternatively develop the color of the ferrous ion with o-phenanthroline.[59]

The Folin phenol reagent determines both gentisic and homogentisic acid. The color develops gradually but changes little at 25° between 15 and 30 minutes. There is interference in acid solution by hydroquinone, bromohydroquinone, pyrogallol, and uric acid.[60] In alkaline solution all phenols react. An alternative reagent is 4 per cent ammonium molybdate in 1:7 sulfuric acid.[61] The wave lengths for absorption of gentisic and salicylic acid are shown under the latter.

Samples—*Serum.* Mix 1 ml. of serum with 8 ml. of water and add 0.5 ml. of 1:54 sulfuric acid. Mix and add 0.5 ml. of 9.75 per cent aqueous sodium tungstate. Mix and centrifuge after 10-15 minutes. Develop the clear decantate with phosphotungstic-phosphomolybdic acid.

For development with the ferric reagent, successively add 1 ml. of serum, 1 ml. of water, 1 ml. of 1:4 sulfuric acid, and 20 ml. of ether. Shake for 3 minutes and centrifuge. Separate the ether layer and repeat the extraction. Wash the ether extracts with water, then evaporate to about 15 ml. with a stream of air. Extract the ether with two successive 4-ml. portions of 5 per cent sodium bicarbonate solution and discard the ether. Add 1 ml. of concentrated hydrochloric acid to the combined extracts and warm to drive off dissolved ether. Cool and develop.

For development by reduction of ferric ion to ferrous ion and reac-

[56] Robert T. Foley and Robbin C. Anderson, *J. Am. Chem. Soc.* **70**, 1195-7 (1948).

[57] A. Camelin, P. Accoyer, J. Pellerat, J. Lafuma, and R. Coirault, *Bull. et mem. Soc. méd. hôp. Paris* **65**, 826 (1949).

[58] P. S. Gerald and B. M. Kagan, *J. Biol. Chem.* **189**, 467-72 (1951).

[59] Julius Lowenthal, *J. Lab. Clin. Med.* **38**, 916-18 (1951).

[60] S. Roseman and A. Dorfman, *Ibid.* **192**, 105-14 (1951).

[61] O. Benati, *Farm. sci. e tec.* (Pavia) **5**, 43-6 (1950).

tion with o-phenanthroline, mix 0.2 ml. of clear serum with 5 ml. of 1:1 acetone-ethanol. Stir, boil, cool, and centrifuge.

Urine. Successively add 5 ml. of serum, 5 ml. of water, 1 ml. of 1:4 sulfuric acid, and 20 ml. of ether. Complete as for serum with the ferric reagent, starting at "Shake for 3 minutes. . . ."

Tissue. Macerate an appropriate sample in a Waring Blendor with 200 ml. of water. Strain through cheesecloth and mix 40 ml. with 10 ml. of 20 per cent trichloroacetic acid. After 5 minutes, filter and mix 10 ml. with 20 ml. of ether. Continue as for serum, starting at "Shake for 3 minutes. . . ."

Procedure—*With ferric reagent.* As reagent dissolve 50 grams of ferrous chloride tetrahydrate in 1:1200 hydrochloric acid. Add 20 ml. of a 1 per cent solution of ferric chloride hexahydrate in that acid and dilute to a liter with the acid. Mix 5 ml. of clarified sample and 5 ml. of reagent. Read at 595 mμ within 1 minute against a reagent blank.

With o-phenanthroline. To a 5-ml. aliquot of deproteinized sample add 10 ml. of an acetate buffer for pH 3.4, 0.1 ml. of 2.5 per cent ferric chloride solution, 0.1 ml. of 4 per cent potassium fluoride, and 1 ml. of 0.25 per cent o-phenanthroline solution. Read at 510 mμ against a reagent blank.

With phosphotungstic-phosphomlybdic acid reagent. To the sample, or an aliquot containing less than 0.05 mg. of gentisic acid, add 1 ml. of the reagent (page 116) and 3 ml. of 20 per cent sodium carbonate solution. Dilute to 10 ml. and, after 20 minutes, read at 660 mμ against a reagent blank.

With ammonium molybdate. As reagent mix equal volumes of 8 per cent aqueous ammonium molybdate and 1:3 sulfuric acid. Dilute a sample containing 0.02-0.4 mg. of gentisic acid to 5 ml. with water. Add 1 ml. of reagent, mix, and heat in boiling water for 30 minutes. Cool and read against a reagent blank.

CINNAMIC ACID

Cinnamic acid is oxidized to benzoic acid by alkaline or neutral potassium permangante solution.[62] In the absence of benzoic acid, ferric chloride is used for estimation of the cinnamic acid in the form of benzoic acid. When both are present a determination of benzoic acid is made without permanganate oxidation and one with the oxidation. The difference between the two determinations is calculated to cinnamic acid.

---

[62] J. R. Nichols, *Analyst* 53, 19-29 (1928).

Procedure—Add to a neutral solution of cinnamate containing about 4 mg., at least double the theoretical quantity of potassium permanganate solution and let stand in a closed vessel for 15 to 20 minutes. Just acidify with 1:3 nitric acid and add just enough oxalic acid to clarify. Proceed as for benzoic acid "Development with ferric ion," starting at the beginning. Multiply the results in terms of benzoic acid by 1.214 to convert to cinnamic acid.

3,4-Dihydroxycinnamic Acid, Caffeic Acid

In aqueous acid solution caffeic acid gives an intense vermillion color with sodium nitrite. Chlorogenic acid gives a yellow color which on addition of excess sodium hydroxide changes to an intense carmine red. Chlorogenic acid can be changed to caffeic acid so that either reaction may be used for its estimation.[63] The color develops slowly and is unstable. Urea decomposes the colors to some extent and the permissible amount of ethanol is strictly limited. As applied to raw coffee the methods are in good agreement and are accurate within 1-2 per cent. The reaction is not applicable to roasted coffee because of interference by protocatechuic acid, protocatechol, and dihydroxystyrol.

Sample—*Raw coffee.* Extract 5 grams of raw coffee for 30 minutes with acetone. Air-dry the fat-free beans and digest for several hours in 50 ml. of saturated sodium chloride solution. Decant, add 50 ml. more, and boil for 15 minutes. Decant, add 50 ml. of water, boil for 15 minutes, and decant. Repeat with 2 additional 50-ml. portions of water. Dilute the combined extracts to 250 ml., filter, and dilute 25 ml. of this extract to 100 ml. for development of color in an aliquot.

Alternatively, add 80 ml. of boiling water to 5 grams of finely ground air-dried but not fat-free coffee. Boil gently for one-half hour, cool, and dilute to exactly 100 ml. Filter with precautions against evaporation. As an average figure the volume of liquid was 96.4 ml., the balance being the coffee. Dilute 10 ml. of this solution to 100 ml. for development of color in an aliquot.

Procedure—*As chlorogenic acid.* Mix 2 ml. of the diluted sample with 8 ml. of water in a test tube. Add 0.3 ml. of a buffer containing 10 per cent of acetic acid and 30 per cent of anhydrous sodium acetate.

---

[63] W. Hoepfner, *Chem.-Ztg.* **56**, 991 (1932); W. Plücker and W. Kielholz, *Z. Untersuch. Lebensm.* **68**, 97-109 (1934); C. Massatsch, *Z. Untersuch. Lebensm.* **67**, 88-91 (1934).

Cool to 8° and add 0.3 ml. of 40 per cent sodium nitrite solution. After 3 minutes at 8° add 0.3 ml. of 10 per cent sodium hydroxide solution. Read against 2 ml. of the sample and 8.9 ml. of water.

As caffeic acid. Cool 50 ml. of extract, obtained directly from the raw coffee, without the last dilution step, to 18°. Add 12 ml. of 30 per cent potassium hydroxide solution. After 1 hour at 18°, add 10 ml. of 1:2 sulfuric acid, with cooling. Filter, extract with 100 ml. of ether, and discard the aqueous layer. Wash the ether 3 times with 25-ml. portions of water. Transfer the washed ether layer and 50 ml. of water to a distilling flask and distil the ether. Dilute the aqueous layer to 100 ml.

To 1 ml. of sample and 9 ml. of water, add 0.15 ml. of the acetate buffer. Cool to 18° and add 0.15 ml. of 40 per cent sodium nitrite solution. Keep at 18° for 10 minutes and read against 1 ml. of extract and 9.3 ml. of water.

Chlorogenic Acid

Chlorogenic acid is estimated in the form of caffeic acid (preceding method). It is also read in the ultraviolet at 324 mμ.[64] For green coffee extracts the reading is a direct one but when extracted from roasted coffee the difference before and after removal of chlorogenic acid with basic lead acetate is used.

Sample—*Green coffee.* For direct reading in the ultraviolet, grind to pass a 1-mm. screen, flake on a chocolate mill, and take a 2-gram sample. Defat by washing with 25, 25, and 25 ml. of 20-40° petroleum ether and let the solvent evaporate. Add about 800 ml. of water and shake occasionally for 20 minutes. Dilute to 1 liter and filter through a Büchner funnel, discarding the first 50 ml. Dilute an aliquot of the filtrate 1:10 with water for reading in the ultraviolet.

Roasted coffee. Follow the technic for green coffee, omitting from "Defat by washing . . ." through ". . . the solvent evaporate." After diluting 1:10 for reading take 100 ml. of the undiluted filtrate and add 1 gram of potassium acetate and 2 ml. of saturated basic lead acetate solution with swirling. Heat at 100° for 5 minutes and chill to 0°. Stir mechanically for 1 hour. Dilute to 200 ml., mix, and filter. Discard the first 50 ml. of filtrate. Use this for reading without dilution.

Procedure—Read the diluted filtrate from green coffee directly at 324 mμ and calculate from $E_{1\text{cm.}}^{1\%} = 526$. For roasted coffee read at

---

[64] R. G. Moores, Dorothy L. McDermott, and T. R. Wood, *Anal. Chem.* **20**, 620-4 (1948).

324 mμ and subtract 20 per cent of the reading for the filtrate treated with lead acetate, this to allow for its lower dilution. Then calculate as usual.

METHYL ANTHRANILATE

The color developed by diazotized methyl anthranilate with naphthols is suitable for colorimetric estimation.[65] α-Naphthol is preferable to the β-derivative. A further modification is to couple with sodium-α-naphthol-2-sulfonate.[66]

Sample—*Non-alcoholic beverages and concentrates.* Dilute 10 ml. or more of sample to 100 ml. and set up to distil through a spray trap and connecting bulb into a condenser dipping below water in a receiver. Heat in boiling water and pass steam until about 300 ml. is collected. Disconnect and wash out the condenser with water. Use all for development with sodium-α-naphthol-2-sulfonate.

Procedure—*With sodium-α-naphthol-2-sulfonate.* Add 25 ml. of 83:917 hydrochloric acid and 2 ml. of 2 per cent sodium nitrite solution to the prepared sample. Mix and after exactly 2 minutes add 6 ml. of 3 per cent hydrazine sulfate solution. Mix for 1 minute and, keeping in rapid agitation, add 5 ml. of 5 per cent sodium-α-naphthol-2-sulfonate solution. At once add 15 ml. of 25 per cent sodium carbonate solution. Dilute to 500 ml. and read against a reagent blank.

With α-naphthol. Dilute a sample to contain 0.005-0.025 mg. of methyl anthranilate to 100 ml. Add 1 ml. of 1:12 hydrochloric acid and 0.5 ml. of 5 per cent sodium nitrite solution. At the end of 30 seconds add to 0.5 ml. of 2 per cent alcoholic α-naphthol solution and 3 ml. of 4 per cent sodium hydroxide solution. Read after 15 minutes against a reagent blank. The color is constant for several hours. A slight color in the α-naphthol solution does no harm as it is removed by the nitrite.

5-HYDROXYANTHRANILIC ACID

Oxidation of 5-hydroxyanthranilic acid in acid solution with potassium iodate yields a violet color,[67] insoluble in ether. Adrenaline develops

---

[65] E. Erdmann, *Ber.* **35**, 24-7 (1902); Frederick B. Power, *J. Am. Chem. Soc.* **43**, 377-81 (1921); R. D. Scott, *Ind. Eng. Chem.* **15**, 732-3 (1923).

[66] Official and Tentative Methods of Analysis of the Association of Official Agricultural Chemists. 7th Ed. pp. 125-6. Association of Official Agricultural Chemists, Washington, D. C. (1950).

[67] Yôichi Shirai and Shûji Uno, *J. Japan. Biochem.* **23**, 51-8 (1951).

the same color but less rapidly. A red to orange color, soluble in ether, is due to 3-hydroxyanthranilic acid, 5-aminosalicylic acid, tryptophan, cysteine, ascorbic acid, *p*-aminophenol, or *o*-aminophenol. A light yellow, soluble in ether, is due to anthranilic acid, pyrocatechol, hydroquinone, resorcinol, orcinol, or pyrogallol. There is no reaction by histidine, tyro sine, arginine, thiamine, riboflavin, nicotine acid, pyridoxine, benzoic acid, salicylic acid, hippuric acid, 3-aminosalicylic acid, 4-aminosalicylic acid, phenol, aniline, or sulfanilamide.

Procedure—*Urine.* Make a 5-15 ml. sample acid to thymol blue with 1:50 hydrochloric acid. Add 3 ml. of 10 per cent phosphotungstic acid solution in 1:30 hydrochloric acid. Dilute to 20 ml. and mix. After 1 hour, filter and shake the filtrate with an equal volume of ether. Separate the extracted aqueous layer and aerate at 40° to remove ether. To 10 ml. of sample solution add about 0.1 gram of sodium acetate to adjust the pH to 2.5. Add 1 ml. of 0.36 per cent potassium iodate in 1.5 per cent potassium iodide solution. Extract with 10 ml. and 10 ml. of ether and dilute the aqueous layer to 20 ml. Read against a reagent blank.

2-Phenyl-4-quinoline Carboxylic Acid, Cinchophen

When cinchophen is precipitated from acid solution with silico-tungstic acid, determination of the excess of precipitant is a convenient device. The titanium chloride reagent so used does not give color with salicylates.[68] Any other precipitant of silicotungstic acid interferes. Accuracy is to ±3 per cent.

Procedure—Adjust a sample solution containing about 50 mg of cinchophen to be about 1:1 with hydrochloric acid. Heat in boiling water and add 5 ml. of 4 per cent silicotungstic acid. Centrifuge and remove a 5-ml. aliquot of the upper layer. Add 7 ml. of water and 10 ml. of a fresh reagent containing 1 part of 15 per cent titanous chloride diluted with 9 parts of 1:5 hydrochloric acid. Shake and read at once at 720 mμ. The precipitate of cinchophen silicotungstate can be dissolved in 1:1 hydrochloric acid and determined by the same reaction.

Phthalic Acid

Ultraviolet spectrophotometry is the best method available for determining small amounts of phthalic acid from phthalic anhydride as iso-

---

[68] André Morel, *Ann. pharm. franc.* **3**, 137-40 (1945).

lated from alkyd resins.[69] Sebacic acid must be filtered out. Other acids absorbing at the same wave length are corrected for provided only one is present. Examples are adipic, succinic, and maleic acids. The phthalyl content of esters of cellulose or polyvinyl alcohol is also read in the ultraviolet at 275 mμ.[70] By subtraction of the phthalic acid determined by titration a measure is obtained of the combined phthalic acid as distinguished from that present as the free acid.

Sample[71]—Reflux for 1.5 hours 3 samples expected to contain about 0.1 gram of phthalic acid each with 5 ml. of benzene and 35 ml. of 5.6 per cent absolute ethanolic potassium hydroxide. Heat at 40° for 1 hour, gradually raise the temperature to gentle boiling, and reflux for 90 minutes. Rinse down the condenser with 1:1 ether-absolute ethanol, remove the flask, and close with a soda-lime tube. Cool in water and rinse down the sides of the flask with ether. Filter as rapidly as possible through a fritted-glass crucible. Use 1:1 ether-absolute ethanol for transfer and washing. Continue to wash until the washings as they come through are not alkaline to phenolphthalein. Finally wash the filter with ether. Do not draw air through the precipitate, which is hygroscopic.

Pass 200 ml. of distilled water by suction through the precipitate in the crucible, thus extracting the soluble salts. Add 10 ml. of concentrated hydrochloric acid to the aqueous extract. A precipitate or cloud indicates the presence of sebacic acid. Filter if even slightly cloudy and dilute to 1 liter. Dilute 50 ml. to 100 ml. with 1:100 hydrochloric acid.

Procedure—Read at 276 mμ against the hydrochloric acid as a blank. If the absorbence is between 0.35 and 0.45, proceed in the same way with the other two precipitates and average the three determinations. If outside that range calculate the dilution necessary in preparation of the other two samples to come within those limits. If difficulty is encountered with scattering of the ultraviolet radiation, use 1:100 hydrochloric acid-absolute methanol or ethanol for the final dilution and read against a corresponding blank.

To correct for one interfering acid completely soluble on acidification of its dissolved potassium salt, calculate from the equations

---

[69] O. D. Shreve and M. R. Heether, *Anal. Chem.* **23**, 441-5 (1951).

[70] Carl J. Malm, Leo B. Genung, and William Kuchmy, *Anal. Chem.* **25**, 245-9 (1953).

[71] 1949 Book of ASTM Standards, Part 4, pp. 237-8, American Society for Testing Materials, Philadelphia, Pa.

$$a_p C_p + a_i C_i = A$$
$$F_p C_p + F_i C_i = B/f$$

where

A = measured absorbence
a_p = absorptivity for phthalic acid
C_p = concentration of phthalic acid
C_i = concentration of interfering ion
F_p = factor to convert phthalic acid to potassium phathalate
F_i = factor to convert the interfering acid to its potassium salt
B = weight of precipitate
f = aliquot of precipitate used.

PHENOLPHTHALEIN

Phenolphthalein is conveniently read by its intense red color in alkaline solution. This is frequently complicated by the presence of other drugs. The method which follows [72] provides for separation from drugs of the emodin type.

Sample—Extract a powdered sample containing 0.005-0.1 gram of phenolphthalein and not over 0.3 gram of emodin drugs with 10, 10, 10, and 10 ml. of acetone. Evaporate the filtered extract to dryness. Take up the residue in 10 ml. of ethanol. Prepare a chromatographic column 10 × 300 mm., using aluminium oxide. Pass the sample through with such suction as is necessary and wash the column with ethanol until the washings show no pink with alkali. Dilute the washings to a known volume.

Procedure—To an aliquot of the sample equal to 0.1-0.5 mg. of phenolphthalein add 2 ml. of 1.25 per cent potassium hydroxide solution and dilute to 25 ml. Read against a reagent blank at 550 mμ.

DIMALONE

Dimalone is the dimethyl ester of *cis*-3,6-endomethylene-Δ^d-tetrahydrophthalic acid, an insect repellant. It is estimated by the methanol liberated on saponification.[73] Amounts of the order of 2.5 mg. separated from fabric are so determined.

---

[72] Sixten Ljungberg, *Pharm. Acta Helv.* **25**, 351-3 (1950); S. Druce, *Pharm. J.* **168**, 76 (1952).

[73] Jerome Goldenson and Samuel Sass, *Anal. Chem.* **20**, 1118-20 (1948).

Sample—*Fabric.* Saponify a 10-gram sample of 1-cm. squares by refluxing for 30 minutes with 50 ml. of 1.2 per cent aqueous potassium hydroxide. Cool, rinse down the reflux condenser, and by suitable additions of water distil 100 ml. into a chilled flask. Use a 5-ml. aliquot of the distillate.

Procedure—Complete as for methanol, developing by any of the methods shown in that procedure (pages 45 and 46).

Melilotic Acid

The technic of determination as a correction in coumarin estimation appears on page 150.

Rosin and Rosin Acids

Rosin is essentially abietic acid. Rosin and rosin acids are estimated by sulfuric acid and acetic anhydride, a modification of the qualitative test for rosin.[74] Rosin esters give a color in benzene. The method will not differentiate different rosin esters. Cellulose derivatives must be absent because the rosin cannot be separated from them. Incomplete esters give values for rosin in agreement with the acid number and cannot be analyzed for rosin ester content. Alkyds do not react. Hydrogenated rosin interferes. The admixture of rosin with waxes such as ceresin or with paraffin is estimated by treating the sample with nitric acid and subsequently making it alkaline with ammonium hydroxide.[75] The waxes give a light yellow which does not interfere with estimation of the deep red-brown color produced by rosin. Cholesterol does not interfere. Since nitric acid does not give soluble colored reaction products with cellulose after neutralizing with ammonia, it is applicable to estimation of the rosin size in paper. The method is accurate to about 10 per cent.

Sample—*Paint or varnish.* Weigh a sample of not over 0.5 gram containing 0.1-0.2 gram of nonvolatile solids into benzene and dilute to 100 ml. with the same solvent. Develop by the procedures for free rosin and rosin soaps, or rosin esters, or both.

Wax or paper. High rosin content. Extract the sample with 50 per cent ethanol, which dissolves none of the wax or paraffin, and weigh

---

[74] C. Liebermann, *Ber.* **18**, 1884 (1884); Melvin H. Swann, *Anal. Chem.* **23**, 885-8 (1951).

[75] E. Donath, *Dingler's Polytech. J.* **205**, 131-7 (1872); *Chem.-Ztg.* **54**, 667 (1930).

directly. Use the extracted residue for estimation of the balance of the rosin.

Low rosin content. Use the sample as received.

Procedure—*Free rosin and rosin soaps.* Dilute an aliquot of benzene solution estimated to contain not over 4 mg. of test substance to about 100 ml. with benzene. If rosin esters are present, this must be further reduced to 1 ± 0.5 mg. of rosin. Mix in a separatory funnel with 5 ml. of 1:1 sulfuric acid and add 1 ml. of acetic anhydride. Shake for 5 seconds and immerse in water at room temperature to at least the level of the benzene. After 45 seconds, remove, add another 1-ml. portion of acetic anhydride, and again immerse for 45 seconds. Repeat until 10 ml. of acetic anhydride have been added.

After removing from the water bath the last time add 80 ml. of 1:1 sulfuric acid and mix without actually shaking. The sulfuric layer separates below. Withdraw at once into a 30-ml. glass filter crucible with a supplementary mat of asbestos fibers. Dilute the aqueous acid layer, after filtration, to 100 ml. with 1:1 sulfuric acid and read at 525 mμ against a reagent blank. Interpret from a standard curve prepared with purified abietic acid. Color in the benzene layer is due to rosin esters.

Rosin esters. Dilute a sample in benzene, containing 2-15 mg. of abietic acid, to 50 ml. with 0.5 ml. of acetic anhydride and benzene. Mix and cool in water at 15-18°. After 3 minutes add 1 drop of concentrated sulfuric acid and shake until color develops, and 3 seconds additional. At once compare against permanganate standards in the same volume as shown in Table 3. Fading starts after 10-15 seconds.

TABLE 3. ABIETIC ACID EQUIVALENTS

0.01% Potassium Permanganate Solution Diluted to 50-Ml. Volume with Water Ml.	Equivalent Ester Gum, Mg.	Equivalent Maleic Rosin Ester, Mg.	Calculated Equivalent Abietic Acid, Mg.
2	3.33	4	3.2
4	6.67	8	6.4
6	10.0	12	9.6
8	13.33	16	12.8
10	16.7	20	16.0

Extract from wax. Mix 1 gram of sample with 5 ml. of nitric acid of d. about 1.32. This is prepared from colorless concentrated acid by diluting 4 parts with 1 part of water. Heat to boiling for 1 minutes and cool. Dilute with 5 ml. of water and render alkaline with concentrated ammonium hydroxide. Cool and dilute to 25 ml. Compare the color obtained with that from a series of standards produced by suitable admixture of rosin with ceresin or paraffin.

CHAPTER 17

COMPLEX ACIDS AND DERIVATIVES [1]

THE SUBJECT starts with complex acids such as uric acid, progresses through derivatives such as allantoin and aloxan, and includes many more complicated acids. Many are sufficiently large in molecular weight so that their salts are colored.

Of course, with such a heterogeneous group of compounds there is no class reaction, and there is no sharp classification between the complex acids here and previous chapters on acids. To illustrate, acetic acid with a reasonably complex substituent is in monosubstituted aliphatic acids, but eventually the substituent becomes so complex that it is in this chapter.

URIC ACID

Uric acid reduces phospho-18-tungstic acid to give a blue color.[2] The phospho-24-tungstic acid is inactive. Such a reduction is also given by other substances present in blood. The convenient method is therefore to correct for a blank in which the uric acid has been destroyed by uricase.[3] Such a blank normally approximates half the uric acid content.

The color development by the reagent from glutathione, glucose, ascorbic acid, resorcinol, tryptophane, tyrosine, ergothioneine, cystine, and mono-, di-, and trimethyl uric acids at concentrations comparable to those in blood is not altered substantially by the uricase which destroys the uric acid. There is no effect by allantoin, alloxan, adenine, guanine, hypoxanthine, xanthine, adenylic acid, creatine, creatinine, and uricase. There is no change in the uric acid content of refrigerated oxalated blood.

While application of heat increases the color it also increases the deviation from proportionality. By cold development accuracy to ±5 per cent is readily obtained. Slow precipitation of proteins improves the

---

[1] See Chapter 1 for details of organization, condensation, etc.

[2] E. Riegler, *Z. anal. Chem.* **51**, 466-70 (1912); Otto Folin and W. Denis, *J. Biol. Chem.* **12**, 239-43 (1912); *Ibid.* **13**, 469-75 (1912).

[3] Mary Brannock Blauch and F. D. Koch, *Proc. Soc. Exp. Biol. and Med.* **38**, 638 (1938); *J. Biol. Chem.* **130**, 443-54 (1939); Harold A. Bulger and Helen E. Johns, *J. Biol. Chem.* **140**, 427-40 (1941); Herman Brown, *J. Biol. Chem.* **158**, 601-8 (1945); E. Leon, *Quaderni nutriz.* **10**, 63-75 (1947).

recoveries. Cyanide intensifies the reaction. In general this is the most accurate method available.[4] Direct reading in the ultraviolet at 290-295 mμ before and after [5] addition of uricase is reproducible to ±3 per cent.

Uric acid reduces arsenotungstic acid to give a blue color, somewhat similar to the reaction of phospho-18-tungstic acid.[6] As with the previous reagent it is necessary to correct for interferences by destroying uric acid in a blank with uricase. The degree of alkalinity of the solution prevents interference by amino acids, and urea prevents turbidity. There is no color developed with this reagent by adenine, guanine, xanthine, methylxanthines, allantoin, and various phenols other than resorcinol. A superior version of the reagent is prepared by precipitation of lithium arseno-18-tungstate.[7] The aqueous solution of this salt is uncontaminated by the chromogenically inert acids and salts present in many uric acid reagents. It is less acidic than other reagents and its reduction can be observed over a wide range of pH. No color develops in a reagent blank.

The two reagents have been chemically combined in an arsenophosphotungstic acid reagent.[8] Glucose interferes and can greatly complicate the corrections required.

A solution of ferricyanide is reduced to ferrocyanide by uric acid in alkaline solution. This is then converted in acid solution to Prussian blue as a measure of the uric acid present.[9] Unlike the previous methods, which are empirical, this is a stoichiometric reaction. Other reducing substances are corrected for by the uricase technic. Usually this value is less than 0.01 mg. per ml. of sample. By operating below 3°, glucose does not interfere.

Uricase —Defat and grind finely 1 pound of fresh frozen beef kidney. Dehydrate at 4° with four successive 500-ml portions of acetone, allowing 12 hours for each treatment. Dry quickly at room temperature

[4] H. Tastaldi, *Anais faculdade farm. odontol. Univ. São Paulo* 3, 41-95 (1942-3).

[5] E. Praetorius, *Scand. J. Clin. Lab. Invest.* 1, 222-30 (1949).

[6] Stanley R. Benedict and E. Franke, *J. Biol. Chem.* 52, 387-91 (1922); Oliver H. Buchanan, Walter D. Block, and A. A. Christman, *Ibid.* 157, 181-201 (1945); Norwood K. Schaffer, *J. Biol. Chem.* 153, 163 (1944).

[7] Eleanor B. Newton, *J. Biol. Chem.* 120, 315-29 (1937).

[8] J. C. D. Hutchinson, *Biochem. J.* 35, 81-90 (1941); J. W. Mull, *J. Lab. Clin. Med.* 28, 1038-42 (1945); O. H. Buchanan, D. Block, and A. A. Christman, *J. Biol. Chem.* 157, 181-7 (1945); Edward J. Bien and Walter Troll, *Proc. Soc. Exptl. Biol. Med.* 73, 370-2 (1950).

[9] F. Montequi, *Anales soc. espan. fis. quim.* 29, 264-6 (1931); Harold A. Bulger and Helen E. Johns, *J. Biol. Chem.* 140, 427-40 (1941); Herbert Silverman and Isadore Gubernick, *Ibid.* 167, 363-8 (1947).

with the aid of a fan. Treat the dry material with 500 ml. of benzene at room temperature for 6 hours, filter, and treat with a second portion for 12 hours. Dry quickly at room temperature, grind to 60-mesh, and store in a desiccator at 4°. Check the activity of the powder by following the rate at which it causes uric acid to disappear from a solution under standardized conditions. Suspend 1 gram of uricase powder in 100 ml. of 0.125 per cent sodium carbonate solution for 2 hours at 45°. Add 36 ml. of water, 1 ml. of 10 per cent sodium tungstate, and 2 ml. of 1:54 sulfuric acid solution. Determine uric acid colorimetrically on the filtrate. One ml. of 1 per cent suspension may be expected to oxidize 4-5 mg. of uric acid.

Sample—*Blood*. To prepare the filtrate containing the uric acid add 2 ml. of 10 per cent sodium tungstate solution to 2 ml. of sample and then slowly add 16 ml. of 1:300 sulfuric acid. For the blank filtrate incubate 2 ml. of sample at 40-48° for 2 hours with 50 mg. of uricase powder. Add 2 ml. of 10 per cent sodium tungstate solution and 16 ml. of 1:300 sulfuric acid to precipitate proteins and the uricase. Centrifuge or filter each to get a clear solution for color development with phospho-18-tungstic acid or ferrocyanide. Trichloroacetic acid filtrates can also be used with phospho-18-tungstic acid reagent.[10]

For development with arseno-18-tungstic acid, first prepare a molybdotungstate precipitant for protein. For this, boil 10 grams of molybdic acid with 50 ml. of 4 per cent sodium hydroxide solution for 5 minutes. Filter, wash the filter with 150 ml. of hot water, and cool. Mix the total filtrate with 80 grams of sodium tungstate dissolved in 600 ml. of water and dilute to 1 liter.

Lake 1 volume of blood with 7 volumes of water and treat with 1 volume of molybdotungstate solution; follow by 1 volume of 1:58 sulfuric acid, and filter.

Serum or plasma. To a 1 ml. sample add 10 mg. of uricase and swirl. This is the background blank. As sample use 1 ml. of serum or plasma. As a reagent blank use 1 ml. of water with 10 mg. of uricase. Incubate the ones containing uricase at 37.5° for 2 hours. Add 8 ml. of 1:300 sulfuric acid and 1 ml. of 10 per cent sodium tungstate solution to each. Shake thoroughly and centrifuge for 5 minutes. Use aliquots for development with ferricyanide.

Cerebrospinal fluid.[11] As sample take 1 ml. of cerebrospinal fluid

---

[10] Pedro N. Herranz, *Mon. farm.* (Madrid) **51**, 265-6 (1945).

[11] Guiseppe Guilio Giordano and Luigi Saitta, *Acta nuerol.* (Naples), **5**, 293-9 (1950).

and 0.75 ml. of 0.125 per cent sodium carbonate solution. In parallel prepare another tube containing the same materials plus 50 mg. of uricase. Incubate the tubes at 45° for 2 hours. Adjust to pH 6 with 0.25 ml. of 1:120 hydrochloric acid. Dilute to 5 ml. for development with phospho-18-tungstic acid.

Urine. Dilute a 24-hour sample to 2 liters with water. To 5 ml. of this add 10 ml. of water and a few drops of thymol blue indicator solution. Titrate to a definite blue tint with 0.4 per cent sodium hydroxide solution, record the volume, and discard. Treat a similar aliquot with alkali without adding indicator. Add 250 mg. of uricase and 5 ml. of borate buffer for pH 9.2 (Vol. II, p. 175). Wash down the sides with 10 ml. of water and incubate at 45° for 2 hours. Add 1 ml. of 10 per cent sodium tungstate solution and mix. Add 1.5 ml. of 1:54 sulfuric acid and mix. Dilute to 50 ml. and filter as the solution to be developed for correction. Similarly dilute 5 ml. of the 2-liter dilution of the 24-hour sample to 50 ml. as the sample. Develop each with arsenotungstic acid reagent.

Renal calculi. Heat 100 mg. of the dried and powdered sample with 5-10 ml. of a warm 10 per cent solution of sodium hydroxide for a few minutes, stirring occasionally. Dilute to 500 ml. and develop an aliquot with phospho-18-tungstic acid, ignoring references to the uricase-treated sample.

Bile. Add 5 ml. of 25 per cent neutral lead acetate solution to 25 ml. of bile. Mix well, filter, and wash the precipitate with 5 ml. of water. Add 10 ml. of 1:35 sulfuric acid and 5 ml. of ethanol. Dilute to 100 ml. and mix well. Filter or centrifuge to remove the precipitated lead sulfate. To 10 ml. of the filtrate add 4 per cent sodium hydroxide solution until neutral to litmus. Add 1:35 sulfuric acid until just detectably acid. Dilute to 50 ml. and develop with phospho-18-tungstic acid, ignoring references to a uricase-treated blank.

Tissue. Cut up a 10-gram sample and rub it in a mortar with 20 grams of clean sand. Add 50 ml. of 0.01 per cent lithium carbonate solution and digest on a water bath for a few minutes. Cool the reddish brown suspension and without filtering treat as a blood sample, starting "To prepare the filtrate . . . ."

Procedure—*By phospho-18-tungstic acid.* Prepare the uric acid reagent,[12] by dissolving 100 grams of pure sodium tungstate in 700 ml.

---

[12] F. C. Koch, "Practical Methods of Biochemistry," Baltimore, 2nd Edit. 130-1, 284 (1937).

of water. Add 75 ml. of 85 per cent phosphoric acid, and reflux gently for 24 hours. To decolorize the resulting solution, add a few drops of bromine, or 30 per cent hydrogen peroxide, and boil for 10 minutes without a condenser. Dilute to 1 liter, filter, and store in a brown, glass-stoppered bottle.

To 5-ml. samples of filtrate treated with uricase and untreated filtrate, add 5 ml. of fresh 2.5 per cent sodium cyanide in 25 per cent urea solution. Then add 1 ml. of uric acid reagent slowly from a buret. Mix, stopper, and allow to stand for 3 hours for color development. Read at 610 mμ. Subtract the uric acid value obtained with the sample treated with uricase from that of the untreated sample to give the true uric acid content.

By arseno-18-tungstic acid. Blood. Prepare the reagent by dissolving 100 grams of sodium tungstate in 500 ml. of water and adding 140 grams of arsenic pentoxide. Reflux for 1 hour, remove the condenser, and continue boiling until the volume is about 200 ml. Slowly pour this solution with stirring on 100 grams of lithium chloride. Stir until all the lithium chloride is dissolved and then chill for about 2 hours below 10°. Filter the lithium arseno-18-tungstate on a Büchner funnel and dry as completely as possible by suction. The yield should be about 130 grams. Dissolve this salt in water and dilute to 500 ml. For use, dilute this solution 1:5.

Mix 5 ml. of 1:10 molybdotungstic acid blood filtrate with 1 ml of a solution containing 7.5 grams of lithium chloride and 35 ml. of concentrated hydrochloric acid per liter. Add 1 ml. of 2.9 per cent silver nitrate solution and shake well. Centrifuge at once, decant the supernatant liquid, and add 3 ml. of 5 per cent solution of sodium cyanide in 20 per cent urea solution. Add 1 ml. of dilute lithium arsenotungstate reagent, mix by inversion, and read at 690 mμ after 10 minutes.

Urine. As reagent boil 100 grams of sodium tungstate, 125 grams of arsenic oxide, and 650 ml. of water for 4 hours. If the color is blue, add sufficient bromine-water to give a yellow color and boil off the excess bromine. Dilute to 1 liter with water. As alkaline urea-cyanide solution dissolve 25 grams of pure sodium cyanide and 50 grams of anhydrous sodium carbonate in 400 ml. of water. Cool and add 75 grams of urea. Dissolve, dilute to 500 ml., and filter. This can be used for several months, but develops a slight precipitate on standing.

Dilute 5 ml. of prepared sample and background blank to 25 ml. with water. Add 2.5 ml. of urea-cyanide solution and 1 ml. of arseno-phosphotungstic acid reagent to each. Dilute to 50 ml. and mix thoroughly. Allow the color to develop exactly 30 minutes before reading at 690 mμ.

With ferricyanide. As alkaline ferricyanide reagent mix equal quantities of 0.4 per cent potassium ferricyanide solution and 1.6 per cent sodium carbonate solution. To prepare ferric reagent suspend 20 grams of gum ghatti on noncorrodable screening just below the surface of a liter of water for 24 hours. Strain the liquid through a double layer of toweling. Dissolve 5 grams of anhydrous ferric sulfate and 75 ml. of 85 per cent phosphoric acid by heating with 100 ml of water. Let cool and mix with the gum ghatti solution. Add 1 per cent potassium permanganate solution, 2-3 ml. at a time until a faint pink color persists for at least 5 minutes. This oxidizes reducing substances in the gum ghatti which would otherwise reduce the ferricyanide.

Chill 5-ml. portions of the deproteinized filtrate and blank in an ice-brine bath for 90 minutes. Add 3 ml. of similarly chilled aqueous 1.65 per cent ferricyanide reagent to each tube and mix by shaking. Replace in the ice bath and allow the oxidation to go on for exactly 60 minutes. Temperature control is very important. Add 2.5 ml. of ferric reagent to each tube, mix by shaking, and incubate at 25° for 20 minutes. Read at 540 mμ against a reagent blank and subtract the background blank from the determined value.

GLYOXYLDIUREIDE, ALLANTOIN

When allantoin is boiled with alkali at pH 9.5-10 for 15 minutes it gives allantoic acid. Following this, hydrolysis in acid solution at a pH of less than 3 for 1-2 minutes at 100° then gives 2 molecules of urea and 1 molecule of glyoxylic acid.[13] The glyoxylic acid is estimated by reaction with phenylhydrazine and a suitable oxidizing agent such as ferricyanide to give a red color.[14] This is preferable to hydrolysis with allantoinase extracted from soybean meal.[15] The reaction is negative with protein, acetaldehyde, formaldehyde, benzaldehyde and urea. Glucose in large quantities interferes because it forms an osazone with phenylhydrazine.

[13] R. Fosse, A. Brunel, and P. de Graeve, *Compt. rend.* **188**, 1632-4 (1929); Gh. Bosson, *Mikrochim. Acta* **2**, 73-9 (1937); Arsène Debeaumont and Jean Desodt, *Bull. soc. pharm. Lille* **1947**, No. 4, 42-9.

[14] E. Gordon Young and Catherine F. Conway, *J. Biol. Chem.* **142**, 839-53 (1942); E. Gordon Young, Catherine Conway MacPherson, Helen P. Wentworth, and Winthrop W. Hawkins, *Ibid.* **152**, 245-53 (1944).

[15] Marcel Florkin and Ghislaine Duchateau-Bosson, *Enzymologia* **9**, 5-9 (1940).

Allantoin is also developed with diacetylmonoxime as described for citrulline.

Sample—*Blood.* Warm 10 ml. of water with 5 ml. of oxalated whole blood at 40° on a water bath. Gradually add 8 grams of anhydrous sodium sulfate with the aid of a mechanical stirrer. Continue stirring for about 30 minutes. Filter through a warmed Büchner funnel as shown in Figure 28. The tube which catches the filtrate has a small hole in the bottom plugged with a piece of rubber. Cool in an ice bath at 0°, mixing occasionally as the sodium sulfate decahydrate crystallizes. The whole tube should become filled with a crystalline paste.

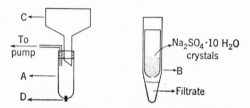

FIG. 28. Filtration apparatus for treated blood

Remove the plug, wipe the tube dry, and encase with Gooch rubber tubing. Place in a tube with a tapered end as shown in Figure 28. Centrifuge for 3-5 minutes. Immerse in the ice bath again for about 5 minutes to be sure that no more sodium sulfate will crystallize at 0°. If it does, centrifuge again and decant.

Procedure—*With phenylhydrazine.* Pipet a 1-ml. aliquot into a tube. Add 0.1 ml. of 4 per cent sodium hydroxide solution and incubate at 37° for 12 hours. Add 0.15 ml. of 1:11 hydrochloric acid. Place in boiling water for exactly 2 minutes and transfer to an ice-water bath. Add 0.2 ml. of fresh 0.33 per cent aqueous solution of phenylhydrazine which has been recrystallized from 98 per cent ethanol and dried over potassium hydroxide.

Mix well and incubate at 30° for 15 minutes. Place in an ice-salt bath at −10° to incipient freezing. Add 0.6 ml. of concentrated hydrochloric acid which has been cooled to −10° and follow with 0.2 ml. of 1.65 per cent aqueous potassium ferricyanide solution. Shake and allow to stand for 30 minutes for color development. Dilute to 5 ml. with water for reading at 520 mμ.

With diacetylmonoxime. Treat as for citrulline (page 360) and make readings at 490 mμ. Then heat a second time for 50 minutes. Cool in the absence of light and read at 470 mμ.

$$\text{Mg. allantoin per 100 ml. plasma} = 100 \ (A_{60} - A_{10})$$

where A_{60} = allantoin equivalent of optical density reading after 60 minutes heating at 470 mμ

A_{10} = allantoin equivalent of optical density reading after 10 minutes at 470 mμ

2,4,5,6(1,3)-Pyrimidinetetrone, Alloxan

The fluorescence of alloxan with *o*-phenylenediamine is appropriate for reading.[16]

Sample—*Blood*. As buffer mix equal volumes of 0.245 per cent acetic acid and 0.064 per cent sodium acetate solution. Mix with 1 ml. of blood, 0.35 ml. of 2.4 per cent solution of *o*-phenylenediamine in glycerol. Add 1 ml. of buffer, 0.3 ml. of 0.4 per cent sodium hydroxide solution, and 4 ml. of 2 per cent zinc sulfate solution. Mix and filter into a tube containing 0.2 ml. of the 4 per cent solution of *o*-phenylenediamine in glycerol.

Tissue. Comminute an appropriate sample with 5 ml. of 1:720 sulfuric acid and 0.5 ml. of 4 per cent *o*-phenylenediamine in glycerol. Centrifuge and treat as for blood, starting at "Add 1 ml. of buffer . . . ."

Procedure—Read fluorimetrically against a fluorescein standard.

Glucuronic Acid

If the product of the reaction of glucuronic acid with naphthoresorcinol is extracted with ether or amyl alcohol a blue-violet color is concentrated in the solvent layer.[17] Glucose, fructose, and urea interfere, sodium chloride does not. The reaction is also applicable to distinguish glucuronic acid from galacturonic acid by different rates of color develop-

---

[16] N. Siliprandi, *Experientia* 4, 228-9 (1948); N. Siliprandi, A. Bonanomi, and N. Simone, *Bull. soc. ital. biol. sper.* 24, 419-21 (1948).

[17] B. Tollens, *Ber.* 41, 1788-90 (1908); A. Ogata and T. Yamanouchi, *J. Pharm. Soc. Japan* 49, 90-1 (1929); *Ibid.* 50, 1059-75 (1930); W. Mozolowski, *Biochem. J.* 34, 823-8 (1939); Marcel Florkin and Roger Crismer, *Compt. rend. soc. biol.* 131, 1277-80 (1939); Wm. B. Deichmann, *J. Lab. Clin. Med.* 28, 770-8 (1943); S. W. E. Hanson, G. T. Mills, and R. T. Williams, *Biochem. J.* 38, 274-9 (1944).

ment,[18] as well as to glucurone, esterol glucuronide, benzoyl glucuronic acid, bornyl glucuronic acid, menthoglucuronic acid, phenolglucuronic acid, and camphor glucuronic acid. Results can be expected to be accurate to ±5 per cent.

Orcin and ferric chloride in hydrochloric acid give the same reaction with solutions of glucuronic acid as with pentoses, a green color on heating, extractable with amyl alcohol.[19] Glucuronic acid is also determined in strong sulfuric acid by reaction with cysteine,[20] a reaction described in some detail for xylose (page 189).

Samples—*Urine.* Dilute to a probably content of glucuronic acid of just under 0.04 mg. per ml.

Blood. Dilute plasma or serum without deproteinizing to just under 0.04 mg. per ml.

Glucose interference.[21] Dilute the sample so that the glucose does not exceed 1 per cent and add 0.5 per cent of sodium chloride. Inoculate with a suitable strain of yeast, such as *Saccharomyces sake* No. 2, and incubate at 28° for 18 hours to decompose the glucose. Centrifuge to separate the yeast and use an aliquot of the clear upper layer.

Procedure—*With naphthoresorcinol.* As reagent, heat a 0.2 per cent solution at 38° for 24 hours with frequent shaking. Filter and keep in the dark at 3-5°. This reagent is stable for about a month. Mix 2 ml. of sample solution containing 0.005-0.04 mg. of glucuronic acid with 2 ml. of the reagent and 2 ml. of concentrated hydrochloric acid. Heat in boiling water for 4 hours, then place in an ice bath for 10 minutes. Add 2 ml. of ethanol to facilitate extraction. Extract with 10 and 5 ml. of peroxide-free anhydrous ether. Dry with anhydrous sodium sulfate and read at 565 mμ against a reagent blank. A convenient standard for preparation of the calibration curve is a 0.1709 per cent solution of pure dry mentholglucuronic acid of which each ml. contains 1 mg. of glucuronic acid.

With orcin and ferric chloride. As reagent add 0.2 gram of orcin and 5 drops of 10 per cent ferric chloride to 100 ml. of concentrated hydrochloric acid. Heat 1 ml. of the sample with 4 ml. of reagent for 10 minutes in boiling water. Cool under the tap for 3 minutes and

---

[18] Eleanor M. Kapp, *J. Biol. Chem.* **134**, 143-50 (1940).

[19] George Scheff, *Biochem. Z.* **183**, 341-9 (1927).

[20] Zacharias Dische, *J. Biol. Chem.* **171**, 725-30 (1947).

[21] Saburo Kakinuma, *J. Pharm. Soc. Japan*, **59**, 635-47 (1939).

extract the color with 1 ml. of amyl alcohol. Read against an amyl alcohol blank.

GLUCURONOLACTONE, GLUCURONE

Glucurone is determined by the same reaction as glucuronic acid (page 442) with napthoresorcinol.

GALACTURONIC ACID

Galacturonic acid gives the same reaction with naphthoresorcinol as glucuronic acid, but the color develops more readily, development being complete in 2 hours of heating. It also is dehydrated to furfural by boiling with acid,·a method described for estimation of pentoses (page 187), and to some lesser extent to other hexoses and derivatives. The reaction in strong sulfuric acid with cysteine is also applicable.[22] It is described in more detail under xylose (page 189).

HEXURONATES

Naphthoresorcinol gives a color with 6-carbon uronic acids available in the body for conjugation.[23] The term "hexuronates" has been applied to these compounds. Hexuronates expressed as glucuronic acid are determined in plasma or serum without removal of proteins or glucose. Essentially hydrolysis of the sample releases free hexuronic acids for reaction with the color reagent, present in large excess to allow reaction with impurities.

Sample—Dilute 0.2-1 ml. of plasma or serum with water to 1.8 ml., add 0.2 ml. of 1:1 hydrochloric acid, and heat for 45 minutes in water at 75°.

Procedure—To the sample, add 2 ml. of concentrated hydrochloric acid and 1 ml. of 10 per cent naphthoresorcinol in ethanol. At the same time prepare a blank. Incubate at 50° for 90 minutes. Cool under the tap and add 8 ml. of ether. Shake vigorously for about 5 seconds, allow the layers to separate, and add another 5 ml. of ether to each. Mix the upper layer by gentle rotation. Add a third portion of ether so that the total volume is 15 ml. and mix the total ether extract again. These further additions of ether dissolve any dispersed water to clarify the

[22] Zacharias Dische, *Arch. Biochem.* 16, 409-14 (1948).
[23] W. B. Deichmann and Marjorie Dierker, *J. Biol. Chem.* 163, 753-760 (1946).

ether layer. Pipet the ether from the sample and read at 570 mμ against the reagent blank. Hemolysis will give high values due to a brown ether-soluble color formed when a constituent of the red blood cell reacts with the naphthoresorcinol-hydrochloric acid mixture.

2-Ketohexuronic Acids

Condensation of 2-ketohexuronic acids with o-phenylenediamine dihydrochloride gives an appropriate reading in the ultraviolet.[24] The reaction is given by 2-keto-d-gluconate, 2-keto-d-galactonate, 2-keto-d-gulonate, 2-keto-d-glucoheptonate, 2-keto-d-galactoheptonate, pyruvic acid, 5-keto-d-gluconate, d-glucose, d-galactose, d-ribose, d-arabinose, d-fructose, d-gluconate, oxalate, dehydroisoascorbic acid, dihydroxyacetone and acetylacetone.

Procedure—To 2 ml. of neutral sample containing 0.01-0.1 mg. of 2-ketohexuronic acids add 1 ml. of 2.5 per cent aqueous o-phenylenediamine hydrochloride. Mix, heat in a boiling water bath for 30 minutes, and cool. Read at 330 mμ or 360 mμ.

Santonin

Santonin, an anhydride of santoninic acid, is estimated by the color of the sodium salt in strongly alkaline solution.[25] Alternatively heat with sulfuric acid and react with diazotized sulfanilic acid.[26]

Procedure—*In alkaline solution.* Mix 3 ml. of sample solution with 4 ml. of 15 per cent sodium hydroxide solution. Compare the yellowish red color against a 1 per cent solution of eosin in ethanol.

By diazotized sulfanilic acid. Dilute the sample with chloroform to 0.5 mg. of santonin per ml. Evaporate 1 ml. of sample to dryness. Add 1 ml. of 1:2 sulfuric acid and heat in boiling water for 7 minutes. Cool and add 6 ml. of 12 per cent sodium hydroxide solution. Add 3 ml. of 1 per cent diazotized sulfanilic acid and heat at 70° for 10 minutes. Cool and store at room temperature for 10 minutes. Read at 510 mμ.

Nucleic Acids

Nucleic acids are combinations of a sugar or sugar derivative with phosphoric acid and a base. The latter is usually a purine or a pyrimi-

[24] Mary C. Lanning and Seymour S. Cohen, *J. Biol. Chem.* **189**, 109-14 (1951).

[25] N. Fucci, *Clin. med. ital.* **1935**, 660 *Rev. sud-americana endocrinol., immunol. quimioterap.* **19**, 595-6 (1936) ; D. Boccia and T. B. DiMatteo, *Ibid.* **20**, 387-97 (1937).

[26] Yoji Iwayama, *J. Pharm. Soc. Japan* **72**, 719-20 (1952).

dine. They are determined as the sugar, the phosphoric acid, or the purine or pyrimidine. The resulting complexity is such as to make subclassification into the different types of determination desirable.

As Sugars

Evaluation of carbohydrate components is satisfactory with free carbohydrates, purine nucleosides, and nucleotides. Difficulties arise from the resistance of pyrimidine nucleotides to hydrolyzing agents, instability of desoxyribose, and the necessity of separating the nucleic acid from the proteins. Nucleic acids are determined as the sugar in the presence of nucleotides by their reaction with ferric chloride and orcinol.[27] The intensity of color decreases in the order adenosinetriphosphoric acid, adenosine, xylose, and arabinose. Likewise ribose [28] is estimated by the same reagent. Diphenylamine [29] reacts with desoxypentose nucleic acid; carbazole [30] with both desoxypentose nucleic acid and pentose nucleic acid. Complete removal of proteins is difficult if not impossible. To avoid interference by pentose nucleic acid, develop desoxyribonucleic acid with phloroglucinol in acid solution.[31] There is no interference by pentoses, glucose, galactose, lactose, and glycogen.

Desoxyribose nucleic acid, when reacted with perchloric acid and tryptophan, gives a red color.[32] For maximum color development for amounts of desoxyribose up to 0.15 mg. per ml., a molar ratio of tryptophan to desoxyribose of 9:1 is required. For stable, rapid color development, the concentration of perchloric acid is at least 30 per cent.

Reaction mixtures containing nucleoprotein represent two means of interference: (1) incomplete solution of colorless protein particles and (2) development of colors due to protein constituents. The first difficulty is eliminated by filtration. In the second case, extract the colored desoxyribose-tryptophan product with isoamyl alcohol.

The reaction of cysteine and sulfuric acid with desoxyribonucleic

[27] H. R. Barrenscheen and Alois Pelham, *Z. physiol. Chem.* **272**, 81-6 (1941); L. Massart and J. Hoste, *Biochem. et Biophys. Acta* **1**, 83-6 (1947); Horace F. Drury, *Arch. Biochem.* **19**, 455-66 (1949); Gail Lorenz Miller, Richard H. Golder, and Elizabeth Echelman Miller, *Anal. Chem.* **23**, 903-5 (1951).

[28] Hans v. Euler and L. Hahn, *Svensk. Kem. Tid.* **58**, 251-64 (1946).

[29] Zacharias Dische, *Mikrochemie* **8**, 4-32 (1930).

[30] Samuel Gurin and Dorothy B. Hood, *J. Biol. Chem.* **139**, 775-85 (1941); *Ibid.* **131**, 211-23 (1939).

[31] Hans v. Euler and L. Hahn, *Arch. Néerland. physiol.* **28**, 423-31 (1944); L. Hahn and Hans v. Euler *Arkiv. Kemi, Mineral., Geol.* **A22**, No. 23, 11 pp. (1946).

[32] Seymour S. Cohen, *J. Biol. Chem.* **156**, 691-702 (1944).

acid results in a pink color.[33] Pentoses do not yield a color reaction with cysteine and sulfuric acid and so yeast nucleic acid does not react. Despite the presence of ribonucleic acid direct estimation of desoxyribonucleic acid can be made.

The color is unusually stable, although there is a slight increase in color intensity with time. There is no interference from ribosenucleic acid. The reagent does not react with phosphoglyceric acid, glycerophosphate, glucose-1-phosphate, glucose-6-phosphate, glucose, arabinose, alanine, xanthine, nicotinic acid, coenzyme 1, adenosine triphosphate, and creatine. Fructose and its derivative, fructose-1,6-diphosphate, give a slight yellow color. However, by nucleic acid extraction,[34] interfering fructose derivatives are removed. To get ribose nucleic acid determine it along with the desoxy compound with orcinol, and subtract the desoxyribose compound specifically determined with cysteine.

Sample—*Tissue.* Shake 2 grams of tissue for 1 hour at 0° with 10 ml. of 10 per cent trichloroacetic acid and dilute to 0.0015-0.02 mg. of pentose per ml. for development with orcinol.

For development with phloroglucinol, grind 1 gram of minced tissue with sand in 10 ml. of 10 per cent sodium chloride solution for 15 minutes. Refrigerate for 2 hours and centrifuge. Repeat this treatment thrice on the residue with 0.8 per cent sodium hydroxide solution. Dilute the four combined extracts to 40 ml. Adjust the pH of 25 ml. to 7 with acetic acid and dilute to 30 ml. Add 3 ml. of 2 per cent lanthanum acetate solution and 50 ml. of absolute ethanol. Cool to 4° for an hour and centrifuge. Wash the precipitate twice with 10-ml. portions of 0.1 per cent lanthanum acetate in ethanol. Decompose the washed precipitate with 1 per cent sodium carbonate and dilute to a known volume.

Procedure—*By orcinol.* As reagent dissolve 0.2 gram of orcinol in 100 ml. of a 0.005 per cent cupric chloride solution in concentrated hydrochloric acid. Mix equal volumes of reagent and sample and heat in boiling water for 10 minutes. Cool and read at 620 mμ against a reagent blank.

By phloroglucinol. Mix 1 ml. of sample containing 1 mg. of pentose or 3 mg. of ribonucleic acid with 8 ml. of 0.1 per cent ferric chloride solution in 1:6 concentrated hydrochloric-acetic acid. Heat in boiling water for 30 minutes and cool. Add 1 ml. of 0.25 per cent phloroglucinol

[33] P. K. Stumpf, *J. Biol. Chem.* **169**, 367-71 (1947).
[34] Walter C. Schneider, *J. Biol. Chem.* **161**, 293-303 (1945).

solution in 1:1:2 concentrated hydrochloric acid-water-acetic acid. After 20 minutes at room temperature heat in boiling water for exactly 4 minutes and cool. After 2 hours read at 720 mμ. If this is followed the color is stable for 20 hours. Greater accuracy is attained at 610 mμ if substances giving a red color are not present. There is a direct relation between ribose and the color developed. Ribose gives 20 per cent more color than ribonucleic acid.

By perchloric acid and tryptophan. To 1 ml. of solution containing 0.05-0.5 mg. of desoxyribosenucleic acid add 0.2 ml. of 1 per cent *dl*-tryptophan in 0.04 per cent sodium hydroxide solution and 1.2 ml. of 60 per cent perchloric acid. Heat in boiling water for 10 minutes and cool rapidly to room temperature. Extract with 2 ml. of isoamyl alcohol, centrifuge, and read at 485-550 mμ against amyl alcohol.

By cysteine. Stir together rapidly with a glass rod 0.05 ml. of 5 per cent cysteine hydrochloride, 0.5 ml. of sample, and 5 ml. of 70 per cent sulfuric acid. Allow to stand for 10 minutes at room temperature and read at 490 mμ against a reagent blank. The color intensifies slightly with time.

As the Phosphorous Acid

For determination of nucleic acids by their phosphorous content the four forms of phosphorous compounds must be separated. They occur in animal tissue as acid-soluble forms, lipids, nucleic acid, and protein. The acid-soluble phosphorus is easily extracted with acid. The lipids are extracted with ethanol. Thereafter the nucleic acids are extracted with 5 per cent trichloroacetic acid. From total phosphorus the four forms are determinable.[35] A related technic[36] bases determination of desoxyribonucleic and ribonucleic acid on selective destruction of ribonucleic acid under the influence of mild alkaline treatment.[37] Incubation for 24 hours at room temperature in 3 per cent sodium hydroxide solution quantitatively splits ribonucleic acid into acid-soluble nucleotides, but desoxyribonucleic remains insoluble in mineral acids. At the same time phospho-proteins are quantitatively liberated as inorganic phosphate. Thus after 24 hours in 3 per cent sodium hydroxide solution on precipitation with strong acid the phosphorus in the precipitate is that of desoxyribonucleic acid, the organic phosphorus in the filtrate is from

[35] Walter C. Schneider, *J. Biol. Chem.* **161**, 293-303 (1945); *Ibid.* **164**, 747-51 (1946).

[36] Gerhard Schmidt and S. J. Thannhauser, *Ibid.* **161**, 83-9 (1945).

[37] H. Steudel and E. Peiser, *Z. physiol. Chem.* **120**, 292-5 (1922).

ribonucleic acid, the inorganic phosphate in the filtrate is from phosphoproteins.

Alternatively, determine the desoxypentose nucleic acid by the carbazole reaction [38] and use the orcinol reaction [39] to measure pentose nucleic acid.

Sample—*Tissue. Separation of phosphorous components.* Chill fresh tissue and homogenize a weighed portion with water at 0°. To remove acid-soluble compounds, mix 1 ml. of homogenate with 2.5 ml. of 10 per cent cold trichloroacetic acid and centrifuge. Resuspend the precipitate in 2.5 ml. of the acid and centrifuge again. Combine these extracts to form the acid-soluble phosphorous fraction. Determine this as molybdenum blue (Vol. II, p. 660 *et seq.*).

To remove the phospholipids, mix the tissue residue which remained after extraction of the acid-soluble fraction with 1 ml. of water. Add 4 ml. of ethanol and centrifuge. Resuspend the residue in 5 ml. of ethanol and centrifuge. Use this extract for determination of the phospholipid (Vol. IV).

To extract the nucleic acids, treat the tissue residue with 1.2 ml. of 0.56 per cent potassium hydroxide solution at 37° for 20 hours. The tissue dissolves. Add 1.3 ml. of cold 10 per cent trichloroacetic acid to precipitate desoxyribose nucleic acid and filter. The filtrate contains pentose nucleic acid. Suspend the residue in 5 ml. of 5 per cent trichloroacetic acid, heat at 90° for 15 minutes, cool, and centrifuge. Resuspend in 2.5 ml. of 5 per cent trichloracetic acid and centrifuge. Combine the acid extracts to give the nucleic acid extract for determination by diphenylamine (page 457).

Destruction of ribonucleic acid. Suspend 0.5-5 grams of finely minced lipid-free tissue in approximately 20 volumes of ice-cold 7 per cent trichloroacetic acid. Stir mechanically for 20 minutes and filter on Hy-Flo filter aid. Wash the residue with ice-cold, 1 per cent trichloroacetic acid solution until the wash water is free of inorganic phosphate. Continue the washings with water till the filtrate is weakly acid towards litmus and then wash with alcohol and ether.

Suspend the residue in 30-40 volumes based on the wet tissue, of a mixture of 75 volumes of alcohol and 25 volumes of ether, and boil for a few minutes. Filter, wash with ether, and grind the dry residue in a

[38] Zacharias Dische, *Mikrochemie* **8**, 4 (1930); Samuel Gurin and Dorothy B. Hood, *J. Biol. Chem.* **139**, 775 (1941); *Ibid.* **131**, 211 (1939).

[39] W. Mejbaum. *Z. physiol. Chem.* **258**, 117 (1939).

mortar. Reflux for 30 minutes with 30-40 volumes of a boiling mixture of equal volumes of methanol and chloroform. Filter on a Büchner funnel and wash generously with ether. Dry in a vacuum desiccator.

Treat the residue for over 15 hours at 37° with 10 ml. of 5.6 per cent potassium hydroxide solution [40] per gram of fresh tissue. The tissue will dissolve. Allow 0.2 ml. in volume for each gram of fresh tissue. Determine total phosphorus in 1-2 ml. of filtrate as molybdenum blue (Vol. II, p. 660 et seq.).

Precipitate desoxypentose nucleic acid by addition of 0.2 volume of 1:1 hydrochloric acid and 1 volume of 5 per cent trichloroacetic acid, to 5 ml. of filtrate and filter. The precipitate contains the desoxyribonucleic acid. The filtrate contains the hydrolysis products of the ribonucleic acid and protein phosphorus. Determine total phosphorus in the to 5 ml. of filtrate [36] and filter. The precipitate contains the desoxyribofiltrate as molybdenum blue. Precipitate inorganic phosphate in another aliquot. Dissolve this precipitate in trichloracetic acid and determine as molybdenum blue. Such separation removes protein decomposition products which would interfere.

The difference between the total phosphorus of the alkaline hydrolyzate and the total phosphorus of the supernatant liquid after acid precipitation is desoxyribonucleic acid. The difference between the phosphorus after acid precipitation and inorganic phosphorus is that of ribonucleic acid. Inorganic phosphorus is that of phosphoproteins.

$$P \times 10.1 = \text{desoxyribonucleic acid}$$
$$P \times 10.6 = \text{ribonucleic acid}$$

Phosphoprotein cannot be so calculated.

As the Purine

The major important purines in nucleic acids are adenine and guanine. For estimation as either purine or pyrimidine the nucleic acid is conveniently hydrolyzed with perchloric acid. The isolated purine, or pyrimidine, is then chromatographed on paper and the purine or pyrimidine is isolated and read in the ultraviolet.[41] With 0.2 mg. of purine the accuracy is ±4 per cent and better than that for pyrimidines. The nucleosides, cytidine, guanosine or guanine riboside, adenosine, and

---

[40] Walter C. Schneider, *J. Biol. Chem.* **164**, 747-51 (1946).

[41] Ernst Vischer and Erwin Chargaff, *J. Biol. Chem.* **176**, 703-34 (1948); Alfred Marshak and Henry J. Vogel, *Ibid.* **189**, 597-605 (1951).

thymidine or thymidine desoxyriboside, can also be separated from each other and most of the free bases.[42]

Chromatography of nucleic acids has been carried to the stage of construction of apparatus for separating and recording the data.[43] This consists of a solvent reservoir, a chromatographic column, and a spectrophotometer modified to record the absorption of the eluate continuously and simultaneously at 4 wave lengths in the ultraviolet, with necessary associated equipment.

After hydrolysis with hydrochloric acid, the purines and pyramines can be separated and read in the ultraviolet.[44] Adenine and guanine are also separable by starch chromatography in alkaline solution.[45]

Sample—*Bacteria.* Extract a centrifuged and washed sample for 1 hour with 50 ml. of boiling acetone-ethanol. Centrifuge and repeat twice more. Extract the residues four times to remove lipids, using 50-ml. portions of chloroform for 24 hours each. Dry the residue and extract with 20 ml. of 7 per cent trichloroacetic acid at 0°. Stir mechanically for 20 minutes, centrifuge at 0°, and re-extract. Wash the residue with 70 per cent ethanol, then twice with 95 per cent ethanol. Dry and store over phosphorous pentoxide. To 0.2 gram of sample add 1.6 ml. of 75 per cent perchloric acid and place in boiling water with occasional agitation, for 1 hour. Cool, dilute to 10 ml. with water, and centrifuge. Use the clear, colorless solution for paper chromatography.

Nucleic acids of yeast and pancreas. Dry at 60° *in* vacuo for 3 hours. To a sample of 5-8 mg. in a Pyrex bomb add 0.5 ml. of 1:70 sulfuric acid, seal, and heat for 1 hour in boiling water. Cool and, for development with BWMD (page 451), adjust to pH 0.8-1 with 30 per cent sodium hydroxide solution. Then dilute to 1 ml. with 1:360 sulfuric acid for development with paper chromatography. For development with BDW (page 452) simply dilute to 1 ml. with 1:360 sulfuric acid.

Desoxypentose nucleic acid and pentose nucleic acid. To 100 mg. of desoxypentosenucleic acid add 2 ml. of 45 per cent perchloric acid or to 80 mg. of pentose nucleic acid add 1.6 ml. of 75 per cent perchloric

---

[42] Rollin D. Hotchkiss, *Ibid.* **175**, 315-32 (1948).

[43] Alfred Deutsch, Richard Zuckerman, and Max S. Dunn, *Anal. Chem.* **24**, 1763-73 (1952).

[44] Hubert S. Loring, James L. Fairley, Henry B. Bortner, and Harry L. Seagram, *J. Biol. Chem.* **197**, 809-21 (1952).

[45] S. R. Elsden and R. L. M. Synge, *Biochem. J.* **38**, ix (1944); R. L. M. Synge, *Ibid.* **38**, 285 (1944); Pehr Edman, Einar Hammarsten, Bengt Löw and Peter Reichard, *J. Biol. Chem.* **178**, 395-8 (1949).

acid and heat at 100° for 40 minutes with occasional agitation. Cool, dilute to 10 ml. with water, centrifuge to remove black residue, and chromatograph by technics which follow.

Separation of adenine and guanine. For chromatographing use strips of S & S 597 filter paper 2.7 × 50 cm., either as individual strips or with 5 parallel lanes on one sheet. A mark 10 cm. below the top represents the starting point. Apply with an accurate microburet 0.007 ml. of aqueous solution containing 0.01-0.03 mg. of the purines. On a blank apply a similar volume of 75 per cent perchloric acid.

For alkaline chromatography expose to the fumes of 1:15 ammonium hydroxide for neutralization of the perchloric acid. For acid chromatography omit this.

For alkaline chromatography, dip the upper part of the strip into a trough containing 7 volumes of n-butanol to 1 volume of 1:150 ammonium hydroxide and thereafter hang over the side. The whole is suspended in a jar with a beaker of the same solvent and a beaker of 1:15 ammonium hydroxide at the bottom of the jar. Let this react until the solvent front has nearly reached the end of the paper, usually about 20 hours. This technic is used with various other substances and solvents.

Dry the paper strips in air. Examine under ultraviolet light. The bases appear as dark spots against a fluorescent background.[46] To elute, cut out rectangles containing the spots. Cut out rectangles of corresponding area from blanks. Cut each rectangle into small pieces and add 5 ml. of 1:120 hydrochloric acid. Shake thoroughly for at least 60 minutes. Decant the eluates and centrifuge for reading in the ultraviolet.

Acid chromatography is the same except that the trough contains 7 parts of n-butanol to 1 part of 1:120 hydrochloric acid and the beaker of ammonia is omitted from the jar.

The relative progress of the areas is represented by the following values.

	Ammonia system	Acid system
Guanine	0.10	
Cytosine	0.22	
Thymine	0.49	0.42
Mixed adenine and uracil	0.28	0.28

Separation of purines. The method of chromatographing is that described for separation of adenine and guanine with differences as noted.

---

[46] E. R. Holiday and E. A. Johnson, *Nature* **163**, 216 (1949).

Solvent BWMD is 4.5 parts of *n*-butanol, 2 parts of water, 1.5 parts of morpholine, and 1 part of diethylene glycol. Solvent BDW is 4 parts of *n*-butanol, 1 part of diethylene glycol, and 1 part of water. Values representing the speed of migration follow.

	BWMD	*BDW*
Adenine	0.53	0.52
Guanine	0.29	0.23
Hypoxanthine	0.35	0.31
Xanthine	0.13	0.15
Uracil	0.56	0.50
Cytosine	0.47	0.50
Thymine	0.71	0.70

In chromatographing with BDW, place a beaker of 1:15 ammonium hydroxide in the bottom of the jar to furnish an ammonia atmosphere.

Sacrifice a duplicate strip to locate the spots as follows. Dry at 105° for 20 minutes. Spray the dried paper with 8 per cent mercuric nitrate solution in 1:30 nitric acid. This fixes the purines as their mercury complexes. Extract with 1:30 nitric acid until a blank, also sprayed with the mercury solution, no longer blackens with ammonium sulfide. This removes the excess mercury salt without affecting the mercury purine or pyrimidine complex. Then immerse the chromatographed strip in a solution of ammonium sulfide. The separated purines are identified by the black spots formed with as little as 0.005 mg. To neutralize traces of acid, store the chromatograms of samples over 1:15 ammonium hydroxide for 15 minutes. Dry at 105° until visible vapors cease. With the strip treated with mercury as a guide remove rectangles, usually 5-6 cm. long, containing the purine.

Place each rectangle treated with BWMD in a tube in an ammonia atmosphere for 15 minutes. Immerse in an 80° bath and add 1 ml. of absolute ether to each in three portions to remove by volatilization the last traces of morpholine. When completely evaporated add exactly 4 ml. of 1:120 hydrochloric acid to adenine samples and 4 ml. of 1:12 hydrochloric acid to guanine samples. Keep overnight at 37°, remove and cool the extracts, and read in the ultraviolet. For BDW dry the strips 3-4 hours, cut out the segments, and extract with acid without the ether treatment.

Procedure—*In the ultraviolet*. Read adenine at 262.5 mμ, guanine at 249 mμ, and subtract the background absorption read at 290 mμ.

Verify the maximum by reading 5 mμ above and below the peak. An appreciable reading at 300 mμ indicates contamination and the test should be discarded.

The maximum absorption [47] of hypoxanthine is at 249 mμ, adenosine (adenine riboside) at 260 mμ, adenosine-3-phosphate at 216 mμ, inosine at 249 mμ.

Total purines. Heat a 10-ml. sample which may contain adenine and guanine in amounts of the order of 100 mg. in 1:35 sulfuric acid in boiling water for 1 hour. Cool and bring to pH 1 by addition of 60 per cent potassium hydroxide solution and warm to about 50°. Add 1 ml. of 20 per cent silver nitrate solution. Cool, ice overnight, and centrifuge. Wash the precipitate three times with small volumes of 1:360 sulfuric acid. Filter the original supernatant liquid and all washings through sintered glass. Extract the purine bases by treatment with four 10-ml. portions of hot 1:150 hydrochloric acid. Stir 3-4 minutes after each addition, centrifuge, and filter the supernatant liquid through the sintered glass. Let stand in the funnel a few minutes before applying suction. Dilute the purine filtrates to 50 ml. with 1:150 hydrochloric acid and similarly dilute 10 ml. of this to 100 ml. for reading at 262 mμ. Recovery of purines is 98-101 per cent.

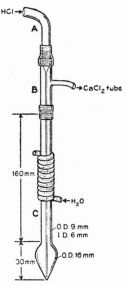

FIG. 29. Arrangement for the hydrolysis of very small amounts of nucleic acid. The capillary tube A is connected through the adapter B with the reaction vessel C.

As the Pyrimidine

Important pyrimidines in nucleic acids are cytosine, thymine, and uracil. Lesser ones are xanthine and hypoxanthine. Paper chromatography is closely related to that for pyrines.

In acid hydrolysis at 175° of nucleic acids to liberate pyrimidines, 1:2 hydrochloric acid largely converts cytosine to uracil. Therefore, less drastic hydrolysis, as with perchloric acid, is required. Desoxyribo-

Sample—*Nucleic acids.* Weigh 15-25 mg. of sample dried *in vacuo* at 60° for 3 hours into C of Figure 29. Add 1 ml. of absolute methanol

---

[47] Herschel K. Mitchell and William D. McElroy, *Arch. Biochem.* **10**, 343-9 (1946).

nucleic acid is also hydrolyzed and the pyrimidines determined without separation.[48]

and pass dry hydrogen chloride through a capillary into the suspension, excluding moisture. The copper spiral with cold water passing makes the neck a reflux condenser. The nucleic acid dissolves in the methanol during about 30 minutes, the solution becomes warm, and purine hydrochlorides begin to precipitate. Continue passage of hydrogen chloride for 4 hours, keeping the mixture at 50°. Chill overnight with exclusion of moisture and centrifuge. Transfer quantitatively to a bomb tube 220 mm. × 65 mm. i.d., 85 mm. o.d. Washing of the purine precipitate is not feasible. The error introduced is about 5 per cent.

Evaporate the yellowish methanol solution at 45° in a stream of dry nitrogen. Add fresh methanol and repeat until the vapors carry only a trace of acid. Usually 15 evaporations will suffice. Dry overnight over calcium chloride and potassium hydroxide. Add 0.5 ml. of 98-100 per cent formic acid, seal, and heat at 175° for 2 hours. Chill to 0° and open.

Add 2-3 drops of 40 per cent potassium hydroxide solution to the brown hydrolyzate. This flocculates and clarifies the solution. Centrifuge and decant. Wash the residue 3 times with 0.1 ml. portions of warm water. Dilute the decantate and washings to 1 ml. for paper chromatography. For details see the separation of adenine and guanine (page 451). Deposit 0.01-0.02 ml. of this solution on the paper strip. Neutralize with gaseous ammonia and develop with n-butanol saturated with water in place of the mixed solvent there described.

Separation of uracil, cytosine, and thymine. For paper chromatography apply 0.01-0.02 ml. of solution containing 0.01-0.03 mg. in aqueous solution following the technic for separation of adenine and guanine (page 451). As solvent in the trough use n-butanol saturated with water. It will require about 12 hours. The relative progress of the areas is adenine 0.28, guanine 0.074, hypoxanthine 0.17, xanthine 0.071, uracil 0.32, cytosine 0.19, and thymine 0.47.

For development dry in air. Then dry one sample chromatograph at 105° for 20 minutes. Prepare a mercuric acetate solution buffered at pH 6.2 by mixing 1 part of 3.2 per cent mercuric acetate solution with 3 parts of 7.2 per cent sodium acetate solution and 6 parts of water. Put the strip in this for 30 seconds. Then bathe the strip for 20 seconds in water and develop with ammonium sulfide to give compact spots identifying the location of the pyrimidines. The limits were about

---

[48] Anthony Pircio and Leopold R. Cerecedo, *Arch. Biochem.* **26**, 209-13 (1950).

0.005 mg. for uracil and cytosine and twice that for thymine. For extraction dry the samples for 4 hours in the air. Extract the 3.5-5 cm. rectangles with 4 ml. of water at 37° overnight. Centrifuge and read.

For determination without chromatography, heat a sample containing 50-75 mg. of the nucleic acid with 1 ml. of concentrated formic acid in a sealed tube for 2 hours at 75°. Dry the brown solution *in vacuo* over calcium chloride and potassium hydroxide. Extract the residue in a few ml. of 1:120 hydrochloric acid. Adjust the pH of the acid extract to pH 1.4 and add 12 drops of 2 per cent palladous chloride solution. Heat to boiling, cool, and filter. Wash the precipitate with cold water, adjust the pH of the filtrate to 5.5-6, and dilute to 50 ml. If a precipitate forms at this point, filter. Use aliquots for estimation of cytosine and thymine if both are present.

Procedure—*In the ultraviolet*. Read uracil at 259 mμ, cytosine at 267.5 mμ, and thymine at 264.5 mμ. Read the background of uracil at 280 mμ; the others, at 290 mμ.

Total pyrimidines. Heat an aliquot of sample solution containing about 10 mg. of disodium uridylate and cyticlylic acid in 1:35 sulfuric acid in boiling water for 1 hour. Cool and adjust to pH 1 by addition of 60 per cent potassium hydroxide solution. Warm to about 50° and add 0.2 ml. of 20 per cent silver nitrate solution. Cool, ice overnight, and centrifuge. Wash the precipitate 3 times with small volumes of the acid and discard the precipitate. Combine the supernatant liquid and washings and precipitate excess silver by adding excess sodium chloride. Warm to coagulate and centrifuge. Wash the precipitate twice with water. Add 2 mg. of prostatic phosphatase to the combined centrifugate and washings and adjust to pH 4.7. Incubate at 38° for 3 hours and cool. Read at pH 2 and 278 mμ.

If tyrosine and tryptophan are to be removed, before reading treat ion exchange resin successively with 200 ml. of 1:15 hydrochloric acid, 200 ml. of 4 per cent sodium hydroxide, and 200 ml. of 2 per cent sodium bicarbonate solution. Pack a 2-cm. diameter column having a sintered glass filter with 6 ml. of 250-500 mesh sodium bicarbonate and the resin.

After phosphatase treatment of the pyrimidine solution, adjust to pH 8.3 with 30 per cent sodium hydroxide solution and pass a 5-ml. sample through the column. Wash with 2 per cent sodium bicarbonate solution until 80 ml. has passed. The amino acids and purines are removed. Adjust the effluent to pH 2.0 with 1:5 sulfuric acid and dilute to 100 ml. with 1:1500 hydrochloric acid. Read at 276 mμ against a reagent blank.

Formation of furfural from ribose furnishes negligible interference. Recovery of cytidylic acid and uridylates is 98-101 per cent.

THYMONUCLEIC ACID

After hydrolysis of thymonucleic acid, the thyminose gives a blue color with diphenylamine in acid solution under controlled conditions.[49] The color can be altered from blue to red by changing the 1:39 sulfuric acid:acetic acid ratio to 1:10. At the 1:39 ratio other hexoses and trioses give a green color; at the 1:10 ratio other hexoses give blue and trioses and pentoses brown. Salts of weak acids and protein decomposition products act as a buffer to diminish the effect of the sulfuric acid. The most favorable concentration for the determination is 5-10 mg. per ml. The error of the method is ±5 per cent.

In the substantial absence of proteins, the aldehyde properties of hydrolyzed thymonucleic acid are estimated by Schiff's reagent.[50] Conditions must be rigidly controlled as the intensity of color depends on the degree of hydrolysis, the amount of fuchsin reagent added, and the pH of the solution in which the color is developed. The maximum color is obtained by hydrolysis for 3-4 hours at 100° at pH 2.3. Best results are obtained with 0.25-1 mg. per ml. The method is accurate to ±2 per cent on a protein-free sample, if both sample and standard are hydrolyzed for the same length of time at the same degree of acidity.

Samples—*Animal organs or tissues.* To 2 grams of macerated sample, add 10 ml. of a 1 per cent solution of pepsin in 1:120 hydrochloric acid and incubate at 40° for 1 hour with frequent shaking. This digests most of the protein matter, leaving the thymonucleates. Centrifuge off the undissolved tissue, suspend it in 5 ml. of 4 per cent sodium hydroxide solution, and dilute to 10 ml. Heat for 2 hours in boiling water to dissolve the suspended matter completely, replacing the water lost by evaporation. Add 0.3 ml. of glacial acetic acid, shake, and let stand for several hours. Filter through a dry filter. To the filtrate add 4 volumes of ethanol and let stand overnight. Centrifuge and dissolve the precipitate of thymonucleic acid in distilled water. Dilute to a concentration of about 5 mg. per ml. for estimation with diphenylamine or Schiff's reagent.

---

[49] Zacharias Dische, *Mikrochemie* **8**, 4-32 (1930); Franz Bielschowsky and Willibald Klein, *Z. physiol. Chem.* **207**, 202-9 (1932).

[50] G. Wilström, *Biochem. Z.* **199**, 298-306 (1928); Torbjorn Caspersson, *Biochem. Z.* **253**, 97-111 (1932).

Procedure—*With diphenylamine.* Prepare the reagent by adding 11 ml. of concentrated sulfuric acid to 400 ml. of a 1 per cent solution of diphenylamine in glacial acetic acid. Mix 2 parts of the reagent with 1 part of the aqueous sample solution. Heat in boiling water for 3 minutes. Cool in running water, let stand for a few hours, and read against a reagent blank.

With Schiff's reagent. The sample and standard are first hydrolyzed in an acid buffer solution. Take a volume of a solution of the sample containing about 1 mg. of thymonucleic acid. Treat with 1:25 hydrochloric acid until just acid to Congo red. Prepare a buffer solution for a pH of 2 ± 0.1 by mixing 30.5 ml. of a solution containing 21.008 grams of citric acid and 200 ml. of 1.0 N hydrochloric acid. Dilute the sample to 10 ml. with this buffer solution. Heat in boiling water for 3 minutes and cool quickly. If necessary, centrifuge and decant.

Add 3 ml. of a mixture containing 1 ml. of fuchsin reagent (page 251) and 2 ml. of buffer to the 10 ml. of sample solution. Read after 10 to 20 hours.

3-Adenylic Acid, Yeast Adenylic Acid, Yeast Nucleic Acid

As with nucleosides, nucleotides, and nucleic acids in general there are three approaches to determination of 3-adenylic acid. It may be determined by a general reaction of nucleic acids, or it may be hydrolyzed and either the purine or the pentose determined. In this case there is the added possibility of determination of the phosphate.

As a general reaction the yellow color of nucleic acid in sodium hydroxide solution is used for its determination in yeast.[51] Values are somewhat higher than those obtained by the purine method, but somewhat lower than those by the ribose method. Hydrolysis with trichloroacetic acid gave results 2-3 per cent higher than by alkaline extraction. Determine by the reaction with cysteine in strong sulfuric acid as described for xylose (page 189).

Sample—*Yeast.* Stir 10 grams of pressed yeast with 30 ml. of 10 per cent trichloroacetic acid solution for 15 minutes. Centrifuge and discard the supernatant liquid. Repeat this extraction three times, wash once with 20 ml. of water, and use the residue as sample.

---

[51] Frederick J. DiCarlo and Alfred S. Schultz, *Arch. Biochem.* **17**, 293-300 (1948); Cf. S. E. Kerr, K. Seraidarian, and M. Wargon, *J. Biol. Chem.* **181**, 761-9 (1949).

Procedure—*Alkaline extraction.* Stir the sample with 20 ml. of 2.2 per cent sodium hydroxide solution at 10-15° for 1 hour. Adjust the pH to 6.5-6.7 and centrifuge. Wash twice by stirring for 10 minutes with 20 ml. each of water. Combine the extracts and dilute to a suitable volume with 0.04 per cent sodium hydroxide solution. Read against a water blank at 260 mμ.

Trichloroacetic acid hydrolysis. Stir the sample for 15 minutes with 30 ml. of 5 per cent trichloroacetic acid at 90°. Wash the residue with 15 ml. of 5 per cent trichloroacetic acid, then with 30 ml. of water. Combine the extracts and dilute to a suitable volume with 0.04 per cent sodium hydroxide solution. Read at 260 mμ.

NUCLEOSIDES

Some methods for nucleic acids (pages 444 to 456) are applicable to nucleosides.

TANNIC ACIDS AND TANNINS

Since neither tannic acid nor tannins are chemical individuals, the methods rely on the availability of a standard of the same general type, one which will develop the same color with the reagent used. If, for example, the tannins being investigated are derived from quebracho, it will be necessary to use a standard from the same source. Alternatively use glucose-free gallotannin derived from Chinese nutgalls,[52] provided it gives a comparable type of color.

Thus, tannic acids and tannins give yellows, reds, and browns with ammonium molybdate. Gallic acid, pyrogallol, and catechol also produce the color; dextrose, resorcinol, glycerol, phenol and ethanol do not. Hydroquinone and phloroglucinol produce a pale yellow color in concentrated solutions.[53] The method is relatively inaccurate since the colors to be compared differ, but it is suitable for rapid control work. An arsenotungstic acid reagent has been applied to give a blue color.[54] Further complicating the reagent the classical phosphomolybdate-phosphotungstate reagent has also been applied.[55]

Another suitable reaction, specific for catechol-type tannins, is that

---

[52] M. Nierenstein, *Analyst* **69**, 91 (1944); C. Ainsworth Mitchell, *Ibid.* **69**, 92 (1949).

[53] G. Spurge, *Chem. Eng. Mining Rev.* **11**, 258 (1919); J. Rae, *Pharm. J.* **120**, 539 (1928); A. B. Shakheldian, *Zhur. Prikladnoi Khim.* **3**, 1117-24 (1931).

[54] Paul Menaul, *J. Agr. Res.* **26**, 257-8 (1923).

[55] A. A. Berk and W. C. Schroeder, *Ind. Eng. Chem., Anal. Ed.* **14**, 456-59 (1942); J. Haslam, J. S. Wilson, and J. E. Edwards, *J. Soc. Chem. Ind.* **63**, 179-82 (1944).

with nitrous acid.[56] Thus it has been used to show the presence of 30-35 per cent of pyrocatechol in pine and quebracho tannins. Modified to use sulfamic acid, it is general for all tannins and for lignosulfates.[57] Nontannins give about 20 per cent as intense a color as tannins. Syntans give no color. The precision of the method is about 1.5 per cent.

For determination of gallotannic acid with ferrous tartrate use the technic described under catechol (page 127). Read at 545 mμ. The optimum pH for this compound is 4.1-11.1. Alternatively determine by osmium tetroxide according to a technic described under gallic acid (page 411). The simple color reaction with ferric chloride is also applicable.[58]

Direct reading photometrically compares favorably with the official hide powder method.[59] At 280 mμ the absorption is not characteristic of any specific tannin.[60] An 0.0084 per cent solution of benzoic acid is an appropriate reference standard for comparing with 0.038 per cent tannin solutions containing 0.1 per cent of sodium sulfite as a stabilizer.

Samples—*Glycerinum acidi tannici.* Dilute 5 ml. of a 20 per cent solution to 100 ml. Use 1 ml. of this for determination by ammonium molybdate.

Tea. Extract 5 grams of tea with 50 ml. of boiling water, then with two 20-ml. volumes. Filter the combined extracts and dilute to 100 ml. for determination by ammonium molybdate.

Grain. Weigh 200 grams of grain and remove fatty matter with petroleum ether in a continuous extractor such as a Soxhlet. Digest the grain with 200 ml. of ethanol overnight, protected from evaporation. Pipet off 10 ml. of the clear supernatant liquid and add 2 ml. of 10 per cent lead acetate solution. Centrifuge and decant the supernatant liquid. Add 0.5 ml. of 10 per cent sulfuric acid to the residue and add a few ml. of water. Mix well and centrifuge. Dilute the supernatant liquid to 25 ml. and take 10 ml. for development with the arsenotungstate reagent.

56 W. Hoepfner, *Chem.-Ztg.* **56**, 991 (1932); Fritz Vorsatz, *Collegium* **1942**, 424-7.

57 Robert S. Adams and Henry B. Merrill, *J. Am. Leather Chemists' Assoc.* **44**, 636-47 (1949).

58 Ilona Klára Király and Endre Schwimmer, *Gyógyszerésztud. Értesito* **22**, 189-95 (1948).

59 D. G. Roux, *J. Soc. Leather Trades' Chemists* **35**, 322-37 (1951); *Ibid.* **36**, 210 (1952).

60 A. W. John, *Das Leder* **2**, 4-8 (1951).

Tannalin.[61] Extract by boiling with antipyrine in ethanol. Develop an appropriate aliquot with ammonium molybdate.

Plantain, banana flour, and peel meal.[62] Treat 10 grams with 60 ml. of petroleum ether in a Soxhlet extractor for 12 hours. Extract the dried residue for 24 hours with ethanol. Wash and dry the residue, take up in water, and dilute to 100 ml. Heat a 10-ml. aliquot with 2 ml. of 10 per cent lead acetate solution at 75° until well coagulated. Centrifuge and decant to waste. Take up the residue in 0.5 ml. of 1:20 sulfuric acid, digest, and centrifuge to separate the lead sulfate. Transfer the supernatant liquid, dilute to 25 ml., and use 10 ml. for development with the arsenotungstate reagent.

Plant tissue. Grind the sample to pass a 40-mesh sieve. Put 20 grams of sample into a flask with 100 ml. of petroleum ether. Stopper, shake occasionally, and let stand overnight. Filter through a dry filter and wash with five 20-ml. portions of petroleum ether. This removes all fats and waxes, and gallic acid. Dry the residue, return it to a flask, and treat with 200 ml. of ethanol. Shake from time to time and let stand for about 16 hours. Gallotannic acid is extracted by the ethanol. Filter through a dry filter. To 10 ml. of filtrate add 2 ml. of a 10 per cent solution of lead acetate. Place in water heated to about 75° and leave until the precipitate, which contains lead tannate, coagulates. Centrifuge. Pour off the supernatant liquid and drain as completely as possible. Add 5-10 drops of 1:20 sulfuric acid to the residue and mix thoroughly. This is to dissolve the tannate and reprecipitate the lead as sulfate. Avoid too much sulfuric acid but use sufficient to complete the reaction. Add about 30 ml. of water, stir, and centrifuge. Develop with arsenotungstate reagent.

Treated waters. For determination of residual tannin use the water as is, with the phosphomolybdate-phosphotungstate reagent.

Tanning solutions. Dilute to around 0.2 mg. per ml. and apply any reagent.

Whiskey.[63] Dilute 1 ml. of sample containing up to 0.25 mg. of tannic acid with an appropriate amount of water and develop with phosphomolybdate-phosphotungstate reagent.

[61] Masaharu Yamagishi, *Japan J. Pharm. and Chem.* **21**, 129-32 (1949).

[62] José H. Ramírez, *Rev. agr., ind. y com.* (Puerto Rico) **35**, 234 (1944).

[63] Official and Tentative Methods of the Association of Official Agricultural Chemists, 7th Ed., p. 134, Association of Official Agricultural Chemists, Washington, D. C. (1950).

Procedure—*With ammonium molybdate.* Dissolve 0.300 gram of pure tannin dried at 100° in 100 ml. of sample solution. This is used as the standard. To 10 ml. of sample and 10 ml. of standard add 10 ml. of 2 per cent neutral ammonium molybdate solution. Mix well and dilute each to 100 ml. After 15 minutes compare by balancing. Knowing that the standard contains 0.3 grams plus x grams of tannin, and the sample x grams of tannin, the calculation of the amount present in the sample is not radically different from the usual colorimetric calculation.

With arsenotungstic acid. As reagent, boil 100 grams of pure sodium tungstate and 30 grams of arsenious oxide with 300 ml. of water and 50 ml. of concentrated hydrochloric acid, until solution is complete, cool, and dilute to 1 liter. To a 10-ml. sample add 2 ml. of reagent and 10 ml. of a 20 per cent sodium carbonate solution. Mix and dilute to a known volume according to the color intensity. Compare by balancing with the color developed from a known amount of tannic acid and diluted to the same extent.

With phosphomolybdate-phosphotungstate reagent. Prepare the reagent by boiling 100 grams of sodium tungstate, 20 grams of phosphomolybdic acid, 50 ml. of 85 per cent phosphoric acid, and 750 ml. of distilled water for 2 hours. Cool to 25°, dilute to 1 liter.

Add 1 ml. of reagent to a 25-ml. aqueous sample. If calcium and magnesium may interfere, add 2 ml. of 25 per cent sodium hexametaphosphate solution. After 5 minutes add 20 ml. of 15 per cent sodium carbonate solution. Compare with a standard after 20 minutes. An appropriate standard contains 2 mg. of tannin per ml.

With nitrous acid. To 5 ml. of tannin solution, add 1 ml. of 10 per cent sodium nitrite solution, 1 ml. of 20 per cent urea solution, and 1 ml. of 1:9 acetic acid. Mix and add 2 ml. of 8 per cent sodium hydroxide solution at the end of 3 minutes. Read against a reagent blank.

With sulfamic acid. Mix 5 ml. of sample solution in the range of 0.2 mg. of tannin per ml. with 2 ml. of 10 per cent sodium nitrite solution. and 2 ml. of 1:9 acetic acid. After 5 minutes add 5 ml. of 10 per cent sulfamic acid solution and swirl to evolve nitrogen from the nitrite. Add 6 ml. of 8 per cent sodium hydroxide solution and dilute to 100 ml. Read at 400 mμ against the 5 ml. of sample solution diluted to 100 ml. The calibration curve must have been prepared from the same tannin or blend.

With ferric chloride. Prepare a 0.01 per cent solution of ferric chloride hexahydrate in 1:2000 hydrochloric acid. Mix 10 ml. of tannic acid solution with 10 ml. of this reagent and dilute to 25 ml. After 90 minutes read at 570 mμ against a reagent blank.

HUMIC ACID AND HUMINS

Humic acid and humus are the ingredients which measure the degree of humification of organic matter in soils.[64] In evaluation of sand for use in concrete sodium carbonate solution is used.[65] The color of sodium humate is either read directly against a standard or photometrically with a light-blue filter. Since the types of humus in different soils can vary widely, the method has potentialities for large errors as an absolute method but not as a relative method in comparing samples of the same soil type. Types of humus in different soils have been classified to clarify the point.[66] The color conforms to Beer's law over the range of 0.001-0.035 mg. per ml.[67] Usual amounts of naturally occuring ions in ground waters do not affect the color. Humic acid extracted with sodium fluoride solution differs fundamentally from that extracted with sodium hydroxide solution.[68]

Other methods determine the oxidizable organic matter by oxidizing agents.[69] The maximum extraction is obtained with 0.4-1 per cent sodium hydroxide-sodium carbonate mixture.[70] The carbonate precipitates calcium. Acid pretreatment is unnecessary.

Sample—*Soil.* Treat 5 grams of soil in a Gooch crucible with 50 ml. of 1:2.6 hydrochloric acid. Wash well with 1:35 acid, discard the washings, and transfer the solid residue to a flask marked to show a volume of 100 ml. in addition to the approximate volume of 5 grams of soil. Add 80 ml. of 12.5 per cent sodium hydroxide solution. Fill the flask

---

[64] S. Odén, *Int. Mitteil. Bodenkunde* **9**, 361-70 (1919); T. Eden, *J. Agr. Sci.* **14**, 469-72 (1924); Josue Gollan and Carlos Christen, *Rev. facultad quim. ind. agr.* (*Univ. Nacl. litoral*) **4**, 149-65 (1936).

[65] L. Tronstad, *Tids. Kjemi Bergvesen* **15**, 18-20 (1935).

[66] A. Hock, *Bodenkunde u. Panzenernähr* **7**, 99-117 (1938).

[67] S. A. Gusinskaya, *Nauch. Zupiski Dnepro petrovsk. Gosudarst Univ.* **15**, 5-13, (1940).

[68] Walter Scheele, *Bodenkunde u. Pflanzenernähr.* **3**, 188-95 (1937); W. Frömel, *Landw. Jahrb.* **92**, 94-154 (1942).

[69] S. A. Wilde, *Soil Sci. Soc. Am., Proc.* **7**, 393-4 (1942).

[70] Amar Nath Puri and Anand Sarup, *Soil Research* **6**, 122-37 (1938).

to the mark with water and heat in a boiling water bath for 15 minutes. Mix well and filter on a Büchner funnel. Collect 20 ml. of filtrate after discarding the first few ml. Dilute 10 ml. of this filtrate to 200 ml. for use as sample.

Sand for concrete. Mix 100 grams of moist sand with 50 ml. of sodium carbonate solution of d. 1.1, approximately 10 per cent. Mix well and let stand for 24 hours for use as sample.

Procedure—*Reading as sodium humate.* To prepare a standard, dissolve 0.3384 gram of well-dried *acidum huminicum* in a slight excess of sodium hydroxide solution and dilute to 100 ml. For comparison, dilute this to a suitable concentration such as one-tenth strength. Report the sample as the percentage by weight of humic acid in the original soil.

ALGINIC ACID

Alginic acid may be estimated as a hexuronic acid by its reaction on heating with carbazole and sulfuric acid.[71] The reaction is a general one given by glucose, mannose, galactose, fructose, sorbose, levoglucosan, arabinose, xylose, rhamnose, barium glucuronate, barium mannuronate, calcium chondroitinsulfate, and sodium alginate. The red-brown color has a maximum at 530 mμ. The uronic acids give the greatest intensity, varying downward through ketohexoses, aldohexoses, and pentoses. Glucosamine, gluconic acid, mannitol, ascorbic acid, and kojic acid give no color. Acetic or benzoic acids give red colors without absorption at 530 mμ. Formaldehyde interferes by giving a dark brown precipitate.

Sample—*Seaweed.* Soak a 0.1-gram sample overnight in 10 ml. of 1:180 sulfuric acid, and filter. Wash on the paper with water and disintegrate the paper in 20 ml. of 3 per cent sodium carbonate solution. Heat at 50° for 2 hours, stir occasionally thereafter, and let stand overnight. Filter, wash with warm water, and finally dilute to 100 ml.

Procedure—Transfer 3 ml. of the prepared solution containing 0.2-2 mg. of alginic acid to a tube equipped with a stirrer and source of compressed air. Chill in ice and salt, and with both forms of agitation in operation, add 18 ml. of concentrated sulfuric acid, dropwise at

71 Huzio Egami, *J. Chem. Soc. Japan* **62**, 277-80 (1941); Zacharias Dische, *J. Biol. Chem.* **167**, 189-98 (1947); E. G. V. Percival and A. G. Ross, *J. Soc. Chem. Ind.* **67**, 4220-1 (1948).

first to avoid darkening. After all the acid has been added, immerse in boiling water for 20 minutes and divide into two parts. Reserve one as the blank and heat the other at 80° for 5 minutes. Add 0.3 ml. of 0.2 per cent recrystallized carbazole in ethanol. After 45 minutes read against the blank.

3,5-Diiodo-4-oxo-1(4)-pyridineacetic Acid, Diodone

Diodone is estimated by the color developed with bromate and formate.[72]

Sample—*Blood.* Use a filtrate from deproteinizing with tungstic acid.

Urine. Dilute to about 0.05 mg. per ml.

Procedure—Prepare a solution containing 1 gram of potassium bromate and 8 grams of sodium bromide per 10 ml. mixed with 4 ml. of 5 per cent phosphoric acid. Mix and let stand for 24 hours before use.

Mix 1 drop of the reagent with 2 ml. of sample containing not over 0.1 mg. of diodone per ml. Heat in boiling water for 3 minutes and cool in ice water. Add 2 ml. of 10 per cent sodium formate in 80 per cent ethanol. After 15 minutes add 2 drops of 85 per cent phosphoric acid and mix. Add a drop of a solution containing 10 per cent of potassium iodide and 4 per cent of sodium hydroxide. Read against a reagent blank after 10 minutes.

Pyrethrins

The color on reaction of neutralized pyrethrins with acid mercuric sulfate is suitable for reading.[73] Pyrethrins react with hydroxylamine to form a hydroxamic acid which in turn gives a colored complex with ferric chloride.[74] As applied to coated paper, this gave 97-98 per cent recoveries with accuracy to 2 per cent if the ratio of pyrethrin I and II is the same in the standard used. Another colorimetric method [75] depends on reduc-

[72] J. A. Barclay and R. A. Kenney, *Biochem. J.* 375-7 (1945).

[73] Walter Fischer, *Z. anal. Chem.* **113**, 1-8 (1938); G. Canneri and G. Mannelli, *Ann. chim. applicata* **28**, 432-40 (1938).

[74] K. A. Lord, *Nature* **165**, 567-8 (1950); Fred I. Edwards and Cipriano Cueto, *Anal. Chem.* **24**, 1357-9 (1952).

[75] C. B. Gnadinger and C. S. Corl, *J. Am. Chem. Soc.* **52**, 680-4 (1930); T. Nagasawa, *Repts. Imp. Ind. Research Inst., Osaka (Japan)* **15**, 1-81 (1934).

tion of copper and its subsequent estimation by a molybdate reagent. For convenience glucose is used as standard. The relation of glucose and pyrethrins is not strictly linear. Pyrethrin I has a slightly greater reducing power than pyrethrin II, which in practice does not cause an error of over 0.04 per cent. Duplicates agree within 0.03 per cent, which is normally within 5 per cent absolute error. Pyrethrins I and II must be separately estimated, when necessary, by noncolorimetric methods. This has been largely superseded.

Procedure—*Powders.* Extract a sample to contain about 0.1-0.15 mg. of pyrethrins, usually about 12 grams of powdered sample, with hexane for 8 hours. Evaporate the solvent at not over 60°. Reflux the residue with 10 ml. of 2 per cent sodium hydroxide solution for 2 hours. Dilute to about 150 ml., add a gram of diatomaceous earth with 10 ml. of 10 per cent barium chloride solution, and dilute to 250 ml. Filter and use 200 ml. of filtrate for steam distillation. In this collect 50 ml. of distillate while the solution is reduced by 15-20 ml. Extract the distillate with 50 ml. of hexane and wash that with 10 ml. and 10 ml. of water.

Neutralize 15 ml. of water to phenolphthalein with 0.02 N sodium hydroxide solution. Add the petroleum ether extract and titrate with 0.02 N sodium hydroxide solution. Separate the aqueous layer as sample and dilute so that each ml. approximates 0.1 mg. of pyrethrin I. Use an aliquot.

Prepare a reagent by solution of 5 grams of mercuric oxide in 230 ml. of 1:11 sulfuric acid. To 2 ml. of this add 3 ml. of concentrated sulfuric acid and chill with ice. Add slowly in dim light 4 ml. of sample. Warm to 25° and read at 570 mμ as soon as the precipitate is dissolved. Continue to read at 1-minute intervals until a maximum is reached. This may take up to an hour.

Coated paper. Cut an amount to contain about 3 mg. of pyrethrins into strips 6 × 0.25 inches. Place in the barrel of the extractor shown in Figure 30. Assemble and add ethanol to fill the barrel to the side arm and about half of the flask. Add several glass beads and heat the extractor in water at 80-85°. Heat the flask in an oil bath at 100-102° to give vigorous but not violent boiling.

After 3 hours of heating, disconnect and concentrate the solution in the flask to about 25 ml. Transfer to a separatory funnel with about 25 ml. of ethanol. Add 350 ml. of water, 7 grams of salt, and 15 ml. of 30-60° petroleum ether. Shake for 1 minute and separate the extract. Again extract with 10 ml. of the petroleum ether for 1 minute and separate. Extract again with 10 ml. of petroleum ether and discard the aqueous layer.

Wash the combined extracts with 5 ml. of water and filter through cotton wet with petroleum ether. Wash with solvent to make 45 ml. Evaporate the solvent at 25° by passing a stream of nitrogen into the flask.

Dissolve the residue by swirling with 3 ml. of ethanol. Prepare a 1:1 mixture of 14 per cent hydroxylamine hydrochloride solution and 14

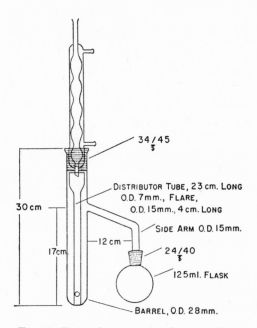

FIG. 30. Extraction apparatus for pyretrins

per cent sodium hydroxide solution within 0.5 hour before use. Add 6 ml. of this to the sample solution and let stand for exactly 10 minutes at $25 \pm 5°$. Add 3 ml. of 1:3 hydrochloric acid and shake. Add 3 ml. of 6 per cent solution of pure anhydrous ferric chloride in 1:150 hydrochloric acid. To this 15-ml. volume add 0.2-0.4 gram of Hyflo Super-Cel and mix. Filter into the cuvet.

The color fades at a rate of 0.13 per cent per minute. Read against a reagent blank at 540 mμ exactly 10 minutes after adding the ferric chloride.

SODIUM CARBOXYMETHYLCELLULOSE, CMC

The green color of carbohydrates with anthrone, 9,10-dihydro-9-keto-anthracene, is applicable to determination of carboxymethylcellulose.[76] Phosphates, silicates, and fatty acids do not interfere. Colored complexes are formed with carbohydrates, carbohydrate derivatives, furfural, and 5-hydroxymethylfurfural. Polyoxyethylene derivatives of fatty acids which may interfere are removable by ethanol extraction. By treatment with sulfuric acid glycolic acid is released. This is determined colorimetrically with 2,7-dihydroxynaphthalene.[77] This method is either appropriate for estimation of the degree of substitution in CMC or the amount of CMC of a known degree of substitution in a sample.

Sample—*Household detergent.* Dissolve a 1-gram sample in 3:2 sulfuric acid and dilute to 100 ml. with the same acid. Filter through an inorganic filter if not clear. Develop with anthrone.

CMC. Grind the sample to 20 mesh. Weigh out about 60 mg. if the material is 25 per cent substituted; 35 mg. if 75 per cent substituted. Dry at 100-105° and cool. Shake with 25 ml. of 6 per cent sodium hydroxide solution until completely dissolved. Dilute with 25 ml. of water and add 36 ml. of concentrated sulfuric acid. This gives a 1:1 sulfuric acid solution of the sample. Reflux for 3.5 hours, cool, and dilute to 100 ml. with 1:1 sulfuric acid. Develop with 1,7-dihydroxynaphthalene.

Procedure—*By anthrone.* As reagent prepare 0.1 per cent anthrone in concentrated sulfuric acid. After 4 hours and less than 24 hours later dilute 65:35 with water and cool to room temperature. Mix 30 ml. of this reagent with a sample containing not over 0.1 mg. of CMC and heat in boiling water for 15 minutes. Cool and dilute to 50 ml. with 6.5:4.5 sulfuric acid. Read at 625 mμ against a reagent blank. Compare with a curve prepared from CMC from the same source.

By 2,7-dihydroxynaphthalene. To 1 ml. of prepared sample add 20 ml. of 0.1 per cent solution of 2,7-dihydroxynaphthalene in concentrated sulfuric acid. Heat in boiling water for 30 minutes, cool, and dilute to 50 ml. Read against a reagent blank at 540 mμ.

HEPARIN

Heparin combines with Toluidine Blue to form a red-violet complex soluble in petroleum ether.[78] The residual unextracted dye is read.

---

[76] Henry C. Black, *Anal. Chem.* **23**, 1792-5 (1951).

[77] R. W. Eyler, E. D. Klug, and Floyd Diephuis, *Ibid.* **19**, 24-7 (1947).

[78] F. C. MacIntosh, *Biochem. J.* **35**, 776-82 (1941).

Azure A gives a similar reaction.[79] One unit of heparin decolorizes 0.15 mg. of Toluidine Blue or 0.1 mg. of Azure A.

Procedure—Dilute a sample of heparin solution containing 20-70 mg. to 10 ml. Add 10 ml. of 0.0025 per cent solution of Toluidine Blue. Shake with 10 ml. of hexane. Read the aqueous layer at 600 mμ.

---

[79] Alfred L. Copley and David V. Whitney III, *J. Lab. Clin. Med.* **28**, 762-9 (1943).

CHAPTER 18

SULFUR DERIVATIVES [1]

BECAUSE so frequently quite diverse types of compounds are determined through the sulfur-derived group, the sulfur compounds in this chapter are heterogeneous. Some not bound to carbon by a covalent bond are included. The compounds having a mercaptan group have a related group of methods of determination by their reducing action. Disulfides are usually susceptible of reduction to mercaptans for such determination. In general such structures as –CSK, –C=S, and –CSSC– are oxidized with a mixture of nitroprusside and hydroxylamine. Sulfanilamides as a group are under aliphatic amines (Vol. IV).

THIOUREA

The color reaction with a nitroprusside-hydroxylamine reagent given with such structures as –C–S–H, –C=S, and –C–S–S–C– is applicable to thiourea.[2] The actual final reagent is of unknown structure. There is interference by thiocyanates but not by sulfonamides. The color intensity varies with pH and the rate of development with temperature. Accuracy to ±2 per cent is to be expected.

Another reaction is to add ferric chloride and pass a stream of air containing nitric oxide, prepared by the reaction of 25 per cent sodium nitrite solution with glacial acetic acid.[3] The color is orange-red.

Sample—*Serum or plasma*. Prepare tungstic acid reagent by mixing equal volumes of 10 per cent sodium tungstate solution and 1:54 sulfuric acid. Mix 1 volume of this with an equal volume of serum or plasma. Filter or centrifuge after a few minutes.

Urine. Dilute to 0.4-4 mg. of thiourea per 100 ml.

Procedure—Mix 10 ml. of 5 per cent sodium nitroprusside solution with 5 ml. of 10 per cent hydroxylamine hydrochloride solution. Exactly

---

[1] See Chapter 1 for details of organization, condensation, etc.

[2] Irvine W. Grote, *J. Biol. Chem.* **93**, 25-30 (1931); Henry J. Nicholes and Raymond C. Herrin, *Am. J. Physiol.* **135**, 113-23 (1941); Thaddeus S. Danowski, *J. Biol. Chem.* **152**, 201-5 (1944); Leon C. Chesley, *Ibid.* **152**, 571-8 (1944).

[3] Fernando De Ritis and Michele Zaccho, *Arch. sci. med.* **85**, 255-62 (1948).

2 minutes later add 10 ml. of 10 per cent sodium bicarbonate solution and mix. At the end of 10 minutes add 0.11 ml. of bromine. Mix and after 10 minutes add 5 ml. of 2 per cent phenol solution to destroy excess bromine. After 10 minutes dilute with 19 volumes of a buffer solution for pH 6 made by mixing 126.3 ml. of 0.71 per cent solution of anhydrous disodium phosphate with 73.7 ml. of 0.96 per cent citric acid solution. This diluted reagent must be used within a few hours. The stock reagent is stable.

To 3 ml. of sample add 3 ml. of the diluted reagent and read at 10-minute intervals at 600 mμ until the maximum color is reached. This may be as long as 3 hours.

SULFHYDRYL GROUPS

By oxidation of sulfhydryl groups with cystine, the cystine is reduced to cysteine and can then be estimated [4] by the phospho-18-tungstic acid reagent. The mount of sulfhydryl groups is conveniently expressed as its equivalent as cysteine. The general subject as here presented should be compared with methods given under cystine and cysteine. The determination of small amounts of sulfhydryls and disulfides in protein hydrolysates shows discrepancies in the extraneous reducers with (1) mercuric chloride and a quantity of ferrous ion equivalent to the –SH inactivated by mercaptide formation, (2) as an average of the colors obtained in the presence and absence of sulfite with the –SH suppressed by mercaptide formation, or (3) with an empirical nomograph. Therefore, it appears most satisfactory for micro work in the photometer to read before and after reduction by zinc, develop in the photometer tube, and evaluate extraneous reducers by formaldehyde and cysteine.[5]

The methylene blue reaction for hydrogen sulfide with dimethyl-p-phenylenediamine hydrochloride is of broad general applicability to disulfides and sulfhydryl compounds such as cystine, cysteine, gluta-thione and thiocresol.[6] The reagent is used in acid solution in the presence of ferric ammonium sulfate. The color is permanent. The sample solution must be substantially neutral. Tyrosine, tryptophan, uric acid, creatine, and acetone do not interfere. For 0.2-1.2 mg. of sulfhydryl in neutral solution, the error is about 1 per cent.

[4] A. E. Mirsky and M. L. Anson, *J. Gen. Physiol.* **18,** 307-23 (1935).

[5] Herbert M. Winegard and Gerrit Toennies, *J. Biol. Chem.* **174,** 45-55 (1948); Joseph J. Kolb and Gerrit Toennies, *Anal. Chem.* **24,** 1164-9 (1952).

[6] I. St. Lorant, *Z. physiol. Chem.* **185,** 245 (1929); Hideo Toyoda, *Bull. Chem. Soc. Japan* **9,** 263-8 (1934).

Sulfhydryl groups are eliminated by iodoacetate or an oxidizing agent. Hydrolysis and comparison of the apparent cysteine content in the treated and untreated protein give a measure of sulfhydryl groups.[4] Sulfhydryl groups react with 1-(4-chloromercuriphenylazo)-naphthol-2 to form a red precipitate.[7] Addition of a strong mineral acid to develop the residual dye makes it applicable to estimation of sulfhydryl groups.[8]

Sample—*Protein in general.* Transfer a 0.25-gram sample to a 19 × 150 mm. Pyrex tube and dry to constant weight. Add 1.2 ml. of 1:2 hydrochloric acid and after this has been absorbed by the protein add 0.8 ml. of 98 per cent formic acid. After gel formation occurs, constrict the neck of the tube, evacuate, and seal. Place upright in a beaker in a pressure cooker containing some water. Heat the cooker to 15 pounds pressure and put in a 120° oven for the period of hydrolysis. Use all precautions of gloves, goggles, and shield, and handle only when cold until the tube has been opened as usual. Dilute the contents to 25 ml. and determine sulfhydryl promptly with phosphotungstic acid.

Egg albumin. Dissolve 1 gram of crystalline egg albumin in 100 ml. of water. Heat with gentle stirring at 90° until the protein is completely coagulated. Add 125 ml. of water, centrifuge, and discard the supernatant liquid. Rub the precipitate to a fine paste with a small amount of water. Add 10 ml. of 20 per cent sodium sulfate solution and water to make about 225 ml. Stir for 5 minutes, centrifuge, and discard the supernatant liquid.

Mix the protein with 200 ml. of water and add 20 ml. of 50 per cent trichloroacetic acid. Centrifuge and discard the supernatant liquid. Repeat as many times as necessary to free the sample from contaminating substances. Mix the washed precipitate with 200 ml. of acetone and stir for 5 minutes. Add 1 ml. of concentrated hydrochloric acid, mix, and centrifuge. Decant and disperse the precipitate in 100 ml. of acetone to which 5-6 drops of concentrated hydrochloric acid have been added. Centrifuge and decant. Warm in water and remove acetone by suction until the protein reaches the consistency of a thick dough. Grind in a hot mortar until the odor of acetone disappears. Dry the fine powder at 108° for 30 minutes, in which time it will reach constant weight.

Edestin. Dissolve 1 gram of dry crystalline edestin in 200 ml. of 1:1200 hydrochloric acid. Add 20 ml. of 50 per cent trichloroacetic acid solution and mix to coagulate. Centrifuge and discard the supernatant

---

[7] H. Stanley Bennett and David A. Yphantis, *J. Am. Chem. Soc.* **70**, 3522 (1948).

[8] Peter Flesch and Ernest Kun, *Proc. Soc. Exptl. Biol. Med.* **74**, 249-51 (1950).

liquid. Complete as for egg albumin, starting at ''Mix the protein with 200 ml. of water . . . .''

Muscle protein. Grind 5 grams of minced frozen muscle in a mortar with 50 ml. of 5 per cent trichloroacetic acid. Dilute to 250 ml. with 5 per cent trichloroacetic acid. Stir and centrifuge. Discard the supernatant liquid and complete as for egg albumin, starting at ''Mix the protein with 200 ml. of water . . . .''

Samples by oxidation. Mix 0.5 gram of sample with sufficient borate buffer for pH 9.6 (Vol. I, page 175) to make the mixture definitely blue to thymol blue. Dilute the buffered sample to 100 ml. Add 5 ml. of 30 per cent hydrogen peroxide and let stand for 30 minutes with occasional shaking. Add 100 ml. of water and 25 ml. of 50 per cent trichloroacetic acid. Centrifuge and decant the supernatant liquid. Rub the residue to a thin paste with water. Stir for 5-10 minutes and add 20 ml. of 50 per cent trichloroacetic acid. Wash four times more by the same procedure and dry the protein.

Reflux a weighed sample of dry protein, usually 50-700 mg., with 5 ml. of 1:5 sulfuric acid and 1 ml. of butanol for 15 hours. At the same time reflux an unoxidized sample. Disconnect the condenser and evaporate the butanol. Cool under the tap, dilute each to 25 ml., and filter.

Procedure—*With cystine and phospho-18-tungstic acid.* Prepare a fresh reagent containing 0.35 gram of cystine in 5 ml. of water and 6.75 ml. of 2.8 per cent potassium hydroxide solution. Draw a vacuum on the container and shake to dissolve. This alkaline solution is unstable.

Mix 0.2 gram of dried sample protein with 45 ml. of water and 2 ml. of 50 per cent trichloroacetic acid. Centrifuge and decant the supernatant liquid. Add 15 ml. of 20 per cent sodium sulfate solution and 30 ml. of water to the precipitate. Stir and centrifuge. Mix the precipitate with 5 ml. of 20 per cent sodium sulfate solution. Add the freshly prepared solution containing 0.35 gram of cystine. Stopper the tube and evacuate. Fill the tube with oxygen-free nitrogen. Evacuate and again fill with nitrogen. Let stand for 30 minutes with occasional shaking.

Add 2 ml. of 10 per cent sodium tungstate solution and mix. Add 6 ml. of 1:56 sulfuric acid and mix. The solution should now turn litmus red but not turn Congo red, blue. This precipitates the protein remaining. Centrifuge and measure the volume of the contents of the tube.

Mix an aliquot of the upper layer with 4 ml. of phosphate buffer for pH 6.7 (Vol. I, p. 174). Add 1 ml. of 2.8 per cent potassium hydroxide solution and dilute to 25 ml. Add 1 ml. of phosphotungstic acid reagent (page 437) and read against a reagent blank. Take the result from a cysteine curve.

Sulfhydryl. With phosphotungstic acid. As the reagent—referred to as PTA in the table—add 100 grams of molybdenum-free sodium tungstate dihydrate to 200 ml. of water and 50 ml. of 85 per cent phosphoric acid. Reflux gently for 1 hour and add 5 drops of bromine. Boil gently for several minutes, then vigorously until excess bromine is expelled. Cool and dilute to 1250 ml.

As the buffer for pH 5.2 dissolve 32.8 grams of sodium acetate and 7.2 grams of acetic acid in water and dilute to 100 ml. As a cysteine standard dissolve 5.25 mg. in 1:40 hydrochloric acid and dilute to 100 ml. with the same acid, using precautions against oxidation. The cysteine solution referred to in the table should be substantially equivalent to the sample and is dissolved in 1:150 hydrochloric acid.

Three readings are necessary for each determination, (1) total color T, (2) formal blank B, and (3) formal control C. Reading T is the total phosphotungstate color; reading B is the color due to extraneous reducers (ER) not prevented by formaldehyde in the presence of known amounts of cysteine; and reading C is the color due to know amounts of cysteine alone. Reading T requires only one tube; readings B and C require 2 tubes. Desirably B_1 and C_1 contain one-third less cysteine than the sample and B_2 and C_2 contain one-third more. Details of the tubes are given in Table 4.

Read at 720 mμ with a PC-4 filter. Then $b_1 - c_1 = ER_1$ at color b_1; and $b_2 - c_2 = ER_2$ at color b_2. By plotting ER_1 and ER_2 against b_1 and b_2, linear extrapolation to T gives ER, corresponding to total color t. Then $t = ER_t$ corresponds to the sulfhydryl concentration.

Sum of disulfide and sulfhydryl. Dilute an aliquot of sample to contain 0.005-0.03 mg. of cystine and cysteine per ml. and adjust the acidity to $0.4 - 1$ N using hydrochloric acid or sodium hydroxide for the adjustment. Add a 10-25 ml. sample to 50-150 mg. of zinc in a container with a magnetic stirring bar of glass, or Duralon or Teflon coated. Cap with provision for inlet and outlet of a nitrogen atmosphere and stir magnetically in that atmosphere for 1 hour with a gentle stream of gas passing. Filter and complete by a modification of the procedure for sulfhydryl. For standardization similarly treat a cystine solution containing 0.06 mg. per ml. in 1:30 hydrochloric acid and compare against an equivalent cysteine solution for color compensation. As the modifications run T tubes at 1, 3, and 3 ml., and one each of B and C tubes containing cysteine nearly identical in amount to the reduced sample.

TABLE 4. COMPOSITION OF MIXTURES FOR SULFHYDRYL DETERMINATION

Tube Designation	R	T	B_{1a}	B_{2a}	C_{1a}	C_{2a}
Hydrolyzate containing 0.03 - 0.12 mg. of cysteine per ml.	..	To 5	To 5	To 5	..	..
Water, ml.	8	..	..	..	To 5	To 5
PTA, ml—See Text	2	2	..	..	..	..
24.6% sodium acetate, ml.	2	2	2	2	2	2
7.4% formaldehyde, ml.	..	..	1	1	1	1
pH 5.2 buffer, ml.—See Text	2	2	..	..	..	..
Water, to make total volume of, ml.	..	14	8	8	8	8

After 1 to 10 min. add to solution below, which has been standing 2 min.

Tube designation	..	..	B_{1b}	B_{2b}	C_{1b}	C_{2b}
Cysteine solution, ml.—See Text	..	..	1	2	1	2
PTA, ml.	..	..	2	2	2	2
pH 5.2 buffer, ml.	..	..	2	2	2	2
Water, ml.	..	..	1	..	1	..

Mix contents of respective a and b tubes.

	R	T	B_{1}	B_{2}	C_{1}	C_{2}
Waiting time, min.	..	10	10	10	10	10
35.7% sodium citrate, ml.	1	1	1	1	1	1
Centrifugation at 2100 r.p.m., min.	..	10	10	10	..	..
Optical density read 30 min. after addition of citrate against tube R, O.D.	..	t	b_1	b_2	c_1	c_2

With ferric salt. To the sample solution add 50 mg. of pure zinc powder and 0.5 ml. of 1:10 hydrochloric acid. Add 0.5 ml. of a 12.5 per cent solution of ferric ammonium sulfate in 1:40 sulfuric acid. Dilute to 25 ml., stopper loosely, and set aside at room temperature for at least 12 hours. Read against a reagent blank.

After oxidation. Take portions of the oxidized and unoxidized sample solutions equivalent to 0.7 mg. of cystine. Dilute each to 5 ml. with 1:36 sulfuric acid. Add 1 ml. of freshly prepared 20 per cent sodium sulfite solution. After 1 minute add 14 ml. of 50 per cent urea solution and 4 ml. of phosphate buffer for pH 6.7 (Vol. I, page 174). Add 1 ml. of phosphotungstic acid reagent (page 437) and mix. After 5 minutes read the oxidized and unoxidized samples against a reagent blank.

Subtract the value for oxidized sample from that for the unoxidized sample as a measure of the sulfhydryl groups originally present, which have been removed by oxidation.

Tissue by 1-(4-chloromercuriphenylazo)-naphthol. Homogenize the chilled tissue with ice-cold 10 per cent sodium lauryl sulfate solution and dilute to a 5 per cent dispersion. As reagent dissolve 3 mg. of 1-(4-chloromercuriphenylazo)-naphthol-2 in 100 ml. of amyl acetate without heating. Filter and store at 4° until used. Add 0.2 ml. of 5 per cent dispersed sample to a 5-ml. portion of this reagent and shake mechanically for 20 minutes. Centrifuge and transfer 4 ml. of the clear upper layer. Add 2 ml. of concentrated hydrochloric acid to develop the color, shake, and let stand for 15 minutes. Read at 540 mμ against a blank of 2 parts of amyl acetate and 1 part of concentrated hydrochloric acid. Interpret from a curve developed with glutathione.

Disulfide Groups

By reduction of disulfides with thioglycolic acid the disulfide is converted to sulhydryl. By estimation of cysteine with phospho-18-tungstic acid before and after reduction, a measure of the disulfide groups is obtained. This is conveniently expressed in terms of cysteine. Results are reproducible to within 1 per cent.

Sample—Dissolve 0.2 gram of sample such as denatured serum albumin in 5 ml. of water in a flask. Slowly add 10 ml. of sodium sulfate solution saturated at 30°, and mix. Neutralize 1 ml. of redistilled thioglycolic acid with 2.25 per cent potassium hydroxide solution saturated with sodium sulfate, until the solution is just red to phenol red. Add 0.5 ml. of additional alkali solution. Dilute to 60 ml. with saturated sodium sulfate solution and mix with the sample precipitated by sodium sulfate solution.

Stopper the flask and let it stand with occasional agitation for 45 minutes at 30°. Dilute to 200 ml. with water and add 20 ml. of 50 per cent trichloroacetic acid solution. Mix, centrifuge, and decant. Repeat the washing about eight times to remove all thioglycolic acid from the precipitate. By reducing in the presence of concentrated sodium sulfate, the albumin is kept precipitated and reversal of denaturation is prevented. Ammonium sulfate cannot be used as it inhibits reduction. A temperature near 30° is required to have the sodium sulfate sufficiently soluble.

Procedure—Determine the cysteine content of a sample of the original protein with phospho-18-tungstic acid. Similarly determine the cysteine content of the reduced protein. Subtract the cysteine in the original protein from that in the reduced protein to give the cysteine from reduction of disulfides.

2-HYDROXYETHANETHIOL

The color of 2-hydroxyethanethiol in 2,2'-dihydroxydiethyl sulfide is developed with nitrite.[9]

Procedure—Dilute a sample containing 0.1-0.4 gram of 2-hydroxyethanethiol to 50 ml. with absolute ethanol. Mix 6 ml. of the solution with 1 ml. of 27.6 per cent sodium nitrite and 2 ml. of acetic acid. Exactly 3 minutes later read against a reagent blank. The content of 2,2'-dihydroxydiethyl sulfide must be standardized if under 6.5 per cent.

2,3-DIMERCAPTO-1-PROPANOL

This 1,2-dithiol is determined by cyanogen chloride and a complex series of reactions following.[10] There is no interference by 1,3-dimercapto-1-propanol. Glutathione, ergothionine, and thiolactic acid interfere.

Procedure—Throughout use water saturated with carbon dioxide and containing 1 mg. of potassium cyanide per 100 ml. This prevents air oxidation. Dilute a sample containing up to 0.01 mg. of test substance to 2 ml. Mix with 0.4 mg. of cyanogen chloride reagent and let stand for 5 minutes. Mix with 0.4 ml. of 4 per cent sodium hydroxide solution and let stand for 10 minutes. Add 0.2 ml. of 1:3 hydrochloric acid and blow moist air through for 30 minutes. Add 0.2 ml. of saturated bromine water and follow with 0.2 ml. of 2 per cent arsenious acid solution. Blow out excess bromine vapor.

As a reagent add 100 ml. of concentrated hydrochloric acid to 1 liter of pyridine. Prepare a 5 per cent solution of benzidine hydrochloride in 1:50 hydrochloric acid. Mix in equal parts. Mix 4 ml. of this reagent with the sample and after 20 minutes read at 520 mμ against a reagent blank.

DIETHYLDITHIOCARBAMIC ACID

The reduced form, diethyldithiocarbamac acid, can be separated from tetraethylthiuram disulfide, by extracting the latter with carbon tetrachloride. The former is then converted to the copper salt,[11] when it can be extracted with carbon tetrachloride and determined in the same manner as the disulfide.

[9] F. N. Woodward, *Analyst* **74**, 179-82 (1949).

[10] W. N. Aldrich, *Biochem. J.* **42**, 52-8 (1948).

[11] Gunnel Domar, Arne Fredga, and Hakan Linderholm, *Acta Chem. Scand.* **3**, 1441-2 (1949).

Procedure—*Urine*. To 20 ml. of urine add 0.1 ml. of 0.1 per cent cupric sulfate solution, 2 ml. of 5 per cent sodium citrate solution as a buffer, and 10 ml. of carbon tetrachloride. Shake and centrifuge. Filter the carbon tetrachloride layer. Read at 660 mμ against a reagent blank.

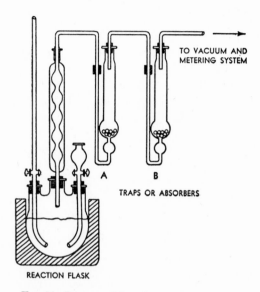

Fig. 31. Decomposition absorption apparatus employed for dithiocarbamate determinations

FERRIC DIMETHYLDITHIOCARBAMATE, FERBAM, FERMATE

Organic dithiocarbamates are important insecticides. These include ferric dimethyldithiocarbamate, zinc dimethyldithiocrabamate, zinc ethylene-bis(dithiocarbamate), and disodium ethylene-bis(dithiocarbamate), all of which are determined by release of carbon bisulfide with dilute acid and its absorption in copper acetate-organic amine.[12]

Sample—*Vegetables and fruits*. Pulp a 300-gram sample with 100 ml. of water. Place the sample in the reaction flask of the apparatus shown in Figure 31. Place 3 ml. of 10 per cent lead acetate solution in the trap A. Add 5 ml. of a solution containing 2 per cent of triethanolamine and 0.005 per cent of cupric acetate in ethanol, to trap B. Apply

[12] F. J. Viles, *Ind. Hyg. Toxicol.* 22, 188-96 (1940); D. Dickinson, *Analyst* 71, 327-8 (1946); D. G. Clarke, H. Baum, E. L. Stanley, and W. F. Hester, *Anal. Chem.* 23, 1842-6 (1951); W. K. Lowen, *Ibid.* 23, 1846-50 (1951).

a gentle vacuum drawing 10-15 ml. of gas per minute. Add 100 ml. of 1:9 sulfuric acid through the dropping funnel. Maintain the reaction flask at reflux temperature for 30-45 minutes.

Procedure—Read the color of the reaction solution in absorber B at 425 mμ. Interpret in terms of the carbon bisulfide derivative present.

Zinc Dimethyldithiocarbamate, Ziram

See ferric dimethyldithiocarbamate.

Disodium Ethylene-bis(dithiocarbamate), Nabam

See ferric dimethyldithiocarbamate.

Zinc Ethylene-bis(dithiocarbamate), Zineb

See ferric dimethyldithiocarbamate.

Bis(diethylthiocarbamyl)disulfide, Tetraethylthiuram Disulfide

When shaken with cuprous iodide, reduction of tetraethylthiuram disulfide to copper diethyldithiocarbamate in carbon tetrachloride gives a sensitive method of determination.[11] Diethyldithiocarbamic acid in the original sample to be extracted with carbon tetrachloride does not interfere.

Procedure—*Urine.* Extract 30 ml. of urine with 10 ml. of carbon tetrachloride. Centrifuge if necessary to give a clear solvent layer. Withdraw the solvent layer, shake with 0.5 gram of pulverized cuprous iodide for 5-10 minutes, and filter. Read at 660 mμ against a reagent blank.

2-Amino-3-mercaptopropionic Acid, Cysteine

A conventional reagent for estimation of cysteine is phospho-18-tungstic acid with in some cases cystine converted to a reduced form and determined at the same time. By working at pH 5 without added reducing agent, cysteine reacts but cystine does not.[13] The color is the conventional molybdenum blue and is stable for at least 6 hours. Thioglycolic acid reacts similarly. Inorganic sulfide slowly develops color,

---

[13] Kamenosuke Shinohara, *J. Biol. Chem.* **109**, 665-79 (1935); *Ibid.* **110**, 263-77 (1935); *Ibid.* **111**, 435-42 (1935); *Ibid.* **112**, 671-721 (1936); *Ibid.* **120**, 743-9 (1937); Alfons Schöberl and Paul Rambacher, *Biochem. Z.* **295**, 377-90 (1938).

but this is easily removed by passing nitrogen or carbon dioxide through the acid solution. n-Butyl mercaptan, ethyl mercaptan, or thiocresol also slowly develop color. Such water-soluble mercaptans are extracted in advance with ether or chloroform.

Amino acids, phenols and cresols, creatinine; furfural, n-butyl disulfide, thiocyanate, thiosulfate, isoamyl sulfide, and diphenyl sulfide are inert. Thiourea will not develop color within 20 minutes. Uric acid develops color at higher pH. Glucose under 3.5 per cent shows no color in 30 minutes. Acetone shows no effect up to 1.5 per cent but does at twice that concentration. Ethanol has no effect at 15 per cent but causes turbidity beyond 30 per cent. Ether does not interfere within 30 minutes. Chloroform does not interfere but mercuric choride does. Formaldehyde does not produce a color with the reagent but reacts with cysteine. Pyruvic acid below 0.035 per cent produces practically no color in 15 minutes. The color from 0.113 per cent of creatinine can be neglected as can also that from 0.2 per cent furfural. Resorcinol below 0.11 per cent produces no substantial color in 2 hours. Catechol and pyrogallol develop some color. Ferrous sulfate reduces the reagent and therefore simulates cysteine. Ferric sulfate causes precipitation. Cuprous chloride produces color; cupric chloride oxidizes the color produced. Stannous chloride reduces the reagent slowly; stannic chloride produces a precipitate. Alkali chlorides, sulfates, and nitrates below 4 per cent do not affect the color if the sample is added before the reagent. Potassium or sodium cyanide inhibit color development. If proteins are hydrolyzed as the sample, use sulfuric acid and neutralize excess with lithium hydroxide. The use of pH 5 prevents some interferences which would occur at other degrees of acidity.

If substantial amounts of acidity are added with the sample, add an equivalent amount of alkali. Minor amounts of acidity are taken care of by a buffer. The color is not altered by dilution. The reaction will detect 0.0005 mg. of cysteine per ml. and can be used on a micro scale. Substantial increase in the amount of reagent used does not affect the intensity of color developed. Accuracy to 0.4 per cent is obtainable.

When both cystine and cysteine are present, the mixture in the presence of sodium sulfite develops a blue with phospho-18-tungstic acid similar to that for uric acid.[14] The cystine is first reduced to cysteine which reacts when the sodium carbonate is added.[15]

---

[14] Otto Folin and J. M. Looney, *J. Biol. Chem.* **51**, 421-34 (1922).

[15] Otto Folin and A. D. Marenzi, *Ibid.* **83**, 103-8 (1929); J. W. H. Lugg, *Biochem. J.* **26**, 2144-59 (1932); Horst Hanson, *Biochem. Z.* **318**, 313-28 (1947).

While reducing agents convert cystine to cysteine for determination, correspondingly oxidizing agents convert cysteine to cystine with development of a red color from sodium nitroprusside.[16] Reducing agents can interfere. Cysteine gives a red color with a chloroform solution of o-benzoquinone, suitable for estimation.[17] Cystine gives no color under the same conditions. Precautions must be used to prevent oxidation of cysteine in the sample to cystine.

Cysteine forms a complex with cobalt in the presence of dissolved oxygen, having a characteristic yellow to brown color. Oxidizing agents convert the cobaltous cysteine complex to a pink cobaltic complex for estimation.[18] Formaldehyde, acetaldehyde, and cyanide decompose the cobaltous cysteine and therefore prevent its oxidation to the cobaltic complex.

Oxidation with hydrogen peroxide is not quantitative; therefore conditions must be carefully standardized. The method qualitatively differentiates from all similar compounds. Pyruvic acid, thioacetic acid, and thiourea give no color. Thioalcohols and thiophenols give a reddish brown precipitate but do not impart color to the solution. A deep brown color is given by thiocarboxylic acids, such as thioglycolic acid. This color can be differentiated from that due to cysteine and fades on standing overnight. Glutathione produces practically no color until oxidizing agent is added, then gives a brownish pink. Disulfides, including cystine, give no color. Of the amino acids only histidine gives a color, which is yellowish brown altered to pink by oxidation with air or hydrogen peroxide. In a mixture of thiol compound and cystine the color of the cysteine complex is obtained, probably due to reduction of cystine to cysteine by the thiol compound. Cystine mixed with hydrogen sulfide gives a brown which is readily differentiated from that due to cystine. With the cobalt salt in slight excess the intensity of color is proportional to the cystine content.

The red color of cysteine with 1,2-naphthoquinone-4-sulfonate is largely applied to estimation of reduced cystine. Details appear under

[16] Vincenz Arnold, Z. physiol. Chem. 70, 300-9 (1911); E. Abderhalden and E. Wertheimer, Arch. ges. Physiol. (Pflügers) 198, 122-7 (1923); A. Blankenstein, Biochem. Z. 218, 321-30 (1930).

[17] E. Hazeloop, Aan. P. van der Wielen 1934, 159-63.

[18] L. Michaelis and E. S. G. Barron, J. Biol. Chem. 83, 191-210 (1929); L. Michaelis and S. Yamaguchi, Ibid. 83, 367-73 (1929); L. Michaelis and M. P. Schubert, J. Am. Chem. Soc. 52, 4418-26 (1930); Maxwell P. Schubert, Ibid. 53, 3851-61 (1931); Ibid. 54, 4077-85 (1932); Ibid. 55, 3336-42 (1933); Kamenosuke Shinohara and Martin Kilpatrick, J. Biol. Chem. 105, 241-51 (1934).

that topic. Cysteine, in the presence of ferric and zinc ions, forms a blue color with p-aminodimethylaniline.[19] Aside from direct application for estimation of cysteine, the cystine in acid hydrolyzates of proteins is reduced by this method and determined. Details of the method are under cystine.

Cysteine reacts with dimethyl-p-phenylenediamine hydrochloride in acid solution containing ferric ion to give a dark red-violet color.[20] Cystine does not react. Glutathione present in a ratio of 25:1 and ascorbic acid present in the ratio 5:1 will interfere. Cystine can be reduced to cysteine by conventional procedures and also determined with this reagent. A complex reaction of cysteine with brucine in acid oxidizing solution gives a red color.[21] Ascorbic acid, adrenaline, thiourea, and heavy metals interfere.

Sample—*General.* Test for hydrogen sulfide. If present, pass nitrogen or carbon dioxide through the solution under reduced pressure. If mercaptans or other chloroform-soluble organic substances are present, acidify the solution and extract twice or thrice with an equal volume of chloroform. Filter the aqueous solution through a wet filter. Titrate an aliquot with a 0.48 per cent solution of lithium hydroxide to an end point with bromocresol purple. Add sufficient lithium hydroxide in development of the standard curve to neutralize the amount in excess of that in the volume of standard used. Develop with phospho-18-tungstic acid for cysteine.

Urine. As sample take 1-10 ml., usually 2 ml. Run one sample through the determination with sodium sulfite. Substitute the sodium sulfite solution in the other portion with water and subtract the value obtained from the total cysteine determined on the other sample. Other reducing substances in the urine are included in the cysteine.

Protein. Reflux 1-5 grams of dried and accurately weighed protein with 20 ml. of 1:2 sulfuric acid, and 2 ml. of butanol to prevent foaming, for 18-20 hours. Remove the condenser and evaporate the butanol. The hydrolyzate is frequently colored with humin-like bodies. These can be removed with kaolin but not with charcoal, Lloyd's reagent, colloidal iron, or lead acetate, because of reduction in the cysteine-cystine content. Add 2 grams of kaolin to the hydrolyzate and shake for 3-5 minutes.

[19] R. Fleming, *Biochem. J.* **24,** 265 (1939); Bruno Vassel, *J. Biol. Chem.* **140,** 323-36 (1941); Dale K. Mecham, *Ibid.* **151,** 643-5 (1943).

[20] Akizi Huzita and Isama Numata, *Biochem. J.* **300,** 264-73 (1939).

[21] Kay Nakamura and Francis Binkley, *J. Biol. Chem.* **173,** 407-10 (1948).

Filter, wash the filter thoroughly, and dilute the filtrate and washings to 100 ml. for estimation of cystine and cysteine in the presence of sulfite or by sodium nitroprusside.

Corn. The preparation of the appropriate solution is described under histidine (Vol. IV).

Solutions. Isolation of cystine and cysteine by cuprous chloride.[22] Wash 0.3 gram of finely powdered cuprous chloride with 25 ml. of 1:100 hydrochloric acid, decant, and dissolve the residue in 2 ml. of a 25 per cent solution of potassium iodide in 1:60 hydrochloric acid. This is the precipitating reagent. To 8 ml. of sample solution containing approximately 0.25 mg. of cystine and cysteine, add 5 ml. of a buffer for pH 4.6. This is a 1:1 mixture of 16.4 per cent sodium acetate solution and 12 per cent acetic acid. Add 10-12 drops of the freshly prepared reagent and mix. Let stand for 30-40 minutes and centrifuge for 5 minutes. Ergothioneine, glutathione, ascorbic acid, and uric acid are not precipitated.

Decant the supernatant liquid. Mix 10 volumes of 16.4 per cent sodium acetate solution and 3 volumes of 12 per cent acetic acid to give a buffer for pH 5.2. Add this to the 8-ml. mark and disperse the precipitate by stirring. Pass in hydrogen sulfide for 3-4 minutes with stirring to break up any lumps of precipitate. Filter and bubble carbon dioxide or nitrogen through the filtrate to remove hydrogen sulfide. Dilute to a known volume and use an aliquot as sample for development of total cystine and cysteine by phospho-18-tungstate in the presence of sodium sulfite.

Procedure—*Cysteine with phospho-18-tungstic acid.* Mix 2 portions containing 10 ml. of 16 per cent sodium acetate solution and 3 ml. of 12 per cent acetic acid. Add water to about 40 ml. Add an amount of sample to contain about 2 mg. of cysteine to each and mix. If lithium hydroxide is to be added, mix it with the sample at this point. To the sample blank add 1 ml. of 37 per cent formaldehyde solution, mix well, and set aside for 2 minutes. This permits cysteine to react completely with the formaldehyde so that this flask will be a blank for other reducing substances which will react with the reagent. Add 4 ml. of phosphotungstic acid reagent (page 437) to each, dilute to 50 ml., and shake vigorously. Read at 760 mμ after 5-10 minutes against water and subtract the sample blank. This color is stable for 6 hours at room temperature or 2 days in a refrigerator.

---

[22] Sarel Rossouw and Tobias J. Wilken-Jorden, *Biochem. J.* **29**, 219-24 (1935); Grace Medes, *Ibid.* **30**, 1293-7 (1936).

Cysteine and cystine with phospho-18-tungstic acid. Slightly acidify a portion of sample such that it contains about 2 mg. of cystine and cysteine. Add 2 ml. of a freshly prepared 20 per cent sodium sulfite solution. After standing for 1 minutes add 8 ml. of 32 per cent sodium carbonate solution. Add 10 ml. of a 40 per cent solution of urea, mix, and add 8 ml. of phosphotungstic acid reagent (page 437). After 5 minutes, dilute to volume with 3 per cent sodium sulfite solution and read at 760 mμ against a water blank. Subtract a sample blank.

With sodium nitroprusside. To 10 ml. of the sample add 6 ml. of 1:2 ammonium hydroxide followed by 5 ml. of 0.13 per cent potassium cyanide solution. Heat in boiling water for 15 minutes, then cool quickly under a tap. Add 6-8 drops of freshly prepared 5 per cent solution of sodium nitroprusside and dilute to 25 ml. with 1:2 ammonium hydroxide. Read against a reagent blank.

With o-benzoquinone. Shake 2 ml. of sample solution, acidified with hydrochloric acid, and 2 ml. of a 1 per cent solution of *o*-benzoquinone in chloroform. Separate the chloroform layer and dry over anhydrous sodium sulfate. Read against a chloroform blank.

With cobaltous chloride. Mix 5 ml. of sample solution with 2 ml. of saturated cobaltous chloride solution at 25°. Add 4 ml. of 2 per cent sodium hydroxide solution and 1 ml. of 3 per cent hydrogen peroxide solution. Filter or centrifuge to remove the cobaltic hydroxide. Read against a reagent blank. The color is stable for at least 12 hours.

With dimethyl-p-phenylenediamine hydrochloride. To 2 ml. of filtrate which has been deproteinized with 2 per cent metaphosphoric acid, add 2 ml. of 2 per cent dimethyl-*p*-phenylenediamine hydrochloride in 1:9 sulfuric acid. Follow with 0.2 ml. of a 10 per cent solution of ferric alum in 1:35 sulfuric acid and mix. Heat in boiling water for 40 minutes, cool, and read at 610 mμ against a reagent blank.

With brucine. To 5 ml. of sample solution containing 0.05-0.5 mg. of cysteine, add 0.5 ml. of 1:1 sulfuric acid, 2 ml. of 1 per cent brucine in 1:20 sulfuric acid, 0.5 ml. of 10 per cent glycine solution, and 0.5 ml. of 1 per cent potassium persulfate solution. Mix, incubate at 30° for 0.5 hour, and read at 660 mμ against a reagent blank.

3,3'-DITHIOBIS(2-AMINOPROPIONIC ACID), CYSTINE

Methods of determination of cystine ordinarily depend on its reduction to cysteine for the reading. Thus by treatment with sulfite or cyanide one mole of cystine gives one mole of cysteine.[23] This can then be reacted with phospho-18-tungstic acid. Extraneous reducing substances are sometimes present and will reduce phosphotungstic acid. Sulfite increases the effects of these.[24] The corresponding treatment of dithioglycolic acid gives thioglycolic acid which reacts the same as cysteine.

Where reduction of cystine by cyanide converts only half the molecule to cysteine, reduction by sodium amalgam causes complete reduction to give two cysteine molecules from one cystine molecule. Comparison of results by the two methods permits calculation of cystine in the presence of cysteine.[25]

The reaction with 1,2-naphthoquinone-4-sulfonate is appropriate for this estimation.[26] The reaction is not given by glutathione, cysteine-amine, or isocystine. If the glutathione present exceeds the cystine by more than 20:1, the amount of naphthoquinone must be increased. Unless the solution is well buffered, the red color is far from proportional to the cysteine content when substantial amounts of other amino acids are present. Ferric ion interferes if present in the sample. The interference is due to catalytic oxidation of cystine to a thiocyanate. Such reducing agents as ascorbic acid, adrenaline, hydroquinone, pyrogallol, diaminophenol, and tannic acid interfere. Larger amounts of simple aldehydes, sugars, and sugar derivatives also cause erroneous results.[27] Amino acids, ammonium salts, and sodium borate inhibit the reaction; sodium and potassium chlorides and sulfates intensify it.

When reduced to cysteine, the complex reaction of p-aminodimethyl-aniline, ferric ion, and zinc ion to give a purple is applicable. Accuracy to ±1 per cent is attainable at 0.01-0.2 mg. per ml.

---

[23] Hans Thatcher Clark, *J. Biol. Chem.* **97**, 235 (1932); Kamenosuke Shinohara, *Ibid.* **110**, 263-7 (1935).

[24] J. W. H. Lugg, *Biochem. J.* **26**, 2144-2160 (1932); Herbert M. Winegard and Gerrit Toennies, *J. Biol. Chem.* **174**, 44-55 (1948).

[25] M. X. Sullivan, W. C. Hess, and H. W. Howard, *J. Biol. Chem.* **145**, 621-4 (1942); Robert John Evans, *Ibid.* **156**, 373-8 (1944); Frank A. Csonka, Harold Lichtenstein, and Charles A. Denton, *Ibid.* **156**, 571-6 (1944).

[26] M. X. Sullivan, *U. S. Public Health Repts.* **41**, 1030-56 (1926); *Ibid.* **44**, 1421, 1599 (1929); *Ibid. Suppl.* **No. 78** (1929); C. E. Neubeck and C. V. Smythe, *Arch. Biochem.* **4**, 435-41 (1944).

[27] James C. Andrews and Kathleen Crandall Andrews, *J. Biol. Chem.* **118**, 555-67 (1937).

Sample—*General.* For development with phospho-18-tungstic acid, make the sample solution more than 1:36 with sulfuric acid. Add tin dust to a measured volume of the sample. Zinc is not satisfactory, tin granules are ineffective. Shake the mixture frequently for 30 minutes. This reduces cystine to cysteine. Filter, neutralize 25 ml. of filtrate with lithium hydroxide solution to an acidity at which tin can be precipitated as the sulfide, and dilute to 50 ml. Pass hydrogen sulfide through the solution and filter the precipitated tin sulfide. For development with 1,2-naphthoquinone-4-sulfonate, add 1 ml. of 0.2 per cent sodium amalgam to 7 ml. of cystine solution which is 1:120 with hydrochloric acid or 1:360 with sulfuric acid and contains 0.1-0.2 mg. of cystine per ml. Allow to stand for 1 hour with occasional shaking.

Protein. Hydrolyze 200 mg. of protein with 2 ml. of a 1:1 mixture of 98 per cent formic acid and 1:1 hydrochloric acid at 120° in a sealed tube. Adjust the pH of an appropriate dilution to 4.5-4.8, after 20 minutes filter through a sintered glass filter to remove turbidity, and develop with phospho-18-tungstic acid reagent.

For development with sodium 1,2-naphthoquinone-4-sulfonate,[28] hydrolyze an amount of protein material containing 4-5 mg. of cystine in 2:1 hydrochloric acid for 24 hours, filter, and wash the humin with hot, dilute, hydrochloric acid solution. Remove excess hydrochloric acid by evaporating to a syrupy consistency. Repeat this procedure twice, after the addition of 5 ml. of water each time. Dilute the residue to a volume of 25 ml.

Add an amount of this solution containing 2-4 mg. of cystine to 2.5 ml. of glacial acetic acid and 3.5 ml. of 20 per cent sodium hydroxide solution. Dilute with water to 40 ml. The pH of the mixture is about 4.2. Prepare a solution of 1.2 per cent of cuprous chloride and 25 per cent of potassium iodide in 1:140 hydrochloric acid.[29] Add 10 drops individually with constant stirring and allow to stand for 40 minutes. Centrifuge, discard the supernatant liquid, and suspend the precipitate in 20 ml. of absolute ethanol. Stir frequently during a 10-minute period. Centrifuge and discard the supernatant liquid again. Dissolve the precipitate in 5 ml. of 1:25 hydrochloric acid. Add 0.5 ml. of pyridine and mix. Add 1 ml. of 10 per cent potassium thiocyanate solution to precipitate the copper. Add enough water to bring the volume to 10 ml. for aliquoting.

---

[28] Frank A. Csonka, Harold Lichtenstein, and Charles A. Denton, *J. Biol. Chem.* **156**, 571-6 (1944).

Such an hydrolysis of protein may be shortened by addition of titanous chloride.[30] Humin formation is also lessened.

Fingernail clippings.[31] Digest 40-50 mg. of nail clippings with 0.15 ml. of 1:1 sulfuric acid solution in an oil bath for 1 hour at 150°. Dilute the hydrolyzate with 5 ml. of water and decolorize by adding 25 mg. of activated carbon and heating gently. Filter, wash the filter with 3 ml. of 1:120 hydrochloric acid, and dilute to 25 ml. with water. Determine cystine by sodium 1,2-naphthoquinone-4-sulfonate.

Human hair.[32] *Cysteine absent.* Dry a 50-mg. sample of hair at 110° for 2 hours. Add 5 ml. of 1:1 hydrochloric acid and seal the tube. Enclose the tube in a metal pipe closed at both ends. Place in an oven at 118-20° for 6 hours. Cool and open the tube. Neutralize the contents of the tube to pH 3.5 by the dropwise addition of 20 per cent sodium hydroxide solution using a glass electrode to determine the end point. Dilute to 100 ml. with hydrochloric acid solution of pH 3.5 and determine the amount of cystine by sodium 1,2-naphthoquinone-4-sulfonate.

Cysteine present. Alkylate a 0.5-gram sample by shaking for 20 hours with 0.5 ml. of ethyl bromide in phosphate buffer at pH 8.3.[33] The ethyl bromide will have alkylated the sulhydryl groups so that they no longer react. Now dry and process as though cysteine had been absent.

Alternatively, transfer a sample of about 0.2 gram to a cold 1 per cent solution of iodoacetic acid for about 1 minute. Strip free of excess liquid, using rubber gloves to protect the hands. Quickly transfer to 50 ml. of 1 per cent solution of sodium iodoacetate at pH 8.3 and heat in boiling water for 30 minutes. Wash thoroughly in water, dry at room temperature, and chop into small pieces. Then proceed as though cysteine had been absent. The cysteine present is determined by difference from analyses of the original hair for total cystine before treatment which has produced more or less cysteine.

Tobacco mosaic virus protein.[34] Inhibit humin formation by hydrolyzing with 1:1 hydrochloric acid containing titanous chloride or with 57

29 S. D. Rossouw and T. J. Wilken-Jordan, *Biochem. J.* **29**, 219 (1935).

30 M. X. Sullivan and W. C. Hess, *J. Biol. Chem.* **117**, 423-8 (1937).

31 M. X. Sullivan, H. W. Howard, and W. C. Hess, *Ibid.* **119**, 721-4 (1937).

32 Dorothy Sanford and Fred L. Humoller, *Ind. Eng. Chem., Anal .Ed.* **19**, 404-6 (1947).

33 Wilbur I. Patterson, Walton B. Geiger, Louis R. Mizell, and Milton Harris, *J. Research National Bur. Standards* **27**, No. 1, 89-103 (1941) (*Research Paper* RP No. 1405).

34 W. C. Hess, M. X. Sullivan, and E. D. Palmes, *Proc. Soc. Biol. Med.* **48**, 353-5 (1941).

per cent hydriodic acid. Determine cystine by means of sodium 1,2-naph-thoquinone-4-sulfonate.

Blood. Digest 0.4 ml. of serum for 18 hours at 115-20° with 2.5 ml. of a solution made up by adding 58 ml. of concentrated hydrochloric acid to 63 ml. of 90 per cent formic acid. Dilute to 10 ml. with 1:1 hydrochloric acid and use an aliquot for development with *p*-aminodimethyl-aniline.

Urine. Mix 7 ml. of the sample with 10 ml. of concentrated hydrochloric acid. This is 7 N in acidity. Develop with *p*-aminodimethylaniline.

Procedure—*By phospho-18-tungstic acid.*[35] As a buffer dissolve 105 grams of citric acid and 52.5 grams of sodium hydroxide in 450 ml. of water with cooling. Add 110 grams of sodium acetate and 250 grams of urea. Add a solution of 13.6 grams of zinc chloride in 20 ml. of water and a solution of 26.8 grams of ammonium chloride in 100 ml. of water. Dilute to 1 liter and preserve with toluene. Filter before use.

As buffered sulfite dissolve 9.5 grams of sodium sulfite in water, add 15 ml. of 54.4 per cent sodium acetate trihydrate solution, and dilute to 100 ml. Keep under refrigeration. Prepare the series of 4 tubes shown in Table 5, using the reagent described on page 437.

Dilute to 25 ml. and read the first three tubes against the blank at 720 mμ. Subtract the average of the second and third tubes as a correction.

TABLE 5. SERIES OF TUBES FOR CYSTINE DETERMINATION

	Cystine and other reducing substances	Other reducing substances with sulfite	Other reducing substances without sulfite	Blank
	Tube 1 ml.	Tube 2 ml.	Tube 3 ml.	Tube 4 ml.
Buffer, Ph 5.7	2.5	2.5	2.5	2.5
Mercuric chloride 6.77 per cent..	0	0.1	0.1	0.1
Water	to dilute to volume of 8 ml. at this point			
Sample hydrolysate	1	1	1	0
Sodium hydroxide solution	To neutralize the sample to methyl red			
Phospho-18-tungstic acid reagent	0.5	0.5	0.5	0.5
Buffered sodium sulfite	0.25	0.25	0	0

[35] Beatrice Kassell and Erwin Brand, *J. Biol. Chem.* **125**, 115-29 (1938).

Cystine as cysteine by sodium 1,2-naphthoquinone-4-sulfonate. Two determinations are necessary. As the first, add 2 ml. of fresh 5 per cent aqueous sodium cyanide solution to 5 ml. of sample solution containing 1 mg. of cystine. Mix and allow to stand for 10 minutes at 25°. Add 1 ml. of 1 per cent solution of sodium 1,2-naphthoquinone-4-sulfonate and shake for 10 seconds. Add 5 ml. of 10 per cent anhydrous sodium sulfite in 2 per cent sodium hydroxide solution and mix. Allow to stand for 30 minutes, then add 1 ml. of 2 per cent solution of sodium hyposulfite in 2 per cent sodium hydroxide and read within 10-40 minutes at 500 mμ against a reagent blank.

The second technic requires a reduction with sodium amalgam. Dilute the usual 2 per cent commercial amalgam with mercury to 0.2 per cent concentration. To 7 ml. of neutral sample add 0.7 ml. of 1:10 hydrochloric acid. Omit any part of this already present as mineral acidity. Add 1 ml. of amalgam and shake occasionally for an hour. Then determine in an aliquot as before starting at "... add 2 ml. of fresh 5 per cent. ..."

The first value is free cysteine plus one mole of cysteine for each mole of cystine. The second value is free cysteine plus two moles of cysteine for each mole of cystine.

With p-aminodimethylaniline. Cystine. Dissolve 35 mg. of *p*-aminodimethylaniline monohydrochloride in 100 ml. of 1:5 sulfuric acid. It keeps about 10 days under refrigeration. As reagent for nine determinations of cystine, react 1 gram of zinc dust with 20 ml. of 20 per cent ferric ammonium sulfate in 1:35 sulfuric acid. Shake occasionally for 10 minutes. Add 2 grams of granulated zinc and 30 ml. of *p*-aminodimethylaniline solution. Allow to stand for 10 minutes, then reflux on a boiling water bath for 25 minutes. Cool and filter.

To 5 ml. of sample solution containing not over 0.2 mg. of cystine and cysteine per ml., add 150 mg. of zinc dust. Stopper loosely until the zinc is dissolved, carefully washing down any particles from the sides of the tube. Add 1 ml. of this reduced solution to 5 ml. of the prepared reagent.

Add an additional 3 ml. of the ferric ammonium sulfate solution, stopper lightly, and place in boiling water for 45 minutes. All of the zinc dust must be destroyed by this heating. Any left will reduce the final color. Wash down the walls with the hot solution to remove any zinc which might adhere. Place in cold water when the greenish-blue color of the solution will change to a deep reddish blue. Dilute to 25 ml. with water and read within 30 minutes at 580 mμ against a reagent blank. Read as cysteine. This value for cystine includes any free cysteine originally present. Therefore, if it was present, determine by the method which follows and subtract from the cystine determined.

Cysteine. Prepare a reagent as for cystine but add 2.3 grams of granulated zinc to allow for that added in the cystine determination as the reducing agent. Add 1 ml. of the unreduced sample to 5 ml. of this reagent. Complete as for cystine starting at "Add an additional 3 ml. of the ferric ammonium sulfate solution. . . ."

GLUTATHIONE

The reduced form of cystine-glutamic acid, glutathione, reacts quantitatively with the phospho-18-tungstic acid reagent because of its free –SH group. The method is similar to one for cystine and cysteine by the same reagent. In their absence it is appropriate for colorimetric use [36] with accuracy to 3 per cent. Uric acid gives a faint interfering color. Ascorbic acid gives the reaction but when rendered alkaline with sodium carbonate is destroyed on standing for an hour. This does not affect glutathione. In contrast with some similar methods with this reagent, sodium sulfite cannot be replaced by sodium cyanide nor sodium carbonate by sodium hydroxide. Such substitution results in an unstable color.

Glutathione in acid solution reduces the arsenophosphotungstic acid reagent for uric acid to give a blue color proportional in intensity to the glutathione content.[37] Thioneine interferes.

Glutathione is estimated by oxidation with ferricyanide and estimation of the ferrocyanide produced by reaction as Prussian blue.[38] Results are best obtained at pH 5.9, where other substances are only slightly or not at all oxidized. An accompanying blank is run with formaldehyde which prevents oxidation of glutathione without interfering with oxidation of other substances. This, therefore, affords a valuable correction for the reducing power of accompanying substances, although formaldehyde is not a specific protection for the sulfhydryl group. Large amounts of salts retard color development, but the effect of the salts in tungstic acid filtrates is negligible. The presence of oxalates sensitizes the solutions to light after addition of ferric ion.

---

[36] G. Hunter and B. A. Eagles, *J. Biol. Chem.* 72, 177-83 (1927); B. Braier and A. D. Marenzi, *Compt. rend. soc. biol.* 109, 319-21 (1932).

[37] Stanley R. Benedict and Gertrude Gottschall, *J. Biol. Chem.* 99, 729-40 (1933).

[38] Harold L. Mason, *Ibid.* 86, 623-34 (1930); *Proc. Staff Meetings Mayo Clinic* 6, 168-9 (1931).

Cysteine behaves in every way like glutathione and is therefore a fully satisfactory standard. Thioneine gives about one-tenth as much color as glutathione, indicating partial reaction, and therefore the results are in error to some extent when it is present. Uric acid does not react. Phenols are oxidized, but are measured in the blank.

Glutathione gives a red color with sodium nitroprusside which can be used for quantitative estimation.[39] The solution must be alkaline. Potassium cyanide in too great excess decomposes glutathione. By using sodium carbonate the color is stable for about 1 minute. Ammonium hydroxide is also used as the source of alkalinity, preferably in the presence of ammonium sulfate. By reduction with hydrogen sulfide total glutathione is obtained. Trichloroacetic acid and metaphosphoric acid are unsatisfactory as deproteinizing agents, but tungstic acid and thiosalicylic acid are suitable.[40]

Sample—*Blood*. Mix 3 ml. of oxalated blood and 3 ml. of water. Add 3 ml. of 10 per cent trichloroacetic acid and shake for 10 minutes. Filter or centrifuge and use as sample for development with phospho-18-tungstic acid. Fresh or coagulated blood can also be used.

For development with arsenophosphotungstic acid prepare a sodium molybdotungstate reagent. For this treat 10 grams of pure molybdic acid free from ammonia with 50 ml. of 4 per cent sodium hydroxide solution and boil gently for 4-5 minutes. Filter and wash the filter with 150 ml. of hot water. Cool the filtrate, mix with a solution of 80 grams of sodium tungstate in 600 ml. of water, and dilute to 1 liter.

Excessive amounts of oxalate retard color development with molybdotungstate reagent, so that not more than 2-3 mg. per ml. are permissible. Dilute 1 volume of whole blood with 7 volumes of water. Add 1 volume of sodium molybdotungstate reagent and 1 volume of 1:60 sulfuric acid. When coagulation is complete, filter. If to be kept for any time, acidify with sulfuric acid to prevent autoxidation.

For development with ferricyanide, mix 5 ml. of blood, 6 ml. of 1:56 sulfuric acid, and 30 ml. of water. Allow the blood to lake and add 5 ml. of 10 per cent sodium tungstate solution. Mix and, when precipita-

[39] R. Fleming, *Compt. rend. soc. biol.* **104**, 831-2 (1930); *Ibid.* **106**, 259-60 (1931); Kurt Uhlenbroock, *Z. physiol. Chem.* **236**, 192-6 (1935).

[40] R. Bierich and A. Rosenbohm, *Z. physiol. Chem.* **215**, 151-63 (1933); C. Mentzer, *J. pharm. chim.* **27**, 145-54 (1938); Frederick S. Hammett and Sidney S. Chapman, *J. Biol. Clin. Med.* **24**, 293-8 (1938); Akizi Huzita and Isamu Numata, *Biochem. Z.* **300**, 246-56 (1939).

tion is complete, filter. The filtrate is slightly acid and thus protects the reduced glutathione from autoxidation. To reduce oxidized glutathione, evaporate 25-50 ml. of the extract *in vacuo* to 1 ml. or less. Extract the residue with small portions of a mixture of 3 ml. of concentrated hydrochloric acid and 100 ml. of absolute ethanol. Centrifuge the extract. Dilute the alcoholic extract with water and evaporate the ethanol under reduced pressure.

Add 10 grams of 2.5 per cent sodium amalgam to a 50-ml. Erlenmeyer flask. Add sufficient mercury to cover the bottom of the flask and chill in ice for a minute or two. Dilute the extract with sufficient water to take up any solids and add to the chilled mercury and sodium amalgam. Add 1:1 hydrochloric acid at 3-4 drops per minute until the sodium has reacted completely. This should require about 10 minutes. Decant the solution from the mercury and rinse the flask and mercury with several small portions of water. Dilute the reduced solution to a known volume and use aliquots for the determination.

Tissue. Triturate 5 grams of finely cut tissue in a mortar with dry sand. Add 5 ml. of water and 10 ml. of 10 per cent trichloroacetic acid. Shake and filter by suction. Develop the clear filtrate with phospho-18-tungstic acid.

For development with ferricyanide treat as for blood samples.

For development with nitroprusside, weigh a 5-gram sample and cut fine. Rub it up in a mortar with sand and distilled water. Transfer to a centrifuge cup and dilute to 45 ml. Add 5 ml. of a 22 per cent solution of thiosalicylic acid and mix. After 30 minutes with occasional shaking, centrifuge and filter the supernatant liquid for use of an aliquot.

Plasma. Dilute 1 volume of plasma with 8 volumes of water. Add 0.5 volume of sodium molybdotungstate reagent and 0.5 volume of 1:60 sulfuric acid, and filter. Acidify unless to be used at once. Develop with arsenophosphotungstic acid.

Corpuscles. Dilute 1 volume of corpuscles with 5 volumes of water. Add 2 volumes of sodium molybdotungstate reagent and 2 volumes of 1:60 sulfuric acid, and filter. Acidify, unless to be used at once, and develop with arsenophosphotungstic acid.

General. Deproteinize the sample solution with 5 per cent metaphosphoric acid solution and determine with sodium nitroprusside. The value will be the reduced glutathione.

For total glutathione, mix 5 ml. of deproteinized filtrate, 4 ml. of 1 per cent mercuric acetate solution, and 0.5 ml. of 1:5 hydrochloric acid. Mix, add 0.5 ml. of 50 per cent sodium acetate solution, and pass in hydrogen sulfide gas. Leave under hydrogen sulfide overnight and then filter. To 8 ml. of filtrate add 0.3 ml. of 1:5 hydrochloric acid and drive off hydrogen sulfide *in vacuo*. Dilute to a volume of 8 ml. The determination by sodium nitroprusside will give total glutathione.

Procedure—*With phospho-18-tungstic acid.* To a portion of sample containing 0.7-2.8 mg. of glutathione, add 0.2 ml. of 20 per cent sodium sulfite solution. Shake and after 1-2 minutes add 0.2 ml. of 20 per cent lithium sulfate solution. Add 2 ml. of 20 per cent sodium carbonate solution and shake. Add 2 ml. of phosphotungstic acid reagent (page 437) and shake. Let stand for 4 minutes to develop the maximum color and dilute to 25 ml. with 2 per cent sodium sulfite solution. This prevents reoxidation. Read in less than 10 minutes against a reagent blank. Results may be taken from a cysteine curve, multiplied by 2.537 to convert to glutathione.

With arsenophosphotungstic acid. As reagent dissolve 100 grams of pure sodium tungstate in about 600 ml. of water. Add 50 grams of pure arsenic pentoxide, 25 ml. of 85 per cent phosphoric acid and 20 ml. of concentrated hydrochloric acid. Boil for 20 minutes and dilute to 1 liter. For use dilute a portion with an equal volume of water.

To 5 ml. of sample add 2 ml. of 50 per cent aqueous sodium acetate solution. Add 0.2 ml. of 2 per cent sodium bisulfite solution and 0.3 ml. of the arsenophosphotungstic acid reagent. Mix and read against a reagent blank after 10 minutes and before 30 minutes.

With ferricyanide. Titrate an aliquot containing 1-2 mg. of glutathione to a Congo red end point to determine how much standard alkali is required to neutralize the sample. Dilute a duplicate sample to a volume which will be 15 ml. after neutralization.

As buffer for pH 5.9, mix 1 volume of 4.77 per cent disodium phosphate dodecahydrate solution with 9 volumes of 1.01 per cent monopotassium phosphate solution.

Add 5 ml. of buffer solution and the necessary alkali for neutralization, thus getting a volume of about 20 ml. Also run a blank of the same or a multiple of the aliquot of sample to which 0.5 ml. of 40 per cent formaldehyde has been added, to measure other reducing substances present. Add salts to the blank equivalent to the amount in the sample taken.

To sample and blank add 0.33 per cent potassium ferricyanide solution free from ferrocyanide drop by drop until oxidation is complete. Add 3-4 drops of ferricyanide in excess, thus getting a distinct yellow color. Let this stand for 15 minutes. The reaction is slow and further addition of ferricyanide may be necessary to maintain an excess.

To prepare a ferric sulfate reagent, heat 60 grams of gum arabic with 600 ml. of water on a water bath with shaking until the gum is completely dissolved, and cool. Mix 5 grams of hydrated ferric sulfate with 75 ml. of 85 per cent phosphoric acid and 100 ml. of water. Heat until the sulfate has dissolved. Cool and add this solution to the gum arabic solution. Mix and dilute to 1 liter. Filtration is not normally necessary. The solution is stable for 4-6 weeks.

When the treated sample and blank have stood for 15 minutes, add 3 ml. of the ferric sulfate reagent and mix. Let stand for 10 minutes in the dark, since ferric ion sensitizes the reducing action of other substances present, and dilute each to 25 ml. Read the sample and sample blank, subtracting the latter prior to calculation.

With sodium nitroprusside. To 1 ml. of deproteinized sample, add 4 ml. of saturated sodium chloride solution, 0.5 ml. of 2 per cent freshly prepared sodium nitroprusside solution, and 0.5 ml. of 1:14 ammonium hydroxide solution. Read at 530 mμ against a reagent blank.

ERGOTHIONEINE

When a solution of ergothioneine is coupled with diazotized sulfanilic acid, the absorption at 510 or 540 mμ is a measure of the ergothioneine content.[41] Conditions are designed to minimize coupling with other blood constituents. Both histidine and tyrosine increase the absorption [42] unless removed by a special method of deproteinizing. Reduced glutathione interferes but can be removed with lead acetate. Otherwise it is accurate to ±3 per cent. Alternatively, in blood filtrates such interfering substances are removed by sorption on an ion-exchange resin, followed by extraction of other interfering compounds with an organic solvent. The method in that form is accurate to ±2 per cent at total concentrations of 4-13 mg. per 100 ml. of blood.

The unusual reactivity of sulfur in ergothioneine with bromine water [43] gives sulfate from compounds which have sulfur linked to carbon

[41] George Hunter, *Biochem. J.* **22,** 4-10 (1928); George Hunter, *Can. J. Research* **27E,** 230-9 (1949); Donald B. Melville and Rose Lubschez, *J. Biol. Chem.* **200,** 275-85 (1953).

[42] E. B. Astwood and Malcolm M. Stanley, *Lancet* **253,** 905-7 (1947); A. Lawson and C. Rimington, *Ibid.* 2, 586-7 (1947); A. L. Latner, *Biochem. J.* **42,** 35 (1948); *Ibid.* **43,** 230 (1949).

[43] D. Blumenthal and H. T. Clarke, *J. Biol. Chem.* **110,** 343-9 (1935).

by a double bond, or as sulfhydryl with nitrogen or oxygen also attached to the same carbon atom. Thus sulfides, glutathione, cystine, and methionine form no sulfate while ergothioneine reacts almost quantitatively.[44] The sulfate is then precipitated as benzidine sulfate and the benzidine determined quantitatively with β-naphthoquinone-4-sulfonate.[45] Recoveries are accurate to 5 per cent and duplicable to 15 per cent. A blank for blood sulfate is necessary. Ergothioneine is estimated by its reduction of phosphotungstic acid reagent.[46]

Sample—*Whole blood.* Mix 0.5 ml. with 4.5 ml. of 0.027 per cent acetic acid containing 0.016 per cent of sodium oxalate. Mix in a boiling water bath. Coagulation occurs in 1-2 minutes. Centrifuge and decant the upper layer.

As the next reagent boil 220 grams of neutral lead acetate trihydrate and 140 grams of lead monoxide with about a liter of water for 30 minutes. Cool, filter, and dilute to 1 liter. Add 1 drop of this to the clarified sample, mix, and centrifuge. Decant and add a drop of 10 per cent monosodium phosphate monohydrate. Again mix, centrifuge, and decant. Develop with diazotized sulfanilic acid.

Alternatively add 1 ml. of heparinized blood to 10 ml. of 0.9 per cent sodium chloride solution, mix, and centrifuge. Pour off the diluted plasma and add water to about 1 ml. Stir, add 0.5 ml. of freshly prepared solution of pure glutathione containing 35 mg. per ml., and mix. Add 25 mg. of sodium hydrosulfite crystals and mix. The reducing agents prevent loss of ergothioneine during precipitation of proteins.

Add 5 ml. of water and 0.5 ml. of fresh, redistilled 35 per cent trichloroacetic acid to precipitate proteins. Mix, centrifuge, and transfer the supernatant liquid to a separatory funnel. Shake with 15 ml. of chloroform which has been thoroughly water-washed on the day of use. Discard any solid-material and the chloroform layer containing interfering substances. Mix the aqueous layer with about 2.4 grams of moist Amberlite IRA-410 resin,[47] and shake the mixture mechanically for 10 minutes. Filter through cotton to remove the resin. Use the filtrate as sample.

---

[44] George Barger and A. J. Ewins, *J. Chem. Soc.* **99**, 2336-41 (1912).

[45] T. V. Letonoff and John G. Reinhold, *J. Biol. Chem.* **114**, 147-56 (1936); Oscar Touster, *Ibid.* **188**, 371-7 (1951).

[46] Jeanette Allen Behre and Stanley R. Benedict, *J. Biol. Chem.* **82**, 11-5 (1929); A. Lawson, H. V. Morley, and L. I. Woolf, *Biochem. J.* **47**, 513-18 (1950).

[47] Sold by the Rohm and Haas Co., Philadelphia, Pa.

For development with β-naphthoquinone-4-sulfonate, centrifuge 1.5 ml. of oxalated whole blood for 25 minutes and wash the corpuscles thrice with 1 ml. portions of 0.9 per cent sodium chloride solution, centrifuging 15 minutes after each washing. Add 1.5 ml. of hot 0.2 per cent uranium nitrate solution to the washed corpuscles. Mix and heat for 15 minutes in boiling water. Minimize evaporation by covering with tin foil. Stir and heat for 15 minutes and decant the supernatant liquid to be saved. Wash the precipitate twice with 0.6 ml. portions of hot 0.2 per cent uranium nitrate solution. Dilute the solution to 2.5 ml. with the uranium nitrate solution and cool.

Dilute 0.45 ml. of the protein-free filtrate with 0.15 ml. of 0.4 per cent cold uranium nitrate solution. Add a drop of bromine and swirl. After 20 minutes add another drop of bromine. If not colored after a minute add another drop. After 30 minutes' total time centrifuge for 15 minutes and pass air through to remove bromine.

Add 3 drops of glacial acetic acid and 1.35 ml. of 1 per cent solution of decolorized and recrystallized benzidine in acetone. Mix well, stopper, and chill for 0.5 hour. Centrifuge, decant, and wipe the lip of the tube with acetone-wet gauze. Wash the precipitate twice with acetone and drain for 3 minutes.

Dissolve the benzidine sulfate by swirling with 3 drops of 1 per cent sodium borate in 0.4 per cent sodium hydroxide solution and heating for 10 minutes in a hot water bath.

For development by reduction of phosphotungstic acid, dilute 0.5 ml. of blood to 5 ml. with 1:1500 acetic acid, heat, and centrifuge. Add 0.05 ml. of 25 per cent basic lead-acetate solution and centrifuge. Decant and add 0.05 ml. of 10 per cent phosphoric acid to the liquid and centrifuge. Decant and add 1 drop of 1:3 hydrochloric acid, cool to 0°, and add 1 drop of iodobismuthous acid to precipitate ergothioneine. Prepare this acid by dissolving 8 grams of bismuth basic carbonate in 10 ml. of concentrated hydrochloric acid and add 28 ml. of colorless hydriodic acid of specific gravity 1.7, freshly distilled over red phosphorus.

Centrifuge the treated solution and decant the liquid to waste. Dissolve the precipitate in 4 ml. of water and determine as described for uric acid (page 437).

Corpuscles. Treat as described for whole blood for development with diazotized sulfanilic acid, except that the acetic acid is 0.018 per cent containing 0.015 per cent of sodium oxalate.

For development with phosphotungstic acid, to 0.5 ml. add 4.5 ml. of 1:5000 acetic acid solution containing 0.016 per cent of sodium oxalate. Continue as for whole blood from ''Add 0.05 ml. of 25 per cent. . . .''

Plasma. Treat as described for whole blood for development with diazotized sulfanilic acid, except that the acetic acid is 0.033 per cent containing 0.016 per cent of sodium oxalate.

Procedure—*With sulfanilic acid.* Prepare a diazo reagent by adding to 1.5 ml. of a prechilled solution containing 0.9 gram of sulfanilic acid and 9 ml. of concentrated hydrochloric acid per 100 ml., 0.15 ml. of a 5 per cent sodium nitrite solution. Let stand for 5 minutes and add 6 ml. of 5 per cent sodium nitrite solution. Let stand for 5 minutes, dilute to 50 ml. with ice-cold water, and mix.

To 1 ml. of chilled diazo reagent add 2 ml. of an alkaline buffer solution containing 1 per cent of sodium carbonate and 10 per cent of anhydrous sodium acetate. Chill this and add at once 4 ml. of chilled sample solution. After 45 seconds, dilute to 10 ml. with 40 per cent sodium hydroxide solution and mix. Warm slightly to promote escape of gas bubbles. Read at 510 mμ against a blank within 15 minutes.

Alternatively, place 3 ml. of sample solution in a tube in an ice bath and mix with 5 ml. of a buffer solution containing 20 per cent of sodium carbonate and 5.7 per cent of sodium citrate dihydrate.

Prepare the reagent by adding 1 volume of cold 8 per cent sodium nitrite solution to 10 volumes of cold 1 per cent sulfanilic acid solution, with mixing. Add 0.5 ml. of the cold diazotized sulfanilic acid and mix. Let stand in an ice bath for 45 seconds. Mix with 1 ml. of clear 72 per cent sodium hydroxide solution. Let stand to permit escape of gas bubbles and read against a reagent blank at 540 mμ.

With sodium-β-naphthoquinone-4-sulfonate. Add 0.15 ml. of water to the sample solution in borated 0.4 per cent sodium hydroxide solution, then 0.15 ml. of 0.15 per cent sodium-β-naphthoquinone-4-sulfonate solution. Mix and let stand for 5 minutes. Add 0.3 ml. of acetone to reduce the color of excess reagent. Read at 500 mμ against a nonbrominated sample similarly developed.

3-Methylthiol-1-aminobutyric Acid, Methionine

When aqueous sodium nitroprusside is added to an alkaline methionine solution, a yellow color develops. Upon acidification, the color changes to red.[48] Many compounds react to give color with sodium nitroprusside, but the change in color upon addition of acid is specific for methionine. Histidine, histamine, carnosine, and tryptophan in amounts of 1 mg. per ml. can cause interference. With carbohydrate present greenish blue sometimes develops.

A practical answer is to work at room temperature, use sufficient alkalinity to inhibit interference other than by histidine, and if necessary add glycine. Glycylmethionine reacts molecularly the same as methionine. The stoichiometric proportion of sodium nitroprusside to methionine is 2:1. This is invalidated by other amino acids, particularly glycine which competes with the test substance for the reagent. The reaction is sensitive to better than 20 ppm.

Methionine reacts with iodine to give a sulfoxide,[49] which after extraction of excess iodine is sensitive to ±0.25 microgram by liberation of bound iodine by reversal of the reaction.[50] This reaction does not respond to peptides containing methionine and responds equally well to the l- and d-forms. The curve does not follow Beer's law. Oxygen must be excluded from the solutions.

Sample—*Proteins*. Reflux 1 gram for 18 hours with 25 ml. of 1:1 hydrochloric acid. Concentrate to 5 ml. and decolorize with activated carbon. Filter, wash the residue with hot water, and dilute to 100 ml. for development of a 5-ml. aliquot with nitroprusside.

Casein. Hydrolyze a 0.5-gram sample with 2 ml. of 1:1 hydrochloric acid solution for 10 hours at 125° in an oil bath. Take up with 2 ml. of water and decolorize by warming with 50 mg. of activated carbon. Filter and wash the residue with 5 ml. of warm 1:10 hydrochloric acid, then with 5 ml. of the same acid but cold. Neutralize the filtrate and washings to pH 3.5 with 20 per cent sodium hydroxide added dropwise with stirring. Dilute to 50 ml. with 1:120 hydrochloric acid and use a 5-ml. aliquot for development with nitroprusside.

Cereals. Treat as for proteins but use a 5-gram sample.

[48] M. X. Sullivan and Timothy E. McCarthy, *J. Biol. Chem.* **133**, C-CI (1940); Timothy E. McCarthy and M. X. Sullivan, *Ibid.* **141**, 871-6 (1941); W. C. Hess and M. X. Sullivan, *Ibid.* **151**, 635-42 (1943); Frank A. Csonka and Charles A. Denton, *Ibid.* **163**, 329-38 (1946); Carl M. Lyman, Olive Moseley, Betty Butler, Suzanne Wood, and Fred Hale, *Ibid.* **166**, 161-71 (1946); Millard J. Horn, D. Breese Jones, and Amos E. Blum, *Ibid.* **166**, 313-20 (1946); R. G. Chitre and A. B. Keni, *Current Sci.* **15**, 130-1 (1946).

[49] Theodore F. Lavine, *J. Biol. Chem.* **151**, 281-97 (1943).

[50] Bohdan Bakay and Gevirt Toennies, *Ibid.* **188**, 1-15 (1951).

For development as sulfoxide. Hydrolyze a 0.15-0.2 gram sample by heating in a sealed tube with 1.2 ml. of 1:3 hydrochloric-52.5 per cent formic acid for 13 hours at 120°. Open, dilute, filter on sintered glass, neutralize, and dilute to 100 ml.

Procedure—*With nitroprusside.* To an acid solution containing about 2 mg. of methionine add 3 ml. of water, 1 ml. of 20 per cent sodium hydroxide solution, and 0.1 ml. of 10 per cent sodium nitroprusside solution. After 10 minutes, if necessary to avoid interferences, add 2 ml. of 3 per cent glycine solution and shake at intervals for 10 minutes. Add 2 ml. of 85 per cent phosphoric acid and after 5 minutes read at 540 mμ against distilled water but correcting for a reagent blank.

As sulfoxide. As solvent use 9:1 isoamyl alcohol-carbon tetrachloride. Extract 500 ml. of isoamyl alcohol with an equal volume of 0.15 per cent silver nitrate solution. Then extract with 10 ml. of 15 per cent sodium iodide solution containing 1 ml. of 1:3 hydrochloric acid. Centrifuge and extract with an equal volume of 1 per cent stannous chloride solution. Wash twice with equal volumes of water. Distill and mix 9:1 with carbon tetrachloride. Extract the mixture with 5 per cent of its volume of 15 per cent sodium iodide solution. Before use, extract 100 ml. with 100 ml. of 1 per cent stannous chloride solution. Wash twice with water and centrifuge. Agitate with 10 ml. of buffer I by passing nitrogen through. Remove the aqueous layer and keep the slightly colored solvent stoppered. Used solvent is similarly repurified.

As buffer I, dissolve as the first solution 13.609 grams of monopotassium phosphate per 100 ml. and as the second solution 17.418 grams of dipotassium phosphate per 100 ml. Mix 1.5 volumes of the first solution with 8.5 volumes of the second solution and 10 volumes of 14.992 per cent sodium iodide solution. Saturate with nitrogen for 10 minutes, let stand for a couple of days, and extract with the 9:1 mixture of amyl alcohol and carbon tetrachloride. Filter, boil while passing nitrogen until the color is at a minimum, and cool with nitrogen passing. Stopper for storage.

As buffer II, mix 40 ml. of buffer I with 10 ml. of 0.0315 per cent iodine solution. As buffer III, mix 80 ml. of buffer I, and 20 ml. of 12 per cent sodium hydroxide solution, so adjust that 5 ml. of this, 1 ml. of the iodate mixture which follows, and 4 ml. of water give a pH of 7. As iodate mixture use equal volumes of 0.214 potassium iodate and 1:1 hydrochloric acid, mixed just before use.

Prepare 4 tubes by the schedule which follows:

	Methionine plus non methionine		Non methionine	
Number	1	2	3	4
Hydrolyzate	0	4	0	4
Water, ml.	5	1	4	0
Buffer II	5	5		
Iodate			1	1
Waiting time, minutes			30	30
Buffer III			5	5
Waiting time, minutes	30	30	30	30
Bubble with nitrogen, minutes	10	10	10	10
Solvent mixture, ml.	10	10	10	10
Bubble with nitrogen, minutes	2	2	2	2
Centrifuge and cool, minutes	5	5	5	5
Volume of aqueous layer, ml.	10	10	10	10
Optical density of aqueous layer, designate	a_0	a_4	c_0	c_4
1:3 hydrochloric acid, ml.	1	1	1	1
Waiting time, minutes	10	10	10	10
Volume of aqueous layer, ml.	11	11	11	11
Optical density of aqueous layer, designate	b_0	b_4	d_0	d_4

Read the solutions at 420 mμ at which it does not have maximum extinction but approaches the maximum degree of linearity. Then expressed in micrograms Δa is $a_4 - a_0$, and similarly for Δb, Δc, and Δd.

$$\text{Methionine} = (\Delta b - \Delta a) - (\Delta d - \Delta c)$$

2-THIOBARBITURIC ACID

Determine by reaction with 2-sulfanilamidopyramidine as described for estimation of the latter. Alternatively develop with nitroprusside-hydroxylamine reagent as described for 2-thiouracil (page 507). The color developed is much less intense than that with 2-thiouracil or its derivatives.

5,5-DIETHYL-2-THIOBARBITURIC ACID

The reaction for 2-thiouracil as modified for 4-thiouracil is applicable with some further modifications to this compound.[51] The color developed is brown.

---

[51] Halvor N. Christensen, *J. Biol. Chem.* **162**, 27-35 (1946).

Procedure—Mix 5 ml. of sample solution with 1 ml. of the buffer as described for 4-thiouracil (page 507). The pH should approximate 7.2. As reagent prepare that described for 2-thiouracil (page 507) but dilute 1 volume of it with 5 volumes of 0.76 per cent glycine solution instead of water and incubate at 38° instead of room temperature for an hour. Add 1 ml. of this to the bufferd sample above and read at 500 mμ as described for 2-thiouracil.

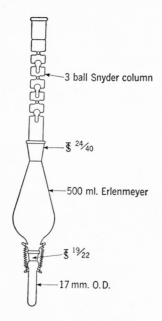

3 ball Snyder column

$\overline{\text{S}}$ $^{24}\!/_{40}$

500 ml. Erlenmeyer

$\overline{\text{S}}$ $^{19}\!/_{22}$

17 mm. O.D.

Fig. 32. Kuderna - Danish evaporative concentrator (*Courtesy A. A. Danish*)

5-Ethyl-5-(1-methylbutyl)-2-thio-barbituric Acid, Penthal

Determine by the nitroprusside-hydroxylamine reagent described for 2-thiouracil (page 507), although the intensity of coloration is much lower.

2-(*p-tert*-Butylphenoxy)isopropyl-2-chloroethyl Sulfite, Aramite

The hydrolysis of Aramite by alcoholic potassium hydroxide or sodium isopropoxide liberates ethylene oxide. This reacts with pyridine to give a brown color. This forms a green with β-picoline.[52] Ethylene oxide with lepidine in the presence of diethylene glycol forms an intense blue color.[53] Ethyleneimine and ethylene sulfide give the same color. Water and isopropanol interfere.

Sample—Recover the Aramite from fruits or vegetables by benzene. Concentrate 200-300 ml. of filtered extract to 3 ml. in the apparatus shown in Figure 32 with the water level below the 19/22 joint but to minimize the reflux have the 500-ml. flask bathed in steam and insulate the column. To avoid bumping add a couple of 3-mm. glass balls.

For the next step, use the apparatus shown in Figure 33. Add to the inulin pressure tube 11.5 grams of 3-mm. glass balls and 6 ml. of fresh

---

[52] Heinrich Lohmann, *J. prakt. Chem.* **153**, 57-64 (1939).

[53] F. A. Gunther, R. C. Blinn, M. J. Kolbezen, J. H. Barkley, W. D. Harris, and H. S. Simon, *Anal. Chem.* **23**, 1835-42 (1951).

5 per cent solution of redistilled lepidine in redistilled diethylene glycol boiling at 243-5° at 735 mm. The outlet tube in this is about 1 mm. from the bottom of the tube. Cool this tube in ice during operation.

To the Aramite concentrate add 5 ml. of 0.8 per cent sodium hydroxide in isopropanol and 2 pellets of potassium hydroxide. Attach to the apparatus, without transfer, and pass oxygen-free nitrogen at 4 ± 0.5 ml. per minute for 3 minutes. Then reflux the hydrolysis mixture by heating with a small burner for 15 minutes while the gas flow continues.

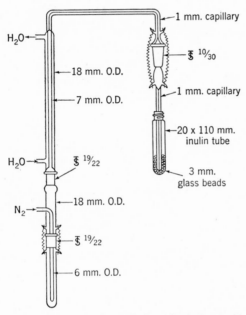

Fig. 33. Apparatus for evolution of ethylene oxide

Remove the inulin tube, and cap with 4 layers of aluminium foil inside the cork-gasketed cap. Screw on tightly and refrigerate until ready for color development.

Procedure—Push the capped tube into a sand bath preheated to $170° \pm 5°$. After exactly 90 minutes remove the tubes and let air-cool for 3 minutes. Shake and cool in running water for 10 minutes. Invert to mix and read at 610 mμ against a reagent blank. If necessary, dilute the sample with isopropanol to read. The blank should be only light-yellow.

THIOPHENE

When a solution of a diketone, such as isatin, in concentrated sulfuric acid is shaken with a sample containing thiophene, a blue color appears,[54] probably due to the formation of indophenin, $C_{12}H_7ONS$. The color produced is more intense than that produced by a similar reaction with alloxan. The addition of ferric sulfate causes development of color in 20 minutes rather than 2 hours, probably due to oxidation.[55] The reaction is appropriate for determining thiophene in synthesis gas derived from coal. It is the only sulfur compound not removable by catalytic treatment.[56]

The temperature of the isatin-acid solution when thiophene absorption takes place affects the color produced. The maximum color is developed at 15°. At higher temperatures, the absorption of thiophene is complete, but the reaction between thiophene and isatin is not. The color is stable for 24 hours.

Carbon disulfide, even if present in concentrations at least 12 times that of thiophene, does not interfere. Mercaptans give high results and must be removed. Amylene and other unsaturated hydrocarbons inhibit color formation. Since it is impossible to remove these unsaturated hydrocarbons selectively or inactivate them without affecting the thiophene, the compounds present must be determined. Ethylene must not be present in amounts greater than 2-3 per cent in the gas analyzed. The reaction is applicable in the reverse direction to isatin without having to remove other sulfur compounds.[57] Usually only 1 ml. of sample is necessary in the range 1-0.002 per cent of thiophene.

Thiophene in producer gas is absorbed in piperidine-ethanol solution and read at 255 mμ, with a correction for benzene as absorbed in ethanol from a similar sample.[58] Alloxan determines thiophene in a manner similar to that outlined for isatin.[59] The presence of ferric sulfate apparently reduces the color. Alloxan does not have a masking

---

[54] A. Baeyer, *Ber.* 12, 1311 (1879); *Ibid.* 16, 1478 (1883); C. Schwalbe, *Ber.* 27, 324 (1894); K. H. V. French, *J. Soc. Chem. Ind.* 65, 15-23 (1946).

[55] Edward Wray, *J. Soc. Chem. Ind.* 38, 83-4T (1919).

[56] H. H. Wainwright and G. I. Lambert, *Bureau of Mines Report of Investigations* 4753 (1950).

[57] Herbert C. McKee, L. Kermit Herndon, and James R. Withrow, *Anal. Chem.* 20, 301-3 (1948).

[58] L. J. Brady, *Ibid.* 20, 512-14 (1948).

[59] Lad. Ekkert, *Pharm. Zentralhalle* 71, 625-6 (1930); K. H. V. French, *J. Soc. Chem. Ind.* 65, 15-23 (1946).

color of its own as does isatin. After being allowed to stand for 30 minutes, the color developed with alloxan shows a tendency to fade.

Procedure—*By isatin. Benzene.* To 1 ml. of sample at 15° add 5 ml. of reagent containing 50 mg. of isatin and 50 mg. of ferric sulfate in 92.5 per cent sulfuric acid. Shake for 1 minute at a rate of 100-120 cycles per minute. Allow to stand 30-60 minutes and read at 580 mμ against a reagent blank.

Synthesis gas. As reagent, add 1.104 grams of isatin and 1.104 grams of ferric sulfate to a liter of water. Heat to 85°, cool to room temperature, and allow to stand 24 hours. Filter off excess isatin.

Slowly add 50 ml. of concentrated sulfuric acid to 4.5 ml. of the isatin-ferric sulfate reagent, keeping the tube in cold water to prevent charring. Age for 1 hour, bringing the solution to the temperature at which the determination is to be made. Equip the tube with an inlet tube which extends to the bottom of the absorber and a gas outlet tube. Pass the gas to be tested over iron oxide on wood shavings to remove hydrogen sulfide, then bubble through alkaline cadmium chloride to remove mercaptans. Finally bubble through the isatin-acid solution, using a wet test meter to measure the volume. Stop the flow when the solution turns blue. Use an aliquot of the sample to read at 580 mμ.

By alloxan. Benzene. To a 2-ml. aliquot at 15° add 5 ml. of a reagent consisting of 0.01 per cent of alloxan dissolved in 90.5 per cent sulfuric acid. Shake for 1 minute and allow to stand for 30 minutes. Compare with standards or with a curve.

Gasoline. As reagent dissolve 0.4 gram of isatin in concentrated sulfuric acid and dilute to a liter with the same acid. To 50 ml. of this reagent add 1 drop of concentrated nitric acid. Add 1 ml. of gasoline, or more if appropriate, and mix. Read at 550 mμ.

p-ANISALDEHYDETHIOSEMICARBAZONE

This compound is read in chloroform solution in the ultraviolet at 335 mμ.[60]

Procedure—*Blood.* Mix 2 ml. of blood with 4 ml. of 2.84 per cent disodium orthophosphate solution. Extract with 40 ml. of chloroform. Filter the chloroform extract and read at 325 mμ.

---

[60] A. Spinks, *Brit. J. Pharmacol.* **4**, 254-9 (1949).

p-(ETHYLSULFONYL)BENZALDEHYDETHIOSEMICARBAZONE

This is determined in the same way as the corresponding anisaldehyde compound but read in chloroform at 332 mμ.

p-HYDROXYBENZALDEHYDETHIOSEMICARBAZONE

This compound is read in alkaline solution in the ultraviolet.[60]

Procedure—*Blood.* Extract a mixture of 2 ml. of blood and 2 ml. of 55 per cent monosodium orthophosphate monohydrate solution with 40 ml. of chloroform. Extract 30 ml. of the chloroform extract with 8 ml. of 1 per cent sodium carbonate solution. Remove and centrifuge the aqueous layer and read at 330 mμ against a reagent blank.

THIODIPHENYLAMINE, PHENOTHIAZINE

A brominated alcoholic solution of phenothiazine gives a red suitable for estimation.[61] The product is probably 3,4-dihydroxyphenazothionium bromide. Ethyl acetate is appropriate for recovery of apple spray residues. Unless the bromine is added rapidly in warm solution, a green may result. Bromine water is usually used for development but an alternative form of reagent is a 1:1 mixture of 1:5 hydrochloric acid with 2.5 per cent potassium bromide solution containing 0.56 per cent potassium bromate.[62] Off-colors are a problem.

Palladous chloride forms a blue complex [63] with the test substance in the presence of a minor amount of acetone. In ethyl acetate the absorption is shifted toward the red and read at 460 mμ. The colors are somewhat unstable. A modified cuprous chloride reagent is also applicable.[64]

Samples—*Soluble in ethanol.* Dissolve a sample containing 0.05 gram of phenothiazine in ethanol and dilute to 200 ml. with the same solvent for use in the procedure with cuprous chloride.

Not completely soluble in ethanol. Extract a sample containing about

---

[61] C. W. Eddy and Floyd De Eds, *Food Research* **2**, 305-9 (1937); L. E. Smith, *Ind. Eng. Chem., Anal Ed.* **10**, 60 (1938); H. L. Cupples, *Ibid.* **14**, 53 (1942); Vincent E. Stewart, *J. Assoc. Official Agr. Chemists* **27**, 343-6 (1944); *Ibid.* **28**, 693-6

[62] Teodor Canbäck, *Svensk. Farm. Tid.* **48**, 77-81 (1944). (1945).

[63] Lyle G. Overholser and John H. Yoe, *Ind. Eng. Chem., Anal. Ed.* **14**, 646-7 (1942).

[64] Vasily Kniaseff, *Anal. Chem.* **20**, 329-31 (1948).

0.05 gram of phenothiazine with petroleum ether in a Soxhlet for 24 hours. Filter, evaporate to dryness, and take up in ethanol for dilution to 200 ml. and estimation with cuprous chloride.

Samples containing pyridine. Mix a weighed sample equivalent to about 0.05 gram of phenothiazine with 20 ml. of 1:20 sulfuric acid. Mix and filter through a paper disc in a Gooch crucible. Wash with 1:20 sulfuric acid to total 80 ml. Discard these solutions and dissolve the phenothiazine in the residue with 150 ml. of hot ethanol. Dilute the ethanol solution to 200 ml. for use in the procedure with cuprous chloride.

Procedure—*With bromine.* Dilute a sample containing not over 4.5 mg. of phenothiazine in ethanol to 50 ml. with the same solvent. Warm to 60° and add 5 ml. of saturated bromine water. Incubate at 60° and add 5 ml. more of the bromine water. After 10 minutes boil to drive off excess bromine and cool. Dilute to 100 ml. and filter. Discard the first 25 ml. and read against a water blank.

With palladous chloride. Add 50 ml. of 7.2 per cent sodium acetate solution to 50 ml. of 1:10 hydrochloric acid and dilute to 250 ml. This buffer should read pH 2.6, on 1:5 dilution read 2.9. As palladous chloride reagent prepare a solution containing 1 mg. of palladium per ml. in 1:10 hydrochloric acid. For use dilute 1:32 with water.

Mix 5 ml. of buffer and 1 ml. of reagent. Add 5 ml. of sample in 20 per cent acetone containing not over 0.1 mg. of phenothiazine. Dilute to 25 ml. with water. Read at once at 550 mμ against a reagent blank.

With cuprous chloride. As cuprous chloride reagent pass sulfur dioxide through a solution of 10 grams of copper sulfate pentahydrate and 2.5 grams of sodium chloride in 75 ml. of water. Cuprous chloride is precipitated. After standing overnight, filter on a Gooch crucible through a paper disc and wash with 50 per cent ethanol until no longer blue. Wash with 95 per cent ethanol, then with ether, and dry on glass. Moisten with 1:1 ethanol, add about 5 ml. of water, and dry slowly. Grind the residue and wash with ethanol and ether. Dissolve 0.2 gram in 1 ml. of 1:1 hydrochloric acid and dilute to 20 ml. with ethanol. Dilute 5 ml. to 50 ml. with ethanol and let stand for 24 hours before use.

Dilute a sample containing 0.05 gram of phenothiazine in ethanol to 200 ml. with the same solvent. To 2 ml. add 2 ml. of copper reagent and 5 ml. of ethanol. Mix and keep at 55° for 4 hours. Let stand in the dark for 48 hours, dilute to 50 ml. with ethanol, and mix. Read at 540 mμ after 15 minutes against a reagent blank.

10(2-DIMETHYLAMINO-1-PROPYL)PHENOTHIAZINE, PHENERGAN, PROMETHAZINE

When Phenergan is oxidized by sodium persulfate, the red color can be measured.[65] The color is stable for more than 1 hour. Separation from ephedrine, benzedrine, pervitin, or caffeine is not necessary.

Sample—*Aqueous Phenergan hydrochloride.* Dilute to 0.05-0.1 mg. per ml.

Solution in physiological saline. Dilute to about 0.06 mg. per ml.

Sirup of Phenergan. Make a sample containing about 8 mg. of Phenergan alkaline and extract the liberated base with ether. Extract the combined ether extracts with 50, 25, and 20 ml. of 1:150 hydrochloric acid. Heat to drive off dissolved ether, cool, and dilute to 100 ml. with water.

Procedure –Add 1 ml. of 2 per cent sodium persulfate solution to a 10-ml. sample and incubate at 45° for 15 minutes. Let cool for 5 minutes and read at 520 mμ.

2-MERCAPTO-4-HYDROXYPYRIMIDINE, 2-THIOURACIL

The details of reaction with cobalt salts in anhydrous media will be discussed under uracil (Vol. IV) with further discussion of interferences. 2-Thiouracil is determined by the green color with a modified sodium nitroprusside-hydroxylamine reagent.[66] The reaction is also given by 6-methyl-2-thiouracil,[67] 6-ethyl-2-thiouracil, 6-propyl-2-thiouracil, 6-hexyl-2-thiouracil, 6-benzyl-2-thiouracil, 6-phenylethyl-2-thiouracil, 6-carboxy-2-thiouracil, and 6-amino-2-thiouracil. Their intensities of coloration are in the same range as 2-thiouracil. Colors are given by 4-thiouracil, 2-thiobarbituric acid, 5,5-diethyl-2-thiobarbituric acid, 2-mercapto-5-amino-1,3,4-thiadiazole, and 2-mercaptoimidazole but are qualitatively different and are not comparable. Thiourea gives a blue with the reagent having a maximum absorption in the vicinity of 600 mμ.

Sample—*Serum.* Mix 2 ml. of serum with 6 ml. of water and add, with shaking, 2 ml. of 19 per cent decolorized *p*-toluene sulfonic acid

[65] Candine Fossoul, *J. pharm. Belg.* **6**, 383-8 (1951).

[66] R. H. Williams, B. J. Jandorf, and G. A. Kay, *J. Lab. Clin. Med.* **29**, 329-36 (1944); H. N. Christensen, *J. Biol. Chem.* **160**, 425-33 (1945); *Ibid.* **162**, 27-35 (1946).

[67] Riva Moscovici, *Arquiv. biol. São Paulo* **30**, 66-8 (1946).

solution. Filter after 20 minutes and add 0.70-0.08 ml. of 72 per cent sodium hydroxide solution to the filtrate. The pH should now be between 5 and 7.5 to indicator paper. Too high a pH will result in turbidity.

Procedure—*By cobalt.* Dissolve a dry sample containing approximately 25 mg. of thiouracil in anhydrous ethanol and dilute to 25 ml. with the same solvent. To 5 ml. of this solution add sequentially 5 ml. of 25 per cent isopropylamine in dry chloroform, 5 ml. of 0.125 per cent anhydrous cobalt acetate in anhydrous methanol, and chloroform to dilute to 25 ml. Mix, read at 530 mμ, and subtract a reagent blank.

By nitroprusside-hydroxylamine. As reagent [68] dissolve 0.5 gram each of sodium nitroprusside and hydroxylamine hydrochloride in 10 ml. of water. Add 1 gram of sodium bicarbonate, mix, and place in water at 20° for 10 minutes. Add 0.1 ml. of bromine and incubate at 37° for 20 minutes. Dilute to 25 ml. and store at not over 5°. As buffer dissolve 5.74 grams of sodium barbital and 2.08 grams of glycine in about 450 ml. of water. Add 1:10 hydrochloric acid dropwise until the pH is adjusted to 8. Dilute to 500 ml. and store at not over 5°. For use mix 1 ml. of the reagent with 9 ml. of the buffer. Age 1 hour at room temperature or 25 minutes at 37° before use. The color changes from purple-brown to light yellow.

To 5 ml. of sample add 3 ml. of the reagent. Mix and read at 660 mμ against a reagent blank after 3 minutes and at 3-minute intervals thereafter until a maximum is reached. This is usually reached in 8-20 minutes. To correct for turbidity add a few crystals of chloramine T to bleach the color, mix, and read after 2-3 minutes. In the absence of turbidity, this approximates the blank.

4-Thiouracil

A modification of the method for 2-thiouracil with nitroprusside-hydroxylamine reagent is applicable to 4-thiouracil. The color is brown rather than green if glycine is not added to the reagent before aging.

Procedure—As a buffer mix 17.4 ml. of 7.1 per cent solution of anhydrous disodium phosphate with 2.6 ml. of 4.8 per cent citric acid solution. To 5 ml. of sample solution add 1 ml. of this buffer. The pH should be approximately 7.2. Add 1 volume of the reagent described for 2-thiouracil which has stood at room temperature only 30 minutes after mixing with its buffer. Read at 700 mμ as described for 2-thiouracil.

---

[68] Irvine W. Grote, *J. Biol. Chem.* **93**, 25-30 (1931).

4-METHYL-2-THIOURACIL

Determine by the technic described for 2-thiouracil [69] with hydroxyl-amine-nitroprusside reagent.

6-METHYL-2-THIOURACIL

Determine by the technic described for 2-thiouracil [70] with hydroxyl-amine-nitroprusside reagent.

2-MERCAPTOIMIDAZOLE

Determine as described for 2-thiouracil with nitroprusside-hydroxyl-amine reagent.

2-MERCAPTO-5-AMINO-1,3,4-THIADIAZOLE

Determine as described for 2-thiouracil with nitroprusside-hydroxyl-amine reagent but read at 700 mμ.

1-DIETHYLAMINOETHYLAMINO-4-METHYLTHIOXANTHONE, MIRACEL D

The test substance couples with bromothymol blue to form a compound soluble in organic solvent.[71]

Procedure—To 10 ml. of sample add 5 ml. of 1 per cent disodium phosphate as buffer. Extract with 5 ml. and 5 ml. of dichloroethane and combine the extracts. Shake the extracts with 10 ml. of 0.05 per cent bromothymol blue solution buffered at pH 7 by 1 per cent of ammonium acetate. After separation read the aqueous phase and interpret in terms of the dye removed.

---

[69] Poul Mørch, *Acta Pharmacol. Toxicol.* (Copenhagen) **1**, 106-11 (1945); E. C. M. J. Hollman and Th. de Jonge, *Pharm. Weekblad* **83**, 1-9 (1948).

[70] K. van Asperen, *Biochem. et Biophys. acta* **6**, 187-91 (1950).

[71] A. L. Latner, R. V. Coxon, and E. J. King, *Trans. Roy. Soc. Trop. Med Hyg.* **41**, 133-40 (1947).

CHAPTER 19

HALOGEN COMPOUNDS [1]

As IN the case of so many other chapters, there are chemically many polyfunctional compounds. In general, the halogen compounds have been classified here unless there was a good reason otherwise. Thus a halogenated urea which is a weed killer appropriately appears here because determined by its substituent groups after hydrolysis. To illustrate, a nitro halogen compound determined by reduction of the nitro group and diazotizing would be classified with nitro compounds because determined only by the nitro group.

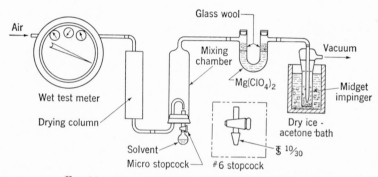

FIG. 34. Apparatus for sampling aliphatic halides

The only general method is a complex reaction of the organic halogen compound with pyridine in the presence of pronounced alkalinity. Aromatic halides can, in general, be nitrated with production of pronounced chromophoric properties.

ALIPHATIC HALIDES

Large numbers of aliphatic halides are read in the infrared.[2] The absorption peaks of many of these are shown in Table 6.

---

[1] See Chapter 1 for details of organization, condensation, etc.

[2] Paul F. Urone and Mary L. Druschel, *Anal. Chem.* **24,** 626-30 (1952); Cf. R. B. Bernstein, G. P. Semeluk, and C. B. Arends, *Anal. Chem.* **25,** 139-42 (1953).

Sample—The apparatus is shown in Figure 34. Air for evaporating the solvent passes through a wet test meter and drying column and through an indicated microstopcock to blow on the surface of the solvent. Thus passing out of the mixing chamber it passes through a tube filled with anhydrous magnesium perchlorate. There is an explosion possibility with very high organic vapor concentrations or back-diffusion of the iso-octane into the drying tube. In case of danger use anhydrous calcium sulfate. The gas then passes into an all-glass midget impinger partially filled with glass beads. This dissolves the chlorinated hydrocarbon for use as sample.

TABLE 6. INFRARED ABSORPTION PEAKS FOR CHLORINATED HYDROCARBONS

Carbon tetrachloride	12.7μ
Chlorobenzene	13.55μ
Chloroform	13.21μ
o-Dichlorobenzene	13.39μ
β-β-Dichloroethyl ether	8.87μ
Ethylene chloride	13.90μ
Ethylidene chloride	9.49μ
Methyl chloroform	14.06μ
Methylene chloride	13.51μ
Pentachloroethane	12.99μ
Propylene chloride	13.53μ
s-Tetrachloroethane	12.56μ
Tetrachloroethylene	11.01μ
1,1,2-Trichloroethane	2.29μ
Trichloroethylene	11.90μ

Place 5 ml. of iso-octane in the unlubricated midget impinger approximately half-filled with 3-4 mm. glass beads. Immerse in a dry ice-acetone bath. Attach a U-shaped magnesium perchlorate tube to the inlet and a suction pump and measuring device to the outlet. All connections must be glass or hydrocarbon-resistant elastomer.

Draw 1-30 liters of air through the impinger at 0.5 liter per minute. After sampling remove the impinger tube and stopper until analyzed.

Procedure—Read in an infrared spectrometer, either over the range 4.5-13.5μ or at the range for reading the specific chlorhydrocarbon expected.

METHYL CHLORIDE

Methyl chloride in air is determined by passing a known amount through an electric spark between carbon electrodes in a portable apparatus. The products of combustion are absorbed in sodium arsenite solution, the solution acidified with nitric acid, and silver chloride turbidity developed with silver nitrate.[3] Details are not given here as it will not differentiate from any other volatile chlorinated hydrocarbon.

CARBONYL CHLORIDE, PHOSGENE

Phosgene reacts with aniline to form diphenylurea.[4] This is isolated, converted to ammonia, and determined by Nessler's reagent.

Sample—*Gas.* Bubble 5 liters of gas sample slowly through 10 ml. of a saturated aqueous solution of aniline. If the concentration of carbonyl chloride is thought to exceed 2 per cent, place a second container of aniline solution in series with the first. Filter the precipitate of diphenylurea on a small disc of paper. Treat the filter paper with the precipitate with 4 ml. of concentrated sulfuric acid. Add 10 mg. of mercuric sulfate and heat in boiling water for 2 hours. The solution becomes colorless. Cool, dilute to 20 ml., and add to 0.25 gram of sodium hypophosphite dissolved in 100 ml. of water. Rinse in with water until the volume of liquid is about 150 ml. Add 4 grams of magnesium oxide and distil about 70 ml. carrying the ammonia into 25 ml. of water to which 1 ml. of 1:100 hydrochloric acid has been added. Dilute to 100 ml. and develop an aliquot.

Procedure—Dilute 10 ml. of the sample to 50 ml. with water and add 2 ml. of Nessler's reagent (Vol. II). Read against standards or at 420 mμ against a reagent blank.

CHLOROFORM

Chloroform and similar halogen compounds give a red color with pyridine in the presence of strong alkali.[5] The same reaction is given

---

[3] J. L. Franklin, E. L. Gunn, and R. L. Martin, *Ind. Eng. Chem., Anal. Ed.* **18**, 314-16 (1946).

[4] A. Kling and R. Schmutz, *Compt. rend.* **168**, 773-6 (1919).

[5] K. Fujiwara, *Sitzber. Abhandl. naturforsch. Ges. Rostock* **6**, 33-43 (1914); W. H. Cole, *J. Biol. Chem.* **71**, 173-9 (1926); Alexander O. Gettler and Human Blume, *Arch. Pathology* **11**, 554-60 (1931); W. Lloyd Adams, *J. Pharmacol.* **74**, 11-17 (1942); R. N. Kulkarni, *Current Sci.* **12**, 324-5 (1943); Hans S. Ussing, *Acta Physiol. Scand.* **9**, 214-20 (1945).

by bromoform, chloretone, chloral, and iodoform. Ethanol retards fading. A correction is often applied to allow for the amount not recoverable by distillation from tissue. The loss occurs more rapidly in an alkaline medium than in an acid medium. The sensitivity is improved by extraction of the distillate with toluene and development of color in that solution.[6] Smaller amounts are aerated from laked blood or tissue extracts directly into the pyridine of the reagent cooled to 0 degrees.[7]

Chloroform gives a red color with resorcinol, stable for 12 hours at ordinary temperatures.[8] The method is only sensitive to 0.1 mg. per ml. Modification of the reagent to α- or β-naphthol gives an intense blue color[9] which is much darker at 50° than at room temperature. The sensitivity of the reaction and the rate of fading are controlled by the concentration of alkali used. β-Naphthol gives better colors and is less subject to interference. Carbon tetrachloride gives a color with α-naphthol, intensified by acetone, but none with β-naphthol. The latter reagent gave no color with reasonable amounts of methylene chloride, acetylene dichloride, ethylidene chloride, ethylene chloride, trichloroethylene, or dichloroethyl ether. Acetone does not interfere. Some of the foregoing may interfere when present in large excess, but such color develops only after 10 minutes.

Sample—*Tissue.* When ice cold, grind about 150 grams of sample. Mix 100 grams with about 100 ml. of water. Add sufficient tartaric acid to make the reaction distinctly acid. Steam-distil, using a long well-cooled condenser and adapter. Collect the distillate in 10 ml. of ice-cold water acidified with hydrochloric acid. Pack this receiver in ice and have the tip of the adapter dip into the water. Collect nearly 250 ml. of distillate, dilute to that volume, and mix well. Develop with pyridine, or resorcinol, or β-naphthol. For increased sensitivity extract the distillate, without dilution, with 10, 10, and 5 ml. of toluene. Then develop with pyridine.

Blood. Mix 1 ml. of blood, 4 ml. of water, and 1 ml. of 10 per cent sodium tungstate solution. Add 0.2 ml. of 1:3 sulfuric acid. Steam-distil until 5 ml. of distillate has gone over and develop with pyridine.

[6] Sheila Habgood and Joan F. Powell, *Brit. J. Ind. Med.* 2, 39-40 (1945); A. S. V. Burgen, *Brit. Med. J.* **1948,** I, 1238.

[7] R. N. Kulkarni, *Indian J. Med. Research* 32, 189-95 (1944).

[8] A. Seyda, *Z. öffentl. Chem.* 3, 333-7 (1897).

[9] Sigmund Lustgarten, *Monatsch. Chem.* 3, 715-22 (1882); W. G. Moffitt, *Analyst* **58,** 2-4 (1933).

Procedure—*Aqueous samples with pyridine.* To 5 ml. of the sample distillate add 5 ml. of colorless pyridine and 10 ml. of 20 per cent sodium hydroxide solution. Mix and heat in boiling water for 1 minute. Cool in running water. Add 20 ml. of water and mix. Read against a reagent blank. Multiply the result in terms of chloroform by 1.087 to correct for loss in recovery from the sample, if fresh.

Toluene samples with pyridine. Mix 5 ml. of the sample in toluene with 5 ml. of colorless pyridine and 10 ml. of 20 per cent sodium hydroxide solution. Heat in boiling water for 5 minutes, cool, and dilute with 10 ml. of water. Separate the aqueous layer and read against a reagent blank.

With resorcinol. Mix 10 ml. of sample solution, 2 ml. of a 10 per cent aqueous solution of resorcinol, and 1 ml. of a 25 per cent solution of sodium hydroxide. Place in a water bath at 80° for 10 minutes and read against a reagent blank.

With β-naphthol. Mix 1 ml. of sample solution with 10 ml. of a 2 per cent solution of β-naphthol in 40 per cent potassium hydroxide solution. Let stand for 5 minutes and read against a reagent blank.

BROMOFORM

The color developed by chloroform with β-naphthol is also applicable to bromoform.[10] Accuracy to ±1 per cent is obtainable. Aside from chloroform, chloral hydrate interferes. Trichloroacetic acid and hexachloroethane do not.

Procedure—As reagent mix 1 ml. of 20 per cent β-naphthol in ethanol and 1 ml. of 50 per cent sodium hydroxide solution. Add 1 ml. of aqueous sample containing 1-4 mg. of bromoform and mix. Warm at 60° for 30 seconds, shake, and heat 60 seconds longer. Cool and dilute to 25 ml. with a 1:9 mixture of concentrated sulfuric acid and 50 per cent ethanol. Read against a reagent blank.

CARBON TETRACHLORIDE

Carbon tetrachloride gives a purplish red with pyridine in alkaline solution. The method gives the same color with chloroform. Bromoform and trichloroethylene react. The reaction is modified for carbon tetra-

---

[10] Robert Paulais, *Ann. pharm. franç.* **2**, 99-102 (1944).

chloride.[11] There is also a blue color with α-naphthol, but its development is not as sensitive.

Sample—*Air.* Pass it through 50 ml. of cold acetone, using fritted glass bubblers and dilute to a known volume.

Soil. Steam-distil in the presence of a little pyridine.

Procedure—Shake 50 ml. of colorless pyridine with 100 ml. of 15 per cent sodium hydroxide solution. After 12 hours, discard the lower layer. Dilute 89 ml. of the upper layer to 100 ml. with water to eliminate turbidity. Mix 10 ml. of this with 5 ml. of the sample solution of carbon tetrachloride in acetone. Heat at 70° for 15 minutes and cool. Read at 540 mμ against a reagent blank.

TRICHLOROETHYLENE

Trichloroethylene gives an orange red with pyridine in alkaline solution. The method gives a purplish red with chloroform and carbon tetrachloride. Bromoform and chloral hydrate also react. It is applicable in various modifications.[12] By distillation with water and xylene the test substance is efficiently separated in the xylene layer. The color can be read between 440 and 480 mμ. Sodium hydroxide solutions of the order of 50 per cent develop the color incompletely. At 1 per cent it does not follow Beer's law. The maximum color developed by heating with 20 per cent sodium hydroxide solution in 4-5 minutes decreases thereafter. When cooled it is stable for at least 10 minutes. Acid gases and light cause rapid fading.

Sample—*Water.* Use as is.

Blood. Mix 1 ml. with 50 ml. of water and add a few drops of tri-*n*-butyl citrate to control foaming. Steam-distil into 5 ml. of anisole until the distillate approximates 45 ml. Dilute to 50 ml. to develop an aliquot.

Vegetable oils. Mix a 10-gram sample with 10 ml. of xylene and add about 75 ml. of water. Add 15-20 glass beads and a few drops of silicone

---

[11] R. P. Daroga and A. G. Pollard, *J. Soc. Chem. Ind.* **60**, 218-22 (1941); F. J. Webb, K. K. Kay, and W. E. Nichol, *J. Ind. Hyg. Toxicol.* **27**, 249-55 (1945); G. W. Rogers and K. K. Kay, *Ibid.* **29**, 227-32 (1947).

[12] Lionel K. Arnold and E. Graham Hollowell, *Proc. Iowa Acad. Sci.* **54**, 181-3 (1947); F. H. Brain and P. J. Helliwell, *Biochem. J.* **45**, 75-9 (1949); F. H. Brain, *Analyst* **74**, 555-9 (1949); F. A. Lyne and T. McLachlan, *Ibid.* **74**, 513 (1949); I. Eisdorfer and V. C. Mehlenbacher, *J. Am. Oil Chem. Soc.* **28**, 307-10 (1951).

defoamer. Distil at 20-30 drops per minute until all of the xylene is collected into a continuous return distillation receiver. This should require about 30 minutes. Rinse down the condenser with five 1-ml. portions of water and distil 60 minutes more. Let cool, transfer the xylene to a test tube, and shake with about 0.5 gram of anhydrous sodium sulfate until clear. Dilute with xylene to not over 0.012 per cent of trichloroethylene.

Soybean meal. Mix 40 ml. of hexane with a 20-gram sample. Let stand for a few minutes without evaporation and develop an aliquot.

Air.[13] Aspirate the sample through 10 ml. and 5 ml. of pyridine at about 2 bubbles per minute. Develop by a special procedure.

Procedure—*Nonaqueous samples.* To 1 ml. of solvent containing not over 0.012 per cent of trichloroethylene add 10 ml. of dry pyridine and 5 ml. of 20 per cent sodium hydroxide solution. Shake vigorously, loosen the stoppers, and heat in boiling water for 4.5 ± 0.5 minutes. Cool below 25° and remove the aqueous layer. Filter the colored pyridine solution through paper and read within 10 minutes at 475 mμ against a reagent blank.

Aqueous samples. Mix 5 ml. of sample, 1 ml. of colorless pyridine, and 1 ml. of 50 per cent sodium hydroxide solution. Heat in boiling water for 5 minutes, cool, and read against a reagent blank.

Air. Mix 5 ml. of the mixed pyridine which has absorbed the trichloroethylene with 1 ml. of 1 per cent sodium hydroxide in ethanol. Keep at 70° for 3 minutes, cool, and add 3 ml. of water. Read between 90 and 180 seconds later at 530 mμ.

ETHYLENE CHLOROHYDRIN

Ethylene chlorohydrin is readily oxidized to an aldehyde in acid solution. The resulting aldehyde condenses with diazotized sulfanilic acid, when heated, to give a red color.[14] Other aldehydes behave similarly and therefore interfere.

Procedure—As reagent dissolve 1 gram of sulfanilic acid in 200 ml. of 1:200 hydrochloric acid. Mix 40 ml. of this solution with 10 ml. of a 0.7 per cent sodium nitrite solution, with cooling.

To 0.5 ml. of a sample solution containing not over 100 mg. of ethylene chlorohydrin, add 4 ml. of the reagent. After 5 minutes of oxidation at

13 Rene Truhaut, *Ann. pharm. franc.* **9**, 175-87 (1951).

14 M. B. Sapadinsky, *Z. anal. Chem.* **74**, 273-5 (1928).

25° add a slight excess of 4 per cent sodium hydroxide solution and heat to 50° for 5 minutes. Cool, dilute to 6 ml., and read against a reagent blank.

CHLORAL HYDRATE

The reaction of chloroform with pyridine and alkali also applies to as little as 0.001 per cent of chloral hydrate.[15] The method does not apply to chloral hydrate conjugated with glucuronic acid. With less than 0.01 mg. of chloral hydrate per ml. a known amount must be added.

Procedure—*Blood*. Mix 2 ml. of a 40 per cent sodium hydroxide solution, 1 ml. of colorless pyridine, and 4 ml. of a tungstic acid blood filtrate. Heat in boiling water for 1 minute. Cool in ice for 1 minute and add 6 ml. of water. Mix and filter. Read within 10 minutes after heating against a reagent blank.

β,β-DICHLORODIETHYL SULFIDE, MUSTARD GAS

Mustard gas, absorbed in aqueous acetic acid, reacts with iodoplatinate to liberate iodine which is determined by its blue color with iodine.[16] It is not applicable in the presence of chlorine, nitrous fumes, and other oxidizing agents, or in the presence of reducing agents. The concentration of acetic acid need not be closely controlled.

Another method is the reduction at 85° of selenious acid in 1:1 sulfuric acid by β,β-dichloroethyl sulfide to give an orange-red suspension of colloidal selenium. Colorimetric measurement of this is unsatisfactory, but nephelometric methods gave results with a maximum error of 0.005 mg. in amounts of 0.01 to 0.1 mg. Sulfur dioxide, hydroxylamine, hydrazine salts, glucose, formic acid, formaldehyde, and a number of organic acids and aldehydes give colloidal selenium sols. Reaction is nearly complete under the conditions outlined. The tendency is toward high results. Either a hot or cold absorption solution may be used. A considerable variation in concentration of the sulfuric acid is permissible. The selenious acid reagent should stand 24 hours before use and is stable for at least two weeks. Any considerable variation in the final

[15] J. H. Ross, *J. Biol. Chem.* **58**, 641-2 (1923); W. H. Cole, *Ibid.* **71**, 173-9 (1926); A. O. Gettler and H. Blume, *Arch. Path.* **11**, 554-60 (1931); Max M. Friedman and Frank A. Calderone, *J. Lab. Clin. Med.* **19**, 1332-3 (1934).

[16] W. J. Stainsby and A. McM. Taylor, *Analyst* **66**, 44 (1941); William Rieman III, *Ind. Eng. Chem., Anal. Ed.* **15**, 411-12 (1943).

concentration of the selenious acid reagent will cause a variation in the intensity of the suspension.

Procedure—*With iodoplatinate.* Absorb by passing at 170 ± 20 ml. of air per minute through 1 ml. of 1:19 acetic acid. To the sample solution so prepared, add one drop of 1 per cent iodoplatinate reagent and one drop of 0.5 per cent solution of potato starch. Compare against standards.

As selenium sol. Prepare a concentrated standard containing 0.02 gram of β,β-dichloroethyl sulfide in 100 ml. of 1:1 sulfuric acid. For use prepare a dilute standard by 1:10 dilution of the above standard with 1:1 sulfuric acid. The latter contains 0.02 mg. per ml.

Draw the sample of gas through an absorption bottle containing 10 ml. of a solution of 1 gram of selenium dioxide in 100 ml. of 1:1 sulfuric acid. The rate should be about one liter per minute. Then add 10 ml. of additional selenious acid reagent. Prepare a standard by addition of a suitable volume of the diluted standard solution of β,β-dichloroethyl sulfide to sufficient 1:1 sulfuric acid to make a total of 10 ml. To this add 10 ml. of reagent containing 2 grams of selenium dioxide per 100 ml. of 1:1 sulfuric acid. Mix both standard and sample and heat for 10 minutes in a bath at $85° \pm 5°$. Cool and compare in a nephelometer.

CHLORALOSE, GLUCOCHLORAL

Neither α- nor β-chloralose after hydrolysis or oxidation to form a CCl_3 group reacts with pyridine and aqueous alkali.[17] Alternative oxidizing agents are sulfuric acid and hydrogen peroxide or periodic acid.[18] An alternative is to develop the chloralose with resorcinol in sulfuric acid.[19]

Sample—*Blood or urine.* Triturate a 20-ml. sample with sufficient anhydrous sodium sulfate to take up the water. Extract the solidified extract with ether. Evaporate the ether and take up the residue in water or ethanol, allowing for the low solubility of β-chloralose.

---

[17] Henri Griffon and Roger Le Breton, *Compt. rend. soc. biol.* **130**, 535-7 (1939); Louis Truffert, *Bull. soc. chim. biol.* **24**, 195-9 (1942); Paul Fleury and Jacqueline Jolly, *Ibid.* **225**, 688-90 (1947); Henri Griffon, *Ann. pharm. franç.* **6**, 165-70 (1948).

[18] Henri Griffon, *Compt. rend.* **226**, 93-4 (1948).

[19] J. Delvenne and G. Barac, *Rev. trav. chim.* **66**, 443-4 (1947).

Procedure—*By pyridine.* To 2 ml. of sample add 2 ml. of 2.94 per cent sodium iodate in 1:1200 sulfuric acid. After 5 minutes at room temperature add 2 ml. of 40 per cent sodium hydroxide solution and follow with 1 ml. of colorless pyridine. Heat for 2 minutes in boiling water. Read the pink to red color of the pyridine layer against a reagent blank.

By resorcinol. Mix 2 ml. of sample containing 0.05-0.2 mg. of chloralose in ethanol with 4 ml. of 0.25 per cent resorcinol in concentrated sulfuric acid. Let stand for 5 minutes and add 2 ml. of water. After 25 minutes read at 500 mμ against a reagent blank.

CHLOROBENZENE

Chlorobenzene is first dinitrated, then reacted with pyridine in alkaline solution to give a red violet color.[20] There is no interference by benzene, toluene, xylene, acetone, ethyl acetate, dichlorobenzene, or turpentine.

Sample—*Air.* Follow the technic for absorption of benzene or toluene as the dinitrocompound (page 16). After 2-3 hours neutralize with concentrated ammonium hydroxide.

Procedure—Mix 5 ml. of neutralized sample with 1 ml. of colorless pyridine and heat for 10 minutes at 80°. Cool, add 3 ml. of 40 per cent sodium hydroxide solution, and mix well. Read against a reagent blank.

BENZENE HEXACHLORIDE, LINDANE

Benzene hexachloride on refluxing with aqueous potassium hydroxide is converted mainly to 1,2,4-trichlorobenzene which is read in the ultraviolet.[21] It is also read in the infrared.[22]

Dechlorination with zinc in acetic acid to form benzene permits estimation of the latter as *m*-dinitrobenzene with methylethyl ketone,[23] butanone, and alkali. It will detect 5 micrograms. The color shows good stability in the presence of alkali in dim light. The conversion to *m*-dinitrobenzene is reproducible but not quantitative.

---

[20] S. L. Ginzburg, *Khim. Prom.* **1947**, No. 2, 23-4.

[21] Bernard Davidow and Geoffrey Woodward, *J. Assoc. Official Agr. Chemists* **32**, 751-8 (1949); John P. Frawley and Bernard Davidow, *Ibid.* **32**, 758-62 (1949).

[22] L. W. Daasch, *Anal. Chem.* **19**, 779-85 (1947).

[23] Milton S. Schechter and Irwin Hornstein, *Anal. Chem.* **24**, 544-8 (1952); Irwin Hornstein, *Ibid.* **24**, 1036-7 (1952).

Commercial lindane contains 99 per cent or more of the gamma isomer of benzene hexachloride. Other chlorinated organic insecticides show no more than a minimal amount of apparent benzene hexachloride. Malonic acid is added to generate carbon dioxide to sweep the benzene vapor through. When benzene hexachloride is refluxed with a large amount of aniline, it forms a mixture of products which on oxidation with sulfuric acid containing vanadium pentoxide give a violet color.[24] It is probable that dichlorodiphenyl is present and possible that diphenylamine and dichlorodiphenylamine are also present. The yield of color by the method described varies with the isomer as follows: gamma 100 per cent, epsilon 110 per cent, alpha 90 per cent, delta 40 per cent, beta 5 per cent, technical mixture 80 per cent. Some chlorinated hydrocarbons containing alkali-labile chlorine interfere. The equivalent of the color from 0.05 mg. of gamma benzene hexachloride is given by the following: Dieldrin 5 mg., Aldrin 5 mg., DDT 4 mg., Aramite 0.95 mg., Toxaphene 0.825 mg., Heptachlor 0.7 mg., gamma-Chlordane 0.675 mg., technical Chlordane 0.450 mg., technical BCH 0.058 mg. Recoveries vary from 61 per cent from peanut butter to 115 per cent from applesauce, but are generally within 5 per cent.

Sample—*Tissue in general.* Grind a weighed sample containing 0.5-15 mg. of benzene hexachloride in a mortar and add about 3 times its weight of anhydrous sodium sulfate. Grind to a coarse powder to insure dehydration and rupture of cells. Extract with ether for 2 hours. Evaporate the ether in a stream of air and add 20 ml. of 8.5 per cent potassium hydroxide in methanol. Reflux for 1 hour and dilute with 250 ml. of water. Extract by shaking for 2 minutes with 25 ml. of hexane. Discard the aqueous layer and wash the hexane with ten 400-ml. portions of water without shaking. Filter the hexane through about 10 grams of anhydrous sodium sulfate to dry it, wash with hexane, and dilute to 25 ml. with hexane. Read in the ultraviolet.

Liver. Extract a 5-gram sample with ether. Continue as for general samples from "Evaporate the ether. . . ." When the hexane extract is obtained, proceed as follows. Wet a column of 1:1 magnesium oxide and Celite, 2 cm. in diameter and about 4 cm. long, with hexane. Pass the hexane through. Dilute the eluate to a known volume for the reading of aliquots in the ultraviolet.

Laboratory diets. Proceed as for liver from "Extract with ether for 2 hours . . ." but use a column of alumina.

---

[24] Wendell F. Philips, *Anal. Chem.* **24,** 1976-9 (1952).

Milk. Mix 200 ml. of milk with 200 ml. of water and add 1.5 ml. of glacial acetic acid with stirring. After letting the precipitate settle for 20 minutes, filter through a 2-mm. layer of Celite on a Büchner funnel. Add anhydrous sodium sulfate to the precipitate and grind to a coarse dry powder. Continue as for liver from "Extract with ether for 2 hours. . . ." For sorption use 1:1 Celite and magnesium oxide in the column.

Solids in general. Use directly if possible, otherwise extract with low-boiling nonaromatic solvent such as carbon tetrachloride. Petroleum fractions are apt to contain cyclic compounds which interfere.

If solvent must be removed, add a glass bead and evaporate on a steam bath. Avoid overheating or the use of an air stream as the test substance is somewhat volatile. Develop as *m*-dinitrobenzene.

Peanuts. Pulverize with a blender. Weigh a sample containing 0.05-0.1 mg. of benzene hexachloride in 90 ml. of redistilled methylene chloride in a 300-ml. conical flask. Place a magnetized glass-sealed stirring bar in the liquid and set the loosely stoppered flask on the stirring apparatus. Stir for 30 minutes, filter under suction, and wash with 50 ml. of methylene chloride. Evaporate most of the methylene chloride and add 100 ml. of glacial acetic acid. Distil 20 ml. of the acid from an oil bath at about 150°, thus removing the residual methylene chloride. Cool and use as a sample for determination as *m*-dintrobenzene. Corrections of the order of 0.3 ppm. are in order for roasted peanuts, depending on the degree of roast. This is obtained by a blank on similar peanuts.

Soil. Extract a sample containing 0.05-0.1 mg. of benzene hexachloride with 75 ml. of glacial acetic acid by magnetic stirring at room temperature for 30 minutes. Filter and wash the residue with acetic acid. Determine as *m*-dinitrobenzene.

Fruits and vegetables. The solvent used must be stable to sulfuric acid and not react with aniline. Strippings may be used according to usual technics. Alternatively, mix a 100-gram sample of the material with 250-ml. of petroleum ether in a Waring Blendor for 4-5 minutes. Add 100 ml. of 1:19 sulfuric acid and blend for 30 seconds. Centrifuge in a stoppered bottle and take a 100-ml. aliquot of the upper layer.

Take 50 grams of Celite, which has had sorbed on each 100 grams a similar weight of fuming sulfuric acid, which latter contains 0.75 gram of vanadium pentoxide per kg. Mix with 20 grams of sodium sulfate and wet with petroleum ether. Add the aliquot of sample in petroleum ether and stir the slurry until the solution is clear. Filter by suction through fritted glass. Wash the residue with two 50-ml. portions of petroleum ether. Treat the combined filtrate and washings with 20 grams more of the acid Celite and stir mechanically for 5 minutes.

Filter by suction through fritted glass and wash the filtrate by shaking for 15 seconds with each of three 50-ml. portions of water. Discard the washings and filter the solvent through a 3-cm. layer of anhydrous sodium sulfate on fritted glass. Wash in with 50 ml. of solvent. If interfering surface waxes are present, they can be removed by chromatographing on magnesium oxide-Celite. Details of this optional treatment are omitted. Otherwise develop by aniline.

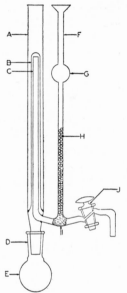

A. Outer jacketing tube
    28-mm. o.d. by 35 cm. ring seal
B. Glass tube 16-mm. o.d. by 26 cm. to ring seal
C. Glass tube 9-mm. o.d.
D. 19/38 standard-taper ground-glass joint
E. Reaction flask with 19/38 standard-taper ground glass
    joint. Bushing adapters may be used for large
    flask
F. Nitrating tube 9-mm. o.d., flared at top
G. Bulb, 20-mm. diameter, center of bulb 11 cm. front
    top of apparatus
H. Solid glass beads 3-mm. diameter packed to height of
    approximately 15 cm.
I. Glass wool plug
J. Stopcock, 2-mm. oblique bore

Fig. 35. Apparatus for dechlorination and nitration

Procedure—*In the ultraviolet.* Read at 284, 286, and 290 mμ against hexane. Plot the points and draw a line from 284 to 290 mμ. The height above that base line at 286 mμ is the measure of benzene hexachloride.

As m-dinitrobenzene. The special apparatus required is shown in Figure 35. Transfer the sample to the flask and dilute to 10 ml. with acetic acid if soluble. If an immiscible liquid or insoluble solid is present use acetic acid equal to at least twice the bulk volume of the sample.

Add 1 gram of zinc dust for each 10 ml. of acetic acid and 2 grams of malonic acid for the first 10 ml. of acetic acid and 0.5 gram for each additional 10 ml. Lubricate the joint and stopcock with 85 per cent phosphoric acid. To the nitration tube add 5 ml. of 1:1 concentrated sulfuric acid-nitric acid of d. 1.49. Fill the outer jacket of the apparatus to the fourth mark with trichloroethylene and add some granulated zinc for smooth ebullition. Reflux vigorously for at least 2.5 hours. Trichloroethylene should boil and just reach a "cold finger" condenser inserted at the top of tube A. The contents of the jacket condense acetic acid without benzene.

Remove the source of heat and detach the flask at once to avoid the contents of the nitration tube being sucked back. To transfer the contents of the nitration tube drain into 10 ml. of water in a separatory funnel. Rinse the apparatus into the separatory funnel with 20, 15, and 15 ml. of water. Follow with similar volumes of ether, then again with water. Shake, let separate, and remove the acid layer. Wash it with 30 ml. of ether and discard the acid layer. Wash the two successive ether extracts with 30 ml. of 2 per cent sodium hydroxide solution, then with 30 ml. of saturated sodium chloride solution.

Filter the first ether extract through cotton. Wash the extraction funnel with the second ether extract and filter it through the same cotton. Rinse the extractors and cotton with 15, 15, and 15 ml. of ether. Add a glass bead and a drop of mineral oil to the combined ether extracts and washings and evaporate on a steam bath to a few ml. Rotate horizontally to evaporate this last trace. The mineral oil prevents vaporization of m-dinitrobenzene.

Dissolve the residue in 10 ml. of methylethyl ketone, or more if the color will otherwise be too dark, add 1 ml. of 40 per cent potassium hydroxide solution, and shake for 1 minute. After 20 minutes away from bright light, decant part of the upper layer and read at once at 565 mμ against a blank of methylethyl ketone shaken with the proportionate amount of 40 per cent potassium hydroxide solution and separated. The calibration curve must have been of the same type, lindane, for example, against lindane.

By aniline. Evaporate the sample in solvent to 5-10 ml., transfer to a test tube with a standard taper, and evaporate to dryness at 40-50° in a stream of air. Add 2 ml. of aniline, fit an air condenser, and reflux vigorously for 90 minutes, the condensation occurring near the standard taper joint. Cool and dissolve in about 50 ml. of ether. Wash by shaking for 10 seconds with 50 ml. of 1:3 hydrochloric acid, then with 50 ml. of water. Filter through a 2-cm. layer of ether-washed sodium sulfate on coarse porosity fritted glass. Wash in with 20 ml. of ether and evaporate to about 1 ml. on a steam bath. Take to dryness at room temperature with a stream of air.

Take up the residue in 0.2 ml. of pentane and add 10 ml. of 0.05 per cent solution of vanadium pentoxide in 1:1 sulfuric acid. Read at 510 mμ against a reagent blank and interpret from a curve derived from the same ratio of isomers.

Chlorinated Naphthalenes

Chlorinated naphthalenes give an appropriate yellow in dimethylaniline.[25] The familiar term for this class of compounds is *Halowaxes*.

Procedure—*Air*. Pass 300-600-ml. of air through ether-washed cotton. Dissolve the collected particles with ether. Dilute to a known volume and separate into two parts. Evaporate the ether solutions and dissolve one residue in dimethylaniline, the other in benzene. Read the solution in dimethylaniline and subtract the value for the benzene solution as a blank.

p-Chloro-m-cresol

The same reaction with phosphotungstic-phosphomolybdic acid which is applied to phenols (page 116) is applicable to isolated p-chloro-m-cresol.[26] Millon's reagent is also applicable[27] to urine, deproteinized blood, and tissue extracts.

Procedure—Acidify a 5-ml. sample to litmus and steam-distil 15 ml. To this add 1 ml. of a mixture of 5 ml. of 20 per cent mercuric acetate solution with 3 ml. of 1:3 nitric acid. Centrifuge after 3 minutes and decant. Add to the decantate 1 ml. of a solution of 50 grams of mercury in 100 ml. of 1:4 nitric acid. After 2 hours, chill in ice water and extract with 5 ml. of cold ether. Read within 1 hour at 500 mμ against a reagent blank.

p-Chloro-m-xylenol

p-Chloro-m-xylenol is determinable with Millon's reagent and can be read in the presence of p-chloro-m-cresol.[27] Samples may be urine directly, deproteinized blood, or tissue extracts.

Procedure—To 6 ml. of sample add 2 ml. of a mixture of 5 ml. of 20 per cent mercuric acetate solution with 3 ml. of 1:3 nitric acid. After

[25] V. I. Kuznetsov and Z. M. Pimenova, *Zhur. Anal. Khim.* **6**, 131-5 (1951).

[26] N. Ray and U. P. Basu, *Indian J. Med. Research* **31**, 221-4 (1943).

[27] B. Zondek, B. Shapiro, and S. Hestrin, *Biochem. J.* **37**, 589-91 (1943).

3 minutes, centrifuge, decant, and add 0.3 ml. of a solution of 50 grams of mercury in 100 ml. of 1:4 nitric acid. After 30 minutes, extract with 4 ml. of cold ether and read at 430 mμ against a reagent blank.

Tetrachlorophenol

This contaminant in pentachlorophenol is determined with the latter.

Pentachlorophenol

The relatively recent wide use of pentachlorophenol for tropical-proofing and as a moluscacide has naturally led to development of methods for its estimation. A complex with methylene blue formed in alkaline solution is soluble in chloroform.[28] The blank is substantial but is due to a removable impurity.[29] Results which include 2,3,4,6-tetrachlorophenate are equally interpretable in terms of sodium pentachlorophenate and the copper salt. Actually the latter as well as iron, calcium, or magnesium will cause cloudiness in the chloroform layer, but this is prevented by a few crystals of sodium citrate. Safranin O forms a more satisfactory complexing agent which does not require prior extraction.

The extraction methods do not permit separation of pentachlorophenol, tetrachlorophenol, and a high-melting polymer. By reading in the ultraviolet the latter is read as pentachlorophenol, but the former is separable in calculation.[30] The sodium pentachlorophenate can also be precipitated as the copper salt, dissolved in isopropanol and sulfuric acid, and the copper determined by the ferrocyanide method.

The action of fuming nitric acid on pentachlorophenol gives a reddish yellow chloroform-soluble compound which is read spectrophotometrically.[31] The nitration is also carried out with lower intensity of treatment. Pentachlorophenol is estimated by reaction with 4-aminoantipyrene as described for G-4 (page 153) but read at 640 mμ after 30 minutes.

Sample—*Tissue.* Mix 10 grams of macerated sample, 20 ml. of water, and 2 ml. of concentrated hydrochloric acid in the flask of the apparatus illustrated in Figure 36. Steam-distil into 10 ml. of 4 per cent sodium

---

[28] G. R. Wallin, *Anal. Chem.* **22**, 1208-9 (1950).

[29] W. T. Haskins, *Ibid.* **23**, 1672-4 (1951); *U. S. Pub. Health Repts.* **66**, 1047-51 (1951).

[30] J. B. LaClair, *Anal. Chem.* **23**, 1760-3 (1951).

[31] Wilhelm Deichmann and Lawrence J. Schafer, *Ind. Eng. Chem., Anal. Ed.* **14**, 310-12 (1942).

hydroxide solution until nearly a liter of distillate is collected. Mix at 75°, dilute to 1 liter, and evaporate 500 ml. to 2 ml. for development with fuming nitric acid.

Blood or urine. Mix 10 ml., 20 ml. of water, and 2 ml. of concentrated hydrochloric acid in the flask of the apparatus illustrated in Figure 36.

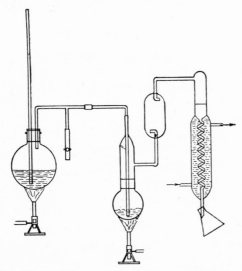

Fig. 36. Distilling apparatus for pentachlorophenol

If necessary add paraffin to reduce foaming. Steam-distil into 3 ml. of 4 per cent sodium hydroxide solution until nearly 300 ml. of distillate are collected. Concentrate to 2 ml. for development with fuming nitric acid.

Water. Use as is.

Procedure—*By methylene blue.* As reagent mix 1 volume of 0.02 per cent methylene blue solution and an equal volume of saturated sodium bicarbonate solution. Extract with successive equal volumes of chloroform until the extract is colorless. Store the extracted solution protected from light. Shake 5 ml. of sample containing 25-100 ppm. of pentachlorophenol, 1 ml. of reagent for each 25 ppm. of test substance, and 5 ml. of chloroform for 15 seconds. After the layers separate, read the color of the chloroform layer if there is still substantial residual color in the upper layer; otherwise add reagent 1 ml. at a time until there is excess. Read within 30 minutes against a reagent blank.

By safranine O. Mix equal volumes of 0.02 per cent solution of safranine O and saturated aqueous sodium bicarbonate. Treat as with methylene blue starting at "Shake 5 ml. of sample. . . ." Read at 520-550 mμ against a reagent blank. Separate the chloroform layer within 30 minutes and read within 1 hour.

In the ultraviolet. Dissolve a sample containing 5-15 mg. of pentachlorophenol in 25 ml. of refined kerosene. Extract the oil solution by shaking for 3 minutes with 10 ml. of 5 per cent aqueous tetrasodium pyrophosphate solution. Repeat this extraction with six 5-ml. portions of that solution. Wash the combined aqueous extracts with 10 ml. of petroleum ether. Wash the ether extract with 2 ml. and 2 ml. of water and add these washings to the aqueous solution.

Add 1:1 hydrochloric acid to acidify the extract of pentachlorophenol. Extract the precipitated phenols with six 10-ml. portions of ether. Wash the combined ether extracts with 2 ml. and 2 ml. of water. Dilute the ether solution to 100 ml. and read at 255 mμ with a 0.3-mm. slit and at 285 mμ with a 0.2-mm. slit against ether.

% Pentachlorophenol =

$$\frac{(7.32 \times D_{255} - 3.26 \times D_{285}) \times \text{vol. of ether solu.} \times 100}{42.255 \times \text{sample wt. in mg.}}$$

% Tetrachlorophenol =

$$\frac{(7.63 \times D_{285} - 4.18 \times D_{285}) \times \text{vol. of ether soln.} \times 100}{42.225 \times \text{sample wt. in mg.}}$$

As the copper salt. Precipitate the sample solution with 20 ml. of 1 per cent copper sulfate pentahydrate solution. Filter and wash the precipitate with water. Dissolve the precipitate in 50 ml. of isopropanol containing 3 drops of 1:54 sulfuric acid. To the solution add 5 ml. of 1 per cent potassium ferrocyanide solution and dilute to 100 ml. Read at 415 mμ against a reagent blank.

With fuming nitric acid. Add 5 ml. of fuming nitric acid to 2 ml. of sample, which may contain precipitated matter from being concentrated. Chill in ice for 20 minutes, then dilute with 100 ml. of water. Extract with 8, 8, and 8 ml. of chloroform, allowing 5 minutes for separation of each. Wash the combined chloroform extracts with 100 ml. of water, allowing 10 minutes for separation. Filter the chloroform layer through paper, prewet with chloroform, and dilute to 25 ml. Read within 10 minutes at 460 mμ against chloroform.

By nitration in benzene. Dilute the sample containing about 5 mg. of pentachlorophenol in 2.5 per cent sodium hydroxide to about 400 ml. Acidify to exactly pH 1.0 with 1:1 hydrochloric acid and a glass electrode, finishing up with 1:120 acid. Filter, wash the filters, and neutralize the filtrate with 10 per cent sodium hydroxide adding 5 ml. in excess. Evaporate to about 25 ml. and cool. Acidify to approximately pH 1.0 with 1:1 hydrochloric acid and extract with three 20-ml. portions of benzene.

Wash the benzene extracts with 5 ml. of water and discard the aqueous layers. Filter the benzene layers through a benzene-wet filter. Add 10 ml. of 10:6 nitric acid and 1 ml. of 1:2 hydrochloric acid. Heat, loosely stoppered, for 20 minutes at 70°. Cool and wash twice with 150-ml. portions of distilled water. Filter the solvent layers through benzene-wet paper and dilute to 250 ml. After 20 minutes read the yellow solution 425 mμ with water as a blank.

3-(p-Chlorophenyl)-1,1-dimethylurea

This urea derivative is present in some weed killers. It can be hydrolyzed completely by acid or alkali to p-chloroaniline and dimethylamine. The former is then determined by N-(1-naphthyl)-ethylenediamine dihydrochloride.[32] The latter is read as the yellow copper dimethyldithiocarbamate. Either is sensitive to 0.004-0.008 mg. of the test substance. Recoveries approximate 100 per cent in the determination, and the availability of the two methods makes it possible to avoid interferences or to obtain check results. Recoveries from soil vary widely depending on the soil composition.

Sample—*Soil.* Homogenize in a ball mill or mortar and weigh out 200 grams containing up to 0.5 mg. of test substance. Add 150 ml. of redistilled acetonitrile containing 10 per cent of glacial acetic acid by volume. Slurry for about 10 minutes and filter through fritted glass under slight vacuum. During the filtration wash the soil with three 30-ml. portions of the solvent. Repeat all of the operations three times with the filter cake and residue left behind in extraction. Combine the results of the four extractions and evaporate nearly to dryness on a steam bath. Transfer to a 50-ml. flask with a minimum of chloroform and evaporate the solvents completely. Add 6 ml. of 1:3 hydrochloric

---

[32] W. K. Lowen and H. M. Baker, *Anal. Chem.* **24**, 1475-9 (1952).

acid and reflux for 16 hours. Transfer to a separatory funnel with 1:30 hydrochloric acid and extract interfering colors and turbidity with 10 ml. and 10 ml. of chloroform. Transfer to a 25-ml. volumetric flask with 1:30 hydrochloric acid and complete by the procedure under acid hydrolysis starting at "Cool and dilute to about 20 ml. with water." A blank on the same soil untreated is necessary.

Procedure—*Acid hydrolysis.* Dissolve the sample containing up to 0.08 mg. of test substance in 5 ml. or less of ethanol and add 6 ml. of 1:3 hydrochloric acid. Reflux for 16 hours in a 25-ml. volumetric flask fitted with a standard-taper air condenser to avoid transfers. Cool and dilute to about 20 ml. with water. Add 1 ml. of 1 per cent sodium nitrite solution, prepared fresh daily. After 15 minutes add 1 ml. of 10 per cent sulfamic acid solution to destroy excess nitrite. Shake occasionally during the next 15 minutes to liberate bubbles of nitrogen. Add 1 ml. of 2 per cent N-(1-npahthyl)-ethylenediamine dihydrochloride solution, prepared fresh daily. Dilute to volume and read at 560 mμ after 15 minutes against a reagent blank. Compare with a standard curve developed with *p*-chloroaniline. If the color is too intense repeat with a lesser amount present prior to diazotizing and coupling.

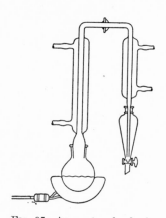

FIG. 37. Apparatus for basic hydrolysis of micro quantities of 3- (p-chlorophenyl) 1-,1-dimethylurea

Alkaline hydrolysis. Add the sample containing up to 0.1 mg. of test substance to the 200-ml. hydrolysis flask shown in Figure 37. Add 50 ml. of 15 per cent sodium hydroxide solution and reflux for 30 minutes. Remove the water from the jacket of the condenser and distil into 5 ml. of 1:150 hydrochloric acid in the separatory funnel. Removal of dimethylamine is complete in the first 15 ml. of distillate.

As a copper reagent dissolve 20 grams of ammonium acetate and 0.2 gram of copper sulfate pentahydrate in 30 ml. of water. Add this to 10 grams of sodium hydroxide in 25 ml. of water. Then add 20 ml. of concentrated ammonium hydroxide and dilute to 100 ml. with water. Add 2 ml. of this to the separatory funnel followed by 5 ml. of 5 per cent solution of carbon bisulfide in chloroform. Warm at 50° for 2 minutes, stopper, and shake vigorously for 30 seconds. Filter the solvent layer through a cotton plug to remove moisture and read against a reagent blank. Interpret from a dimethylamine curve.

p-CHLOROPHENYL-p-CHLOROBENZENESULFONATE, K-6451

This icaricide is hydrolyzed to p-chlorophenol for conversion to a red compound with 4-aminoantipyrine in the presence of potassium ferrocyanide [33] as developed for determination of other phenols. Rigid standardization and controls on untreated fruit permit recoveries of 94.5-100 per cent. Any phenolic impurity will interfere.

Sample—*Fruits.* Place 30 items of fruit such as apples, peaches, or plums in a jar, leaving a void of one-fourth to one-third over the fruit. Add benzene and tumble end-over-end for 5 minutes. Drain the stripping solution and allow it to stand until clear, or filter.

Evaporate a sample equivalent to 3.5 mg. of test substance in flask C of Figure 38. Complete by passing a jet of air through the warm flask. Add 10 ml. of 0.56 per cent ethanolic

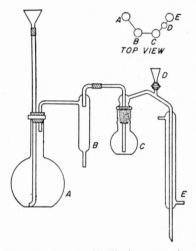

FIG. 38. Steam distillation appartus for p-chlorophenol

potassium hydroxide and digest at 100°. The compound hydrolyzes readily. After boiling for at least 3 minutes again evaporate to dryness as before. Add 15 ml. of 1:1 sulfuric acid and insert in the apparatus of Figure 38. Steam-distil until 90 ml. is collected and dilute to 100 ml. Apply sufficient heat to flask C to prevent dilution. Filter through fine fritted glass for the use of aliquots.

Procedure—Add 0.1 ml. of 2.5 per cent sodium carbonate solution to 10 ml. of sample and adjust the pH to 10.5-10.6 to a meter, using 1:15 hydrochloric acid or 0.4 per cent sodium hydroxide solution. Add 0.5 ml. of 2 per cent 4-aminoantipyrine, mix well, and dilute to 25 ml. with 0.025 per cent sodium carbonate solution. Add 0.25 ml. of 8 per cent potassium ferrocyanide solution, mix, and keep in the dark for 5 minutes.

[33] A. H. Kutschinski and E. N. Luce, *Anal. Chem.* **24**, 1188-90 (1952).

Read at 500 mμ against distilled water with a PC-4 filter. Check that this is the minimum time for complete color development.

CHLOROPICRIN

Chloropicrin reacts with dimethylaniline in the presence of oxygen to give a pale yellowish red to dark bluish red color. The method can be applied upward from 0.01 mg. per ml. of solution.[34]

Sample—*Aqueous solution.* Extract 10 ml. of an aqueous solution of chloropicrin with 2 ml. of a 1:1 solution of benzene and colorless dimethylaniline. Repeat the extraction three times more and combine the extracts.

Food. Extract a sample of suitable size with benzene. To each ml. of benzene extract add 1 ml. of dimethylaniline.

Milk. Acidify 50 ml. of milk with 0.5 ml. of 1:1 sulfuric acid and heat in boiling water for 5 minutes. Add 5 ml. of xylene and steam-distil until all the xylene has been collected in the turbid distillate. Filter to remove the water which was distilled over. To each ml. of xylene solution add 1 ml. of dimethylaniline.

Fats. Dissolve in five times the amount of warm xylene and distil. The first 5 ml. of xylene distilled contains the chloropicrin.

Air. Pass a suitable volume of air, such as 5 liters, through a column of silica gel for sorption of chloropicrin. Extract with undiluted dimethylaniline.

Procedure—To a volume of sample solution containing about 10 mg. of chloropicrin add 1 drop of 30 per cent hydrogen peroxide for each ml. of solution, and warm. Read against a reagent blank.

DIODRAST, IODOPYRACET

Diodrast is a loose combination of 3,4-diiodo-4-pyridone-N-acetic acid and diethanolamine containing almost 50 per cent of iodine. For determination of the iodine content it is converted to iodate, color is developed by liberation of the iodine from the iodate and intensified, then finally the color intensity is read.[35] Diodrast can be recovered quanti-

---

[34] W. Deckert and Butra Prathithavanija, *Z. anal. Chem.* **113**, 182-9 (1938).

[35] Jack Flox, Isadore Pitesky, and Alf S. Alving, *J. Biol. Chem.* **142**, 147-57 (1942); A. C. Corcoran and Irvine H. Page, *J. Lab. Clin. Med.* **28**, 1514-16 (1943).

tatively from protein-free filtrates of plasma or urine when cadmium is used as the precipitating agent.

The method will detect 0.001 mg. or more of diodrast iodine per ml. of plasma or urine. It is applicable to the determination of sodium iodomethamate and iodides. Hippuran and skiodan cannot be oxidized to iodate by bromine and, hence, it is possible to analyze for diodrast, sodium iodomethamate, or iodides in the presence of hippuran or skiodan. Potassium oxalate, sodium citrate, and crystalline heparin do not interfere with the analysis. The method determines 2-65 mg. of diadrast iodine in 100 ml. of plasma with an accuracy of ±2 per cent.

Sample—*Plasma*. Prepare acid cadmium sulfate solution by mixing 13 grams of cadmium sulfate and 63.5 ml. of 1:17 sulfuric acid and diluting to 1 liter with water. To 1 volume of plasma add 8 volumes of acid cadmium sulfate reagent, then 1 volume of 4.4 per cent sodium hydroxide solution. Agitate gently while adding the sodium hydroxide, then shake vigorously for a few seconds. Allow to stand for 30 minutes, filter, and dilute the filtrate to contain 0.001-0.005 mg. of diodrast iodine per ml. Proteins must be precipitated before the sample is diluted.

As an alternative technic prepare an acid zinc sulfate as follows. Dissolve 27 grams of zinc sulfate heptahydrate, 30 ml. of 1:35 sulfuric acid, and 1 gram of Duponol PC in water, and dilute to 1 liter. Titrate 10 ml. of this solution with 0.6 per cent carbonate-free sodium hydroxide solution. From the value obtained, dilute the zinc sulfate solution until 10 ml. exactly neutralizes 11.2 ml. of the sodium hydroxide solution.

To 1 volume of heparinized plasma add 5 volumes of the acid zinc sulfate. Let the treated plasma stand for 30 minutes, then add 5 volumes of the 0.6 per cent sodium hydroxide solution, dropwise, with constant stirring. Filter immediately and use the filtrate as sample.

Urine. If proteins are absent dilute appropriately and use. If present treat as for plasma.

Procedure—To 10 ml. of sample add 0.2 ml. of 85 per cent phosphoric acid and 1 ml. of saturated bromine water. Shake until homogeneous. Place in boiling water for 3 minutes, then cool in an ice bath. Add 1 ml. of 10 per cent sodium formate solution, mix, let stand 20-30 minutes, and read at 365 mμ against a reagent blank.

DIIODOTYROSINE

Diiodotyrosine gives a yellow color with nitrite which is altered to red in strongly alkaline solution.[36,37] It can also be determined with phosphotungstic-phosphomolybdic acid phenol reagent.[38] Hydrolysis of a protein with alkali does not convert the iodotyrosine to tyrosine, but hydrolysis with alkaline stannite does. Thyroxine is converted to a phenolic compound at the same time, presumably to diiodothyronine or thyronine. If the total organic iodine is from these two substances, they can each be calculated. Alternatively, the diiodotyrosine is determined by a different method and subtracted.

Another technic is to couple with either diazotized N'-diethylsulfanilamide [39] or diazobenzenesulfonic acid.[40] The diazo compound is conveniently extracted from alkaline solution into butanol for reading, thereby avoiding interfering colors of the sample solution.

Sample—*Iodized proteins.* Reflux a 0.1-gram sample for 8 hours at 125° with 2 ml. of 20 per cent sodium hydroxide solution. Cool and add 2 ml. of 40 per cent sodium hydroxide solution. Dilute to 7.5 ml. with water and shake mechanically for 2 hours with 7.5 ml. of butanol. Centrifuge, remove the butanol layer which contains anthyroxine, and add 3 ml. of concentrated hydrochloric acid to the aqueous layer. Dilute to 15 ml. with water for the development of aliquots with nitrite.

Procedure—Dilute an aliquot of hydrolyzate containing 0.05-0.2 mg. of diiodotyrosine, usually 2-4 ml., to 5 ml. with a solution made up of 10 ml. of 40 per cent sodium hydroxide solution and 10 ml. of concentrated hydrochloric acid diluted to 50 ml. with water. Add 2.5 ml. of ethanol and 1 ml. of 1 per cent aqueous sodium nitrite. After 10 minutes at 15-20° an orange color will have developed. Add 1.5 ml. of 1:4 ammonium hydroxide which produces a red color. Centrifuge and read at 500 mμ against a reagent blank.

As a correction for tyrosine, neutralize 1 ml. of the sample hydrolyzate with 1:1 sulfuric acid and add 10 ml. of 1:72 sulfuric acid. Add 1.5 ml. of 15 per cent mercuric sulfate solution in 1:6 sulfuric acid. Heat at

[36] Jean Roche and Raymond Michel, *Compt. rend.* **221**, 521-3 (1945); *Ann. pharm. franç.* **4**, 1-6 (1946).

[37] For more detail of possible interferences see page 533. Tyrosine gives about 1.25 per cent as much color and is corrected for. Thyroxine is completely separated. The method is accurate to ±2 per cent.

[38] Erwin Brand and Beatrice Kassell, *J. Biol. Chem.* **131**, 489-502 (1939).

[39] Dora Winikoff and V. M. Trikojus, *Biochem. J.* **42**, 475-80 (1948).

[40] Hermann Moser, *Experientia* **3**, 119-20 (1947).

100° for 10 minutes and add 1 ml. of 1:4 sulfuric acid. Add 1 ml. of fresh 1 per cent sodium nitrite solution. Centrifuge and read at 500 mμ. Calibrate by a curve obtained by carrying various amounts of tyrosine through the technic for diiodotyrosine.

THYROXINE

Hydrochloric acid solutions of *o*-diiodophenols, such as thyroxine and diiodotyrosine, give an orange color on addition of sodium nitrite which becomes red upon the addition of ammonia.[41] The color is proportional to the quantity present over the range 0.1-0.3 mg. Diiodotyrosine must be separated by butanol extraction. Monoiodotyrosine does not give the color.

The only noniodinated amino acids which give color are dihydroxyphenylalanine which is not found in proteins, tryptophan if present in larger amounts than the test substance, and tyrosine which is not extracted with the thyroxine. The method is accurate to ±2 per cent.

Sample—*Iodized proteins or thyriod tissue.* Reflux a 0.1-0.2-gram sample with 10 ml. of 8 per cent barium hydroxide solution for 6 hours and cool. Adjust to about pH 3.5-4 with 1:10 hydrochloric acid. Dilute to 15 ml. and extract with 15 ml. of butanol. This not only extracts the thyroxine but much diiodotyrosine, etc. Wash the extract twice with 15-ml. portions of 20 per cent sodium hydroxide, finally with 7.5 ml. Evaporate the butanol at not over 70°.

Take up the residue in 15 ml. of water, and repeat the preceding paragraph from "Adjust to about pH 3.5-4. . . ."

This time take up the residue in exactly 15 ml. of a mixture of 10 ml. of 40 per cent sodium hydroxide solution, 10 ml. of concentrated hydrochloric acid, 30 ml. of water, and 25 ml. of ethanol. Use an aliquot for development by diazotizing.

Procedure—*By diazotizing.* Use a 7.5-ml. sample containing 0.1-0.3 mg. of thyroxine. Add 1 ml. of fresh 1 per cent sodium nitrite solution. A yellow color develops on standing at 15-20° for 10 minutes. Add 1 ml. of 1:1 ammonium hydroxide to alter the color to red. Centrifuge if necessary to clarify and read at 500 mμ within 15 minutes.

[41] Thorsten Ingvaldsen and A. T. Cameron, *Trans. Roy. Soc. Can.* **20**, Sect. V, 297-306 (1926); Jean Roche and Raymond Michel, *Compt. rend soc. biol.* **139**, 1102-3 (1945); Jean Roche and Raymond Michel, *Ann. pharm. franç.* **4**, 1-6 (1946); *Biochem. et Biophys. Acta* **1**, 335-56 (1947); Jean Roche, Raymond Michael, and Marcelle Lafon, *Ann. pharm. franç.* **5**, 337-43 (1947).

Coupling with diazotized N-diethylsulfanilamide. The reagent must be prepared. Add 40 grams of 4-acetamidobenzenesulfonyl chloride in 20 ml. of acetone to a cold aqueous solution of 44 grams of diethylamine hydrochloride in 200 ml. of 8 per cent sodium hydroxide solution. Chill and add 16 grams of sodium bicarbonate. Let stand overnight at room temperature, then distil off the acetone and add 200 ml. of water. Filter the precipitated N-diethyl-4-acetamidobenzenesulfonamide and dissolve the major portion of it by boiling with 40 ml. of 1:1 hydrochloric acid. Filter while hot, cool, and make alkaline with 10 per cent sodium hydroxide solution. Filter the precipitate and wash with water. Recrystallize from 60 per cent ethanol, decolorizing with carbon.

As diazo reagent dissolve 1.14 grams of the recrystallized amine in 9 ml. of concentrated hydrochloric acid and dilute to 100 ml. with water. For use cool 5 ml. to 0° and add 5 ml. of 4.5 per cent sodium nitrite. Dilute with 20 ml. of ice water and use after 10 minutes.

Mix a 2-ml. sample containing 0.002-0.01 mg. of thyroxine, 1 ml. of 8 per cent sodium hydroxide solution, and 2 ml. of redistilled butanol. Mix 2 ml. of the diazo reagent with 1 ml. of 8 per cent sodium hydroxide solution and 2 ml. of redistilled butanol. Mix 2 ml. of the diazo reagent with 1 ml. of 8 per cent sodium hydroxide and add it to the sample. Agitate at 25° for 24 hours. Separate the butanol layer and to a 0.75-ml. aliquot add 0.2 ml. of 4 per cent alcoholic sodium hydroxide. Read at 540 mμ against a reagent blank.

BROMOSULFONAPHTHALEIN

The indicator properties of bromosulfonaphthalein permit its reading in biological fluids which are rendered alkaline.[42]

Procedure—Mix 0.5 ml. of sample, such as serum, 2.5 ml. of water, and 3 ml. of 0.4 per cent sodium hydroxide solution. Read at 620 mμ against a water blank. Correct for a sample blank in which the sodium hydroxide solution was replaced by water.

TETRACHLOROPHENOLPHTHALEIN

The indicator properties of tetrachlorophenolphthalein are used to read it in biological samples by the violet color in alkaline solution.[43]

[42] Oliver H. Gaebler, *Am. J. Clin. Path.* **15**, 452-5 (1945); Augusto Lattanzi, *Riv. gastro-enterol.* **2**, 299-302 (1950).

[43] Giovanni Toffanelli, *Riv. mensile* **11**, 337-9 (1940).

Sample—*Plasma*. Mix 5 ml. of plasma with 10 ml. of absolute ethanol to precipitate proteins. Filter.

Procedure—Mix 5 ml. of sample with 0.3 ml. of 33 per cent sodium hydroxide solution and read against a reagent blank. If the sample is not entirely transparent, correct for a sample blank.

1,1,1-TRICHLORO-2,2-BIS(p-CHLOROPHENYL)ETHANE, DDT

When DDT is nitrated, the color in benzene with sodium methylate in methanol is an appropriate method of estimation.[44] The end product is primarily the tetranitro compound.

The by-products and products of hydrolysis must also be considered. By this method, p,p'-DDT—1,1,1-trichloro-2,2-bis(p-chlorphenyl)ethane —and p,p'-DDD—1,1-dichloro-2,2-bis(p-chlorophenyl)-ethane—give blue colors; o,p'-DDT—1,1,1-trichloro-2-o-chlorophenyl-2-p-chlorophenyl)ethane—gives a violet-red; and dehydrochlorinated DDT—1,1-dichloro-2,2-bis (p-chlorophenyl)ethylene—and p,p'-DDA—bis(p-chlorophenyl)acetic acid—give red colors. If the p,p'- and o,p'-isomers are to be resolved after nitration and treatment with sodium methylate read at 510 mμ and 560 mμ and correct each value for the curve obtained from the other. Accessory spray materials such as nonionic surfactants interfere to a minor degree.

Significant losses occur in the nitration of very small quantities of DDT in the presence of 100 or more times as much of vegetable waxes unless about 10 per cent of oleic acid is added when results are close to theoretical. This does not occur with spray residues. Small amounts can be masked by interferences, particularly from cauliflower and alfalfa.

[44] Milton S. Schechter and H. L. Haller, *J. Am. Chem. Soc.* **66**, 2129-30 (1944); M. I. Smith and E. F. Stohlman, U. S. Public Health Service, *Pub. Health Repts.* **59**, 984-93 (1944); Milton S. Schechter, S. B. Soloway, Robert A. Hayes, and H. L. Haller, *Ind. Eng. Chem., Anal. Ed.* **17**, 704-9 (1945); Ruth R. Ofner and Herbert O. Calvery, *J. Pharmacol* **85**, 363-70 (1945); P. A. Clifford, *J. Assoc. Official Agr. Chemists* **29**, 195-206 (1946); Baidyanath Ghosh, Annada Bhattacharya, and Nihar Kumar Dey, *J. Proc. Inst. Chemists* (India) **18**, 144-50 (1946); Milton S. Schechter, H. L. Haller, and Milton A. Pogorelskin, *Agr. Chemicals* **1**, No. 6, 27, 46 (1946); P. A. Clifford, *J. Assn. Offic. Agr. Chemists* **30**, 337-49 (1947); F. Adar and A. Zust, *Mitt. Gebeite Lebensm. Hyg.* **38**, 371-5 (1947); Milton S. Schechter, Milton A. Pogorelskin, and H. L. Haller, *Anal. Chem.* **19**, 51-3 (1947); R. H. Carter, *J. Assoc. Official Agr. Chemists* **30**, 456-63 (1947); *Ibid.* **32**, 353-9 (1949); *Ind. Eng. Chem.* **40**, 716-17 (1948); L. B. Norton and Barbara Schmalzriedt, *Anal. Chem.* **22**, 1451 (1950); George Donning and L. B. Norton, *Anal. Chem.* **23**, 1870-1 (1951); H. D. Mann and R. H. Carter, *Anal. Chem.* **23**, 929-30 (1951).

The color after nitration is also developed in alcoholic alkali [45] and in ether and acetone with ammonia and hydroxylamine hydrochloride.[46]

The coupling of DDT with benzene by the Friedel-Crafts reaction gives a colored compound suitable for reading at 420 mμ.[47] Temperatures above 66° for development of color decrease the intensity. The same reaction can be applied in ethylene dichloride at 52° to give a product with a maximum transmittance at 530 mμ. This therefore provides for interference by other materials present in fruit strippings.

A reagent containing anhydrous pyridine, xanthydrol and potassium hydroxide is green but turns red when boiled with DDT. Otherwise it fades to a yellow.[48] Moisture inhibits color formation. All compounds which contain an aliphatic halogen give the reaction. The method is the simplest and most rapid available and nearly as precise as that with pyridine.[49]

A yellow color is obtained by heating a DDT residue with sulfuric acid and glacial acetic acid [50] with accuracy to ±1 per cent for 0.05-0.5 mg. Variations in the concentration of acetic acid affect the color developed. The color from p-p'-DDT is much more intense than from o-p'-DDT. Another applicable reaction [51] is to convert to the unsaturated derivatives in benzene with alcoholic potash, oxidize in acetic acid by chromic acid to the dichlorobenzophenones, and treat with 2,4-dinitrophenylhydrazine to the corresponding hydrazones. These are read in alkaline solution. This method is less accurate. A turbidimetric method compares the silver suspension after saponification to dehydrohalogenate and treatment with nitric acid.[52]

Samples—*Fruit*.[53] Place 25 grams in a 3-gallon churn washer and

---

[45] A. Quintana y Marí and Ana María Cid Capella, *Ministerio agr., Inst. nacl. invest. agron.* (Spain), *Cuaderno* **No. 81**, 229-51 (1946).

[46] E. T. Iling and M. H. Stephenson, *Analyst* **71**, 310-14 (1946).

[47] Eugene L. Bailes and Merle G. Payne, *Ind. Eng. Chem., Anal. Ed.* **17**, 438-40 (1945).

[48] Julio C. Castillo and Henry A. Stiff, Jr., *Military Surgeon* **97**, 500-2 (1945); Henry A. Stiff, Jr., and Julio C. Castillo, *Science* **101**, 440-3 (1945); *Anal. Chem.* **18**, 316-17 (1946); Filadelfo Irrevarre and N. E. Sharpless, *Ibid.* **102**, 304-5 (1945).

[49] Jack A. Fahey and Harold W. Rusk, *Anal. Chem.* **23**, 1826-9 (1951).

[50] Saul W. Chaikin, *Ind. Eng. Chem., Anal. Ed.* **18**, 272-3 (1946).

[51] H. V. Claborn and W. I. Patterson, *J. Assoc. Official Agr. Chemists* **29**, 206-18 (1946).

[52] Frances A. Gunther, *Ind. Eng. Chem., Anal. Ed.* **17**, 149-50 (1945); Henk Kemp and Hilda Almeida de Aguiar, *Rev. brasil. malariol.* **2**, 318-25 (1950).

[53] H. J. Wichmann, W. I. Patterson, P. A. Clifford, A. K. Klein, and H. V. Claborn, *J. Assocn. Official Agr. Chemists* **29**, 188-90 (1946).

add 500 ml. of benzene. Operate for 5 minutes at 75-100 rpm. Drain as completely as possible, shake with about 10 grams of anhydrous sodium sulfate and 5 grams of Filter-Cel, and filter. Dilute to a known volume for development of aliquots by nitration. Other tumbling apparatus is applicable.

Milk.[54] Shake 50 ml. of milk with 35 ml. of glacial acetic acid mechanically until the butterfat rises to the top. Add about 45 grams of potassium acetate and shake again. Add 150 ml. of chloroform and extract the fat carrying the DDT with it. Filter the chloroform layer through a plug of cotton. Extract the aqueous-acid layer with 150 ml. more of chloroform and filter into the previous extract as the chloroform extract. Extract again with 150 ml. of chloroform but keep separate on filtration as a chloroform wash.

Extract the chloroform extract successively with 75 ml. of 0.1 per cent sodium sulfate solution in concentrated sulfuric acid, 75 ml. of the same, 75 ml. of a 1:1 mixture of 20 per cent fuming sulfuric acid and concentrated sulfuric acid, 75 ml. of the same, and 75 ml. of 1 per cent sodium sulfate in concentrated sulfuric acid. If this last extraction is not very light in color, repeat it. Wash each extract successively with the 150 ml. of chloroform wash to recover any emulsified chloroform solution of DDT carried over with the acid washings. It will require about 15 minutes to separate after shaking with each acid extractant. In the rare case of a persistent emulsion, break by centrifuging or with acetic acid. Combine the acid extracts to recover any chloroform which separates.

Filter the chloroform extract through a 5-cm. tight plug of cotton in a Gooch crucible holder. Recover any chloroform separated from the combined acid washings and add to the chloroform wash. Finally make quantitative by washing with 50-100 ml. of chloroform. Add 5 per cent aqueous sodium bicarbonate—usually about 40 ml.—so that it remains alkaline to litmus after shaking with the combined chloroform extracts. After 10 minutes refilter the chloroform through cotton as before. Wash the aqueous sodium carbonate with 30 and 30 ml. of chloroform and filter these. Refilter if not clear. Distil the chloroform down to about 10 ml. in an all-glass apparatus. Transfer this quantitatively to a test tube with chloroform as the sample for evaporation in the procedure by nitration.

The sulfonation with fuming acid removes *p,p'-DDA*. It is also ex-

[54] Cf. F. R. Olson, D. M. Hegsted, and W. H. Peterson, *J. Dairy Sci.* **22**, 63-6 (1939).

tractable from ether solution of the sample or extract with sodium bicarbonate solution from which it can be recovered by acidification and extraction with ether, separately determined by nitration. If not to be removed, omit the wash with fuming acid and that with sodium bicarbonate.

Alternatively, separate the fat chromatographically [55] as follows. Mix 100 ml. of milk with 100 ml. of ethanol and add 5 ml. of hexane. Shake for 1 minute and separate the layers by centrifuging. If necessary to break emulsions add a drop or two of concentrated hydrochloric acid. Repeat the extraction three times. Combine the extracts and evaporate the solvent with the help of a gentle air stream. Take up the extracted fat in about 15 ml. of carbon tetrachloride.

Triturate 30 grams of Celite 545 with 9 ml. of concentrated sulfuric acid and 9 ml. of 15 per cent fuming sulfuric acid in a mortar to a damp powder. Add carbon tetrachloride in portions until 100 ml. have given a smooth slurry. Add to 25 ml. of carbon tetrachloride in a chromatographic tube to give a uniform firm column, developed by experience to flow at about 120 drops per minute.

Add the sample in carbon tetrachloride and follow with more carbon tetrachloride until 250 ml. of eluate is collected. The fat will flow slowly down the column as a yellow band which should not approach the exit. Evaporate the eluate and take up in an appropriate volume of benzene.

Butter or fat. Such samples are treated by either of the technics described for milk fat. For the first warm and decant the fat layer from water or sediment. Dissolve a 5-gram sample in 150 ml. of chloroform and filter through cotton. Continue as for milk from "Extract the chloroform solution successively. . . ."

For the chromatographic technic dissolve a 5-gram sample in 15 ml. of carbon tetrachloride and proceed from "Triturate 30 grams of Celite. . . ."

Water. Acidify 200 ml. strongly to litmus with acetic acid and extract with 50, 25, and 25 ml. of ether. Combine the ether extracts and develop an aliquot with pyridine and xanthydrol.

Removal of interference by sorption from benzene. Interfering materials in benzene solutions are so removable. Prepare a sorption column by pouring a slurry of ignited aluminum oxide of about 100 micron mean particle diameter in benzene with a column 2.5×450 cm. closed with a cotton plug. A bed 50 cm. deep is sufficient. When the benzene reaches the top of the bed, pass an aliquot, usually 5-50 ml., of the benzene solu-

[55] Bernard Davidow, *J. Assoc. Official Agr. Chemists* **33**, 130-2 (1950).

tion containing DDT through the bed. Follow with 50 ml. of benzene added in small portions to wash through the unsorbed DDT. Neither pressure nor suction is required. The benzene solution is then the sample for development.

An alternative is to shake 25 ml. of sample in benzene for 1-2 minutes with 4 grams of Attapulgas clay. Let settle and pipet an aliquot of the clear supernatant layer for development. More clay may be used if necessary and does not remove DDT. Activated carbon does not settle clear and necessitates filtration.

Procedure—*By nitration.* Evaporate a sample containing 0.5 mg. of DDT to dryness in a tube appropriate for nitrating. Add 5 ml. of ethanol or chloroform and again evaporate to remove any residual aromatic solvent as an azeotrope. Cool and add 2 ml. of 1:1 fuming nitric acid of d. 1.50 and concentrated sulfuric acid with all precautions against violent reaction. Heat in a steam bath for an hour. This destroys most extraneous matter. Cool, add 25 ml. of ice-cold water, and mix. Add 25 ml. more of water and extract with 50 ml. of hexane by shaking continuously for 10 minutes or intermittently for 5 minutes. Thiophene-free benzene is an alternative extractant. Discard the acid layer and wash the hexane with 10-ml. portions of 2 per cent sodium hydroxide solution until the washings remain alkaline. Two are usually sufficient. Wash the hexane with 10 ml. and 10 ml. of water saturated with sodium chloride. Wash the hexane solution with six 10-ml. portions of 10 per cent aqueous potassium hydroxide, shaking each for 2 minutes, if substantial amounts of contaminants may still be present. Filter the hexane through oven-dried fine glass wool, first extracted and air-dried. Wash the filter with about 50 ml. of hexane used to rinse the extractor. Completely evaporate the solvent, using a gentle stream of air near the end. Heat for 1 hour at 100° to volatilize some impurities. Add a measured volume of benzene to the residue and dissolve.

As sodium methylate reagent dissolve sodium in purified and redistilled methanol to exceed a 10 ± 0.1 per cent solution. Dilute and titrate an aliquot, and dilute with methanol to that concentration. This must be colorless and optically clear. Mix an aliquot of sample in benzene with twice its volume of this reagent. Read at 596 mμ exactly 15 minutes after adding this reagent. Subtract a blank. This assumes the mixture of *p,p'*- and *o,p'*-isomers usual in the commercial product.

For samples which may be contaminated, read at 600, 620, and 640 mμ and average the readings.

By Friedel-Crafts reaction. The sample must be dissolved in benzene. Dilute a sample containing 1-3 mg. of DDT to 10 ml. with benzene. Heat to 66° for 5 minutes and add 0.5 gram of anhydrous aluminum chloride. Continue to heat for 1 hour at 66°. Cool and add 3 ml. of ether and 30 ml. of benzene. Add 1.5 grams of anhydrous calcium chloride, let stand until turbidity disappears, and decant. Dilute the decantate and washings of the residue to 100 ml. with benzene and read at 420 mμ against benzene.

With pyridine and xanthydrol. Evaporate a sample containing 0.01-0.2 mg. of DDT to dryness until all odor of solvent has disappeared. A gentle stream of air will assist. As fresh reagent daily, reflux 50 ml. of 0.2 per cent xyanthydrol in colorless pyridine containing 0.2 per cent of water and add about 2.25 grams of dry pellets of potassium hydroxide. Swirl every 20 seconds until the upper layer is the same dark green as 5 mg. of dithizone per liter of carbon tetrachloride. Decant from solid alkali. The dark green color must be reproduced to give a comparable reagent. The green changes to yellow on cooling and the reagent is ready for use. It will keep for 2 hours.

Add 10 ml. of reagent to the DDT residue and heat at 120° for 8 minutes. Cool for 1 minute and read within 10 minutes at 520 mμ against a reagent blank.

With acetic and sulfuric acids. Evaporate the solution of sample to give a residue containing 0.05-0.5 mg. of DDT. Take up in 2 ml. of glacial acetic acid and add 10 ml. of concentrated sulfuric acid. Mix, cool, and immerse in boiling water for 10 minutes. Cool and read at 435 mμ.

1,1,1-Trichloro-2,2-bis(p-methoxyphenyl)ethane, Methoxychlor, Methoxy DDT

After isolation, methoxychlor is nitrated with fuming acid, separated, and developed as a blue with sodium methylate.[56] There is no interference by DDT or TDE. When dehydrochlorinated, this gives a red color.[57]

Sample—*Beef fat.* Agitate 10 grams of sample with 125 ml. of hexane for 2 minutes. Add about 1 gram of anhydrous sodium sulfate and blend for a minute. Mix with a gram of Filter-Cel, let settle, and filter. Extract by shaking with 50, 50, and 50 ml. of nitromethane for 2 minutes each. Shake the combined extracts with 50 ml. of hexane. Wash the

---

[56] H. V. Claborn and Herman F. Beckman, *Anal. Chem.* **24**, 220-2 (1952).

[57] C. S. Prickett, Frieda M. Kunze, and Edwin P. Laug, *J. Assoc. Official Agr. Chemists* **33**, 880-6 (1950).

separated hexane layer with 50 ml. of nitromethane and add it to the previous extracts. Distil the nitromethane to about 10 ml., then evaporate the last few ml. carefully.

Procedure—Transfer to a nitration tube with acetone and evaporate the acetone. Remove the last traces with a gentle stream of air. Cool and add 5 ml. of fuming nitric acid, d. 1.50. Heat in boiling water for 30 minutes. Remove the tube and add 25 ml. of ice-cold water. Shake with 50 ml. of hexane for about 2 minutes. Wash the hexane by shaking with 10 ml. of water. Shake the hexane layer with 20 ml. of 5 per cent sodium hydroxide solution for 1 minute. Repeat with 10 ml. and 10 ml. of saturated sodium chloride solution. Filter the hexane through a plug of hexane-wet cotton. Wash with 10 and 10 ml. of hexane. Evaporate the hexane, removing the last traces with a gentle current of air. Cool and add 2 ml. of dry benzene. When dissolved add 4 ml. of 10 per cent sodium methylate in absolute methanol. After 15 minutes read at 590 mμ against benzene containing the sodium methylate.

Bis-(p-chlorophenyl)-methylcarbinol, 4,4'-DMC

DMC is read in the ultraviolet by dehydration to 1,1-bis-(p-chlorophenyl)ethylene.[58] It is also nitrated in a manner analogous to DDT.

Procedure—*Ultraviolet*. Read a solution in iso-octane containing about 0.01-0.015 mg. of original sample per ml. at 240 mμ and 260 mμ. This is a reading of 1,1-bis-(p-chlorophenyl)ethylene. Then the ethylene derivative is expressed by 1.27 $(D_{240} - 0.108) - 2.98 (D_{260} - 0.029)$ for later use.

Dissolve a 0.1-0.15 gram sample in 10 ml. of hexane and reflux with 0.3 ml. of thionyl chloride for 1 hour. A bath at 90-100° is appropriate. The thionyl chloride, which must be pure, dehydrates the DMC to the unsaturated hydrocarbon. Rinse down the condenser with 10 ml. of petroleum ether and evaporate nearly to dryness on a steam bath. Add 10-ml. portions of hexane and evaporate nearly to dryness 3-4 times, and finally dry for 10 minutes. This operation removes all the thionyl chloride. The material must not go to dryness until the thionyl chloride is all volatilized. Take up in iso-octane and dilute to 0.01-0.015 mg. of original sample per ml. Read at 260 mμ and calculate from the specific

---

[58] Oliver Grummitt, Dean Marsh, and James A. Stearns, *Anal. Chem.* **24**, 702-8 (1952).

extinction before dehydration, E, and after dehydration, E'. The factor

$$\% \text{ DDM} = 2.02 \ (E'_{260} - E_{260})$$

2.02 takes account of incomplete reaction with thionyl chloride, the specific extinction of 60 for the unsaturated hydrocarbon, etc. The amount of 4,4'-ketone present is estimated by difference.

By nitration. Evaporate a benzene solution of sample to dryness in a large test tube. Add 10 ml. of absolute ethanol and reevaporate. Repeat and remove the last organic vapors with a vacuum line drawing air through the tube. Cool in ice and add 2 ml. of 1:1 fuming nitric acid of d. 1.50 and concentrated sulfuric acid. Exercise precautions against violent reaction. After the initial reaction, heat in a steam bath for 1 hour. Halt the nitration with 25 ml. of ice water. After further dilution with 25 ml. of water in transfer, extract by shaking for 1 minute with 50 ml. of ether. Discard the aqueous layer and wash the ether with 10-ml. portions of 2 per cent sodium hydroxide solution until the lower layer remains alkaline to litmus. Wash the ether with 10 ml. and 10 ml. of saturated sodium chloride solution. Filter the ether solution through cotton moistened with ether and evaporate the ether. Take up the residue in 25 ml. of benzene. Add 5 ml. of this solution to 10 ml. of 10 per cent sodium methylate solution.[59] After 15 minutes read at 530 mμ against a blank of the benzene and sodium methylate.

CHLORDANE

Chlordane is 1,2,4,5,6,7,8,8-octachloro-2,3,3a,4,7,7a-hexahydro-4,7-methanoindene. The technical product is estimated by the color developed with diethanolamine and potassium hydroxide in methanol.[60] A roughly quantitative method comprises mixing with 2 ml. of 1:4 pyridine-ethylene glycol monoethylether and 1 ml. of 5.6 per cent potassium hydroxide in ethanol. Heating in boiling water for 5 minutes gives a wine-red with no absorption peak.[61].

Sample—*Biological tissue.* Grind a sample containing 0.05-0.7 mg. of chlordane with about thrice its weight of anhydrous sodium sulfate. Extract the coarse dry powder with ether for about 2 hours. Evaporate the ether and take up the residue in 15 ml. of hexane.

---

[59] For details of the reagent see page 539.
[60] Bernard Davidow, *J. Assoc. Official Agr. Chemists* **33,** 886-94 (1950).
[61] J. S. Ard, *Anal. Chem.* **20,** 858-9 (1948).

Prepare a chromatograph column as described for DDT with Celite (page 538) but substitute hexane as the solvent throughout. Add the sample to the column filled with hexane and percolate at 120 drops per minute. Use hexane for washing until 200 ml. of eluate are collected.

Spray residues. Shake a weighed sample of fruit or vegetables with 250-500 ml. of benzene for 5 minutes and drain all benzene possible. Shake the extract with 10 grams of a mixture containing 10 parts of activated carbon, 5 parts of Filtercel, 5 parts of Attapulgas clay, 10 parts of silica gel, and 5 parts of anhydrous sodium sulfate. Filter after 5 minutes of shaking. Dilute or concentrate to a known volume.

Commercial chlordane. Prepare a solution containing 1 mg. per ml. of hexane.

Procedure—The sample will be in hexane. Concentrate a volume to contain 0.05-0.5 mg. of chlordane to about 1 ml. As a reagent mix 2 volumes of 5.6 per cent potassium hydroxide in methanol with 1 volume of diethanolamine. Add 3 ml. of this to the sample and heat in boiling water for 30 minutes. Cool in water, let stand for 15 minutes, and dilute to 5 ml. with methanol. Read at 521 mμ against a reagent blank.

ALDRIN, COMPOUND 118

The insecticide aldrin, known as compound 118, must necessarily be determined in spray or dust residues, in biological fluids, and in tissues. The product is 1,2,3,4,10,10-hexachloro-1,4,4a,5,8,8a-hexahydro-1,4,5,8-dimethanonaphthalene which reacts with phenylazide at the double bond of the halogen-free ring,[62] another form of the Diels-Alder reaction. This triazole reacts with diazotized 2,4-dinitroaniline to produce a colored compound of unknown structure. Probably the triazole ring is opened. The absorption maximum is at 515 mμ; a suitable range for filter instruments is 490-540 mμ. A minimum sample of 0.01 mg. is necessary.

Sample—*General.* Extract a sample with hexane, the size being that expected to yield 0.002-0.25 mg. of aldrin. If so large an amount of hexane is used that it must be concentrated by evaporation with a stream of air blowing on the surface, there will be 2-3 per cent loss for each 250 ml. of hexane evaporated. The final concentration is to be 0.021-0.04 mg. per ml.

Cow's urine. Extract a 100-ml. sample with two 50-ml. portions of

---

[62] A. A. Danish and Rex E. Lidov, *Anal. Chem.* **22**, 702-6 (1950).

hexane. If emulsions form, break by centrifuging. Dry the hexane extract with anhydrous sodium sulfate and concentrate or dilute to such degree as necessary to contain 0.02-0.05 mg. per ml.

Procedure—Prepare diazotized 2,4-dinitroaniline [63] as reagent. For this warm 1.5 grams of 2,4-dinitroaniline in 30 ml. of concentrated sulfuric acid to 90°. Cool to 0° and sift 0.7 gram of sodium nitrite on the surface. This dissolves in 1-2 hours below 15°. Add 40 ml. of 85 per cent phosphoric acid with stirring, controlling the temperature below 40°. Let stand for 2 hours after which the pale yellow solution is ready for use. It will keep for at least a week; when deep orange it must be replaced.

Transfer 1 ml. of sample in hexane containing 0.02-0.04 mg. to a cuvet, and 1 ml. of hexane as a blank to another. Add exactly 2 drops of chilled freshly distilled phenyl azide, boiling at 45-50° at 5 mm. Evaporate the hexane *in vacuo* at room temperature. To avoid undue chilling set the cuvet in a small dish of oil, and to minimize decomposition of phenyl azide avoid direct sunlight. After 10-20 minutes a drop of oily residue should remain. Heat at 75-80° for exactly 30 minutes to form the triazole. Then completely remove excess phenyl azide by heating at 45-50° and 1-2 mm., usually for about 3 minutes. A colorless film remains for coupling. This contains appreciable amounts of decomposition products of phenyl azide which give color with the diazo reagent; hence, the necessity of the parallel blank.

Dissolve the triazole in 5 ml. of absolute ethanol and add 1 ml. of concentrated hydrochloric acid and 0.3 ml. of diazotized 2,4-nitroaniline solution. Mix and let stand for 20 minutes to develop an orange color. Add 3.7 ml. of 2:1 sulfuric acid to make a total volume of 10 ml. Mix and let stand for 3 minutes to develop an intense red color. Read around 515 mμ within the next 5-7 minutes and compare with a standard curve obtained under the same conditions, correcting for the blank run in parallel.

When the developed color is far outside the optimum of the instrument, it can be diluted with a fresh menstruum consisting of 5 volumes of absolute ethanol, 1 volume of concentrated hydrochloric acid, and 4 volumes of 2:1 sulfuric acid to not less than one-fifth the original concentration developed.

---

[63] H. A. J. Schoutissen, *J. Am. Chem. Soc.* **55**, 4535-41 (1933).

1,4,5,6,7,8,8-Heptachloro-3a,4,7,7a-tetrahydro-4,7-methanoindene, Heptachlor

Heptachlor forms a permanganate-like color with ethanolamine and potassium hydroxide in butyl Cellosolve.[64] The reagent must be aged about 30 days to give the maximum color development. Otherwise a fresh calibration curve must be run daily. Heating will not give the same effect as natural aging. There is no interference by DDT, toxaphene, parathion, aldrin, or benzene hexachloride. Commercial chlordane gives a similar reaction.

Procedure—As reagent prepare a solution in butyl Cellosolve containing 3 per cent of ethanolamine and 5.6 per cent of 50 per cent aqueous potassium hydroxide. Mix 1 ml. of sample in benzene or hexane and 1 ml. of reagent. Heat in boiling water for 15 minutes and cool. Dilute to a known volume with ethanol and read after 20 minutes at 564 mμ against ethanol.

N-Trichloromethylthiotetrahydrophthalimide, SR-406, Orthocide 406

This pesticide reacts with fused resorcinol to form an intensely red phthalein soluble in ethanol.[65] This will determine as little as 0.05 mg. of SR-406. The color shows no change in 24 hours and slight intensification in 72 hours.

Sample—Wash a 100-200-gram sample of fruit or foliage expected to yield at least 0.1 mg. of the test substance with two 150-ml. portions of warm chloroform. Filter the extract and wash the paper with 10 ml. of chloroform. Evaporate the chloroform filtrates to about 3 ml. and dilute to an appropriate volume, usually 5 ml.

Procedure—To a 1-gram portion of resorcinol in a tube add 1 ml. of sample with a pipet so that it will not run down the side. When absorbed, heat in an oil bath at 135-138° for 20 minutes and let cool. Dissolve in 5 ml. of ethanol and dilute to a known volume. Read at 425 mμ against a reagent blank.

[64] Percy B. Polen and Paul Silverman, *Anal. Chem.* **24**, 733-5 (1952).
[65] Allen R. Kittelson, *Anal. Chem.* **24**, 1173-5 (1952).

AUTHOR INDEX

Hossein, A. M., 175
Hoste, J., 445
Hotchkiss, R. D., 450
Houghton, G. U., 108
Housewright, R. D., 47
Hove, E. L., 92
Howard, H. W., 484, 486
Howie, D. L., 420
Howland, F. O., 241
Hubbard, R. S., 195
Hudlicky, M., 302
Huang, L. S., 313
Huber, L., 357
Hughes, J. P., 196
Hughes, J. S., 30, 76, 87
Hugonnet, J., 198
Hume, E. M., 74
Hume, R. M., 71
Hummel, J. P., 385
Humoller, F. L., 486
Hunter, G., 489, 493
Hunter, M. O., 325
Hurka, W., 93
Hutchens, J. O., 306, 332
Hutchinson, J. C. D., 435
Hutchinson, W. S., 29
Huzita, A., 27, 361, 363, 481, 490
Hyams, F. C., 176

Il'ina, A. A., 26
Iling, E. T., 536
Immink, H. J., 33
Iugier, A., 130
Ingvaldsen, T., 533
Inichof, 269
Inihov, G. S., 271
Innes, R. F., 77
Irreverre, F., 164, 536
Irvin, J. L., 372, 373
Isaac, M. L., 363
Isaacs, T. L., 381
Ishler, N. H., 177
Ito, K., 195
Ivanova, Z. V., 168
Iwayama, Y., 444
Iyengar, N. K., 76
Izumi, S., 378

Jackerott, K. A., 130
Jacobs, M. B., 22, 247, 255
Jacobs, M. D., 406
Jacobs, P., 420
Jacobsen, N. L., 79
Jacobson, M., 182
Jaerger, W., 99
Jaffe, J. H., 57
Jakob, F., 401
James, A. E., 241
James, W. O., 133
Jandorf, B. J., 506
Janot, M. M., 88
Jefferson, M. E., 31
Jeffreys, C. E. P., 31, 38
Jenke, M., 373
Jenkins, D. M., 153
Jensen, C., 76, 82
Jensen, C. O., 201
Jervis, G. A., 357
Jetter, W. W., 46
John, A. W., 459
Johns, H. E., 434, 435
Johnson, C., 102
Johnson, C. R., 363
Johnson, E. A., 451
Johnson, G., 197
Johnson, H. R., 42, 256, 258
Johnson, H. W., 413
Johnson, K. E., 63
Johnson, M. J., 195, 309, 390
Johnson, R. M., 29
Johnston, C. G., 372, 373
Jolles, A., 244
Jolly, J., 517
Jones, A. J., 401
Jones, D. B., 497
Jones, G. I., 75
Jones, H. A., 180, 183
Jones, J. H., 128
Jones, J. I. M., 71
Jones, M., 412
Jones, M. A., 180
Jones, V. F., 285
Jonna, J., 225
Jordan, R. C., 208, 219
Jorgensen, K. S., 133
Jorpes, E., 187

SUBJECT INDEX